At last—a single volume examining b
compe tent in biology, theology, philo
important, Dr Best's book is admirably
compr ehensive without being overly
read' book in the field, a necessary resource not only ... ,
and la ypersons who share her Christian convictions, but also for anyone
who w ants to participate knowledgeably in current bioethical debates.

DA Carson
Trinity Evangelical Divinity School, Chicago

This is an outstanding resource for concerned Christian laypeople, health
professionals, church leaders and students. It is authoritative, up to date,
meticulously researched and pastorally sensitive. I strongly recommend
this remarkable book. Megan writes honestly and compassionately from her
personal experience as an ethicist, palliative care doctor, Christian speaker
and parent.

John Wyatt
Emeritus Professor of Ethics and Perinatology, University College London

Dr Megan Best's ambitious work covers every aspect of the science and ethics
of the beginning of human life. She has made accessible the best research
and much helpful theology to offer a robust Christian account. The book is a
welcome reply to much of what passes as 'bioethics', and will become a point
of first reference for anyone seriously wrestling with this bewildering area.

Andrew Cameron
Lecturer in Ethics, Social Ethics and Philosophy, Moore College, Sydney

In clear and theologically informed language, Dr Best discusses a wide range
of issues and problems in contemporary bioethics. Her training in medicine
and bioethics is evident on every page. Of particular interest to Christian
health professionals and clergy will be her discussion of the basis for ethical
decision making, and the way she continually draws readers back to the biblical
teaching in seeking to explain and critique various arguments. Her final
chapter exploring whether we are playing God when we try to control when
and how we have children, confronts head-on several of the instrumental and
utilitarian temptations many of us face today. This will be a valuable resource
for anyone engaged in teaching, pastoral care or clinical practice.

Rev. Rod Benson
Ethicist and public theologian, Tinsley Institute (Morling College), Sydney

In *Fearfully and Wonderfully Made* Dr Megan Best offers an intelligent and deeply felt defence of the Christian vision of the beauty and goodness of the human person, sexuality and marriage. Although we clearly part company on certain fundamental issues such as contraception and IVF, I commend Dr Best's much-needed work in bringing the tradition of Anglican Reformed theology and her love of Scripture to the crucial field of contemporary bioethics in an engaging and practical way.

Cardinal George Pell
Catholic Archbishop of Sydney

Finally, a bioethics book written by someone who is both a specialist doctor and an ethicist. Dr Megan Best helps us to navigate through the medicine and theology that we need to know for complex issues such as contraception, reproductive technology and antenatal screening. I especially like how Dr Best covers everything so thoroughly, yet also explains it clearly and sensitively.

Fearfully and Wonderfully Made is for everyone who wants to know what a biblically informed viewpoint should be on these current issues. I will be using Dr Best's book as a reference in the preparation of my own lectures on ethics, and as the basis for any bioethical advice I give as a Christian doctor.

Dr Sam Chan MB BS BTh ThM PhD
Theology, Ethics, Preaching and Evangelism Lecturer, Sydney Missionary and Bible College, Sydney

Fearfully and Wonderfully Made addresses the crucial matters pertaining to the beginning of life. In our world in which technology and choice are often promoted over truth and compassion, Megan Best has applied a biblical framework to reproductive and early-life issues. The book is informative and instructive for both those who seek guidance about early-life questions and those health professionals who are consulted to provide answers.

The book is also more. It represents a journey of exploration by Megan Best through the prevailing attitudes to human life over the centuries. Her conclusion as to the point that modern medicine and society have reached challenges readers to question how they are advocates for some of life's most vulnerable.

Professor Jonathan Morris
Associate Dean and Head, Sydney Medical School—Northern
Director, Kolling Institute of Medical Research, University of Sydney

Fearfully and Wonderfully Made

Ethics and the beginning of human life

DR MEGAN BEST

Matthias Media is an evangelical publishing ministry that seeks to persuade all Christians of the truth of God's purposes in Jesus Christ as revealed in the Bible, and equip them with high-quality resources, so that by the work of the Holy Spirit they will:

- abandon their lives to the honour and service of Christ in daily holiness and decision-making
- pray constantly in Christ's name for the fruitfulness and growth of his gospel
- speak the Bible's life-changing word whenever and however they can—in the home, in the world and in the fellowship of his people.

It was in 1988 that we first started pursuing this mission, and in God's kindness we now have more than 300 different ministry resources being used all over the world. These resources range from Bible studies and books through to training courses and audio sermons.

To find out more about our large range of very useful resources, and to access samples and free downloads, visit our website:

www.matthiasmedia.com

How to buy our resources

1. Direct from us over the internet:
   – in the US: www.matthiasmedia.com
   – in Australia and the rest of the world: www.matthiasmedia.com.au

2. Direct from us by phone:
   – in the US: 1 866 407 4530
   – in Australia: 1300 051 220
   – international: +61 2 9233 4627

> Register at our website for our **free** regular email update to receive information about the latest new resources, **exclusive special offers**, and free articles to help you grow in your Christian life and ministry.

3. Through a range of outlets in various parts of the world. Visit **www.matthiasmedia.com/contact** for details about recommended retailers in your part of the world, including www.thegoodbook.co.uk in the United Kingdom.

4. Trade enquiries can be addressed to:
   – in the US and Canada: sales@matthiasmedia.com
   – in Australia and the rest of the world: sales@matthiasmedia.com.au

For you formed my inward parts;
    You knitted me together in my mother's womb.
I praise you, for I am fearfully and wonderfully made.

Ps 139:13-14a

Fearfully and Wonderfully Made
© Matthias Media 2012

Matthias Media
(St Matthias Press Ltd ACN 067 558 365)
PO Box 225
Kingsford NSW 2032
Australia
Telephone: (02) 9233 4627; international: +61 2 9233 4627
Email: info@matthiasmedia.com.au
Internet: www.matthiasmedia.com.au

Matthias Media (USA)
Telephone: 330 953 1702; international: +1 330 953 1702
Email: sales@matthiasmedia.com
Internet: www.matthiasmedia.com

ISBN 978 1 921896 61 3

Cover and interior design by Lankshear Design.
Typesetting by Matthias Media.

Contents

Acknowledgements

I'M NOT SURE IF IT WAS ever any different, but it is certainly no longer possible to study bioethics in isolation. This book would not have been possible without the input of many people who have generously shared their knowledge and experience with me. Thank you all.

This book was greatly enhanced by the generosity of a grant from The Center for Bioethics and Human Dignity at Trinity International University in Deerfield, Illinois, USA, through their Global Bioethics Education Initiative. I would also like to thank the 'Free Money for New Lives' campaign, which contributed a substantial sum to this project.

I have been humbled by the graciousness I have been shown during the five years I have worked to put this book together. I have spoken to countless people who have lived through the challenges discussed within these pages, and I am deeply indebted to them all for sharing part of their lives with me. Many experts have kindly answered my questions as I have studied the current practice of medicine at the beginning of life, and the associated theology. I appreciate the assistance given by Andrew Cameron, Don Carson and my research assistant Elizabeth Hegedus. Thank you Andrew and Penny Wilkinson for your hospitality. A particularly big thank you to those who gave the time to read through chapters at draft stage and make suggestions: Kirsten Birkett, Peter Bland, Patrina Caldwell, Anne and Geoff Campbell, Patricia Chan, Sam Chan, Sarah Condie, Angela Ferguson, Andrew Ford, Peter Jensen, David Kardachi, Jonathon Morris, Kirk and Lisa Patson, Jeff Persson, Karin Sowada, Rob Smith, Joseph Thomas Thenalil and Ron Vaughan. Some of those chapters were really long. All remaining errors are my own.

To the staff at Matthias Media, a big thank you for all your work in putting the book together, especially my editors Tony Payne, Lee Carter and Emma Thornett, and to Hayley Boag who had to bear with my late additions. The book would not have been what it is without your long hours of labour.

Finally, a big thank you to my family, who have put up with me being distracted by all things embryonic for such a long time—to Amoni and Susannah, who bring me so much joy, and finally to my husband, John, without whose care, support and cups of tea this book would never have been written. In acknowledgement of his invaluable contribution I dedicate this book to him.

Preface

I READ A NEWSPAPER article the other day, with this headline:
'Are these babies really a crime?'

Underneath were photographs of two adorable children lovingly clasped in their parents' arms. It was a story about gestational surrogacy, prompted by the birth of children to high-profile parents through the use of a surrogate mother.

Are they a crime? Of course not. All babies are beautiful, and these children are loved by their families and no doubt bring much joy. But it highlights the difficulty in evaluating the morality of issues in reproduction, because reproductive technologies are aiming to provide things that are in themselves good—things that are normal for humans to desire; things that we all desire. Because these technologies aim to satisfy these good desires, we hesitate to brand them as wrong. Nonetheless, evaluating them objectively is a necessary task if we are to put all areas of our lives under the lordship of Jesus Christ.

I have written this book in response to many requests from Christians who are struggling to find the information they need to think clearly about the morality of reproductive technology. I write from the perspective of believing that human life begins at fertilization and deserves protection from that time. I will give my reasons for this position, but I accept that some will not agree with me. This book may not be for them (although I hope and trust that it will provide clear and useful information on the current state of play in medicine and technology for all readers). The book will be particularly relevant to those who hold the Christian Bible as authoritative, and want to see how it can be applied to modern

9

reproductive dilemmas.

These matters involve personal decisions for which we will answer to God alone. No blame is intended for those whose past choices are now regretted. We make the best decisions we can with the information we have at the time. I now know from experience how difficult it is to get accurate information on some of these topics. This information is intended to help us look forward, not back, and make the best choices we can in the future. We live in a fallen world and none of us is free from the ravages of sin. Thank God that he knows our hearts and forgives our sins when we confess them to him (as 1 John 1:9 promises). Finally, I realize that some of the subject matter in this book refers to unspeakable personal suffering. May the God of all comfort hold you in the palm of his hand.

Megan Best
July 2012

The dilemma

Is IT EVER RIGHT to have an abortion? What about the case of a young girl who has been raped? Or what if the baby has something seriously wrong with it and we know it can't survive?

What about the right to have a child? When we 'create' test-tube babies, are we saying we know better than God who should be a parent? Is IVF ever okay for Christians?

These are all very good questions. However, they are also difficult questions that affect the whole of our lives. Children are a blessing from the Lord, and it is right and good to desire them. Yet the technology that can make fertility control possible does not always operate within a framework where human beings are valued from the time they are created. Not only that, but as more and more extreme manipulations of unborn humans become available, the less extreme ones seem more reasonable by comparison. Before we know it, as a community we find ourselves regarding unborn human life as a resource to use rather than a gift to cherish. We contemplate our ethical dilemmas and say to ourselves, 'How did we end up here?'

Due to the development of reliable contraception and assisted reproductive technologies (ART) we are told that we can now have sex without children, and children without sex. The question is: should we? The urge to have a baby can be powerful, and the fear of an unplanned pregnancy can be overwhelming. Faced with unmet desires in a world where anything seems technologically possible, in a climate where we are used to being in control, the pull between what is possible and what is ethical can create an unbearable tension.

People in church circles often feel this tension strongly, but discussions about practical issues arising from our sexuality can be awkward and embarrassing, involving as they do images of "glistening eyes and soft dark orifices, moisture and menses, muscle and bones and blood".[1] However, God made us as embodied creatures, and our physicality is an important part of what it means to be human. As the way society views our bodies moves further and further from the biblical understanding, we need to think through a truly Christian understanding of human procreation.

Reformed Christianity has not always been strong in this area. In fact, it is difficult to find a comprehensive theology of the issues surrounding human procreation. Whatever the reasons in the past, as the science involved gets more complex, it is imperative that we get a clear theologically driven handle on the questions it raises. Recent controversies about the morality of research on human embryos have made many people think more carefully about other ways we treat humans in this early stage of development. I am regularly asked, "If it's not okay to kill a human embryo for research, why aren't we more careful to check which contraceptives do the same thing?"

This book, then, is an attempt to examine the different aspects of the quest for married couples to plan their families. It is not intended to replace a medical consultation at any level, but to give information that allows the reader to prepare ahead, and to think through the issues from a biblical point of view.

As we do so, there will be some inevitable clashes with the prevailing views of our society. Sometimes we will need to go against the flow, and not fall in with accepted modern practices. We will examine things carefully, and if necessary, do things differently, in order to be faithful to God. This can be hard. You might be seen as a nuisance or a crackpot. But Jesus Christ has called us to be salt and light in the corruption of our generation. We are the people of God. We *should* look different, and when we live out the kingdom's values we bring glory to God.

Modern reproductive technology is very complex, and it is difficult to make ethical judgements about reproductive therapies if we don't understand what is actually being done. This book is therefore organized to help you understand those areas with which you may be unfamiliar. As you read, please remember that this is an international publication, and so the availability of some practices will vary in different countries.

---

1.   J Budziszewski, in 'Contraception: a symposium', *First Things*, December 1998, pp. 17-29.

Many of the key topics in medical ethics revolve around the question of when human life begins, so it is important we clarify that issue at the outset. We start by considering the biology of how human life develops in the womb, before looking in chapter 3 at the philosophical and theological questions of when life begins. Human beings are made for relationships, and we cannot make important life decisions in any other context, so chapter 4 looks at the background of biblical teaching on human relationships. A model for ethical Christian decision-making is offered in chapter 5 so that we can determine a biblical way to decide right from wrong, and see how this will differ from others in our community.

Following that we will consider separately the areas that can hold ethical problems for those who believe life begins at fertilization. This book assumes that the place for sexual relationships for Christians is within marriage. At the beginning of our married lives, there is usually more interest in contraception than child-bearing, so we begin with that topic in chapter 6. The easily available option of reversible contraceptives has, however, reduced the tolerance for unplanned pregnancy, so the corollary of legal abortion was almost inevitable. We deal with it next in chapter 7.

We look at normal pregnancy and find out the new and sinister agendas underlying many modern practices in chapter 8. In chapter 9 we go on to consider what can be done when you discover there is something wrong with your longed-for child.

Of course, not all couples will be able to have the baby they wish for, so in chapter 10 we examine infertility, before touching on the silent sorrow of miscarriage and stillbirth in chapter 11. One 'solution' to infertility is assisted reproduction and we look at that in chapter 12, before considering why you may decide against it in chapter 13. A common problem for Christians pursuing assisted reproduction is deciding what to do with leftover embryos. Options are discussed in chapter 14. Chapter 15 on human embryo research, stem cells and cloning helps clarify some of the options available to parents in this situation.

In the midst of all the discussion about assisted childbirth, we need to take time to consider whether it is ethical for Christians to embrace modern technology in the quest for a child. After all, if God had wanted us to be parents he could have made it happen naturally, couldn't he? When is it permissible to take things into our own hands? We look at this in chapter 16.

We end by considering how the Christian view of the value of unborn human life has changed over the ages, and whether pastors need to rethink the guidance they offer their members in the new millennium.

The appendices allow us to consider in more depth a few issues raised in the text: whether the oral contraceptive pill causes abortions, what are the commercial markets created by abortion, advances in the study of human genetics, and what is meant when someone asks you if you want your baby's cord blood cells collected at birth.

Many of the papers and journal articles I refer to in the footnotes—and even some of the books—are available online and can be freely read or downloaded. Internet search engines are great tools for this purpose, and I encourage you to follow up on those references that interest you.

I think it is important that in all our discussion of these topics, we remember that we will touch on painful issues for real people who have had to come to terms with terrible sadness in their lives. My prayer is that this information will help those who are making decisions, and those who are supporting them, to bring glory to God.

Biology

ONE OF THE DIFFICULTIES in discussing the morality of medical technology is that in order to understand the ethics, we first need to understand the technology and the science that underlies it. In this chapter, I am providing a biology lesson to remind us how life begins at fertilization. I will also examine arguments that suggest human life begins *after* fertilization.

Human development

Human conception begins with fertilization of an egg[1] by a sperm. Cells in the human body have 46 chromosomes, made up of 23 pairs. Chromosomes carry the genetic material, or DNA (deoxyribonucleic acid), that guides our individual growth and development. Both the egg and sperm carry half the usual number of chromosomes, so their union creates a single cell with the full complement of chromosomes. This single cell is called a *zygote* and has its own unique genetic code.[2] Both the sperm and the egg cease to exist individually at this point. It is not a 'fertilized egg' so much as the first cell of the new human, physically representing the 'one flesh' (Gen 2:24) of the father and mother. All the genetic material required for full maturity of the human being is present in this single cell, and from this point on it will direct its own growth. From this point, development of the individual will be a continuum

---

1.   The correct term for the human female gamete is 'oocyte'. However, even though it is a more culinary term, 'egg' is used here for familiarity.
2.   For a more detailed explanation of human genetics, see appendix III.

through pregnancy and childhood to adulthood. We therefore have in the human zygote a member of the species *homo sapiens*.

A human being is conceived when a sperm penetrates the wall of a human egg, which normally happens in a woman's fallopian tube.

Diagram 1: Female reproductive organs

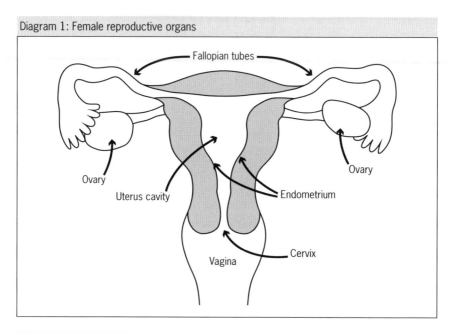

Diagram 2: Early embryo development

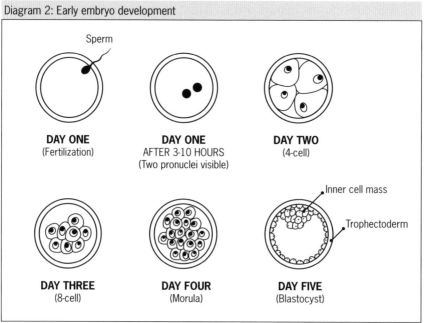

The first cell division occurs within 24 hours of conception, and cellular division continues while the embryo travels down the fallopian tube towards the uterus.[3] At day 5 a *blastocyst* is formed, at which point the cells have divided into those which will become the baby and those which will become the placenta; an inner cell mass surrounded by a hollow ball of cells. The blastocyst will normally be floating in the uterus at the end of the first week, when implantation begins. The blastocyst attaches to the uterine wall and the mother's blood supply starts to nourish it. Sadly this doesn't always happen successfully and instead an early miscarriage occurs.

At around 14 days, the mother will notice that she has missed her menstrual period—the first outward sign of the pregnancy. Embryonic development from this point is quite rapid. Note that babies can vary in their development and the information below is a rough guide only, counting weeks from fertilization.[4]

Table 1: Human embryological development

Age (weeks)	Length (mm)[5]	Development
3	1	Future spinal cord begins to develop and heart tubes begin to fuse. Blood cell production begins.
4	3	The embryo's own heart begins to beat regularly. Early development of the brain, thyroid, eyes and ears, arms and legs. Embryo begins to curve into typical C shape.
5	8	Continued development of eyes and mouth, arms and legs. Nose, sinuses, lungs, and hands begin to grow.
6	16	Beginning of formation of feet, ears, nipples and bones. Continued development of face and brain. Fingers are growing on hands and toes on feet.

---

3. The first week of embryo development is covered in more detail in chapter 12.

4. Working out the duration of pregnancy can be confusing, as some people date it from the first day of the last menstrual period (this is known as *gestational age*, which actually starts counting before fertilization takes place). This was traditionally used because most women know this date. Embryologists describe development in *ovulation age* (time from ovulation) or *postconceptional age*, which is used here. You can translate this number into gestational age by adding two weeks to the postconceptional age. For greater detail of embryology see R O'Rahilly and F Müller, *Human Embryology and Teratology*, 3rd edn, Wiley-Liss, New York, 2001; for fetal development see F Cunningham, K Leveno, S Bloom, J Hauth, D Rouse and C Spong, *Williams Obstetrics*, 23rd edn, McGraw-Hill, New York, 2010, chapter 4.

5. From 3-5 weeks greatest length is given; from 6 weeks crown-heel length is given.

| 7 | 22 | Trunk lengthens and straightens. Upper limbs are longer and bent at elbow. Hands approach each other, feet likewise. Kidneys and tastebuds start to develop. Hormones are beginning to be produced by the embryo. |
| 8 | 43 | Eyelids and external ear more developed. Limbs longer and more developed. Beginnings of all essential external and internal structures are present. |

You can see that even while still at the *embryonic* stage (that is, from 0-8 weeks), an enormous amount of development has taken place. After 8 weeks, the *fetal* period begins. At 3 months, the fetus is fully formed and all organs are beginning to function. The remainder of the pregnancy is the time during which the fetus will mature.

Table 2: Human fetal development

Age (weeks)	Crown-rump length (mm)[6]	Development
9	50	Eyes closing or closed. Head more rounded. Intestines are in the umbilical cord.
10	61	Intestines in abdomen. Early fingernail and bone development. The fetus can move spontaneously when seen on ultrasound. Fetus begins to swallow amniotic fluid.
12	87	External genitalia distinguishable as male or female. Well-defined neck. Tastebuds mature. Kidneys start to make urine. Fetal chest wall movements are starting.
14	120	Head erect and lower limbs well developed.
16	140	Ears stand out from head.
18	160	Early toenail development.
20	190	Head and body (*lanugo*) hair visible.
22	210	Skin wrinkled and red. Eyebrows and eyelashes usually recognizable.
24	230	Fingernails present. Lean body. May be able to suck and hear.
26	250	Eyes partially open. Eyelashes present.
28	270	Eyes open and sensitive to light. Good head of hair. Skin slightly wrinkled.

6. Average measurements are given, variation increases with age.

30	280	Toenails present. Body filling out. Testes descending.
32	300	Fingernails reach fingertips. Skin pink and smooth.
36	340	Body usually plump. Lanugo hair is disappearing. Toenails reach tips of toes.
38	360	Prominent chest; breasts protrude. Fingernails extend beyond fingertips.

Language

I have noticed in my research that language is often used to confuse the debate regarding when life begins. Depending on your purpose, early embryos can be called many things, including 'pre-embryos', 'fertilized eggs', 'pre-syngamy eggs', 'little clusters of cells', and 'genetic material (which is going to be thrown away)'. And the problem isn't just euphemisms for early embryos; I have also seen the term 'conception' used to describe the beginning of fertilization (fusion of sperm and egg), the end of fertilization (syngamy), full genetic expression (around the 8-cell stage) and implantation (around 7-10 days). Then there are various options for the term 'cloning': we have 'therapeutic cloning' (which sounds downright good for you), 'cloning for research' (which also sounds fairly harmless), and 'somatic cell nuclear transfer' (which for most people means nothing at all). Although the technical terms can be difficult for those not used to them, there is a lot to be said for clarity. Any terms that obscure the truth instead of increasing transparency should be avoided.

Common objections to the argument that human life begins at fertilization

In public debate, no educated person questions the humanity of the human embryo any more. The argument now focuses on *when* the embryonic human deserves protection. Nonetheless, despite the straightforward embryology, you may still hear arguments that suggest the embryo is not human.[7] I have listed the most common of these below, along with a response to each one.[8]

---

7.   Some of these arguments are also used to deny the moral significance of the unborn human.

8.   I have heard these arguments from many sources and have not listed them all. This topic is treated in great detail in RP George and C Tollefsen, *Embryo: A Defense of Human Life*, Doubleday, New York, 2008.

1. Twinning and the problem of individuality

This objection states that, because it is possible for an embryo to divide into two identical twins, or indeed (rarely) for two embryos to meld into one, and because the early embryo is totipotent (each individual cell retains the capacity to develop into a separate embryo), it is not possible to say that a single human individual exists from zygote stage (because you could end up with two). It is argued that it is only at around 14 days, when totipotency and the possibility of twinning no longer exist, that the human individual exists.

Response: This argument confuses individuality with indivisibility. While most individual humans are indivisible, it is not *necessary* for them to be indivisible in order to be human individuals. Consider conjoined (Siamese) twins. Despite the fact that they are permanently joined, we talk about them as two persons rather than one. In any case of fertilization, an individual embryo exists from day one. It may or may not divide during the next two weeks. At present we don't know enough about the twinning process to be able to know from day one whether or not the embryo will divide. However, the possibility of division does not remove the fact that the individual embryo exists. Should it divide, then two individuals exist. The existence of one has begun in a way that is unusual for a human being (i.e. twinning), but this does not alter the fact that it has begun to exist as an individual. The other embryo continues to exist, as it has since day one, maintaining its identity (ontological continuity) for the rest of its life. The unusual process of generation does not change these facts, and our inability to identify which is the 'new' embryo and which is the 'continuing' embryo also does not change these facts. The objection that two embryos can become one (mosaicism) can be responded to in the same way.[9]

2. The problem of destiny

This objection notes that most of the substance of the early embryo does not contribute to the future fetus. The developing cells of the embryo do not separate into those that will become the embryo and those that will become the extraembryonic membranes (such as the placenta) until the

---

9. Further discussion is found in JJ Davis, 'Human embryos, "twinning", and public policy', *Ethics and Medicine*, vol. 20, no. 2, Summer 2004, pp. 35-46; and J Finnis, 'Abortion and Health Care Ethics', in R Gillon (ed.), *Principles of Health Care Ethics*, Wiley, Chichester, 1994, pp. 547-57.

blastocyst stage, and all tissues supporting the development of the fetus are discarded at birth. How can we call the early embryo a human being when this excess tissue makes up more than half of it?

Response: Our inability to distinguish those cells that will become the body from those cells that will become the placenta after the first week does not change the fact that a human individual is represented in an early embryo. It is just a human individual with extra tissue. The lack of clarity should make us more careful in our handling of it—not less.

3. The problem of wastage

It is estimated that roughly up to 75% of all embryos created naturally will fail to implant after fertilization, often without the woman ever being aware that she was pregnant. It has therefore been suggested that the destruction of human embryos which is sometimes part of the reproductive technology process is the equivalent of this normal 'wastage', and therefore of no moral concern. This argument suggests that the sheer number of lost embryos in either process reduces the significance of each individual one.

Response: It is true that there is a high rate of loss of human embryos before natural implantation (the range is 30%-70%). This is frequently due to a genetic abnormality, such as the wrong number of chromosomes or missing/extra bits of chromosomes, which can be fatal for embryos. Other reasons that some embryos don't make it include local endometrial (womb lining) factors affecting receptivity to the blastocyst; or a lack of energy in the embryo due to mitochondria problems, especially if they were made from an older woman's eggs (the mitochondria is the 'power house' of the cell). However, this is not an expression of the unimportance of early embryos so much as a problem of living in a fallen world. In countries where many children die before 12 months of age, you would not consider each child less important, but as a casualty of disease in a fallen world. You certainly would not say they weren't human. Furthermore, how can a statistical argument (which speaks in percentages) give us a sufficient indication of discontinuity in the individual embryo to justify destruction?[10] As we do not know in advance which embryos will live and which will die, we need to treat them all carefully.

---

10. See O O'Donovan, *Begotten or Made?*, OUP, Oxford, 1984, p. 57.

4. The problem of environment

This is really an extension of the 'wastage' argument. It is suggested that until implantation, the embryo is not in a secure environment where nurture is ensured. In the 10 days or so before implantation, the embryo could still be flushed out of the uterus with the next menstrual flow and there is no guarantee that it will remain in an environment where it will be able to flourish.

Response: Location is not a biologically significant factor when deciding what an embryo is. It is either a human being or not, regardless of where it is. None of us would survive long if we were not in an environment conducive to our survival.

5. The problem of syngamy

The continuity of the human being from fertilization is linked to its unique genetic code (DNA), which results from the fusion of egg and sperm. However, as we have discovered more about the embryo we have realized that fertilization is not so much an event as a process. We now know that there is a gap of about 20 hours between the penetration of the egg by the sperm and the total fusion of male and female DNA (*syngamy*). It is suggested that if personhood is linked to the genetic continuity of the individual from embryo to live birth, then the human embryo should be protected only once syngamy (and therefore fertilization) is complete.

This may seem petty—arguing over a few hours time difference— but it is significant because some scientists want to conduct research into aspects of fertilization that occur before syngamy (for example, the microinjection of a single sperm into the egg). This has led to a change in the definition of an embryo in some jurisdictions so that it is said to exist only after syngamy has occurred.

Also, a few hours before syngamy, the genetic material from the sperm and the egg are visible as separate *vacuoles* (storage bubbles) called *pronuclei*. Some ART[11] clinics offer the service of freezing embryos at this stage (they may call the embryos 'fertilized eggs that have not yet become embryos') to avoid producing more 'embryos' than will be used, yet still have the benefits of freezing.

Those who believe that legislation should protect the human embryo only after syngamy is complete are not necessarily arguing against the

---

11.   Assisted reproductive technology.

view that a new human life begins at fertilization. Rather, they may be attempting to explain the traditional view more precisely.

Response: There are many points at which the embryonic human life is said to have begun: on penetration of the egg by the sperm; at syngamy; on implantation; at viability; and at birth. Certainly there are significant milestones reached at each of these points, and each milestone is necessary for the ongoing development of the human being involved. However, the first 'significant moment' is when a particular sperm penetrates the egg so that the sperm and the egg individually no longer exist. At this time the structure of the egg wall changes so that no other sperm can enter. This is the moment when the unique combination of genetic material of the new individual is first together within one cell, and all other genetic combinations (had a different sperm won the race) are no longer possible. The gender of the embryo is decided. To choose any later 'significant' point is arbitrary.

Although it is possible for the normal sequence of events in fertilization to fail in some way—for example, more than one sperm may enter the egg—this is unusual and leads to significant abnormalities in the embryo. I would not change my definition of the embryo on this basis. We create definitions based on the common manifestation rather than the exception. So while it is possible for a man to have one leg, he usually has two. We would not say he was not a man because of this difference, nor would we refrain from defining 'man' as a two-legged creature because an exception is possible.[12]

We also know that the beginning of fertilization (prior to syngamy) is significant in other ways. The organization (orientation) of the embryo's development seems to be present from the start, and may be related to the sperm's point of penetration.[13] In addition, the embryo is a separate organism that will direct its own growth and development from that point on.

Furthermore, the argument from syngamy seems to me to be trying consciously to follow the letter of the law while avoiding the spirit of the law.

---

12. This point is challenged in S Buckle, K Dawson and P Singer, 'The syngamy debate: When precisely does a human life begin?', *Law, Medicine and Health Care*, vol. 17, 1989, pp. 174-81.

13. The very early development of the embryo is still not fully understood. See T Hiiragi, VB Alarcon, T Fujimori, S Louvet-Vallée, M Maleszewski, Y Marikawa, B Maro and D Solter, 'Where do we stand now? Mouse early embryo patterning meeting in Freiburg, Germany (2005)', *International Journal of Developmental Biology*, vol. 50, no. 7, 2006, pp. 581-88.

We all know that a human being comes from the joining of the sperm and the egg. If it is not a nascent human being prior to syngamy then what is it?

6. The problem of potential

This argument concedes that the early human embryo has the potential to develop into a fully conscious human being, but denies that this potential means it deserves to be given moral significance. This argument does not grant moral significance on merely biological grounds.[14]

Response: The words used in ethical debates can make a difference to how the community thinks. One problem of discussing embryos in terms of 'potential' is that it gives us the impression that the embryo is not fully human, when what is meant is that it is not fully developed. It would be more helpful to describe an embryo as a 'human with potential' than as a 'potential human'.

However, this helps us clarify some of the confusion. If we mean that the embryo *will become* a fully conscious human, it would be fair to say we imply that the embryo is not fully a human being *yet*. But that is not what I mean when I say an embryo deserves protection because of its potential. I am indicating that there is continuity between the embryonic human and the fetal human and the child human and the adult human. This is referred to as *ontological continuity*. We were all embryos once. And when we were, we looked exactly like an embryonic human is supposed to look.

We should also remember that in biblical terms, no-one reaches their potential in this life. Philippians 1:6 tells us that God is still working in each one of us. In this sense, we are all 'humans with potential' until we are face to face with God.

7. The problem of appearance

According to this argument, early embryos are not human because they do not look human. For one thing, they are very small (smaller than a full stop). They are also a different shape, and they can't do anything.

Response: It is obviously true that embryos in the first month of development look different from the way we do now. But you also look different now from the way you did one month after birth. You may not like it, but that's what you looked like at that stage of development. It does not help us determine what your moral value is. Appearance is not morally relevant.

---

14. This argument is expanded in S Buckle, 'Arguing from potential', *Bioethics*, vol. 2, no. 3, July 1988, pp. 227-53.

8. The problem of detection

This argument notes that there is no test for the mother to identify that an embryo has been created until after implantation when her *human chorionic gonadotropin (hCG)* level is checked. Therefore, it is claimed, the pregnancy (and by implication, human life) cannot start until then. This argument is sometimes expanded to include the idea that 'conception' is a process that begins with fertilization and ends with implantation, and cannot be said to have definitely occurred until the embryo is implanted in the mother's womb.

Response: This argument seems to be saying that something cannot exist if you can't confirm it with a test. Indwelling Holy Spirit aside, years of scientific research should have taught us by now that just because you can't detect something, it doesn't mean it's not there. It would make sense that there are no biochemical markers detectable in maternal blood before the embryo physically attaches to the wall of the mother's uterus and makes contact with her blood supply. (In much the same way, there is no evidence I have taken medication until it is absorbed into my system, but that doesn't mean the tablet is not in my tummy.)

Perhaps this argument supports the idea that *pregnancy* begins with implantation, but our inability to test for the embryo's existence prior to this does not mean that *human life* begins at implantation. There was a time when English law did not confidently extend protection to an unborn child until the mother felt it move (known as 'quickening') because that was how they knew it was definitely there. Times change. Perhaps we should simply say that we cannot routinely detect the presence of an embryo in the womb prior to implantation *yet*.

However, it so happens that studies have demonstrated that hCG in the mother's blood is not the earliest signal of pregnancy. Although the test has only been done in research laboratories, Early Pregnancy Factor (EPF) has been detected in maternal blood within 24 hours of fertilization. It is thought that the embryo releases EPF to prepare the nearby endometrium for implantation.[15] This may yet provide us with an earlier test for pregnancy, but technically it is quite difficult to do.

It is also important to realize that the existence of embryos fertilized

---

15.   H Morton, AC Cavanagh, S Athanasas-Platsis, KA Quinn and BE Rolfe, 'Early pregnancy factor has immunosuppressive and growth factor properties', *Reproduction, Fertility and Development*, vol. 4, no. 4, 1992, pp. 411-22.

outside of the body (as in the case of IVF) is not questioned just because implantation has not occurred. Their importance may be questioned, but not their existence as embryological human beings. If confirmation of existence is the requirement for humanity, on these grounds embryos are human beings before implantation.

9. Difference in kind

This is more of a moral significance issue, discussed by philosopher Michael Sandel in the prestigious *New England Journal of Medicine*.[16] Using the analogy of an acorn and an oak tree, he argues that just as we do not value an acorn as much as an oak tree, so we do not need to value embryos as we would adult human beings. He dismisses the developmental continuity, saying that embryos and adult humans (like acorns and oak trees) are different kinds of things and so do not have the equivalent moral value.

Response: It is important to note that human beings and oak trees are not moral equivalents. Indeed, it is because of the *kind* of thing it is that we value an adult human more than an oak tree. In the same way, it is because of the kind of thing it is that we value a human being at all stages of development. Made in the image of God, our value lies in what we are rather than in what we can do. It is our essential nature that gives us moral value. In contrast, the reason we value an oak tree over an acorn is because of what RP George and C Tollefsen call its "accidental characteristics"—the shade it provides, its magnificence and perhaps its sentimental value.[17] These 'accidental characteristics', and not its essential nature, explain why an oak tree might be valuable to us—indeed, why a large, beautiful, oak tree would be highly valued while a small, ugly one would not.

The oak tree analogy does not work, although it does help us understand that when we grieve the loss of an adult more than an embryo, it is because of the 'accidental characteristics' of the human adult with which we have become familiar as we have been in relationship with them. Just because the embryo and adult human have equivalent *moral value* does not mean they are *identical*. I would suggest it is not true that loss of a human embryo is never mourned,[18] but it is certainly mourned less, on the whole, than loss of a more mature human.

16.　MJ Sandel, 'Embryo ethics: The moral logic of stem-cell research', *New England Journal of Medicine*, vol. 351, no. 3, 15 July 2004, pp. 207-9.

17.　Full discussion of this argument can be found in George and Tollefsen, op. cit., pp. 176-84.

18.　See 'Moving on' at the end of chapter 12.

10. Confusion with gametes

I have heard many arguments where embryos are confused with gametes (sex cells; sperm and eggs). It is argued that if sperm and eggs are alive but are not treated as if they are human, why should embryos be treated as if they are human? The reverse is also argued: that if we treat an embryo as if it is morally significant, why would we not have to treat sperm and eggs just as carefully?

Response: As mentioned above, sperm and eggs each consist of a single cell that is different from other types of cells in the body. Each has a half complement of DNA (genetic information)—that is, they have 23 chromosomes each rather than the usual 46. As such, they cannot grow individually as they do not contain all the required genetic material for maturation. Therefore, neither is a human being at an early stage of development, and so neither has moral significance. When the egg and sperm combine to make a zygote, however, a cell is created with a new set of the full 46 chromosomes—a unique individual with its own unique genetic code, combining the mother and father's DNA in a new way. This cell also has the ability to continue to divide and direct its own development from that point until it is a fully grown human. As a genetically distinct human being even at this early embryonic stage, it has moral value.

11. Confusion with somatic cells

Following on from the previous argument, it has been suggested that if the other cells in the body apart from the sex cells (called *somatic cells*) each have 46 chromosomes just like an embryo, *and* we now know that they can each grow into an embryo through the cloning process, then it follows that every cell in the human body has as much potential for development as any human embryo. Therefore it is suggested that embryos have no greater significance than ordinary somatic cells. And since we obviously don't treat every cell in our body as morally significant, it is argued, we shouldn't give this status to an embryo.

Response: This is, once again, a mistake in biology. Although an embryo *can* be generated from a somatic cell through the cloning process, the somatic cell *of itself* is not a distinct organism, and is only able to change into an organism with the introduction of other factors.[19] In contrast, a human

---

19. For further discussion of cloning, see chapter 15.

The strange case of the clone

How can a cloned embryo have the same moral status as a fertilized embryo? Isn't the definition of a human embryo based on sexual reproduction—the joining of a sperm and an egg? Now that we can make 'embryos' from single cells (with a bit of extra help—asexual production), what does that mean in terms of moral significance? Are they the same kind of thing?

Yes. Despite their different origins, once you have created an embryo that continues to promote and direct its own growth, the two types of embryo are indistinguishable. You could only identify the clone genetically by showing that its DNA was the same as another person's (this is the definition of a clone). Furthermore, the development of the two types of embryos will be a continuum through pregnancy to birth and further growth. Should any children come to birth through asexual production they will be fully human, made in the image of God, and morally valuable.

embryo is *of itself* a "unified, unique, dynamic, self-directed whole",[20] distinct from other organisms, as soon as it is created. A similar argument to this—that stem cells are equivalent to embryos because they can also be used to create an embryo—can be refuted on the grounds that, once again, a stem cell cannot *of itself* develop into an individual organism.

Having said that, if a human embryo *were* to be created through any of the cloning techniques, it would deserve to be treated with respect similar to that of a human embryo that was created by fertilization, just as we treat other human beings whose beginnings were atypical with similar respect. But by that stage it is no longer a somatic cell or a stem cell.

12. The problem of Christian apathy

According to this argument, human embryos should not be treated as morally significant human beings today because they have been routinely destroyed for years through the use of certain contraceptives and the development of assisted reproduction, and the church has not made any significant objection to this in the past.

Response: Ouch. It is true that we have failed to protect human embryos, those most vulnerable of human beings, in the past. This reflects not so much on the nature or

---

20. H Pearson, 'Developmental biology: Your destiny, from day one', *Nature*, vol. 418, no. 6893, 4 July 2002, pp. 14-15.

value of those embryos as on our own indifference. Maybe we should change. We will address this issue below—but for now, I will end this section by directing you to the *real* experts.

The view of embryologists

Embryologists are the experts in this field. They are quite clear about what fertilization represents. There are many references I could quote to make the point; here are just some:

> Almost all higher animals start their lives from a single cell, the fertilized ovum (zygote)… The time of fertilization represents the starting point in the life history, or ontogeny, of the individual.[21]

Embryologist Ronan O'Rahilly originated the international Carnegie Stages of human embryological development, used for many decades now by the international Terminologica Embryologica committee, which determines the scientifically correct terms to be used in human embryology around the world. This internationally pre-eminent human embryologist has no doubt that in biological terms we are dealing with a human being from the time of fertilization:

> Although life is a continuous process, fertilization… is a critical landmark because, under ordinary circumstances, a new, genetically distinct human organism is formed when the chromosomes of the male and female pronuclei blend in the oocyte [egg]. This remains true even though the embryonic genome is not actually activated until 2-8 cells are present, at about 2-3 days…
>
> During the embryonic period proper, milestones include fertilization, activation of the embryonic genome, segregation of embryonic from extra-embryonic cells, implantation, and the appearance of the primitive streak and bilateral symmetry.
>
> Despite the various embryological milestones, however, development is a continuous rather than a saltatory process, and hence the selection of prenatal events would seem to be largely arbitrary.[22]

---

21. BM Carlson, *Patten's Foundations of Embryology*, 6th edn, McGraw-Hill, New York, 1996, p. 3.
22. O'Rahilly and Müller, op. cit., p. 8.

Prenatal life is conveniently divided into two phases: the embryonic and the fetal...

...it is now accepted that the word embryo, as currently used in human embryology, means "an unborn human in the first 8 weeks" from fertilization. Embryonic life begins with the formation of a new embryonic genome (slightly prior to its activation).[23]

The embryo, from the time it is created, is a unified, unique, dynamic, self-directed whole, not just a collection of cells. There is evidence that organization exists from the first cell division.[24]

So if there is no doubt that, biologically, the human embryo is indeed a human being at an early stage of development, why is there confusion about how it should be treated? We shall consider this question in the next chapter.

---

23. ibid., p. 87.
24. Pearson, loc. cit.

The moral status
of the embryo

DURING THE 2002 PUBLIC debate in Australia about whether destructive research on human embryos should be allowed, I remember reading the newspapers with frustration. In the same week, different reports claimed that the frozen excess embryos in question were: (a) dead; (b) merely human cells; and (c) not human at all. These are all incorrect, though (a) involves an interesting metaphysical question.[1]

Thankfully those days are over, and we no longer need to argue in informed circles that human embryos are indeed embryonic humans. The question we now face in public policy is: at what stage of development does the nascent human deserve protection? It is the answer to this question that has informed our community's treatment of unborn humans, and therefore the way medical practice has developed. However, the question is complicated, not only by the differing definitions used by each side of the debate, but also by how each party decides what is and is not ethically permissible. Our motives also complicate the discussion— it has long been recognized that people tend to choose their definition and select their preferred moral calculus according to the result they want to achieve.[2]

We have examined the biological view in the previous chapter, which

---

1.   Although we can be confident that (at least most of) the frozen excess embryos are not dead (a permanent state from which one does not return to life—biblical examples excluded, of course), can we say that a frozen embryo—being in a state of suspended animation—is actually alive, or do we have to wait until they are thawed to give them this status? If the latter, we would have to say that the embryos in question are neither alive nor dead.
2.   Editorial, 'A question of tolerance', *Times*, 24 April 1990.

demonstrated the undeniable humanity of the embryo in physical terms. However, human beings are more complex than just biology, and as we have already mentioned, biological facts do not determine moral significance. In view of this, how has our society justified the destruction of unborn humans at embryonic and fetal stages? The answer lies in the way the developing human is considered in philosophical terms.

Personhood

The proponents of destructive embryo research and abortion usually advocate that protection is only due to human *persons*, and that personhood is not conferred merely on biological grounds. The modern view is that the status of 'personhood' is not automatically given to any human being, but only to those who can perform certain functions. It is worth pausing here to look a bit closer at the idea of 'personhood'.

The concept of human personhood has been incorporated into Christian doctrine since its earliest writers, to express the biblical understanding of individuality. Boethius (480-524 AD), in his *Fifth Tractate*, coined the traditional definition of a person—"the individual substance of rational nature"—to defend the Chalcedonian definition of Christ as "one person in two natures". The substance (a person) is separated from a specific property, its nature (human/divine).[3] For much of its history, this definition of personhood was understood to mean 'an individual (human) being of a rational nature'. As explained by Thomas Aquinas, the classical understanding was that those who possess a human nature possess a rational nature, even if they are unable freely to exercise their reason at a certain time (for example, it they are too young). Therefore, it was considered that all human beings were human persons.

During the 20th century, the definition of personhood underwent a change, largely for political reasons. Over time, the origins of Boethius' definition were lost, and it began to be interpreted as meaning that a person was merely a *particular instance* of a rational nature. The 'nature' gradually became more important than the 'substance'.

In 1954, Episcopalian minister Joseph Fletcher published an account of human personhood in which he claimed that the human person must not merely possess a rational nature, but *be able to exercise it*. His

---

3. O O'Donovan, *Begotten or Made?*, OUP, Oxford, 1984, pp. 50-7.

motivation was a desire to justify legal abortion, which at the time was seen by some Christians as an expression of compassion toward women in a difficult situation (unwanted pregnancy).[4] This was at a point when the birth control movement had shifted the focus of the abortion debate away from the humanity of the fetus. Fletcher's definition was driven less by scientific discovery and more by the political debate around abortion. If the embryo was not a fully human person then abortion would be much easier to justify.

Fletcher argued that what sets humans apart from other animals is their possession of reason. He claimed this is what grounds human dignity and is signified by the term 'person'. He went on to argue that if the human embryo is not a human person then it does not merit legal protection. His approach is based on the work of the English philosopher John Locke, focusing on the actual intelligence and reflective powers that people can display, and requiring someone to have a high degree of self-awareness before they can be defined as a 'person'. For Fletcher, the possession of human nature with the latent ability to reason was insufficient, and thus not only embryos and fetuses but also newborn infants would have to be classed as non-persons. He explicitly accepted the conclusion that infanticide would be justifiable on these grounds. Those in a prolonged coma or suffering dementia would likewise be excluded from personhood status. Technically, you would also have to exclude a perfectly normal adult who was asleep or unconscious, because their reasoning is also latent.[5]

In response to this argument, many people (Christians especially) would suggest that surely this is an unacceptable way to decide which humans deserve protection in our legal system. Obviously, any ethic allowing infanticide is not consistent with the Christian desire to defend the weak and helpless.

Traditionally those who are unable to speak for themselves and who thus become socially vulnerable are seen to be in *more* need of protection rather than less, which suggests that we should stick with the standard definition of 'person'—that is, a living human being. If you are a human being, you possess a human nature, which means you have a rational nature even if you are unable to express it at the time.

There is some concern (amongst Christians especially) that attempts

---

4. To understand how some Christians came to support legal abortion, see DA Jones, *The Soul of the Embryo*, Continuum, London, 2004, chapter 13.
5. More detailed analysis of Fletcher's theory is found in Jones, ibid., chapter 14.

to redefine personhood are a foil aimed at political expediency—in this case, to allow the destruction of human embryos for research. Arguments about 'personhood' certainly became more important once embryos were created in isolation for use in IVF. Suddenly the focus was more on what the embryo actually was in and of itself, rather than just its importance in relation to the mother.

There are many theories regarding the point at which personhood begins, or when independent moral status is acquired. Generally these theories require the unborn child to have particular features or abilities before being considered worthy of protection. Some of these views are summarized below in table 3.

Table 3: Personhood theories

Point at which personhood begins	Rationale	Noted proponents
Fertilization	Genetic union of parental gametes (one flesh) and continuum of self-directed development from this point	Embryologists and many Christians
14 days	Primitive streak visible in embryo; twinning no longer possible	Warnock committee 1984, United Kingdom Parliament (see below)
Implantation	Embryo is in an environment where maturation will occur *or* Definitional change[6]	Many obstetricians and gynaecologists
Quickening (first time at which mother is aware of fetal movement; 17-20 weeks)	Confirms presence of fetus	Medieval writers
Sentience (capacity to feel pain)	Includes higher-order animals	Philosophers LW Sumner and Peter Singer, and some animal rights activists
Viability (ability to survive outside the womb; varies with geographical location; 22+ weeks)	"With respect to the State's important and legitimate interest in potential life, the 'compelling' point is at viability"[7]	Supreme Court of the United States in *Roe v. Wade*

---

6. See 'Marketing strategies' under '3. Understanding different contraceptives' in chapter 6.

7. *Roe v. Wade* (1973) 410 US 113 at 163.

Birth	Physical independence from mother	Most Western federal courts
Self-consciousness	"Life without consciousness is of no worth at all"[8]	Philosophers Peter Singer and Michael Tooley

Public debate on these competing theories continues without any sign of resolution. My main objection to the claim that personhood begins at any point after fertilization is that these are arbitrary points. Yes, each one of these points is a significant milestone in the life of the human involved. But there will be many more significant moments that come afterwards. Once you go beyond fertilization, that's all it is: the next stage of development, then the next, one after another.

Some of the 'requirements' for personhood listed above are not actually intrinsic properties of the fetus. For example, in pre-ultrasound times *quickening* (the first movements of the fetus felt in the uterus) was used to confirm that a live baby was present. But the timing of quickening varies according to the sensitivity of the pregnant woman, with first-time mothers regularly noticing fetal movement later than their more experienced sisters. And viability depends on biology *and* the standard of care available. The gestational age for viability keeps changing as technology in neonatal intensive care units improves. Likewise, the timing of birth can be dependent on a host of factors outside of the baby itself.

The idea of personhood that has most influenced international debates on human embryo research is that proposed by the Warnock committee, which reported to the United Kingdom government in 1984. While acknowledging that embryonic humans should have a special status, the committee decided to avoid answering the question of when life or personhood began. Instead it discussed how the embryo should be treated. Despite criticisms of this approach (how do you know how to treat it if you don't know what it is?), the committee's recommendation—that destructive human embryo research can be justified up to 14 days—has influenced policy makers around the world ever since. The introduction of *in vitro* (in the test tube) *fertilization* (IVF) in the United States was

---

8.   P Singer, *Rethinking Life and Death*, St Martin's Griffin, New York, 1994, p. 190. Later in the book, Singer suggests that a period of 28 days should be allowed to lapse before the child has a right to life, during which time the parents could decide whether they want the baby. If not then infanticide is, according to his view, morally permissible.

also approved after 'putting aside' the question of the moral status of the embryo.[9] Interestingly, at the time IVF was approved, the maximum length of time anyone had been able to grow human embryos in the laboratory was 14 days. How convenient.

The Warnock committee conferred *emerging* personhood on the embryo—that is, they indicated that personhood increases with age. They chose their time limit for destructive embryo research on the grounds that 14 days was the time when the primitive streak was visible in the embryo ("this marks the beginning of individual development"),[10] and also the time when twinning was no longer possible.[11] We now know that this science is out of date. Subsequent research has shown that the human embryo is organized from its very first day.[12] However, the Warnock report remains influential. Its assumptions permeated the United Kingdom's most recent review of the Human Fertilisation and Embryology Act in 2005;[13] and the '14-day rule' has been confirmed as an ethical principle by various government ethics committees, including United States federal committees[14] and Australian parliamentary reviews.[15]

The interesting thing to notice in the literature about the moral status of the embryo is that most philosophers—regardless of whether they think the embryo deserves protection or not—do not support the arguments used in the Warnock report to justify the '14-day rule'.[16]

---

9.   MO Steinfels, 'In vitro fertilization: "ethically acceptable" research', *Hastings Center Report*, vol. 9, no. 3, June 1979, pp. 5-8.

10.   Department of Health and Social Security, *Report of the Committee of Inquiry into Human Fertilisation and Embryology*, M Warnock (Chairman), London, 1984, paragraph 11.22.

11.   For further explanation of why these markers where chosen, see chapter 2.

12.   See 'Human development' in chapter 2.

13.   Department of Health, *Review of the Human Fertilisation and Embryology Act: A Public Consultation*, London, 2005.

14.   National Institutes of Health, *Report of the Human Embryo Research Panel*, 1994; American Society for Reproductive Medicine, *Ethical Considerations of Reproductive Technology*, 1986, 1990 and 1994; National Bioethics Advisory Commission, 1997, 1999; The President's Council on Bioethics, 2002, 2004.

15.   Legislation Review Committee, Review of the *Prohibition of Human Cloning Act 2002* and the *Research Involving Human Embryos Act 2002*, Justice John Lockhart (Chairman), Canberra, 2005 (known as the Lockhart review).

16.   For further discussion of the philosophical approaches to justification of embryo research, see M Suttie, 'Embryo research and the fourteen day rule: What implications does this global bioethical and legal standard have for human dignity?', paper presented to the Global Bioethics: Emerging Challenges Facing Human Dignity conference, Chicago, 13-22 July 2009.

According to the philosophical literature, either the pre-14 day embryo is being unjustifiably exploited (because it deserves protection), or research on embryos is being unjustifiably limited (because they don't deserve protection until later).

How do we decide which is correct? Certainly not by asking the researchers. The moral status of the human embryo is not a scientific question but a philosophical or metaphysical one, dependent on one's world view rather than calculated by an equation. It does not lend itself to numerical values and deadlines.

Proponents of destructive embryo research further justify their position (that the human embryo does not deserve protection) by pointing to examples in modern life where our society already condones the discarding of embryonic and fetal humans. These include the marketing of contraceptives that work after fertilization, assisted reproductive technology (ART) research, and legal abortion.[17] The high rate of embryo loss before implantation in normal pregnancy is also considered to support this view.[18]

Despite the time given to discussions of personhood, it's hard to avoid the impression that its place in the debate is really an excuse to justify what some people want to do anyway.

The philosophical theory that underlies the position that approves of human embryo destruction is ultimately *consequentialism*. Consequentialism is the ethical theory that right and wrong can be determined by looking at the consequences of our actions alone (leaving out consideration of things like motives, intentions, actions and the character of the person involved). Many national governments have decided that while the destruction of developing humans (usually in the form of excess frozen embryos left over from assisted reproduction) may be regrettable, the consequences of their destruction is sufficient justification—for example, potential medical cures through embryonic stem-cell research, babies through ART research, and freedom for

---

17. Incidentally, this should remind us of the need to voice our concerns with public policy at the time it is being discussed and decided. In the current public debates in Western society it is regularly pointed out that Christians did not strongly oppose the embryo destruction associated with the introduction of IVF—thus implying that we should not start making a fuss now.

18. See '3. The problem of wastage' under 'Common objections to the argument that human life begins at fertilization' in chapter 2.

women desiring abortion.

Yet the secular world is not entirely committed to the idea that early human life is unimportant. The Warnock committee recognized the mood of the community when they "agreed that the embryo of the human species ought to have a special status".[19] However, without biblical grounding, many people are unsure as to why this should be so. One secular expression of the preciousness of human life is reflected in human rights declarations, which since World War II have been designed to protect the welfare of human research subjects. Technically, destructive research on human embryos contravenes documents such as *The Nuremberg Code*[20] and the WMA *Declaration of Helsinki*, which requires that "in medical research involving human subjects, the well-being of the individual research subject must take precedence over all other interests".[21] The Council of Europe *Convention on Human Rights and Biomedicine* ensures "adequate" protection of the embryo where *in vitro* research is allowed (although I'm not sure exactly what "adequate" includes), and also prohibits research on human embryos *in vivo* (in the body) and the creation of human embryos for research.[22]

However, when economic opportunity and political expediency call, such documents may fail to impact legislators. In Australia, amidst concerns expressed in the media that lucrative biotechnology opportunities would be lost if embryonic stem-cell research was not approved by parliament, laws were passed in 2002 to allow it—despite a previous Senate committee recommendation that human embryos be protected from destructive experimentation.[23] It is interesting that in Western Europe, countries that witnessed the worst of the World War II atrocities, such as Germany and Italy, have been among the most reluctant legislatures when it has come to approving destructive

---

19. Department of Health and Social Security, op. cit., paragraph 11.17.

20. 'The Nuremberg Code (1947)', *British Medical Journal*, vol. 313, no. 7070, 7 December 1996, p. 1448.

21. World Medical Association, *Declaration of Helsinki: Ethical principles for medical research involving human subjects*, 6th revision, adopted by the 18th WMA General Assembly, Helsinki, 1964 and amended by the 59th WMA General Assembly, Seoul, 2008, paragraph 6.

22. Council of Europe, *Convention for the Protection of Human Rights and Dignity of the Human Being with regard to the Application of Biology and Medicine: Convention on Human Rights and Biomedicine*, Oviedo, 1997.

23. Australia, Parliament, *Human Embryo Experimentation in Australia*, Report of the Senate Select Committee on the Human Embryo Experimentation Bill 1985, Parl. Paper 437, Canberra, September 1986, p. xiv.

research on human embryos.

Another group that has decided fetal life can be valued without establishing formal independent moral status is a body of doctors involved with antenatal care.[24] Chervenak and Kurjak have argued that if a human being is presented to the physician, and if that human is expected to benefit from the application of the physician's clinical skills, then that human being can be viewed as a patient. Certainly many doctors who work with newborn babies hesitate to advocate abortion once they realize how similar their tiny patients are to those in the womb.

Chervenak and Kurjak's arguments ground the value of the fetus in the ontological continuity of its identity with the human who is reliably expected to achieve independent moral status later, after birth. While they respect the autonomy of the pregnant woman, they note that her expectation that the doctor will care for the child is expressed in her presentation to the doctor for antenatal care in the first place. They recognize the possibility of conflict should the mother refuse the physician's advice, but suggest that beneficence (doing good) towards the baby should be their motivation, in balance with obligations to the mother (for instance, in regard to her safety). They endow the unborn child with moral significance by referring to codes of professional medical ethics. Those who take the Hippocratic Oath (historically the most influential declaration of the moral obligations of the medical practitioner) specifically promise not to "give a woman means to procure an abortion".[25]

Despite difficulties in understanding why it should be so, the reality of our community's instinctive attribution of special status to the human embryo is seen in the fact that in Western countries where destructive research on human embryos is legal, it requires official approval and is permitted only up to 14 days of development. There is societal hesitation to go further. Bioethicist Leon Kass, when discussing human cloning, famously referred to this hesitation as "the wisdom of repugnance".[26]

---

24. FA Chervenak, LB McCullough and A Kurjak, 'An essential clinical ethical concept', in FA Chervenak and A Kurjak (eds), *The Fetus as a Patient*, Parthenon, New York, 1996, pp. 1-9.
25. GER Lloyd (ed.), J Chadwick and WN Mann (trans.), *Hippocratic Writings*, Penguin, London, 1978, p. 67.
26. LR Kass, 'The repugnance of wisdom', in LR Kass and JQ Wilson, *The Ethics of Human Cloning*, AEI Press, Washington DC, 1998, p. 19.

While accepting that repugnance is not a moral argument, he nonetheless sees it as "the emotional expression of deep wisdom, beyond reason's power fully to articulate it".[27] He expands the point:

> We are repelled by the prospect of cloning human beings not because of the strangeness or novelty of the undertaking, but because we intuit and feel, immediately and without argument, the violation of things that we rightfully hold dear. Repugnance, here as elsewhere, revolts against the excesses of human willfulness, warning us not to transgress what is unspeakably profound. Indeed, in this age in which everything is held to be permissible so long as it is freely done, in which our given human nature no longer commands respect, in which our bodies are regarded as mere instruments of our autonomous rational wills, repugnance may be the only voice left that speaks up to defend the central core of our humanity. Shallow are the souls that have forgotten how to shudder.[28]

We shall return to the idea of personhood in a moment, after we have considered what the Bible has to contribute to this question.

The biblical view

Christians have a moral compass, the Bible, which should inform all our decisions regarding right and wrong.[29] We do need to understand that in issues relating to modern technology, the Bible may not specifically address the point at hand. It is an ancient collection of texts written in times vastly different from our own. Nevertheless, despite its antiquity, the Bible is God's revelation of the unchanging principles that should guide the lives of those who follow his Son, Jesus Christ. To elicit such principles it is necessary both to pay attention to explicit biblical statements and to look for biblical themes that can inform our decision-making.

Over the years many helpful frameworks have been developed for distilling and applying the Bible's teaching on ethical questions—

---

27. ibid., p. 18.
28. ibid., p. 19.
29. Ethical decision-making is explained in more detail in chapter 5.

see, for example, those used by Michael Hill and John Stott.[30] Most approaches suggest that the Bible's teaching is best applied to current ethical dilemmas by considering biblical revelation in 4 stages: creation, fall, redemption and future consummation. In other words, we need to consider the world firstly as God originally made it; then as it is affected by sin; then in light of the salvation that is possible through the work of Christ; and finally in view of the glorious future awaiting us. It is important to consider the whole of Scripture in our task so that our conclusions are not distorted by a partial appreciation of God's purposes.

In considering the Bible's teaching on the moral status of the human embryo, I acknowledge that opinion in the Christian community is divided on this issue. After examining the texts, I will explain my own view and the reasons for it.

Creation in the image of God

We can learn a lot about the way God wants us to treat humans by considering the way we have been made. All humans are made in the image of God, and this is the basis on which we are all to be treated equally and with dignity. There has been much debate over what it means for humankind to be made in God's image, but it at least refers to embodied individuals who live out a role in history.[31] The creation story shows us that humanity has been brought into this world by God's creative word and, like the creation around us, we constantly depend on his will, purpose and upholding presence:

> Then God said, "Let us make man in our image, after our likeness. And let them have dominion over the fish of the sea and over the birds of the heavens and over the livestock and over all the earth and over every creeping thing that creeps on the earth."
>
> So God created man in his own image,
> > in the image of God he created him;
> > male and female he created them. (Gen 1:26-27)

---

30.   M Hill, *The How and Why of Love*, Matthias Media, Sydney, 2002; JRW Stott, *Issues Facing Christians Today*, 4th edn, Zondervan, Grand Rapids, 2006. These texts are recommended for those who would like to explore further ethical issues from a biblical perspective. John Wyatt has provided an expansion of Stott's scheme in the context of modern biology in his book *Matters of Life and Death*, 2nd edn, IVP, Leicester, 2009, pp. 51-82.
31.   This idea is implied by biblical references to divinely ordained vocation (e.g Jer 1:5). For exploration of this theme, see O'Donovan, loc. cit.

Human beings have been uniquely made in the image and likeness of God. This sets us apart from all the other creatures, which were made "according to their kinds" (Gen 1:21, 24, 25). If what qualifies you to be treated with equal dignity to others is the fact that you are a person, then all human beings have this 'right', for we are all persons made in the image of God. In contrast to the modern philosophical view that personhood must be earned, the Bible teaches that our personhood is inherent because of the nature of the God whose image we reflect. We are to treat all human beings with respect for the whole of their lives, regardless of their particular characteristics. It is not our respect that gives them dignity; rather, it is because they have dignity that we owe them respect.

The reality of sin and the Fall does not change this fact. Just as taking a $20 bill and screwing it up, throwing it in the mud and jumping on it does not reduce its intrinsic value (it's still worth $20), so the ravages of sin have not reduced the value of human beings made in the *imago dei*. Man still retains the image of God (Gen 9:6).

When God said 'Let *us* make man in *our* image', and then created 'man' to be both man and woman, he underscored our need for community and relationships (reflecting the differentiated unity of the Godhead). In other words, we have been made for relationships both with him and with each other. This is further emphasized by the fact that when the solitary Adam was placed in the garden of Eden, God himself declared that it was "not good that the man should be alone" (Gen 2:18). Up to this point in time, this was the only thing in the whole creation that was "not good". This means that man can only truly understand himself as a finite embodied being in the context of relationships.

It also means that we do not make decisions independently of those around us. Even if we do not care about others, our actions will nonetheless affect them. Moreover, as human persons with a history, we each have a 'story' that is inextricably linked to the 'story' of others. Whether we realize it or not, we cannot act without being influenced both by our own narrative and by the narratives of others. We may like to think about issues like reproduction in an abstract or individualistic way, but biblically informed Christians will always accept that our choices profoundly affect others.[32] Our freedom, therefore, must be guided and

---

32. Modern 'science fiction' examples used to debate the moral status of the embryo (these will be known to those familiar with the philosophical debate regarding abortion, violinists, etc.) are invalid on these grounds.

limited by what the Bible says it means to be truly free—part of which is to live in loving relationship with others.

As mentioned, after the sin and judgement of the Fall in Genesis 3, humanity retains God's image and likeness, passed down from father to son (Gen 5:1, 3; 9:6; also see Jas 3:9). Of course, sin has corrupted the image. That is why those in Christ "have put on the new self, which is being renewed in knowledge after the image of its creator" (Col 3:10). One day this renewal will be complete (Rom 8:29), but not this side of glory (Phil 3:12-14). Nevertheless it is because we retain God's image, even in our fallenness, that the book of Genesis informs us that shedding human blood is judged with capital punishment:

> "Whoever sheds the blood of man,
>   by man shall his blood be shed,
> for God made man in his own image." (Gen 9:6)

This somber warning, together with other parts of Scripture, tells us how seriously God views murder. For example:

- Such a crime is not only against man but against God himself, in whose image man is made (Gen 9:6).
- The murderer himself is liable to be killed and is not protected by the 6th commandment, which prohibits the taking of innocent life (Exod 20:13).
- The judicial code for retributive justice (i.e. the 'eye for an eye' of Exodus 21:24 and Leviticus 24:20) is clarified and qualified elsewhere in the Scriptures, with manslaughter specifically distinguished from murder (Num 35:10-28).
- Murder pollutes the land in which it is committed, and atonement can only be made by shedding the blood of the one who has committed it (Num 35:33).

As far as God is concerned, the taking of human life is a very serious crime.

Continuity before and after birth

But when does human life begin?

It is quite clear that it does not begin at birth. The Bible indicates that all human beings have a relationship with God while still in the womb. Several passages attest to God's careful moulding of the human form, while not identifying exactly when this relationship begins:

> For you formed my inward parts;
>   you knitted me together in my mother's womb.

43

I praise you, for I am fearfully and wonderfully made.
Wonderful are your works;
> my soul knows it very well.
My frame was not hidden from you,
when I was being made in secret,
> intricately woven in the depths of the earth.
Your eyes saw my unformed substance;
in your book were written, every one of them,
> the days that were formed for me,
> when as yet there was none of them. (Ps 139:13-16)

The psalmist, David, uses a variety of words here to evoke the picture of God as a craftsman: "formed", "knitted", "made", "woven". All of these point to the fact that each human being is a carefully modelled masterpiece. Furthermore, the passage does not refer to the fully developed fetus so much as to the early embryo. This is clear from David's use of the Hebrew word *golem* (translated "unformed substance" in verse 16), a term used in Jewish literature to denote the first stage of human life after conception.[33] David Jones associates the idea of our being created in the "depths of the earth" with Adam's creation from "dust from the ground" in Genesis 2:7.[34] Whether or not this link is present in David's mind as he writes the psalm, Psalm 139 clearly portrays the mystery of human development long before the availability of antenatal ultrasound. It is also clear that David identifies with his unborn self in his mother's womb. He is in no doubt that life outside the womb is a continuation of the life that began inside, and he acknowledges God's full knowledge of his future even as he knows his past (cf. Ps 139:1-10; Heb 4:13). Similar ideas are found in several apocryphal texts (e.g. Wisdom 7:1-4; 2 Maccabees 7:22-23) and also in Job's words:

"Your hands fashioned and made me,
> and now you have destroyed me altogether.
Remember that you have made me like clay;
> and will you return me to the dust?

33. The term is used by JRR Tolkien in *The Lord of the Rings* to denote the creature Gollum, who is 'deformed' by the malignant influence of the ring.
34. Jones, op. cit., p. 7. I recommend this book for those who would like to further examine the Christian tradition regarding the moral status of the human embryo. It has informed much of this discussion.

Did you not pour me out like milk
    and curdle me like cheese?
You clothed me with skin and flesh,
    and knit me together with bones and sinews.
You have granted me life and steadfast love,
    and your care has preserved my spirit." (Job 10:8-12)

Further status is given to the developing embryo in Exodus 21:22-25. This passage outlines the penalties for injuring a pregnant woman during a fight, and appears to give the unborn human equivalent importance to one who has been born:

> "When men strive together and hit a pregnant woman, so that her children come out, but there is no harm, the one who hit her shall surely be fined, as the woman's husband shall impose on him, and he shall pay as the judges determine. But if there is harm, then you shall pay life for life, eye for eye, tooth for tooth, hand for hand, foot for foot, burn for burn, wound for wound, stripe for stripe." (Exod 21:22-25)

This passage seems to be saying that if men who are fighting injure a pregnant woman and she gives birth prematurely to a live child, the offender is to be fined. But if there is serious injury and miscarriage, you are to take life for life (the life of the unborn child is equated to the life of the attacker). This reading of the Hebrew is reflected in the NIV and ESV translations, among many others. However, consider another translation:

> If men struggle with each other and strike a woman with child
> so that she gives birth prematurely, yet there is no injury, he shall
> surely be fined as the woman's husband may demand of him; and
> he shall pay as the judges decide. But if there is any further injury,
> then you shall appoint as a penalty life for life, eye for eye, tooth for
> tooth, hand for hand, foot for foot, burn for burn, wound for wound,
> bruise for bruise. (Exod 21:22-25 NASB)

If this translation is correct, then a different interpretation follows. The attacker is not to be executed for bringing about the death of the child, but only for bringing about the death of the mother. In other words, it is the mother's life that is equated with that of the attacker, not the child's. This could be understood as suggesting that "the unborn do not have the same value or rights as those born".[35] This is the common Jewish reading of the text, and is also reflected in a number of English Bible translations (notably KJV, NEB and RSV).[36] However, since the death of a (non-pregnant) woman has already been dealt with earlier in the chapter, it's hard to see why it would be mentioned again.

Much of the confusion surrounding the interpretation of Exodus 21:22-23 stems from the influence of the Septuagint (or LXX).[37] The Septuagint version of the text yields a different translation again:

> And if two men are fighting and strike a pregnant woman and her infant departs not fully formed, he shall be forced to pay a fine: according to whatever the woman's husband shall lay upon him, he shall give with what is fitting. But if it is fully formed, he shall give life for life… (Exod 21:22-25, LXX)

According to this version, the death of a "formed" infant demands "life for life", but the death of a "not fully formed" infant only warrants a fine. Many early Christians read this version of the Old Testament, and its influence lasted well into the Middle Ages. However, at this point, the Septuagint badly mistranslates the original Hebrew, using the word 'form' where the Hebrew clearly means 'harm' or 'injury'. In other words, the formed/unformed distinction is nowhere present in the Hebrew text. In fact this distinction derives from the ancient Greek philosopher Aristotle, whose (incorrect) explanations of early human development were widely accepted at the time.[38]

That the writer of Exodus is making a distinction between an unharmed child and an injured child is clear from his use of the term *yeled*—the normal term for a child. If the writer had wished to signify the miscarriage of an undeveloped fetus, he could have used the term

---

35. DP O'Mathuna, 'Bodily Injuries, Murder, Manslaughter' in *Dictionary of the Old Testament: Pentateuch*, TD Alexander and DW Baker (eds), IVP, Downers Grove, 2003, p. 93.
36. It is noteworthy that these three biblical translations belong to the same 'family' and therefore share much in common.
37. The Septuagint, or LXX, is a Greek translation of the Old Testament that was begun by the 3rd century BC and completed sometime before 132 BC. It was used by Greek-speaking Jews throughout the Mediterranean world, and also by the early Christians.
38. I have come across the suggestion that the LXX was never meant to be a faithful translation so much as a culturally relevant interpretation of the Hebrew for Greeks at that time. See Mark Scott, 'Quickening in the Common Law: The legal precedent Roe attempted and failed to use,' *Michigan Law and Policy Review*, vol. 1, 1996, p. 204.

sakal (the normal word for a miscarriage; cf. Exod 23:26) and referred to the fetus by either *golem* or *nefel*.[39] But this is not what is said, nor what is meant. The Hebrew word used is *yatsa*, which is a more general verb meaning 'to come out'. In the context of pregnancy this nearly always refers to giving birth (as in Gen 25:24-26 and 38:28-30). Consequently, in the ancient world the Exodus text was not seen as a justification for abortion except, in rabbinic interpretation, to save the mother's life.

However, the Septuagint was used as a basis for the 'Old Latin' version of the Bible (the Vulgate). This in turn was used by Augustine (among others), who felt obliged to embrace a formed/unformed duality. The popularity of his commentaries kept that version of Exodus 21:22-25 alive.[40] Yet it did not change people's thinking that deliberate destruction of an unborn child was wrong. Indeed Augustine himself "disapproved of the abortion of both the vivified and unvivified fetus, but distinguished between the two".[41] As I've argued, this distinction is based on a misunderstanding of Exodus 21:22-25. But however you interpret it, this passage only refers to accidental injury. Therefore, it "cannot be used to imply support for the intentional destruction of human life in abortion".[42]

Furthermore, despite an acknowledged lack of understanding of the process involved in embryological development (see Eccl 11:5), the link between conception and birth was clearly understood in biblical times:

> Adam knew Eve his wife, and she conceived and bore Cain… (Gen 4:1)

---

39. The one place in the Old Testament where the Hebrew word *golem* is used is in Psalm 139:16. And as we've already seen, it is certainly not used there in a way that implies the fetus is less than fully human. *Nefel* is the usual word for a stillborn child (Job 3:16; Ps 58:8; Eccl 6:3).

40. The idea of delayed ensoulment developed from the embracing of Aristotle's science. Delayed ensoulment is not a biblical idea. Aristotle believed that formation of the human embryo was not complete until 40 days for males and 90 days for females. He believed that the embryo did not belong to the human species, and therefore obtain a soul, until then. Augustine picked up these ideas and they were subsequently propagated by Thomas Aquinas. Aristotle's embryology was accepted as fact until the 17th century. However, by then both Calvin and Luther had taught that the soul was given at conception. With Aristotle's biology discredited, Catholic theologians increasingly came to agree. See Jones, op. cit., chapter 4.

41. JC Bauerschmidt, 'Abortion', in AD Fitzgerald (ed.) *Augustine Through the Ages*, Eerdmans, Grand Rapids, 1999, p. 1.

42. O'Mathuna, op. cit., p. 94.

The birth of Christ was similarly announced:

> ...an angel of the Lord appeared to him in a dream, saying, "Joseph, son of David, do not fear to take Mary as your wife, for that which is conceived in her is from the Holy Spirit. She will bear a son, and you shall call his name Jesus, for he will save his people from their sins." (Matt 1:20-21)

Indeed, a strong argument for the importance of the nascent human comes from the incarnation of Jesus. It is clear from the Gospels that Jesus' human existence commenced at his conception. This was certainly the understanding of the early Christian church.[43] As John the Baptist's prenatal life is similarly described, Jesus' prenatal life cannot be attributed to his divinity. If Jesus assumed human nature at the point of conception, it follows that all human existence commences at conception.

Luke's account of the meeting between Mary and Elizabeth in Luke 1 is interesting in this regard. Mary had just been visited by the angel Gabriel, and was in early pregnancy when she hurried to visit her relative Elizabeth, who was 6 months pregnant with John the Baptist:

> And when Elizabeth heard the greeting of Mary, the baby leaped in her womb. And Elizabeth was filled with the Holy Spirit, and she exclaimed with a loud cry, "Blessed are you among women, and blessed is the fruit of your womb! And why is this granted to me that the mother of my Lord should come to me? For behold, when the sound of your greeting came to my ears, the baby in my womb leaped for joy." (Luke 1:41-44)

Luke is suggesting that Jesus and John, both *in utero*, were as present as Mary and Elizabeth at this meeting: John the Baptist is noted to have 'recognized' Jesus. Furthermore, the Greek word *brephos*, used to describe the unborn John, is the same word used later on to describe the baby Jesus (Luke 2:12) and also the little children who came to Jesus in Luke 18:15.

Luke's account is also interesting because if Mary went to visit as soon as she received the news ("with haste", v. 39), and given a journey of approximately one week, Jesus would have been a blastocyst (a 5-7 day

---

43. Jones, op. cit., p. 129.

old embryo) at the time Mary met Elizabeth, who acknowledged him as her Lord (v. 43).[44]

Pulling the above biblical strands together, then, we can only conclude that God recognizes and interacts with embryonic humans from the time of conception through to birth and beyond.

There are Christians who have argued against this understanding. RJ Berry, an ecological geneticist awarded for his advocacy of the Christian faith in the world of science, argues that Psalm 139 cannot be used to argue for continuity except in retrospect by a rational being (i.e. 'Since I know I am here now, I realize it was me in my mother's womb'). He argues it is not legitimate to say that God is in relationship with every fetus and embryo created (including those lost early in development). He makes a point of saying that continuity can only apply to *persons*:

> Once a *person* exists [which Berry seems to define as one who is able to reason], one must reckon with his or her whole life history as a linked sequence of divinely guided and appointed processes and events. But Psalm 139 says nothing whatsoever about those who are not 'persons'.[45]

Berry says that if we are honest, we should admit that we don't know what relationship God has with the early embryo.

In other words, if I say that Psalm 139 seems to show God clearly interacting with a human person *in utero*, Berry would respond by saying we can't know that, because by his definition of 'person' (derived from elsewhere) the fetus or embryo in Psalm 139 is not a person. This just seems to be an *a priori* ruling out of inconvenient evidence.

Berry also says we can't count the incarnation of Jesus because that was a special case. This is a question of who has the burden of proof. Is it those who continue the teaching of the moral worth of the unborn, which extends since Old Testament times, or those who now want to disregard embryonic humans for the sake of scientific research?

Sadly, it appears that the late Anglican theologian Gordon Dunstan was influential in persuading Bishop Harries—the Chair of the House of Lords Select Committee on Stem Cell Research in the United

---

44. JJ Davis, 'The status of the human embryo: religious issues', plenary session at the Genetic and Reproductive Ethics Conference, The Center for Bioethics and Human Dignity, Deerfield, 14-16 July 2005.

45. RJ Berry, *God and the Biologist*, Apollos, Leicester, 1996, p. 73.

Kingdom—to allow destructive research on embryos in that country.[46] Dunstan appealed to Christian tradition to downgrade the importance of the human embryo. He pointed out in a 1984 article that medieval Christians such as Aquinas believed the embryo did not have a soul until it was fully formed. He claimed it was only since the late 19th century that Christians had given absolute protection to the human embryo "from the moment of conception".[47] Unfortunately, he based his ideas on the inaccurate translation of Exodus 21:22-23 in the Septuagint, and on the outdated embryology of Aristotle.

Conclusion

How does the Bible suggest we treat this being who is "fearfully and wonderfully made" (Ps 139:14)? We will discuss the Christian ethical framework in chapter 5, but for now I simply want to point out that our God has a special concern for the vulnerable in society, and his expectation is that we will be likewise concerned. He upholds the cause of the weak and oppressed. He shows no partiality, and neither should we (e.g. Deut 10:17-18; 24:14; Isa 1:17). While these passages obviously don't refer to embryonic human life, is there any member of society more vulnerable than an unwanted human embryo?

Should we give a human embryo the same moral status as a human adult? As we've seen, that depends on our view of human personhood. However, even if you are unsure whether the early embryo has the same moral status as a fully developed human adult, this is very different from saying that it has no moral status whatsoever, and is not entitled to any protection or any respect. (Specific exceptions are discussed throughout this book.)

It seems to me that logic obliges us to contend that human life and human personhood begin at fertilization. This is our experience. At no point during my pregnancies did I think of the child I was carrying as an embryo or a fetus. They were always babies, and I think this is a very normal and common perception.

We are now able to see why the public debate regarding when life begins has been so heated and protracted. Issues including the

---

46. DA Jones, 'Dunstan, the embryo and Christian tradition', *Triple Helix*, Summer 2005, pp. 10-11.
47. GR Dunstan, 'The moral status of the human embryo: a tradition recalled', *Journal of Medical Ethics*, vol. 10, no. 1, March 1984, p. 43.

destruction of human life and the potential cure of disabling disease will inevitably arouse emotion. But it is obvious to me that consensus will never be reached, because of the different ways in which those on either side of the debate are addressing the question. Proponents of embryo and fetal destruction are looking at the favourable consequences they expect to result. Opponents will not permit this destruction of human life on any terms, despite anticipated consequences. For those who hold them, absolute moral values will stand regardless of the context.

This may make those opposed to destructive embryo research, for example, seem hard and uncaring to our community. It is suggested that such citizens do not care about human suffering, about those who live in hope of a miracle. There is no equivalent visual symbol for embryos as powerful as the disabled men and women, boys and girls who sit patiently in wheelchairs. We do have 'snowflake children'—those born from donated 'excess' embryos left over from IVF. But they are relatively few in number, and it will be years before they can articulate their opposition as coherently as those who support human embryo destruction and sit eye to eye with politicians in parliamentary hearings.

We cannot expect those who do not acknowledge the authority of the Bible to agree with us, especially when Christians do not even agree with one another. We have not always taken the lead we should have when our community was trying to decide how unborn human life was to be treated. We have at times failed to be salt and light to a society seeking moral guidance. Around the time of the Warnock committee's enquiry, there were many people looking to the church for direction as to how to treat the human embryo. Our failure is summarized in a comment by philosophers Peter Singer and Deane Wells at the time:

> The difficulty here is that those upon whom God could most reasonably be expected to have vouchsafed revelation do not all seem to be in possession of the same information.[48]

This is a challenge for our churches. We need to equip Christians with a sufficiently sophisticated biblical understanding of our culture, including modern biotechnology, so that they are able to participate meaningfully in the public discourse that decides what scientific developments are acceptable to our community on moral grounds.

---

48. P Singer and D Wells, 'In vitro fertilization: The major issues', *Journal of Medical Ethics*, vol. 9, no. 4, December 1983, p. 193.

As for the moral status of the embryo, I would suggest that we need to recognize the personhood argument for what it is: pure expediency, designed to justify political decisions that allow the development of medical technologies and procedures that come with the cost of sacrificing early human life. I recognize that the overwhelming majority of those who want these technologies developed do so with good motives. Treatments for debilitating disease; avoidance of suffering; a child of one's own—these are good things that we all value, and that we should value. However, we need to ask whether we should seek these things at the cost of another human's life.

Human relationships

IN THE PREVIOUS CHAPTER, we looked to the Genesis account to understand what it means to be human. We can see that we are dependent, embodied creatures who are designed to live within the limits set for us by our loving creator God. This is central to the Christian understanding of freedom. Even though when we have children we are 'co-creators' with God, we are unlike God in that we are not omniscient, and so even as co-creators we are to continue to observe the limits he has put in place. We are not to take on the role of God for ourselves.

Moreover, as relational creatures, we need to understand what is permissible for us in the context of our relationships. We do not make our decisions in an isolated or abstract way, but as embodied creatures who have a history and experience of life and who live in relationship with others. The aim of this chapter, then, is to understand from the Bible what our relationships are intended to be, and what our responsibilities are within them. Only then will we be able to make ethical decisions that are aligned with God's will.

When talking about the birth of children, for example, what is the best word to use? Bioethicist Leon Kass underlines the importance of this point when he writes:

> Consider the views of life and the world reflected in the following
> different expressions to describe the process of generating new life.
> Ancient Israel, impressed with the phenomenon of the transmission
> of life from father to son, used a word we translate as "begetting" or
> "siring" [meaning creating the same moral value as the begetter]. The
> Greeks, impressed with the springing forth of new life... called it

genesis, from a root meaning "to come into being"… The premodern Christian English-speaking world, impressed with the world as given by a Creator, used the term "pro-creation". We, impressed with the machine and the gross national product (our own work of creation), employ a metaphor of the factory, "re-production".[1]

It can be terrifying to see how easily we can slip into the thought patterns of the world, and how the language we use can lead us unconsciously to embrace a non-Christian world view.

Let us see now what is distinctive about the biblical teaching on the subject of marriage and family.

What is marriage?

In most cultures, marriage is a legal institution. In the West it has traditionally been regarded as a voluntary lifelong union between one man and one woman. Understandably, the state has an interest in marriage as the domestic unit where children are born and raised, thereby renewing society. While the community understanding of marriage has been weakened in recent years, it is still usually seen as a mutually supportive and sexually exclusive relationship.

Although it has come down to us through English common law, this understanding of marriage is grounded in the Bible's teaching that marriage is a binding covenant between a man and a woman, a covenant witnessed by God himself. So Malachi says:

> …the LORD was witness between you and the wife of your youth, to whom you have been faithless, though she is your companion and your wife by covenant. (Mal 2:14)

This is why God is so against divorce, for divorce is the breaking of a commitment that should never be broken. For this reason, divorce was carefully regulated in ancient Israel and only permitted under exceptional circumstances (Deut 24:1-4). Jesus is even more restrictive in his teaching, permitting divorce and remarriage only for unfaithfulness (Matt 19:8-9).[2]

---

1. LR Kass, *Toward a More Natural Science*, The Free Press, New York, 1988, p. 48.
2. Many commentators conclude that Paul also allows divorce and remarriage for believers who have been deserted by an unbelieving spouse (1 Cor 7:15-16). Historically, this view is given expression in chapter XXIV of *The Westminster Confession of Faith* (1646), which says, "nothing but adultery, or such willful desertion as can no way be remedied by the Church or civil magistrate, is cause sufficient of dissolving the bond of marriage" (paragraph 6).

Marriage, however, is not merely a secular institution endorsed by God; it is essentially a sacred institution, ordained by God. The origins of marriage predate its legal formalization. Indeed, Genesis 2 reveals that marriage is at the centre of God's purposes in creating humanity male and female:

> Therefore a man shall leave his father and his mother and hold fast
> to his wife, and they shall become one flesh. (Gen 2:24)

Marriage thus involves leaving one's family of origin and cleaving to one's spouse, thereby creating a new family unit that is a new one-flesh entity. The one-flesh state is expressed in sexual intercourse between husband and wife, but it is fundamentally a new creative act of God. This is why Jesus says, "What therefore God has joined together, let not man separate" (Matt 19:6). Consequently, Scripture repeatedly warns that marriage commitments should be guarded carefully (Matt 5:27-32, 19:3-9; Mark 10:2-12; 1 Thess 4:3-6; Heb 13:4).

Polygamy

Does it have to be just one man and one woman? Is monogamy the only divinely sanctioned pattern for marriage?

While it is true that polygamy was practised by godly men in the Old Testament era (such as Jacob and King David), it often led to discord between the wives and their various children: consider Abraham with Sarah and Hagar (Genesis 16), Jacob with Leah and Rachel (Gen 29:31-30:24), and Elkanah with Hannah and Peninnah (1 Sam 1:1-20). Nevertheless, while it was clearly a practice that was tolerated,[3] it was also regulated (Exodus 21:10-11 outlines a husband's obligations to his first wife when he marries a second).

---

3. Although the Bible is silent on the reasons for this, there is no question that polygamy enabled the people of Israel to multiply more rapidly (although not all households would have been able to support more than one wife). It also compensated for the high fatality rate amongst men due to the brutality of ancient warfare, which would have often meant that there were more women than men in Israelite society. Added to that, as it was difficult for an unmarried woman to provide for herself, there were clearly compassionate reasons for tolerating the practice of polygamy. There is debate as to whether the law of the Levi (Deut 25:5-10) commands a married man whose brother has died to marry his wife and give her children. Since the law is incomplete (with no mention of what is required if there is no brother, for instance), it is possible there were unwritten assumptions of what was required—for example, that the law referred to the oldest *unmarried* brother. See C Ash, *Marriage: Sex in the Service of God*, IVP, Leicester, 2003, p. 251.

On the other hand, it is noteworthy that it was first introduced by the evil Lamech (Gen 4:19) and was not God's plan in the original creation, as he gave Adam only one wife (Gen 2:18-25). Certainly in the New Testament church, it is clear that a man in leadership is to have only one wife (1 Tim 3:2, 12).

Monogamy, then, is God's ideal.

The place of sexual intercourse

That sexual intercourse is intended for heterosexual marriage is clearly taught in Scripture and is, therefore, a foundational assumption for the argument of this book. The Hebrew word for the act of intercourse (*yada*) literally means 'to know' (Gen 4:1, 17, 25). In the Bible, 'knowing' someone involves personal, intimate involvement. The term applies to coitus, where the penis is placed in the vagina, but the Bible does not count it just as a physical act in humans (as compared to animals). It is also the giving of oneself in an act that can lead to the begetting of new life.

Christians recognize two primary purposes of sex in marriage: it is *unitive*—expressing and strengthening their common love while providing mutual enjoyment (Gen 2:24); and it is *procreative*—for having children and perpetuating the human race (Gen 1:28). However, different understandings of the connection between these two purposes are at the basis of the difference between Protestant and Roman Catholic views on sexual relations.

Catholic v Protestant doctrine

In his 1968 encyclical, *Humanae Vitae* ('Of Human Life'), Pope Paul VI argued that the meaning of sex and marriage lies only in the combination of the unitive and procreative. As we've seen, the unitive refers to the strengthening of the bond between the man and woman, and the procreative refers to the production of offspring. The Catholic Church teaches that each and every marital act (i.e. of sexual intercourse) must retain its relationship to the procreation of human life.[4] In other words, marital sex that only has unitive intention is improper.[5] This is one of the

---

4. Encyclical of Paul VI, *Humanae Vitae: On the Regulation of Birth*, Rome, 25 July 1968.

5. Pope Paul VI bases his arguments in *Humanae Vitae* on arguments of natural law, which basically maintains that all created things have a 'natural' and presumably divinely intended use (e.g. sex = procreation) that humans can rationally work out. Traditionally Protestants have rejected this line of argument on grounds that, since the Fall, man's reason has been damaged by sin, and it is only through biblical revelation that we can be sure of God's intended purposes. Paul VI did not refer to Genesis in his encyclical.

reasons the Catholic Church forbids most contraception.

Protestant churches, on the other hand, teach that the unitive and procreative aspects of marital sex should apply to the overall marriage relationship, but not necessarily to each individual act of intercourse. The Protestant understanding is that the prevention of fertilization through contraception is permissible, as long as the marriage is open to procreation at some time unless serious considerations exclude it.[6] The views put forward in this book will be Protestant unless otherwise indicated.

The nature of the 'one flesh' union

Given that sexual intimacy is intended for heterosexual marriage, what more might be said about the 'one flesh' union and the purposes of sex in marriage? As we've already seen, the language of two becoming "one flesh" (Gen 2:24) is a powerful and evocative way of combining notions of kinship with sexual intimacy, whilst at the same time highlighting a number of the other God-given purposes of marriage. These are listed below.

1. Purposeful companionship

As a gift of God, married love is a good, in and of itself. More than that, it is an expression of our creation in the image of the God who does not exist in solitude, but is a 'being in relation', a 'trinity' of three persons within one godhead. Marriage is thus intended to provide intimate companionship for image-bearers who are wired for relationship. Not surprisingly, this is the first purpose of marriage mentioned in the Bible. As God himself declares: "It is not good that the man should be alone; I will make him a helper fit for him" (Gen 2:18). However, as Christopher Ash notes:

> …we must not conclude that the final *goal* of this delightful and intimate companionship is to be found in the delight, the intimacy or the companionship. This is delight with a shared purpose, intimacy with a common goal, and companionship in a task beyond the boundaries of the couple themselves.[7]

Relationship and task go hand in hand.

---

6. Karl Barth notes the need to take into account "various considerations regarding… physical and psychological health" that may make it impossible for a couple to assume responsibility for children. See K Barth, 'Parents and Children', in *Church Dogmatics*, vol. III.4, GW Bromiley and TF Torrance (eds), T and T Clark, London and New York, 2010, pp. 272-3. This will be discussed further in chapter 6.

7. Ash, op. cit., p. 121.

2. Equality and partnership

In creating Eve as a "fit" helper, God is affirming her equal status as a bearer of his image despite her different sexuality. The Hebrew word for 'helper' (*ezer*) underscores this, as most of its uses in the Old Testament refer to God (Israel's 'helper' in times of trouble). Therefore, as Carolyn C James notes, the traditional translation of this word as 'helpmeet', and its restriction (in English) to marriage, has led to a diminished understanding of its meaning and application to marriage.[8] The term is a strong one, which contains no suggestion of inferiority. Rather, it implies Eve's necessity (for Adam needs her), and emphasizes the fact that husband and wife together are to exercise dominion and labour alongside each other to advance God's kingdom.

3. Differentiated unity

Because he has created Eve directly, God 'gives away the bride' at the first marriage. When he presents Eve to Adam, Adam responds ecstatically, describing her as "bone of my bones and flesh of my flesh" (Gen 2:23). This highlights the unity of the man and the woman, a unity that is expressed most fully in marriage. Indeed, the image of shared flesh and the subsequent statement about the 'one flesh' nature of the marriage union (Gen 2:23-24) point to the intimacy of this unity when it takes sexual expression. However, it is important to appreciate that it is a differentiated unity. This is captured in the Hebrew word translated as "fit for him" (*kenegdo*) in verse 18 (literally, 'like opposite him'), which suggests "both likeness and difference or complementarity".[9]

4. Ordered complementarity

The unity of the man and the woman is also an ordered unity. This is seen in the fact that Adam was formed first (cf. 1 Tim 2:13), that Eve was taken from him and made for him (cf. 1 Cor 11:8-9), and finally in the fact that Eve was named by him (Gen 3:20). This order, far from undermining the equality of husband and wife, serves and enhances their unity. This is seen most powerfully in Ephesians 5, where the image of human marriage given in Genesis 2 (in both its unity and order) is shown to be a prototype of the union between Christ and his church, his body and bride (Eph 5:22-33). Despite the strain that has come upon all human marriages

---

8.   CC James, *Lost Women of the Bible*. Zondervan, Grand Rapids, 2005, pp. 335-6.
9.   A Perriman, *Speaking of Women*, Apollos, Leicester, 1998, p. 180.

as a consequence of the Fall (Gen 3:16b), the Ephesians passage shows us that a profound solidarity between spouses, which embraces their different roles and responsibilities, is still God's intention.[10]

5. Relational priority

Another facet of Genesis 2:24 is that the union of man and woman in marriage takes priority over responsibilities to parents. This is seen in the fact that the man leaves his family of origin to create not an extension of his family, but a new and distinct "public social unit".[11] This idea is conveyed by the Hebrew word for 'flesh' (*basar*), which is often used of a clan or family group (e.g. Gen 29:14, 37:27). This does not mean that family connections are severed or that the command to honour one's parents has no further application to those who are married. But it does mean that the responsibilities of husband and wife to each other take precedence over all other relational obligations.

6. Permanence and exclusivity

A clear implication of this relational priority is the fact that the relationship of husband and wife is to be lifelong and exclusive. In other words, in two becoming one flesh we see God's intention for marriage to be both monogamous and inviolable. In commenting on Genesis 2:24, John Murray says that as for divorce so for polygamy: "from the beginning it was not so… The indissolubility of the bond of marriage and the principle of monogamy are inherent in the verse".[12] This is why God condemns adultery (Exod 20:14; Lev 20:10) and is so against divorce (Mal 2:13-16). The ultimate theological reason for this understanding is to be found in the model of Christ and the church (Eph 5:22-33). Christ has only one bride, whom he regards as his "body" (v. 30), and he literally loves her to death (v. 25)!

7. Mutual enjoyment and enrichment

The shared intimacy of sex allows for the expression of love that strengthens the bond of the couple. Before the Fall (Gen 2:25), Adam

---

10. Ephesians 5 also confirms that order in marriage (i.e. headship and submission) is not a consequence of the curse. The Fall distorted the God-given order, but it did not create it. True headship means love and self-sacrifice (Eph 5:25), and true submission is not a matter of enforced subservience but of voluntary service and respect (Eph 5:33).

11. Ash, op. cit., p. 348.

12. J Murray, *Principles of Conduct*, Eerdmans, Grand Rapids, 1957, p. 30.

and Eve share physical intimacy without shame. This changes after the Fall (Gen 3:7), although the enjoyment of sexual union and its ability to enrich marriage relationships persists. Passages such as Proverbs 5:18-19 and the Song of Solomon describe the delight the husband and wife should find in each other:

> Let your fountain be blessed,
>> and rejoice in the wife of your youth,
>> a lovely deer, a graceful doe.
> Let her breasts fill you at all times with delight;
>> be intoxicated always in her love. (Prov 5:18-19)

This combination of mutual pleasure and marriage enrichment is another purpose of human sexual expression within the one flesh union of marriage.

8. Mutual satisfaction and protection

A further purpose of sex within marriage, which we learn from the New Testament, is to suppress the temptation to be sexually immoral:

> Do not deprive one another, except perhaps by agreement for a limited time, that you may devote yourselves to prayer; but then come together again, so that Satan may not tempt you because of your lack of self-control. (1 Cor 7:5)[13]

Therefore, as Christopher Ash notes:

> In marriage there is a mutual moral obligation on both husband and wife each to surrender their body to the other in willing sexual relations sustained so far as health permits over the lifetime of their marriage.[14]

Of course, the duty to provide each other with mutual sexual satisfaction is not only a defense against unfaithfulness but also protects and nourishes the "one flesh" union. This in turn benefits not only the couple and their children, but also their neighbours and wider human society.[15]

9. The birth of children

Finally, the procreation of children is expected within marriage as a result of sexual intercourse. Indeed, "the intrinsic structure of the act between the man and the woman is intended and designed towards this

---

13.   See also 1 Thessalonians 4:3-4.
14.   Ash, op. cit., p. 190.
15.   ibid., p. 110.

end".[16] For as husband and wife come together, so may their gametes (the sperm and egg) result in a child for whom both are responsible. Children, then, are an intended part of the blessing of marriage, and are themselves a rich blessing from God. As the psalmist writes:

> Behold, children are a heritage from the LORD,
>   the fruit of the womb a reward.
> Like arrows in the hand of a warrior
>   are the children of one's youth.
> Blessed is the man
>   who fills his quiver with them! (Ps 127:3-5a)

Procreation, then, is a good gift of God and a vital part of the divine intention for the "one flesh" union of marriage.

The blessing of children

While the words of Genesis 1:28—"Be fruitful and multiply and fill the earth and subdue it"—are often described as a command, not only are they preceded by a statement of blessing ("And God blessed them"), but the Hebrew is also suggestive of a blessing.[17] Nor does this blessing disappear after the Fall, for it is repeated to Noah and his family following the flood (Gen 9:1, 7). Obviously (and for many, painfully), not all couples are able to have children—a reality that is repeatedly acknowledged in Scripture.[18] Nevertheless, children within marriage are presented as the norm, for it is through the birth of children that the image of God is perpetuated (Gen 5:1), and the creative and redemptive purposes of God achieved.

However, it also needs to be said that the life-partnership of marriage should not be seen as *subservient* to the procreation and training of children. Karl Barth notes the Roman Catholic teaching (derived from Thomas Aquinas)[19] that it *is* subservient, and insists the opposite is true. Barth's view is that the family is subordinate to the marriage, the life-partnership, which does not depend on the coexistence of children to be valid. This would seem to be supported by Genesis 2:18-22, which

---

16. ibid., p. 248.
17. BK Waltke and CJ Fredricks, *Genesis: A commentary*, Zondervan, Grand Rapids, 2001, p. 67.
18. I will address the issue of childlessness in chapter 10.
19. Thomas Aquinas, *Summa Theologica*, 2nd edn, trans. the Fathers of the English Dominican Province, Part III, Burns Oates and Washbourne, London, 1926, p. 39.

contains no explicit mention of children and where the emphasis falls on the relationship between the man and the woman. But this point should not be overstated, for the 'command' to multiply has already been supplied in Genesis 1 and Scripture nowhere encourages 'chosen childlessness'.[20] Marriage as a loving life-partnership is indeed a highly significant work in itself, and one that mirrors the union of Christ and the church. And so it is a valid end in itself.[21] Nevertheless, marriage, as the basic unit of society, is the God-ordained context within which the raising of children occurs.[22]

Ironically, the blessing of children was not experienced by Adam and Eve prior to the Fall. Furthermore, following the Fall, the experience of childbirth becomes a difficult one for Eve; the Lord God says to her, "I will surely multiply your pain in childbearing; in pain you shall bring forth children" (Gen 3:16). In addition to this, the task of filling the earth has also become more difficult, for mortality has entered the scene. So Adam is told that he will return to dust (v. 19).

Nevertheless, God's creative and redemptive purposes will prevail. For, although Adam and Eve have been barred from access to the tree of life (Gen 3:22-24), "Immortality is replaced by progeny, opening the door to redemptive history".[23] Adam subsequently calls the woman 'Eve'—mother of all the living (v. 20), trusting the Lord's promise that she will bear offspring who will finally defeat Satan. For this reason, parenthood is closely related to the salvation story. So the Scriptures trace the children of the promise from Eve's seed or offspring (Gen 3:15), through the line of Abraham, all the way to Jesus (Matt 1:1-16), God's Son, who was "born of woman" (Gal 4:4), and then through Jesus to all who have received his Spirit (Gal 4:5-6, 28)—a multiethnic multitude that no-one can number (Rev 7:9).

For those who take the time to go looking for them, there are a lot of creative lists on the internet explaining why people should have children. In my experience the usual reasons include things like:

---

20. As we have already noted, there are sometimes good and valid reasons (of a medical or psychological or even financial kind) that require some couples to choose (albeit reluctantly) not to have (more) children. See further in Ash, op. cit., pp. 175-9.

21. Barth, op. cit., p. 258.

22. See chapter 6 for discussion of the altered nature of this command under the New Covenant.

23. Waltke and Fredricks, op. cit., p. 94.

- to continue the family line
- to look after you when you're old
- for self-fulfilment
- as a physical representation of your "one flesh"
- to help in the family business.

There is no doubt that the desire to have children can be strong, and we should sympathize with those who are unable to fulfil it. We can even understand why people in our community talk about a 'right to reproduce' and seek ever-expanding technologies to achieve it (Prov 13:12). However, the Bible teaches us to view children rather differently.

Christians see child-bearing not as a way to find self-fulfilment so much as to raise up "Godly offspring" (Mal 2:15). A new generation must learn how to exert responsible dominion over the creation, and while we are waiting for Christ to return we are called to proclaim the gospel. Therefore, we will do better to consider our responsibilities rather than our rights. The Bible does not suggest we possess our children, but that we receive them as a gift:

> "Behold, children are a gift of the Lord;
> the fruit of the womb is a reward." (Ps 127:3, NASB)

The responsibilities of parenthood

The Bible speaks of parenthood not just in terms of procreation but also in terms of the subsequent time, effort and love involved in childrearing, regardless of the child's biological origins. The honour of parenthood is lifelong and to be lived out according to God's commands. When a child is biologically related to its parents, this relationship usually begins before the birth. The responsibilities of parenthood remain for both parents even if they are not married, although this situation will inevitably be more difficult.

Parents are to stand as a witness and a godly example to their children. This seems to be part of the reason the apostle Paul regards the children of even just one believing parent as "holy" (1 Cor 7:14). Such children are not only acceptable to God (rather than being "unclean"), but also stand in a place of privilege. Consequently, they will be "marked by an element of shaping and 'difference' from a wholly pagan environment".[24]

---

24. A Thiselton, *The First Epistle to the Corinthians*, Eerdmans, Grand Rapids, 2000, p. 530.

This does not mean they are born Christians, or that they will inevitably become Christians, but that there is a saving and sanctifying influence adults can have over their children merely by the fact of their existence and presence as Christians.

Parents are called to nurture their children. God expected Abraham to "command his children and his household after him to keep the way of the LORD by doing righteousness and justice" (Gen 18:19). With regard to the Law, God's words, Moses instructed Israel to "teach them diligently to your children... talk of them when you sit in your house, and when you walk by the way, and when you lie down, and when you rise" (Deut 6:7). In Proverbs, children are repeatedly exhorted to heed the wisdom of their parents (e.g. 1:8).

In teaching their children about the ways of God, parents are also expected to exercise authority over their children—not in a domineering way, but by modelling their own obedience to God and discipling the children on his behalf. Ephesians 3:14-15 tells us that God is the Father from whom all fatherhood is named. Our children are his children. Any way we can serve our children, he can surpass, whether it be in giving good gifts (Matt 7:9-11) or administering discipline (Heb 12:7-11).[25] Therefore, we must model our parenting on his. This is why the New Testament says to fathers: "do not provoke your children to anger, but bring them up in the discipline and instruction of the Lord" (Eph 6:4). Similarly, "do not provoke your children, lest they become discouraged" (Col 3:21).

This latter teaching, that fathers should be careful to avoid overburdening their children and arousing rebellion, reminds us how important it is to operate in a framework of grace. Christian parents, no less than their children, stand in constant need of the mercies of God. The extended contact they have with their children provides a unique opportunity to communicate this, for the time God gives them. The end must come, either with the child returning to God or with the child leaving his or her parents. Then the cycle will begin again (1 Tim 5:4).

If the gracious love of God is the reason he "makes his sun rise on the evil and on the good, and sends rain on the just and on the unjust" (Matt 5:45), so we must seek to lovingly provide the things that our children

---

25. Barth reconciles the teaching regarding discipline in Proverbs (3:11-12, 13:24, 19:18, 22:15, 23:13-14, 29:15) with Hebrews 12 by explaining that the task of parents since the coming of Jesus is to teach their children not the law but the gospel. See Barth, op. cit., p. 271.

need regardless of their response (1 John 3:11-16).

These needs will include the material. Responsibilities to our families in this regard will be ongoing. In 1 Timothy 5:8, Paul tells us that "if anyone does not provide for his relatives, and especially for members of his household, he has denied the faith and is worse than an unbeliever". Parents should be aware of whether the needs of each child are being met, and this will include being responsible stewards when they reach the point at which their resources cannot provide for additional children.

We also know that a sense of belonging is important for children. In the Old Testament we see examples of God encouraging the children of Israel to remember the stories of his deliverance (such as with the memorial stones in Joshua 4:4-7, 20-24), which belong to the generations. Furthermore, as embodied, finite creatures, we are all linked by lines of kinship and have a place in time and space. Our very existence is, in one way or another, embedded in a family line. This is easy to forget at times in our individualistic society.

But does this have to be within a nuclear family?

Other definitions of 'family'

A nuclear family consists of a married couple and their children. There has been public pressure in recent years to broaden the definition of 'family' to reflect what is happening in our society. While there have always been step-families, children raised by grandparents, and other combinations resulting from the vicissitudes of life, the advent of 'children without sex' has opened up new ways of becoming parents. Every now and then a single, female Hollywood star decides she can't wait any longer for a man, and decides to have a child without one. Actress Sharon Stone, single mother of three adopted sons, has said:

> I'd urge anyone who is even considering it to go ahead and make their own family, instead of sitting around dreaming and hoping that their Prince Charming is going to come and give them children. What's the point?… Make it happen for yourself. If your Prince Charming does come, then he's going to walk in and say, 'Oh, just what I've been looking for, a family waiting for me'. We can do that these days.[26]

---

26. M Freedman, 'Women are looking for standing ovation as curtains threaten to close on fertility', *Sun-Herald*, 16 March 2008, p. 28.

Same-sex couples can now 'reproduce' with the assistance of donor gametes and ART procedures. Many of the biological barriers to child-bearing in the past no longer apply.

There are numerous examples of family structure in the Bible. The Old Testament features the ancient extended tribal families, while the more urbanized New Testament exhibits a pattern of households (which often included servants). The modern Middle Eastern experience of family is still quite different from the experience of family known to most Westerners. None are identified as being superior. However, married couples remain central within all these models, along with the expectation that their relationship is permanent and exclusive.

Interestingly, Jesus taught us that it is our brothers and sisters in Christ who are our true family: "whoever does the will of God, he is my brother and sister and mother" (Mark 3:31-35; cf. Matt 12:46-50; Luke 8:19-21). He also taught that our allegiance to God is more important than family ties (Matt 10:34-38; cf. Luke 12:49-53, 14:26; Mark 10:28-31). However, we know from Genesis that God's original plan was for a child to be brought up in a home with a male and female parent.

In other words, the biblical norm is for family to proceed from a married couple. Whilst this is not everyone's experience, there is a significant difference between missing out on this through tragedy or misadventure, and creating an alternative situation on purpose.

How does this influence decisions about procreation?

In a world where we have the options of surrogacy, donor sperm, frozen embryos and genetic testing, how do Christians respond to the God-given desire for a child?

According to the Bible, children are the result of the "one flesh" union between husband and wife, a physical sign of their mutual love. The family is the intended place for the raising of children. Does this mean that married couples have a *right* to have children? In view of the technology now available to assist with reproduction, do we have a right to pursue a child at all costs?

In answering such questions, several points need to be considered. First, because human beings are creatures under the authority of the creator, we are free to act within the limitations of God's design. Our God-given drive to procreate is meant to function within that design. We are free to try to carry out the God-given instruction to be fruitful. We are free to pursue healing if our bodies are damaged in some way that makes child-bearing difficult.[27] But not at any cost. We are not to disobey God's word in our efforts to become parents.

Second, the responsibilities parents have in caring for their offspring will be another limiting factor on what we decide as we go about making reproductive choices. We will aim to witness to a gracious, generous God. We will aim to provide a sense of belonging, whether biological ties exist or not, as our children grow. We will aim to protect our embryonic children from destruction, our fetal children from harm. This does not give us clear ethical guidance in every instance, as all child-bearing involves risk of some kind, both to mother and child. We must pray for wisdom in our decision-making. Yet some things are clear. We will respect human life, its dignity and its value, for each person is made in the image of God throughout the entire procreative process; that is, from fertilization on.

The Bible also talks about our responsibilities to our spouse. In our desire for a child we should not risk our marriage. The stresses of coping with issues of childlessness are well known. Nowhere in the Bible are we promised that every married couple will be able to have children. Nowhere are we promised that if we do have children, they will be healthy. Children are a gift of God, and we are to nurture them in the time they are with us. We will extend to them the same love and hospitality that has been shown to us and is therefore expected of us. Above all, we will stand united with our spouse as we seek to serve our heavenly Father, whether that be as parents or not.

In Western culture (including Western Christian culture), it is now customary for married couples to delay child-bearing while the marital bonds are being strengthened. During this period, husband and wife will be more interested in considering and ensuring contraception than in actively building a family. We therefore need to consider whether it is ethically acceptable for Christians to use contraceptives, and if so, which ones. However, before embarking on this task, we first need to examine a model for ethical Christian decision-making.

---

27.   See chapter 16.

Which ethical basis?

I N A PLURALIST SOCIETY it is difficult to find moral consensus, because we no longer have a common process for working out right from wrong. We hope our legislators will consider an ethical perspective as they make decisions, but there is no guarantee that their ethics will be consistent with biblical ethics.

Let me illustrate some common ways of making ethical decisions in our community by using the example of abortion.

The most common approach to deciding right from wrong in our society is to judge actions solely by their consequences—that is, the rightness or otherwise of a course of action is determined by looking at the outcome. As I mentioned briefly in chapter 3, this ethical theory is called *consequentialism*. If you expect a good outcome, then it is a morally good decision. If you anticipate a bad outcome, it is the wrong ethical choice. For example, a consequentialist finds that she has an unplanned pregnancy. She worries that this unwanted baby will have a bad effect on her health, her career, and her general happiness. She reasons that since an abortion would remove these threats to her future and provide a better outcome, then an abortion is the ethically correct choice for *her*.

Another popular theory involves evaluating choices in terms of an individual's *rights*. In the case of abortion, we often hear the classic argument of a woman's 'right to choose' what happens to her body. While there are some recognized lists of rights (such as *The Universal Declaration of Human Rights* by the United Nations),[1] nowadays many people use

---

1.   UN General Assembly, *The Universal Declaration of Human Rights*, 10 December 1948.

'rights' language simply to demand something they really, really want, but which is not actually a valid 'right' at all.

Cuts both ways

Note that each of these common ethical theories could also be used to argue against abortion. The consequentialist might decide that missing out on being a mother is a bad outcome, so she may decide against abortion. The rights advocate might consider the right of the baby to life. The relativist might just prefer not to have the abortion, and the communitarian might decide it is bad for the community to allow the devaluing of human life, and decide that abortion is wrong on these grounds. The ethical theory you use is just an instrument that gives you a method to work through the question; it does not necessarily determine what you decide. Your presuppositions (the basic principles that you accept as true— such as believing that life starts at fertilization) will also make a big difference to your conclusion. This demonstrates that, even without using biblical principles, non-Christians will at times agree with Christians on issues of morality, though possibly for different reasons.

In many heated public debates on topics such as abortion, you often hear an argument like this: "If you don't like abortion then don't have one, but don't stop someone else from having one". This argument is based on a theory called *moral relativism*. According to this theory, there is no absolute right or wrong, and moral rules are just an expression of personal preferences (influenced by cultural factors). Therefore choosing an abortion is a matter of expressing your personal preferences and values, and does not need any other reason to justify it—just as if you were choosing what to eat for breakfast. Furthermore, no-one should judge another's choice and ask for abortion to be banned.[2]

Sometimes the ethically correct healthcare for an individual is decided by what is best for the community as a whole—a theory called *communitarianism*. Consider, for example, when public policy needs to determine what public funds will be spent on, or which procedures will be legal. Some people justify abortion for disabled babies on the grounds that it is better for the community if disabled children are not born, so that they don't have to be

---

2. For a comprehensive refutation of moral relativism in the abortion debate, see F Beckwith, *Defending Life*, Cambridge University Press, New York, 2007, chapter 1.

supported, which costs society time and money. Note that you would need to combine another theory with this one, because the main feature of communitarianism is its assumption that what is right for the individual can be determined by working out what is best for the group. (Christian responses to all these arguments are given below.)

Christian decision-making

Serious ethical deliberation involves a logical process of working through basic principles to determine what is the right thing to do. Human reason therefore plays a role in evangelical ethics, but a Christian will not operate without the guiding authority of Scripture. However, because human reason is fallible, and because we don't all have exactly the same priorities or the same perceptions of the way the world is, it is possible that two Christians will approach the same ethical question and come to different, but valid, conclusions. They would not come to a conclusion that is contrary to Scripture, but there are many issues on which Scripture is silent. For example, given that government is operating under God's authority (as Romans 13 teaches), what mode of government is correct? While we would probably all prefer democratic government on grounds of human equality, some of us might support a more capitalist version of democracy because it encourages human enterprise, and others might favour a more socialist version because it aims to support the poor and the weak.[3] Both conclusions make sense. That is why there are Christians in different political parties.

In order to make informed and biblical decisions, we really need two things: a clear understanding of the facts related to the decision, and a sound biblical framework for making sense of them and working out what is the right and wrong thing to do. In medical decision-making, many Christians often struggle with the first of these factors—that is, they simply don't have a good knowledge of the facts, often because of rapidly changing technologies that are emerging. Much of the rest of this book will be concerned with providing this information.

However, knowing the facts is not enough. We also need a clear and applicable biblical foundation on which to base our decision-making. In this chapter, I will introduce one basic approach, but there are excellent

---

3.   This example is taken from J Stott, *New Issues Facing Christians Today*, rev. edn, HarperCollins, London, 1999, p. 46.

accounts elsewhere which provide comprehensive explanations.[4]

All explanations of evangelical Christian decision-making will use the Bible as the moral compass. The Bible contains some specific guidance—for example, we are told to obey God's commands as an expression of our love for him (John 14:15). We also find some general moral principles in its pages that we can confidently follow (e.g. Matthew 5-7). However, just as important is the Bible's portrayal of the character of the God we seek to emulate—his goodness, justice, mercy, grace and forgiveness (Exod 34:6-7). There are also numerous lists of the qualities of character (virtues) that we should seek to develop as we grow in godliness (Gal 5:22-23; Eph 4:1-3, 32; Phil 4:8; Col 3:12-13; 1 Tim 4:12, 6:11; 2 Tim 2:22, 3:10-11; Titus 3:1-2; 1 Pet 3:8; 2 Pet 1:5-7). Furthermore, the Bible teaches us the context of our lives—what we are as human beings, what kind of world we live in, and what lies in our future.

As we already began to see in chapter 3, it is also important to consider the whole of Scripture as it unfolds so that our conclusions are not distorted by a partial appreciation of God's purposes. This will involve reflecting on what is often called 'biblical theology'—the framework of God's unfolding revelation in the Bible:

1. Creation: the world as God originally made it
2. Fall: the world as it is affected by sin
3. Redemption: the world in light of salvation through Christ
4. Future consummation: the world in view of the glorious future awaiting us

So, for example, with regard to the principles for moral behaviour given to Israel in the Old Testament, we need to remember that the biblical revelation is progressive, and that these principles will need to be interpreted in light of the New Testament. Paul tells us in Romans that we are no longer under the law—in fact, we are delivered from the law (Rom 6:14, 7:6)—and so we will look carefully at the validity of Old Testament ethical instruction, using it as a source of Christian wisdom rather than a strict code of law.[5]

As Michael Hill points out, many of the New Testament virtues

---

4. For a detailed explanation of ethical Christian decision-making, see M Hill, *The How and Why of Love*, Matthias Media, Sydney, 2002.
5. For further discussion of the place of Old Testament laws in Christian ethics, see A Cameron, *Joined-up Life*, IVP, Nottingham, 2011, pp. 135-40.

are related to personal relationship and community—virtues like compassion, kindness, hospitality, gentleness, generosity, peaceableness, truthfulness, humility, patience and forbearance.[6] This reminds us that we are creatures made for relationship, which will be an important consideration in all our decision-making.

So how do we put it all together? Below is a framework that can help us combine the important considerations for any decision and check whether we are indeed following biblical principles.

A model of ethical decision-making for Christians

In any moral choice, we are first moved to act by our *motivation*, which leads to an *intention* to achieve a certain goal. We then take *action* to achieve that goal, and our action will have certain *consequences*. How does the Bible judge the importance of each of these components of our ethical choice?

We begin by recognizing that we face an ethical decision, and developing the *motivation* to respond. This will determine not what we are going to do so much as *why* we are going to do it. Christian motivation is grounded in the summary of the commandments given by Jesus in Matthew 22:37-40: "Love the Lord your God with all your heart and with all your soul and with all your mind" and "love your neighbour as yourself". For example, if a Christian (let's call him Tom) sees a woman suffering from unrelieved pain, he will be moved by love and compassion to want to help.

Once we have been motivated to act, we consider what we want to achieve. This is our *intention*. We begin to consider a particular goal, which will help us to decide on an appropriate course of action. Mind you, good intentions are not enough on their own. Good intentions do not justify wrong actions (as Paul insists in Romans 3:8); nor are good intentions an excuse for doing nothing (as James reminds us in James 2:16). However, if we have bad intentions, this can be as bad as having performed a wrong action (Matt 5:21-22, 27-28).

Both intentions and actions are significant. Jesus told us that our actions are a reflection of what is in our hearts and minds (Mark 7:21-23). We therefore will see some overlap between our intentions and our actions.

To take our example to the next step: having been motivated to help,

---

6.   Hill, op. cit., p. 38.

Tom now decides to try to stop the woman's suffering by relieving her pain. He has formed an intention, but what *action* will he take?

In recent times, some people advocate euthanasia—that is, killing those who are in pain and suffering, in the (usually erroneous) belief that it is the only way to stop their pain. However, Tom is aware that there is a biblical prohibition on killing people (Gen 9:6; Exod 20:13; cf. Matt 5:21-22), so he rules out that course of action. The action itself is wrong, even if the intention is noble or good (in this case, compassion for the suffering person). Compassion moves us to act, but does not inform the content of our actions.

Tom decides to give the woman medication to stop the pain. This is a compassionate response that does not violate any biblical principles.

The last aspect of our choice involves examining the *consequences* of our action. Consequences are important, and we do need to consider them. However, we cannot decide right from wrong by looking at consequences *only*. There are a few reasons for this. We might remember, firstly, that the end does not justify the means (there are some things we should never do regardless of the consequences, as Romans 3:7-8 makes clear). Moreover, God knows our hearts and minds, and he is concerned by our motivation and intention as well as our actions and their consequences (cf. Matt 5:27-28). Besides, consequences are enormously difficult to predict and to assess—even after the fact, let alone in advance. So in the case of euthanasia, there is on the one hand the consequence of a sick person's suffering being eased. But on the other hand, there is the distinct possibility that allowing euthanasia will certainly lead to some people being killed against their real wishes. How do we weigh these consequences against one another, let alone all the other possible outcomes and consequences? And can we do so credibly in advance, when we simply cannot predict or control what will eventuate? Consequences alone are an inadequate basis for ethical decision-making.

However, we do need to consider what effect our actions will have, for good or ill. Now, before we go any further, we need to acknowledge that all things are in our sovereign God's hands, and that we cannot foresee all consequences. God knows this, and we are judged according to those things for which we are responsible, not those things that are out of our control. God's judgement will be just (Rom 3:19). We should aim for a good outcome, but if a bad outcome intervenes through circumstances beyond our control, we are not morally liable.

That said, Christians will judge consequences in light of gospel values.

If we are aiming to love our neighbours and do what is best for them, we will look for outcomes in which suffering is eased, loving relationships are fostered, justice is done, and so on (see Mic 6:8). Sometimes we will need to be creative in considering what options are available to us. Sometimes we will have to choose an option that has a difficult and personally costly outcome. Sometimes we will be surprised by the way God works to bring good out of evil (Rom 8:28). But God has promised that we will never be forced to submit to the ethically wrong but easy way out when we are tempted to give way (1 Cor 10:13). We also need to remember that we cannot control the actions of others, and that we must expect to see troubles in this fallen world (John 16:33).

To return to our example: the consequence of Tom's action is that the woman's pain is relieved and her suffering eased. He considers this a satisfactory result by biblical standards.

MOTIVATION — Love for God and for our neighbours. Christian character is developed according to the virtues listed in the New Testament.

INTENTION
ACTION — Both intentions and actions should be obedient to God's word and keep in mind the nature of the creation.

CONSEQUENCES — Will be measured according to God's standards for justice; we will be concerned for the vulnerable, we will be merciful and we will keep in view the future consummation.

Note that to maintain a Christian ethic in decision-making, the following is necessary:
- study of the Scriptures to identify relevant themes and rules
- development of Christian character (put on virtues, take off vices)
- development of a Christian world view by making it our practice to think things through in a gospel context and collecting any extra information we need
- prayer that God's spirit will give us wisdom and the power to change.

A retrieval ethic

Sometimes we find ourselves having to choose between two 'evils'. As Michael Hill acknowledges, the tensions of living in a fallen world mean that love for God and for our neighbours cannot always be sustained as we would like. At these times, we will find that the Bible permits a retrieval ethic—an allowance from God in view of the hardness of our hearts. To justify this approach Hill looks to passages like 1 Corinthians 7:10-16, where God, who hates divorce, will allow it when mutual love cannot be accomplished, as a way of salvaging what good is possible and minimizing harm (cf. Matt 19:8).[7] Sometimes all we can do is try to minimize the damage that results from actions we cannot control.

This needs to be carefully evaluated. A retrieval ethic is not based on a different system of morality to that I have described. Rather, "the same value system [is] operating in two different ways".[8] As Hill describes it, good and evil remain constant, but where sin has limited the opportunity to act as we would wish, some goods may need to be abandoned and others taken up. His example refers to divorce, where the oneness of marriage is no longer possible if one party leaves the relationship for an adulterous union. However, a cordial relationship may be able to be maintained through legal separation and formal divorce. This is particularly helpful if children are involved.

Decision-making in medical matters

It is difficult to make choices if we are not sure what it is we are choosing between. As mentioned above, one of the challenges of decision-making in bioethics is that we need to understand something of the science before we can start talking about ethics. Christians have at times been discredited for speaking out on scientific issues about which they were ignorant.

I am not saying we shouldn't speak out until we know every single detail. But we will be taken more seriously in public debate if we know our facts and we know our limitations. This is a challenge for our churches, but we need to trust that God will provide people, if not in our own congregations then in our geographical areas, who can educate us about current controversial bioethical issues.

Responding to alternative ethical theories

At the beginning of the chapter we looked at several ethical theories that are popular in modern society. Having looked at the Bible's

---

7. Hill, ibid., pp. 132-4.
8. ibid., p. 133.

ethical framework, how might Christians respond to these alternative approaches?

Let us start with *consequentialism*. While the Bible teaches that we should consider the consequences of our actions, it does not support the idea that consequences are the *only* things that matter, or that consequences should overrule all other considerations. We would therefore reject the argument that a good outcome (such as the mother's emotional or financial or career wellbeing) justifies abortion on grounds that killing an unborn child is an unjust and immoral action in itself. The mother's desire to secure her future wellbeing does not justify taking human life any more than, say, inheriting a valuable property justifies killing your parents.

Regarding *rights theory*, we will be more interested in loving our neighbours than in asserting our rights over them (1 Cor 10:24). We would also point out that the proliferation of 'rights' (usually self-claimed) results in impossible conflicts. So, for example, if I have a right to personal happiness or prosperity, what happens when my neighbour's right to the same thing conflicts with mine? Whose right should have priority? Likewise, why does a woman's right to control her own body override a baby's right to life and liberty? In the end, these conflicts are usually resolved by the more powerful trampling on the rights of the weak. The mother decides that the baby's right to life is not morally relevant or not as important as her right to happiness, and so aborts the baby. And the baby is in no position to stop her.

Moral relativism is often regarded as 'politically correct', and necessary for maintaining community harmony. But while it may appear to promote tolerance, insisting that all moral positions are personal and relative is both illogical and impractical. It is illogical because moral relativism is itself claiming to be *the* correct ethical theory. And it is impractical because no-one ever sticks to it. You don't have to push a moral relativist very far before they admit that some things are universally good or evil (whether it is racism or sexism or child abuse or whatever). Also, by reducing the abortion argument to 'Don't have an abortion if you don't approve', moral relativists are avoiding the question of right and wrong entirely and confusing it with personal preference. But for those opposed to abortion, personal preferences are beside the point when you are fighting for an absolute moral value such as the protection of innocent human lives. And personal preferences certainly shouldn't be the basis for the law that provides the moral standard for a whole society.

With regard to *communitarianism*, we will always consider the needs and welfare of those around us, and will desire to build strong and loving communities. But working out what is best for a community will depend on one's vision of the good life, and what constitutes the 'best'. So whereas supporters of abortion would argue that it is better to abort disabled babies so that the community does not have to bear the cost of supporting them throughout their lives, Christians would say that this is not only a morally wrong action in itself, but is also based on a morally defective view of what makes a good community. In a truly good community, everyone would be treated with love, dignity and respect, not dispensed with if they are weak or disabled or become expensive to care for.

Christians do support communitarianism in that we believe there are absolute moral truths that are the good gift of the God who made the world, and that upholding and living out these truths will be for the benefit of everyone in the community.

For doctors

Medicine has for some time focused on the 'four principles' approach to healthcare ethics developed by Tom Beauchamp and James Childress (often called 'principlism').[9] The principles they identified as important in this context were:

1. *Beneficence (the obligation to provide overall benefits to patients when balanced with risks)*
2. *Non-maleficence (the obligation to avoid causing harm)*
3. *Respect for autonomy (the obligation to allow mentally competent patients to make decisions on matters that affect them)*
4. *Justice (the obligation to treat patients fairly regarding benefits and risks)*

However, the authors never intended this framework to be used as an independent ethical theory. Beauchamp recommended it be used "together with other moral considerations".[10] In fact, it is extremely difficult to decide what to do using only these four principles.

---

9. TL Beauchamp and JF Childress, *Principles of Biomedical Ethics*, 3rd edn, Oxford University Press, New York, 1989.

10. TL Beauchamp, 'The "four principles" approach' in R Gillon (ed.), *Principles of Health Care Ethics*, Wiley, Chichester, 1994, pp. 3-12.

For one thing, it does not tell you whose autonomy ought to be respected if more than one patient is involved. If you were deciding whether abortion was the right or wrong thing to do, you may consider going ahead if you wanted to respect the autonomy of the woman requesting one. But what of the unborn child whose autonomy is being radically terminated? Moreover, you are denying the unborn child justice by intentionally killing it—an act that can only be described as harmful (maleficent). From this perspective it would be the wrong thing to do. Obviously, further principles are required to work out what to do in this situation. If we consider the principles with regard to the mother, abortion is the right thing to do. If we look at it from the baby's perspective, it isn't.

Furthermore, the way the principles are used in medical practice usually makes them a form of consequentialism (deciding right from wrong only on the basis of the consequences of an action). That is, beneficent actions are determined as those with good outcomes; maleficent actions are determined as those with harmful outcomes; and so on. As such, the 'four principles' approach suffers from the problems and inconsistencies that all consequentialist moral theories share. We know from Scripture that we are not to decide right from wrong purely by consequences—the end does not justify the means. We need to consider the morality of motive, intentions and actions as well, as we have discussed above. The 'four principles' approach will be inadequate on its own to assess morality for Christians.

The usefulness of the principles lies in reminding us that we should aim to do good and not harm, to take into consideration our patients' wishes where appropriate, and to treat them justly. This is not the complete list of our obligations, but it is a start.

Doctors interested in engaging with medical ethics would do well to do further reading about ethical theories. This will put you in a position not only to formulate and understand your own ethical approach, but also to be able to analyse and interact with the arguments of others. Beauchamp is right when he says that "it is insupportably optimistic to think we will ever attain a fully specified system of norms for health care ethics".[11] There is no longer sufficient societal consensus for this to happen. I agree

---

11. Beauchamp, op. cit., p. 12.

with Pellegrino that the most likely candidate to allow development of a unique 'professional medical ethic' is virtue theory (which looks at the preferred virtues, or qualities of character, of a good doctor). His writing on this topic is recommended.[12] This style of approach is becoming loosely categorized as 'Hippocratic medicine', and you could do a lot worse than aim for that.

Now that we have covered the basics of biology, theology and ethics, we will look at specific areas of the beginning of life that need to be evaluated from a Christian perspective. We will start with contraception.

---

12.   ED Pellegrino, *The Philosophy of Medicine Reborn*, University of Notre Dame Press, Indiana, 2008, chapter 12.

Contraception

T HE CURRENT GENERATION of fertile adults has not known a time when contraception was not safe and easily available. As a result, they have grown up with the unquestioned belief that was expressed with the arrival of the oral contraceptive pill: you can have 'sex without reproduction'.

But is this really true? Has there really been a rupturing of the link between sex and pregnancy? The abortion rate would seem to indicate not. While unwanted pregnancy does not account for all cases of abortion performed annually in Australia (as opposed to abortion where the pregnancy poses a threat to the mother's life, for example), it certainly accounts for most of them. In fact, one of the factors that drove the demand for accessible abortion was the belief that it was no longer necessary to accept pregnancy as an inevitable consequence of being sexually active. But regardless of what our society would like to think, the reality is that fertile couples who engage in sexual relations will always have a chance of becoming pregnant.

Yet the myth that sex is no longer connected to child-bearing persists, and the thought that there might be ethical objections to the use of contraceptives in marriage does not occur to many Protestant couples. We may take time to consider *which* form of contraception we should use, but very few couples pause to consider whether they should use it at all. We are used to the worldly idea that we can control our child-bearing just as we can control (at least, we like to think so) most other areas of our lives. It is interesting to note, however, that contraception was opposed by Protestants from the time of Luther right through until 1930, when the first institutional moves towards its acceptance occurred. Even today, many churches (most notably the Roman Catholic Church) reject most forms of artificial contraception.

Is it morally permissible for married Christian couples to use contraceptives? There are at least two important ethical questions to be answered:

- Is it ever morally permissible for Christians to use contraception?
- If so, are there any particular methods of contraception that should be avoided?

This chapter will look at both of these questions. I apologize in advance that doing so will take some time—but the issues are complex and have a long history. The chapter falls into three parts:

1. **A brief history of contraception**, which looks at how views towards contraception have developed and changed in Christian history (depending on level of interest, some readers may wish to skip this section).
2. **A theology of contraception**, which looks at the Bible's teaching on whether it is morally permissible for Christians to use contraceptives.
3. **Understanding different contraceptives**, which looks at the wide range of contraceptives available, and at the moral implications of using each of them.

In all of this, my intention is not to make anyone feel guilty for past choices. I would like to encourage you to think about this subject prayerfully, and use the information given to inform your future choices.

1. A brief history of contraception

There are ancient Egyptian records dating from between 1900 and 1100 BC providing recipes for women to avoid pregnancy. Formulas include ingredients such as crocodile dung, honey, acacia tips and dates, which were smeared around the vulva or placed in the uterus in an attempt to prevent sperm from entering the uterus.[1] Ingredients like sodium carbonate appear in recipes for contraceptives in European literature, so it is likely that some of this knowledge persisted to Christian times. We can be confident that the withdrawal technique was known amongst

---

1.   Modern science has demonstrated that acacia does indeed act as a spermicide, so it may have worked. The early history of contraception here has been adapted from JT Noonan, *Contraception*, Mentor-Omega Press, New York, 1965, pp. 23ff. This book is highly recommended reading for those interested in this topic.

the Hebrews by the story of Onan (Gen 38:8-10). The Talmud contains references not only to this technique, but also to pessaries, sterilizing potions and sterilizing surgery. Ancient Graeco-Roman society was educated by Aristotle's *History of Animals* and Pliny's *Natural History*. Although these writers were more interested in the underlying science, they did give instructions for contraception. By the 2nd century AD, the Greek gynaecologist Soranus of Ephesus wrote about the association between ovulation and fertility, and promoted a flawed version of the rhythm method. He also gave information on potions and pessaries, as well as a rather less scientific method of contraception which involved the woman getting up after sex, squatting, and sneezing loudly to dislodge the sperm! (Don't try that one at home.) Some of his contemporaries recommended an ointment to be applied to male genitals (possibly as a spermicide), and amulets (perhaps suggesting, if magic was worth a try, that none of the known contraceptives were particularly reliable). Soranus' book, *Gynecology*, was the most important guide to contraception not only during the time of the Roman Empire but also, through the Arabs, throughout medieval Europe.

There is no doubt that *knowledge* of contraceptive techniques existed in biblical times. Use of them, however, was not thought to be common in Israel due to the value placed on child-bearing in the Old Testament. God blesses humanity in Genesis 1:28, and commands the man and woman to "Be fruitful and multiply". This instruction is repeated after the flood (Gen 9:1), and in Deuteronomy, Israel is told that God "will love you, bless you, and multiply you. He will also bless the fruit of your womb… There shall not be male or female barren among you" (Deut 7:13-14). (See further biblical references to contraception below.)

While the use of contraceptive methods is not thought to have been widespread amongst the Hebrews, there is no doubt that it was widespread amongst the Romans. Although sexual immorality was rampant in the late Roman Empire, so was childlessness and declining birth—so much so that laws were introduced to ban contraceptives in an attempt to increase the population size.[2] It is unlikely that the Jews or the New Testament Christians would have been ignorant of such a prevalent social phenomenon.

---

2.   This legislation was introduced by Augustus in response to the falling birth rate in the upper class: *Lex Julia de maritandis ordinibus* (18 BC) and *Lex Papia Poppaea* (9 AD). It disqualified the childless from high office and the right of inheritance.

Philo (20 BC-50 AD) was the earliest Jewish philosopher to discuss contraception, and he is thought to provide an example of Jewish thought on marriage at the time of Jesus. He was influenced by the Stoics, an austere school of Greek philosophy. The Stoics mistrusted emotion and tried to control bodily desires by rational thinking. They were more interested in justice than in love. Marriage based on passion, therefore, was suspect. According to Stoic beliefs, there must be another reason for marriage, and plainly that was reproduction. While Philo rejected the Stoic elimination of all emotion, he nonetheless regards overly strong desire for one's spouse as a source of wickedness: "Now even natural pleasure is often greatly to blame when the craving for it is immoderate and insatiable… as the passionate desire for women shown by those who in their rage for sexual intercourse behave unchastely, not with the wives of others, but with their own".[3] From other writings, it seems that 'behaving unchastely' refers to having sexual intercourse for pleasure. He interprets the Old Testament as teaching that God blesses married couples who have intercourse specifically for children, such as Abraham and Sarah, and curses those who don't, such as Onan, who used Tamar without impregnating her (Genesis 38). His writings influenced a number of 2nd-century Church Fathers.[4]

Noonan comments that the development of Christian doctrine is usually a response by the Christian community both to meditation on Scripture and to the pressures of the environment.[5] Further development of an early Christian doctrine of contraception is thought to have been a reaction to the two most influential attitudes in the Greco-Roman world—the Gnostics and the secular pagans.

The Gnostics were a heretical sect within early Christianity who regarded the physical world as evil and corrupt. For the Gnostics, true spirituality was mystical and non-physical. Accordingly, they believed in total celibacy and condemned marriage as a sinful impediment to true spirituality and godliness, bolstering their arguments by appealing to the example of Jesus. They pointed to those parts of the New Testament (such as 1 Corinthians 7) that teach that singleness and celibacy are valid options for Christians.

Clement of Alexandria (c150-215 AD) argued against the Gnostics

---

3.   Philo, *The Special Laws* 3.2.9.
4.   Noonan, op. cit., pp. 74ff.
5.   Noonan, op. cit., p. 77.

that marriage was legitimate, its purpose being procreation. He turned to the law of nature as described by Paul in Romans 2:15 to construct a natural law of marriage, contrasting the natural and purposeful act of procreation with both sexual license and forced abstinence within marriage. He taught that to have sexual intercourse in marriage "other than to procreate children is to do injury to nature".[6]

Thus 'nature' became a key factor in orthodox Christian teaching, and has been the basis for Roman Catholic teaching on sexuality ever since. Interestingly, the early Church Fathers (such as Origen, Clement, Ambrose and Jerome) used the concept of 'nature' in three distinct senses. One sense compared sex and the sowing of a field. The idea here was that a pattern discovered in a process uncontaminated by humans was 'natural', and so could safely be translated into law for humans. In a second sense, the natural was seen to be what animals do—once again, since human sin was not involved, such activity could be held up as a universal pattern for behaviour. The third sense of 'natural' related to what was observed in the human body, particularly the function of different organs—so the fact that 'eyes are to see with' told us what was natural to eyes. Such functions were held to be self-evident, requiring no further proof; and they were not necessarily seen in context of the whole body.

In summary, the natural law approach led the early Church Fathers to conclude that sexual desire was evil, as it could lead a man to use his wife for purposes other than procreation. Once you sow the seed, you should wait for the harvest, not keep sowing more seed upon it.[7] While a husband should love his wife, love and sex were seen as separate. This meant that sex for pleasure alone, sex during menstruation, sex during pregnancy, sex in old age and sex with contraception were all evil. Unnatural sexual acts were also condemned.[8]

There were some dissenting voices. In the late 3rd and early 4th centuries, Lactantius and St John Chrysostom defended Paul's teaching that marriage was not just for parenthood but also to promote sexual purity, implicitly allowing some license for more frequent sexual union

---

6.   Clement of Alexandria, *Pedagogus* 2.10.95.3.
7.   This was the Christian philosophy as explained by the Greek philosopher Athenagoras in 177 AD.
8.   Oral and anal sex, and probably coitus interruptus (which will be discussed later in this chapter).

in marriage. However, they did not extend their arguments to allow for contraception.[9]

Church opposition to contraceptive use is most strongly influenced by the writings of Augustine of Hippo (354-430 AD). As a young man, Augustine was involved for 11 years with a new religion, Manicheanism, which promoted frequent non-procreative intercourse and abortion. It is thought that Augustine's teachings on sex and contraception were a direct reaction to his involvement with the Manichees, against whom he wrote two books within a year of his conversion.[10]

Augustine held that the purpose of marriage, and therefore of sexual intercourse within marriage, was procreation. He reasoned that if, as the Bible teaches, man and wife become one flesh in sexual intercourse (Gen 2:24; Matt 19:5; Eph 5:31), then man becomes all flesh in intercourse, which is a threat to his spiritual freedom.[11] Marital sex must therefore have an external purpose to justify this danger (i.e. procreation). Furthermore, in opposition to the heretical teaching of Pelagius,[12] Augustine taught that since original sin was transmitted through sexual generation, sexual desire (which he saw as bad) had to be balanced by the good of possible procreation. Otherwise, sexual relations, even within marriage, were sinful.[13] He opposed contraceptive use even within marriage as morally corrupt, suggesting that it turned matrimonial intercourse into prostitution and the wife into a harlot.[14] He used the story of Onan as an example of judgement for avoiding the propagation of children in marriage.[15] He particularly opposed the method of 'natural family planning', which was the contraceptive strategy used by the Manichees. (It is ironic that the main method singled out and condemned by such a prominent church spokesman on sexual matters is the only one allowed by the Catholic Church today.)

Augustine summarized his position by claiming that the goods of

---

9.   Noonan, op. cit., pp. 103-4.

10. Noonan, op. cit., p. 151.

11. Augustine, *Sermons* 62.2.

12. Pelagius was a British monk (360-420 AD) who taught that salvation could be achieved by one's good moral nature and that grace was unnecessary. He and Augustine argued about the nature of original sin. Pelagius was condemned as a heretic by the Councils of Carthage in 416 and 418.

13. Augustine, *Marriage and Concupiscence* 2.5.14.

14. Augustine, *The Morals of the Manichees* 18.65.

15. Augustine, *Adulterous Marriages* 2.12.12.

marriage are offspring, fidelity and symbolic stability—*proles, fides, sacramentum.*[16] There is no mention of love between spouses. Procreation was only to be avoided by complete abstinence. And, according to his reading of the Bible, since virginity is preferable to marriage, continence in marriage is also preferable to intercourse.[17] Augustine's powerful presentation of the case against contraception was hugely influential, and persisted within the Western church for 1000 years.

In the centuries following Augustine, opposition to contraception and sexual pleasure in marriage continued within the church largely unopposed. Pope Gregory 'the Great' (pope from 590-604), managed even to 'out-Augustine' Augustine not only by limiting married intercourse to the purpose of procreation, but also by condemning any pleasure gained during the exercise. Since most people found it difficult to separate the two, copulation itself became an unavoidably sinful activity. Contraception was unthinkable. Gregory did not consider this policy to be anti-marriage or to be a new doctrine, citing Psalm 51:5 ("in sin did my mother conceive me").

The monastic movement, which did so much to preserve and pass on Christian teaching during the period from 500-1100, was also staunchly opposed to contraception. The monastic attitude to sexuality and contraception is reflected in their 'penitentials'—lists of sins, each with prescribed penances. Looking at penitentials written between the 6th and 11th centuries, the contraceptives described are potions drunk by women. While we don't know how seriously penances were enforced, use of contraception was seen as a serious sin, with penance by fasting for 7-15 years (bread and water only). This indicates the gravity with which contraceptive use was viewed. At the same time, anal or oral intercourse was also regarded as a serious sin, often viewed more seriously than homicide or abortion. (This suggests that control of lust was the key factor, rather than the protection of life.) *Coitus interruptus* (the withdrawal method) earned a penance of up to 10 years. Intercourse where the woman is on top of the man was rejected on grounds that it impedes procreation (actually untrue) and is 'doglike'. It received a penance of 40 days (and even more if it was customary behaviour).

---

16. Augustine, *The Good of Marriage* 29.32.
17. Inherent in Augustine's argument is the idea that the command to multiply no longer applies after the coming of Christ. This idea is elaborated below.

The most significant outcome of the penitentials for the doctrine of contraception was the text *Si aliquis*, which became canon law in the 13th century. Its first expression was as follows: "If someone (*Si aliquis*) to satisfy his lust or in deliberate hatred does something to a man or woman so that no children be born of him or her, or gives them to drink, so that he cannot generate or she conceive, let it be held as homicide".[18]

In 1230, Pope Gregory IX directed Dominican monk Raymond of Pennaforte to make a collection of decrees (the *Decretals*), which was to become Catholic Church law for the next 685 years. *Si aliquis* was included, with artificial contraception once again being equated with homicide. Along with 6 centuries of sexual behaviour interpreted by the penitentials, this created the mentality that marriage was for procreation, that sexual behaviour beyond the 'missionary' position was objectionable, and that contraception was evil.

By this time, the Catholic Church's opposition to contraception was settled, based on the natural law approach pioneered by Clement, on Augustine's teachings, on the rules and penances of the monks, on *Si aliquis*, and on a consistently expressed theology that saw procreation as the only legitimate purpose of marital intercourse.

Thomas Aquinas (1224-1274 AD) provides us with the classical expression of the Catholic view. Highly influenced by the teaching of Augustine, he took Genesis 1:28 to mean that the procreation of children is the primary purpose of marriage. He promoted 'natural law', arguing that what is in nature comes from God himself, and that while using contraception may not seem so severe a sin as, say, sins which harm our neighbour, it is still in fact a sin against God.[19] Thomas condemned contraception because it was homicide (it destroyed potential life), it was against nature (by frustrating the aim of intercourse, which was insemination), and it destroyed marital relations (by violating the main/only purpose of marital intercourse). In this presentation, the ban against contraception could rationally be argued as necessary for the good of man. It is noteworthy that in the case of a woman being unable to conceive due to sterility or pregnancy, intercourse was not deemed unnatural. It was not the lack of procreation but the avoidance of depositing semen in the vagina that made the act 'unnatural'.

---

18. Noonan, op. cit., p. 209.
19. Thomas Aquinas, *Summa Theologica*, part II, in Noonan, op. cit., p. 291.

Thomas reinforced the norm that became the basic assumption of later writers: heterosexual marital coitus, the man above the woman, with insemination resulting. This is the 'natural' act, established by God, deliberate departure from which is an offence against God. The gravity of the offence lies either in the harm done to the potential human life or in the frustration of the normal process of preserving the human race. Thomas also accepted the ideal of married love, and considered it possible to have marital intercourse without sin, as even animals seemed to enjoy sex.

I will not continue the story of the Roman Catholic approach to contraception, except to say that although Augustinian ideas were challenged and sanctions softened, and contraception was no longer viewed as homicide but simply as a violation of the purposes of marriage, contraception remained condemned.

With the arrival of the Reformation, Protestant church leaders such as Martin Luther and John Calvin broke with Roman Catholicism on many subjects. However, on contraception they remained largely in line with Catholic doctrine. Luther largely held to Augustinian teaching on sexuality, as well as emphasizing that children are a blessing from the Lord (Gen 1:28). Calvin argued for three purposes of marriage: companionship (Gen 1:27; 2:18, 21), procreation (Gen 1:28), and the controlled exercise of God-given sexuality (Gen 2:22). He rejected the idea that singleness/celibacy was a superior state to marriage.[20] Both Calvin and Luther opposed contraception on the basis of Genesis 38. Noonan suggests that the Protestants' holding of the Catholic line encouraged the Catholic Church not to change its position.[21] The Protestant position on contraception remained largely unaddressed until the 19th century. Discussion did not really proceed beyond the condemnation of *coitus interruptus* on the basis of the story of Onan. Meanwhile, the use of contraceptives quietly spread.

In the late 19th century, in response to lobbying by Protestants, legislation began to be passed in the United States to suppress contraceptive use. Laws such as the Comstock Act, passed in the United States in 1873, prohibited distribution of contraceptives and birth control information (on grounds of it being obscene material). Such

---

20. J Calvin, *Institutes* 2.8.42-3.
21. Noonan, op. cit., p. 423.

laws not only limited access to information about contraception but also created a public perception that contraception was to be equated with pornography (which may explain why the discussion of contraception was often seen as shameful). It was not until 1960 that the United States Supreme Court overturned a law in Connecticut that prohibited the use of contraceptives by married couples.

By the 1920s, the physiology of reproduction was being understood accurately for the first time, and the calendar rhythm method was introduced in 1932. At the same time, the birth control movement grew in the late 19th and early 20th centuries in response to the Comstock laws. Led by Margaret Sanger and Marie Stopes, the movement used arguments about the need to limit population growth in view of available resources,[22] and the need to save poor women from abortion in the event of unplanned pregnancy.[23] The turning point came in 1930 when Anglican bishops at the Lambeth Conference controversially voted to approve limited contraceptive use within marriage—a reversal of the strong opposition voiced ten years previously. The 1930 resolution recognized that there may be moral grounds for restricting parenthood and that limited use of contraceptives was permissible:

Resolution 15: The Life and Witness of the Christian Community—Marriage and Sex

Where there is clearly felt moral obligation to limit or avoid parenthood, the method must be decided on Christian principles. The primary and obvious method is complete abstinence from intercourse (as far as may be necessary) in a life of discipline and self-control lived in the power of the Holy Spirit. Nevertheless in those cases where there is such a clearly felt moral obligation to limit or avoid parenthood, and where there is a morally sound reason for avoiding complete abstinence, the Conference agrees that other methods may be used, provided that this is done in the light of the same Christian principles. The Conference records its strong

---

22. These arguments had been offered by Rev. Thomas Malthus in a 1798 publication where he warned that, without measures to restrict population growth, by 1900 food in England would feed only one third of the population. As the remedy, however, he advertised not contraception but abstention.

23. This argument had been recommended in an 1832 essay by Charles Knowlton, using utilitarian arguments. There is evidence that Sanger and Stopes were also motivated by eugenic aims to reduce the fertility of the genetically inferior.

condemnation of the use of any methods of conception control from motives of selfishness, luxury, or mere convenience.

Voting: For 193; Against 67.[24]

The Roman Catholic Church responded with *Casti Connubii* ('On Christian Marriage'), an encyclical written by Pope Pius XI. He reiterated the Augustinian teaching that the goods of marriage were offspring, fidelity and sacrament, with offspring the primary good. God had spoken to all married people when he commanded them to "Increase and multiply, and fill the earth".[25] He reinforced the ban against contraception, but made an ambiguous comment about the 'rhythm method' of birth control, which was seen as a possible endorsement. (The confusion did not clear until 1951, when Pope Pius XII formally approved the rhythm method for all Catholic couples.)

Contraception was formally approved by the United Church of Canada in 1932, the Federal Council of Churches in the United States in 1931, and the Lutheran bishops of Sweden in 1952. In each case it was noted that the decision needed to be made carefully by individual couples according to their consciences and in light of scriptural teaching.[26] Most Protestant denominations have since followed suit.

In the early 1960s, the oral contraceptive pill became available. R Albert Mohler Jr has noted that:

> Lacking any substantial theology of marriage, sex, or the family, evangelicals welcomed the development of 'The Pill' much as the world celebrated that discovery of penicillin—as one more milestone in the inevitable march of human progress and the conquest of nature.[27]

Protestant contraceptive use continued, unquestioned.

The next Catholic Church pronouncement came in 1968 with *Humanae Vitae* ('Of Human Life'), issued by Pope Paul VI. It was expected

---

24. Secretary General of the Anglican Consultative Council, 'Resolution 15: The Life and Witness of the Christian Community—Marriage and Sex', Resolution from the 1930 Lambeth Conference.

25. Encyclical of Pius XI, *Casti Connubii: On Christian Marriage*, Rome, 31 December 1930, paragraph 11.

26. KD Blanchard, 'The gift of contraception: Calvin, Barth and a lost Protestant conversation', *Journal of the Society of Christian Ethics*, vol. 27, no. 1, 2007, pp. 234-5.

27. RA Mohler Jr, in 'Contraception: A Symposium', *First Things*, December 1998, p. 24.

that he would relax the traditional stand on contraception, in keeping with the recommendations of a papal commission and the spirit of the Second Vatican Council (1962-1965). But it was not to be. He proclaimed that "each and every marital act [of sexual intercourse] must of necessity retain its intrinsic relationship to the procreation of human life".[28] He pronounced that both the unitive meaning (where the married couple grow in love and companionship) and procreative meaning (where the potential for children is realized) of the sexual act within marriage are to be realized in every sexual act. The traditional opposition to artificial contraception was reiterated.[29]

The motivation for Roman Catholic teaching is understandable: "to experience the gift of married love while respecting the laws of conception is to acknowledge that one is not the master of the sources of life but rather the minister of the design established by the Creator".[30] However, while wanting to acknowledge God as the one on whom all life depends (Job 1:21), Protestants do not agree with the Catholic view that observing God's design in nature can be a reliable guide to establishing a theology of marriage and contraception. We derive our beliefs not from observation of nature but through careful reading of Scripture. Furthermore, we would not agree with the implication that contraception is as offensive as abortion, as *Humanae Vitae* seems to suggest.[31]

The contemporary Protestant view recognizes the validity of sexual intercourse for "completion of marital fellowship" independent of any intention to conceive children.[32] The resolution of the 1930 Lambeth Conference first permitted contraceptive use when chosen according to "Christian principles".[33] In the discussion of contraception in his multi-volume *Church Dogmatics*, Protestant theologian Karl Barth argues that

---

28. Encyclical of Paul VI, *Humanae Vitae: On the Regulation of Birth*, Rome, 25 July 1968, paragraph 11.

29. According to *Humanae Vitae*, natural family planning is permissible for Catholics (see below for explanation of this contraceptive method). *Humanae Vitae* is discussed in HOJ Brown, J Budziszewski, CJ Chaput, E Chevlen, SE Hinlicky, G Meilaender, P Turner, R Albert Mohler Jr, A Mosier and JE Smith, 'Contraception: A Symposium', op. cit., pp. 17-29. The position of *Humanae Vitae* was affirmed in 2008 in *Dignitas Personae* ('The Dignity of a Person').

30. Paul VI, op. cit., paragraph 13.

31. Paul VI, op. cit., paragraph 14.

32. K Barth, 'Parents and Children', in *Church Dogmatics*, vol. III.4, GW Bromiley and TF Torrance (eds), T and T Clark, London and New York, 2010, p. 269.

33. Secretary General of the Anglican Consultative Council, op. cit.

the unitive aspect is the "first essential meaning" of sexual intercourse, and that intercourse does not need to be associated with the desire for children.[34] He advises that use of contraception is permissible at times in marriage, but that the decision to use it should be "under the divine command and with a sense of responsibility to God, not out of caprice".[35] Such "Christian principles" and "divine commands" can only be worked out if we look to the ultimate guide for Christian ethical decision-making: the Bible.

2. A theology of contraception

From our historical overview we can see that the contemporary Protestant position on contraception has not been the prevalent view in the history of Christianity. How has the modern Protestant view been formed? How have we decided that it is permissible for sexual intercourse in marriage to be used for the unitive purpose only?

As we seek the Bible's guidance on the subject of contraception within marriage, we need to look at its teaching on the purpose of marriage, and the place of sex within marriage.

This teaching begins with the divine command of Genesis 1:28 to Adam and Eve: "Be fruitful and multiply and fill the earth and subdue it". This command is repeated to Noah and his sons after the flood (Gen 9:1). We can then see it being worked out through the story of Israel. The promise of plentiful offspring was an important part of God's covenant with Abraham in Genesis 15, and continued through his sons. The Old Testament ends with God's reminder through Malachi that he desires to see "godly offspring" as a result of marriage (2:15). Indeed, in one sense the whole Old Testament story is a working out of God's promise in the garden of Eden that, through the descendants of Eve, a saviour will be raised up (Gen 3:15).[36] This promise culminates in the New Testament with the coming of Christ.

The Old Testament considers children to be a blessing:

> Behold, children are a heritage from the LORD,
> the fruit of the womb a reward.

---

34. Barth, loc. cit.
35. ibid., p. 270.
36. See the discussion of the word 'offspring' in BK Waltke and CJ Fredricks, *Genesis: A commentary*, Zondervan, Grand Rapids, 2001, p. 93.

Like arrows in the hand of a warrior
>   are the children of one's youth.
Blessed is the man
>   who fills his quiver with them! (Ps 127:3-5)

Your wife will be like a fruitful vine
>   within your house;
your children will be like olive shoots
>   around your table.
Behold, thus shall the man be blessed
>   who fears the LORD. (Ps 128:3-4)

Marital intercourse is seen as a duty in the Old Testament:

"If [a man] takes another wife to himself, he shall not diminish her
food, her clothing, or her marital rights." (Exod 21:10)

In the Mishnah (the Rabbinic teachings recorded in the Talmud), Rabbi
Eliezer is recorded as saying that the frequency of conjugal duty "for men
of independent means was every day, for laborers twice a week, for ass-
drivers once a week, for camel-drivers once in thirty days, for sailors
once in six months".[37] According to the Rabbinic school of Shammai, if a
man vowed to avoid intercourse with his wife, the period should not be
more than two weeks, and according to the school of Hillel it was only
one week.[38]

In the New Testament there is less emphasis on procreation, and
discussions of marriage include mention of the legitimate place of
celibacy. For example, Jesus' discussion of marriage in Matthew 19:10-
12 opens up the possibility that some will choose to make themselves
eunuchs (i.e. renounce marriage) for the sake of the kingdom. Paul also
identifies chosen celibacy as a gift that allows the receiver to remain free
from the troubles of this world, and instead to be concerned with the
Lord's affairs and pleasing him (1 Cor 7:32-35). Some also see Revelation
14:1-5, where John sees 144,000 who have not defiled themselves with
women, as being a further commendation of celibacy—although in light
of the symbolic nature of Revelation, it is best not to push this verse too
far.

While there is little specific teaching in the New Testament on the

---

37. Noonan, op. cit., p. 73.
38. ibid.

procreative aspect of marriage and sex, it is very possible that this was simply a given. When Paul commended the mutual duty of marital intercourse (1 Cor 7:2-5), it is unlikely he did not expect children to result—although it is noteworthy that he doesn't actually mention procreation in the entire passage.

Some have suggested that there is a significant difference between the Old and New Testaments on this issue. Karl Barth, for example, argues that since the coming of Christ, the propagation of the human race as commanded in Genesis 1:28 has ceased to be an unconditional command. The Old Testament necessity to procreate the "holy sequence of generations" has reached its goal in the birth of Jesus. In the Christian community, therefore, heirs do not have the same significance that they did in Israel, because all men are children of God through their spiritual unity with the Son of God (John 3:6). Marriage remains as a valid option for God's children, but it now represents Christ and his community (Eph 5:22-33; 2 Cor 11:2). This new state of affairs explains why it is no longer shameful to bear no children, or to be unmarried, as all God's elect are part of Christ's bride and will be invited to the marriage feast of the Lamb.[39]

Christopher Ash has challenged this view.[40] He notes that the forward-looking character of the Old Testament was focused not only on the Messiah, but also on the building of Israel and the continuance of humanity. He notes that the genealogies do at times follow the Davidic line, but not always (e.g. Genesis 10, 36). He questions the idea that pious Israelites sought offspring through marital intercourse only with the hope of contributing to the genealogy of the Messiah, because this would make the whole ethical underpinning of marital intercourse a kind of 'procreational lottery'. Besides, Ash adds, if that is the case, there is the irony that the Messiah was eventually conceived *without* parental intercourse.

Whilst the difference between the Testaments can easily be overstated on this point, the emergence and endorsement of chaste singleness in the New Testament supports the claim that God does not require all humans to reproduce. This establishes the honour of the *single* person's vocation. However, it does not clarify what married couples should do. As long as

---

39. Barth, op. cit., pp. 142-4.
40. C Ash, *Marriage: Sex in the Service of God*, IVP, Leicester, 2003, pp. 170ff. This passage contains a detailed critique of Barthian and Augustinian positions on marital procreation.

the world lasts, someone has to provide the human generations needed to rule and care for it. But does that mean that all married couples need to have the maximum number of children possible, or, in fact, any children at all?

Even in the Old Testament, there are suggestions that maximal propagation of the human race was never God's intention. Proverbs 5:18-19, for example, calls upon the husband to delight himself in his wife; and Song of Songs is famous for its celebration of the delights of sexual love. Neither passage mentions children. Marital intercourse is not portrayed in these passages as merely a procreational duty. According to Pope Paul VI in *Humanae Vitae*, marriage is honoured only when *every* act of marital intercourse is open to the conception of a child. But Anglican theologian Oliver O'Donovan points out that this claim fails to recognize that sexual intercourse over the course of a marriage has its own cumulative quality, building intimacy in the context of regular physical union during the whole of the life together. The use of contraception does not reduce marital sex to the same level as a series of one-night stands, which the Pope's view could seem to imply.[41]

Furthermore, we know that not every act of sexual intercourse results in a child. It is not physically possible. God did not make women fertile for the whole of their adult life (unlike other animals). Whilst some couples, sadly, are completely sterile, all couples experience episodes where procreation simply is not possible—for example, during the infertile phase of a woman's monthly cycle, and after menopause. Even if we were to build our theology of contraception on the observation of nature (as Roman Catholicism does), we would be forced to conclude that while procreation is naturally inherent to the marriage overall, it cannot be so for each and every sexual act.

Nonetheless, it is evident that God encourages child-bearing as the norm in marriage, even if it is not always possible. Apart from the original divine command to be fruitful, God encourages his people to increase in number, even in times of adversity (Jer 29:6). Similarly, in the New Testament widows are encouraged to remarry and have children (1 Tim 5:14). Biblical eschatology doesn't overturn or contradict the created order. That is, God's will for married couples in 'the last days' is the same

---

41. O O'Donovan, *Resurrection and Moral Order*, 2nd edn, Apollos, Leicester, 1994, p. 210.

as it was in 'the first days'; they are to be open to having and welcoming children. The burden of proof would seem to rest on anyone who wanted to argue that children are no longer inherent to God's purposes for marriage.

Some authors have identified prohibitions against specific forms of contraception in verses such as Deuteronomy 23:1, where we are told that "No-one whose testicles are crushed or whose male organ is cut off shall enter the assembly of the LORD". However, this is more likely a condemnation of corrupt Canaanite religious practices involving castration than a prohibition against male sterilization. Whatever the case, we are no longer bound by such requirements under the new covenant.

Onan has the dubious honour of providing the one explicit example of contraceptive practice in the Bible:

> And Judah took a wife for Er his firstborn, and her name was Tamar. But Er, Judah's firstborn, was wicked in the sight of the LORD, and the LORD put him to death. Then Judah said to Onan, "Go in to your brother's wife and perform the duty of a brother-in-law to her, and raise up offspring for your brother". But Onan knew that the offspring would not be his. So whenever he went in to his brother's wife he would waste the semen on the ground, so as not to give offspring to his brother. And what he did was wicked in the sight of the LORD, and he put him to death also. (Gen 38:6-10)

According to the later Levirate law (Deut 25:5), Onan's duty was to raise an heir for his deceased brother by having intercourse with his brother's widow, Tamar. But because the child born from this relationship would not be considered his, he intentionally did not complete the sex act with Tamar to avoid impregnating her. He appeared to accept the obligation placed upon him to marry his sister-in-law, but then failed to carry it through. It was a repeated sin. While this story has often been used in support of a contraceptive ban for Christians, Onan's subsequent punishment was unlikely to be because he used a contraceptive method.

We have noted above that contraceptives were known and widely used in biblical times. If all contraceptive use was forbidden, we would expect to see it mentioned in the text. However, a passage such as Leviticus 20:10-21, which contains a long list of sexual crimes, contains no mention of a prohibition on contraceptive practices. If use of contraception deserved the death penalty, how much more would we expect it to appear? It is more likely that Onan's punishment was due to his failure to honour his dead brother and obey God's command. His motives were sensual and selfish, agreeing to have intercourse but preventing conception so that his own inheritance would not be diminished by the birth of a nephew. Although the penalty for defying the Levirate law in Deuteronomy was public shaming, Onan's actions were particularly exploitative. He displeased God, and God judged him by putting him to death.

The Bible, then, does not expressly forbid contraception. Does it specifically endorse it? In 1 Corinthians 7, Paul permits abstinence from sex within marriage for spiritual purposes, but only as a temporary and mutually agreed practice:

> Do not deprive one another, except perhaps by agreement for a limited time, that you may devote yourselves to prayer; but then come together again, so that Satan may not tempt you because of your lack of self-control. (1 Cor 7:5)

United States theologian John J Davis sees this as implying a larger principle where "Christian couples have the right to choose to 'override' the usual responsibility to procreate (Gen 1:28) for a season in order to pursue a spiritual good".[42] However, considering the restrictions placed on this activity by the apostle (i.e. that this is the exception, not the rule; that it is only for a set time for a specific reason, after which the couple is to come together again; and that it does expose you to moral danger), it is very hard to see that Paul is recommending abstinence in this passage as a regular method of birth control. Indeed, the passage does not even discuss child-bearing, but rather the need to be united sexually in marriage in order to be holy.

In the absence of any scriptural prohibition against contraception, and given that the Bible was written in a world where contraception was well known and widely practised, it would seem that there is a legitimate place for contraception in marriage. If this is the case, when is it acceptable?

The Genesis account of creation, where mankind is commanded to procreate, helps us approach this question. If we consider that humanity is made in the image of God and called to be God's representatives in the

---

42. JJ Davis, *Evangelical Ethics*, 3rd edn, P and R Publishing, Phillipsburg, 2004, p. 54.

world, we are not only dependent on God, without whose help no child is born (cf. Gen 4:1), but we are also persons who are free to make choices, whether good or bad (Gen 2:16-17; Gal 6:7-8). We have the responsibility to act as good stewards—as parents as well as individuals. As parents, it is not enough just to beget offspring; we are also called to nurture our children as they grow.[43] And we know from our ethical framework that we should seek to have godly motives and perform actions that are consistent with God's will.

With regard to our motives, as mentioned previously, we should begin sexual relations with the understanding that parenthood may be a consequence (sex without children being a myth). In view of the Bible's high regard for children, any attempt to avoid their birth must be done with a clear conscience and not for arbitrary or self-interested purposes. If we seek to honour God in all our decision-making, we will be aware that such self-interest is clearly opposed to God's will. However, even when our motives are right, decisions are not always simple and some situations are clearer than others.

Contraception may have a place in Christian marriage when its purpose is to time the arrival of children. Birth control allows married couples time to strengthen their love and commitment at the beginning of a marriage, before the arrival of children. Care of newborns can be demanding and tiring, and contraception can give the couple time to prepare for parenthood.

Since the responsibilities of parenting extend beyond birth, factors such as temporary financial or ministry restrictions may make timing of the arrival of children an important consideration. In 1 Timothy 5:8, Paul tells us that we are to provide for our relatives and especially our immediate family. This suggests that parents need to be responsible stewards regarding their ability to support children, and be realistic about how many they can effectively provide for. And 'provision' includes physical, emotional and spiritual needs. The wellbeing of children already born may require extra time between children to allow for the proper fulfilment of parental responsibilities—especially if, for example, a child is born with a disability. Such decisions should be made prayerfully and jointly between husband and wife, and with an awareness that God may overrule our plans.

---

43. See chapter 4.

Chosen childlessness

A couple may have valid reasons for deciding against having children. In our fallen world, there may be times when a couple may long for the blessing of children, yet sadly see this path as unwise given their particular circumstances. For example, if we view contraception as an expression of permissible medical care for promoting health,[44] it is possible to envisage how it might be used for such a purpose. Some contraindications to child-bearing will be straightforward, if tragic—such as life-threatening complications for the wife if she became pregnant. Selflessness may lead a mother to pursue parenthood regardless of risk while trusting God for deliverance, but it could also be argued that in the face of expected complications, it is better stewardship to preserve the woman's life. Sometimes it is the child who would bear the burden of a poor outcome, such as through complications of pregnancy or inherited genetic disease. In such a situation some parents may pursue other means of becoming parents, for example through adoption.

Often contraindications to child-bearing may be less straightforward and require clinical judgement on the part of medical staff, as well as prayerful consideration by those involved. Reasons to consider putting off child-bearing may include seasons of poor physical or psychological health. The same decision by two different couples may derive from entirely different motives, so we must be careful not to judge others. The decision to use contraception should be made consciously, thoughtfully and with the desire to glorify God in our choices. This is not a place for legalism.

However, none of this is to say that we should choose not to have children merely from our own selfish motives. In our ethical framework, motives are important. It is wrong to avoid having children (by using contraceptives) simply to make our lives more convenient or affluent.

Some argue that it is wrong to bring children into a world in which evil is so prevalent. But as theologian Stanley Hauerwas has argued, "Christians do not place their hope in their children, but rather their children are a sign of their hope, in spite of the considerable evidence to the contrary, that God has not abandoned this world".[45] While Jeremiah

---

44. See chapter 16.
45. S Hauerwas, *The Hauerwas Reader*, ed. J Berkman and M Cartwright, Duke University Press, London, 2001, p. 499.

was instructed not to marry and have children because of the coming judgement (Jer 16:1-4), once the exiles were in Babylon he wrote encouraging them to build families (29:6) as a sign that God had not forgotten his promise and would in time bring them back from captivity (29:10-14). Procreation is aligned with hope.

There are Christian couples who say they have chosen to be childless so that they may "please the Lord" (1 Cor 7:32-35), but this is faulty on at least two levels. Firstly, the passage in 1 Corinthians is discussing the situation of an unmarried Christian, for whom the intended purposes of marriage are not relevant. Secondly, it implies that an increased commitment to ministry is pleasing to God in a way that the nurture of children is not.

While I am conscious that sometimes couples who are childless through infertility are wrongly accused of selfishness, in other circumstances selfishness is indeed the reason for childlessness. There are websites dedicated to supporting those who make the choice to be 'childfree'. They regularly deny the charge of selfishness, but the reasons given for their choice include reluctance to change lifestyle, avoiding stress on their relationship, and not wanting to take responsibility for children. Rodney Clapp sees this as a logical outcome of a society which has become increasingly individualistic, with autonomy promoted as an important ethical value: "What could hinder my autonomy more than responsibility for children, who will surely impose their own expectations and limitations on my life?"[46] I am not saying these claims are unfounded. Research into childfree couples in recent years has repeatedly shown that they tend to be happier and wealthier than their child-bearing peers.[47] But that is not the point.

As Oliver O'Donovan has written:

> A deliberate intention to prefer other goods (such as career or
> wealth) to the good of children, would, in my opinion, constitute
> a lack of understanding consent and so, in traditional terms, a
> ground of nullity. A couple who do not see what children have to
> do with it are as far from understanding marriage as a couple who

---

46. R Clapp, *Families at the Crossroads*, IVP, Leicester, 1993, p. 136.
47. S Basten, *Voluntary Childlessness and Being Childfree*, The Future of Human Reproduction: Working Paper 5, St. John's College, Oxford, and Vienna Institute of Demography, June 2009.

do not see what permanence has to do with it. But I would wish to distinguish very carefully between this couple and another who, while seeing quite clearly what children have to do with it, are persuaded for reasons that seem good to them (their age or health or genetic endowment, for example) that this good cannot be realized in their own marriage. There is a *reluctant* 'intention' not to have children which is perfectly compatible with a full understanding of marriage.[48]

But overall, justifiable reasons for avoiding children will be relatively few. It is not up to us to redesign the model of marriage we are given in the Bible and to which we commit at our wedding. Most marriages will be open to children at some point—in fact, we are to welcome children as a good gift from God.

Children as a gift

The Western world is far more affluent than any society before us. Sadly, our affluence at times seems to make us more selfish rather than less. We can now see in our society the growing acceptance of a lifestyle that excludes children entirely and allows adults to live in a completely self-centred way. In such communities, children may be seen not so much as a gift but as a threat. Life is fast-paced in the city and children make us less efficient. Kathryn Blanchard says that for Christian couples within this milieu, there is a risk that contraceptive freedom paradoxically "ends up being troubling (rather than a relief) to... Christian consciences, in that children are no longer seen as gifts from God but as consumer choices in need of explanation".[49] This endangers the ability of Christian couples to truly welcome children. It robs us of the space to slow down and offer children the open hospitality that we ourselves have received from a gracious, loving God. In a perfect world we would have many children, and would greet them with relaxed joy and not time-pressured expectations. It is a form of Christian freedom to allow God to bless us in this way if he so chooses.

Christopher Ash has summed it up well:

> If the Creator declares procreation a blessing, given to us to
> enable us to participate in the privilege of being his stewards in

---

48. O O'Donovan, *Marriage and Permanence*, Grove Ethical Booklets, no. 26, Nottingham, 1978, p. 12, cited in Ash, op. cit., p. 179.
49. Blanchard, op. cit., p. 243.

this world, we ought to value this as gift and blessing. It may be, and often is, an alarming blessing (because we are not sure if we can cope with it), an inconvenient blessing (impacting deeply on lifestyles) and a costly blessing, but it is to be esteemed as blessing not curse. This ought to be our fundamental attitude with regard to procreation.[50]

3. Understanding different contraceptives

If we accept that contraceptive use can be ethically permissible for Christians, our next question relates to whether our choice of contraceptive is morally important. Answering this question is necessary to help us judge whether our actions will be pleasing to God. However, to answer this question we first need to understand the biology of conception.

The biology

Women of child-bearing age will usually produce an egg every month, which comes from the ovary and is released into the fallopian tube (ovulation). During sexual intercourse, sperm is released from the man's penis and travels from the vagina through the cervix into the womb and into one of the fallopian tubes. If there is an egg there, fertilization can take place.

In our biology lesson in chapter 2, we saw that this is the first step of *conception*. Therefore, you might be forgiven for thinking that a *contraceptive* (i.e. something which opposes conception) would just be working to keep the sperm and egg apart. Not so. Contraceptives usually work in one of three ways:

- by stopping production of eggs
- by preventing the egg and sperm from coming into contact with each other
- once the embryo has been formed, by preventing it from implanting in the uterus.

However, any action occurring after fertilization means that a human life is already present when it occurs. How can a device with such an action be labelled a 'contraceptive'?

---

50. Ash, op. cit., p. 175.

Marketing strategies

Some history is needed to understand the marketing of contraceptives. After the introduction of the oral contraceptive pill (OCP) in 1958, Albert Rosenfeld was concerned that rather than only preventing the sperm from fertilizing the egg (the classic definition of 'conception'), the pill might also terminate embryonic human life by inhibiting implantation (which you may remember occurs at the end of the first week). Since such interference would occur after conception, he realized that some people would say this represented an abortion. He recommended the 'solution' to this problem suggested by Dr AS Parkes of Cambridge: "Equate conception with the time of implantation rather than the time of fertilization—a difference of only a few days".[51] That is, he got around the fact that these drugs might cause the termination of a pregnancy by changing the definition of when a pregnancy started—because if there were no pregnancy, you couldn't say you were causing an abortion. (Whether this abortive mechanism does actually operate for the pill is still not clear, as we will see.)[52]

Following Rosenfeld's logic, the subsequent printing of the American College of Obstetricians and Gynecologist's terminology text in 1972 saw a deliberate change of the definition of 'conception'. The accepted scientific view that conception was the result of the process of fertilization was altered to define 'conception' as implantation.[53] As a result, the link between fertilization and conception was broken. Pregnancy was still defined as "the state of a female after conception and until termination of the gestation",[54] but the text now dated a pregnancy (and by implication a human life) from the time of the *implantation* of the embryo into the wall of the mother's uterus. Under the new definition, any device that prevented the embryo from implanting in the uterus could be marketed as a contraceptive.

There are then two categories of marketed 'contraceptives': those that prevent fertilization, and those that cause an early abortion by acting after fertilization. Note that those who made this definitional change had no authority to do so—they weren't embryologists. Despite many medical

---

51. A Rosenfeld, *The Second Genesis*, Prentice-Hall, Englewood Cliffs, 1969, p. 108.
52. See the oral contraception pill section later in this chapter, and also appendix I.
53. It is sometimes explained in terms of conception being a 'process' that commences at fertilization and is not complete until implantation, with the pregnancy in place only after the 'process' is complete.
54. EC Hughes (ed.), *Obstetric-Gynecologic Terminology*, Committee on Terminology, American College of Obstetricians and Gynecologists, FA Davis, Philadelphia, 1972, p. 327.

textbooks adopting the new definition, current respected embryology textbooks still mark conception (and human life) at fertilization.[55] Very few doctors currently practising are aware of this definitional change.[56]

Two kinds of contraceptive

Now, if as Christians we hold that human life begins at fertilization, we need to separate these two categories, since we would say that contraceptives that act prior to fertilization are ethically acceptable, whereas those acting after fertilization are not. We have already established that God's law prohibits the destruction of a human embryo.[57] However, working out which contraceptive methods fit into which category is not a completely straightforward process, as we will see below.

First we must consider how a contraceptive works. This can be a problem because, surprisingly, it is still not known exactly how some standard contraceptives work. Such research is hampered by the fact that it is difficult to know exactly when fertilization occurs in any individual woman.[58] It also seems that contraceptive manufacturers are quite happy to have some doubt surrounding the precise mechanisms of contraceptives, as it makes it more difficult for pro-lifers to object to them on factual grounds. I will do my best to clarify how particular contraceptives work as I discuss each one.

In the discussion of individual contraceptives below, effectiveness ratings are included as failure rates. No contraceptive works perfectly. Sometimes they fail. Failure rate refers to how well it works in terms of preventing pregnancy, and the way it is listed refers to the percentage of couples who will become pregnant in the first year of use. It does not refer to how ethical it is in terms of function. I have included this information not only because reliability will obviously be a factor worth considering when choosing a contraceptive, but also because some people have the idea that by making ethical choices in this area they are opening themselves up to the risk of unreliable birth control. The figures don't support this.

In this chapter, failure rates are recorded as a range between

---

55. As explained in chapter 2. For example, see R O'Rahilly and F Müller, *Human Embryology and Teratology*, 3rd edn, Wiley-Liss, New York, 2001, pp. 8, 87; and BM Carlson, *Patten's Foundations of Embryology*, 6th edn, McGraw-Hill, New York, 1996, p. 3.
56. My informal research has elicited none.
57. See chapter 3.
58. For further discussion of this point, see '8. The problem of detection' under 'Common objections to the argument that human life begins at fertilization' in chapter 2.

'consistent and correct use' (which looks at how well the method of contraception works if used perfectly according to the instructions) and 'as commonly used' (which takes into account someone forgetting a dose or experiencing drug interactions, and other aspects of real life).[59] 'Failure rate' of using no method at all is 85%, meaning that 85% of couples will become pregnant in the first year if no contraception is used.

Check with your doctor regarding how a particular contraceptive method should be used, any risks involved, and how long you need to be using it before it starts working properly.

Choosing a contraceptive

A final note of caution: this section is not designed to take the place of the medical consultation that is necessary to ensure contraception will be safe and appropriate for your own situation. This is because choosing which contraceptive you would like to use involves consideration of more than ethics alone. Once you have determined which contraceptives are ethically permissible, you will also need to take into account factors such as the state of your health, side effects of different methods, availability and cost. Before deciding which one suits you, I recommend you discuss the issue with your doctor. Most doctors will be happy to take your ethical position into account while exploring the alternatives.

Some people may reject a certain contraceptive (such as the pill) because of the social context in which it was developed. I would suggest that while this may make us look at an individual method more carefully, it should not lead us to reject it out of hand. Ethics is a rational process of inquiry that, in medical decision-making, should be based on the facts.

This chapter discusses the use of contraceptives for the purpose of avoiding pregnancy.[60] The discussion below assumes that the reader is in a Western industrialized society. There may be different ethical factors to consider in a developing country where maternal mortality and

---

59. Unless indicated otherwise, all effectiveness rates are taken from J Trussell, 'Contraceptive efficacy', in R Hatcher, J Trussell, A Nelson, W Cates Jr, FH Stewart and D Kowal (eds), *Contraceptive Technology*, 19th rev. edn, Ardent Media, New York, 2007, pp. 747-826; rates for monthly injectables and cervical caps are from J Trussell, 'Contraceptive failure in the United States', *Contraception*, vol. 70, no. 2, August 2004, pp. 89-96; both as cited in the World Health Organization (WHO) Department of Reproductive Health and Research and Johns Hopkins Bloomberg School of Public Health/Center for Communication Programs (CCP), *Family Planning*, appendix A, Knowledge for Health Project, CCP and WHO, Baltimore and Geneva, 2011, p. 319.

60. For discussion of the use of these medications for other purposes, see chapter 16.

associated newborn mortality need to be taken into account.

For convenience I will group the various methods under the following headings:

  a. Hormone contraceptives
  b. Barrier contraceptives
  c. Intrauterine Devices (IUDs)
  d. Fertility awareness
  e. Male contraceptives
  f. Other methods
  g. Permanent contraception
  h. Emergency contraception

a. Hormone contraceptives[61]

There are two main types of hormone contraceptive formulations available:
- combined, which contain both an oestrogen and a progestin (a synthetic form of the natural hormone progesterone)
- progestogen-only, which contain only progesterone or progestin.

It is easier to understand how these contraceptives work if you are aware of the normal 28-day human female reproductive cycle. The changes that occur in the ovary and uterus during each cycle serve to develop and release the egg for possible fertilization by the sperm, and prepare the endometrium (uterine lining) for implantation of the fertilized egg.[62]

During the first half of her menstrual cycle, an egg develops in a follicle of a woman's ovaries in response to a hormone stimulus (follicle stimulating hormone, or FSH). The follicle increases oestrogen production, which acts on the uterus to stimulate growth of the endometrium. It reaches a peak about one day before *ovulation* (release of a mature egg into the fallopian tubes). The surge of oestrogen stimulates her pituitary gland to secrete another hormone (luteinizing hormone, or LH), which in turn triggers ovulation.

The follicle that released the egg then transforms into another type of cell (a corpus luteum) under the influence of LH. The corpus luteum produces high levels of oestrogen and progesterone, which stimulate continued growth of the endometrium to prepare it for implantation of an

---

61. Brand names for hormone contraceptives vary throughout the world. I have included a few examples of each type, but if you would like to check other brand names for hormonal contraceptives you can do so through the IPPF website's directory: http://contraceptive.ippf. org. I do not endorse the content of this website overall, but the contraceptive directory is accurate and regularly updated.

62. See diagram 1: Female reproductive organs in chapter 2.

embryo if there is one. During an ovulatory cycle, estradiol levels increase by 10-16 times, and progesterone increases by 20 times, compared to pre-ovulatory levels. If fertilization does not occur, the corpus luteum reduces in size and stops secreting hormones, leading to the shedding of the endometrium as a menstrual period. If fertilization does occur, the corpus luteum continues to secrete its hormones for 8-10 weeks until the placenta takes over production of the hormones to support the pregnancy.

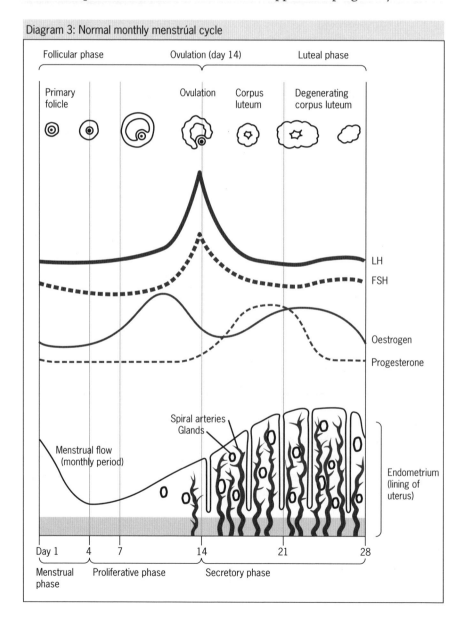

Diagram 3: Normal monthly menstrúal cycle

There are several different types of hormone contraceptives, including the oral contraceptive pill, progestin-only pills, implants and injectables, and hormone-containing patches and rings. As they vary in method of action and effectiveness, they will be considered individually.[63]

(i) The oral contraceptive pill (OCP)

Also known as the combined oral contraceptive (COC), the birth-control pill and 'The Pill', this is an oral contraceptive that contains low doses of two hormones—a progestin and an oestrogen. There are many brands available that vary in strength and other factors, but they essentially all work the same way. The OCP is taken daily for 3 weeks followed by a week when either a sugar pill or no pill is taken before resuming the OCP.

OCPs inhibit follicular development and prevent ovulation as their primary mechanism of action. This is achieved through suppression by progestin of the release of FSH and LH. Oestrogen was originally included in the OCP for better cycle control (stabilizing the endometrium to reduce breakthrough bleeding), but was also found to inhibit follicular development and help prevent ovulation.[64] This means there is no egg available to be fertilized.

A secondary mechanism action of all progestogen-containing contraceptives is inhibition of sperm penetration through the cervix by decreasing the amount and increasing the viscosity (stickiness) of the mucous in the cervix. This reduces the chance that sperm will be present to do the fertilizing.

The OCP also has a third effect. It makes the lining of the womb thinner and hostile to the embryo. These changes to the endometrium may prevent implantation of an embryo in the uterus, should one be present.[65] If the first two mechanisms failed and this post-fertilization mechanism did operate, then use of the OCP may sometimes cause early abortions, in which case its use is unethical. However, if this third mechanism does not operate alone, then there are no ethical objections to use of the OCP. Although in scientific terms this controversy is currently unresolved, my own view is that the weight of evidence supports OCPs as being ethically acceptable—but see appendix I for a fuller discussion of these issues.

---

63. See also hormonal IUD (*Mirena*) under 'c. Intrauterine devices' below.
64. J Trussell, 'Contraceptive efficacy', loc. cit.
65. For further discussion of this issue, see appendix I.

It is well known that the mechanism of the OCP is less reliable in suppressing ovulation in certain circumstances: in the first month of use, when a dose is missed, when the tablets are not absorbed from the gut (e.g. due to vomiting and diarrhoea), and when other drugs interfere with the pill (e.g. some antibiotics). At these times I would advise using an alternative method of contraceptive (such as a condom). This is because the OCP will be less effective, not because I think you are risking an early abortion. You need to discuss these things with your doctor, but they explain why the OCP failure rate is wide at 0.3%-8.0%.

For doctors

For added security, to reduce the likelihood of ovulation you could consider shortening the pill-free interval to 4 days on a regular basis, or recommend 2-, 3-, 4-monthly or continuous extended use of the pill. Monophasic pills (where there is the same amount of oestrogen and progestin in each pill) are recommended for extended use.[66] It is important to take the time to educate patients regarding the significance of the pill-free period—that is, that missing a pill at the start of a packet or extending the pill-free period for more than 7 days significantly increases the chance of ovulation occurring.[67]

As there is no research into the residual effects of hormonal contraceptives when they are stopped, it is impossible to tell whether post-fertilization effects are possible while ovulation is being re-established. To avoid any risk for those who wish to avoid this, it is recommended that a couple use a barrier method of contraception until after the woman's second period when ceasing the OCP.[68]

(ii) Extended cycle and continuous use birth control pills

These are usually known by their brand names: *Seasonique, LoSeasonique, Lybrel* (all contain levonorgestrel and ethinyl estradiol).

In 2003, the FDA approved use of extended regimen birth control,

---

66. J Guillebaud, 'When do contraceptives work?' *Triple Helix*, Summer 2003, pp. 12-13.
67. J Guillebaud, *Contraception*, 4th edn, Churchill Livingstone, Edinburgh, 2004, p. 112.
68. OEO Hotonu, *Contraception: A pro-life guide*, The Christian Institute, Newcastle on Tyne, 2005, p. 26.

which was intended to let women have fewer periods (withdrawal bleeds) or none at all. It has a similar makeup to older OCPs but is packaged differently. The extended use involves taking one pill for 84 days continuously, followed by a different pill for 7 days, which means a woman will have only 4 periods a year. The continuous use is just one pill taken without a break, with no period until she stops. At this stage it is thought that extended use pills are as safe as the conventional pill in the short term (obviously no long-term studies are available yet), and of similar effectiveness, although details of the failure rate are not known at the time of writing. Missing a period is safe—but many women are reassured by the appearance of a period, to know that pregnancy is unlikely. Ethics of use will be similar to the OCP (see above).

Seasonique and *LoSeasonique* are taken 84/7. *Lybrel* is taken continuously. They currently have limited distribution.

For doctors

You will recognize this application as similar to tricycling conventional OCPs, which has long been done by women wanting to avoid a monthly withdrawal bleed. This has often been used to treat endometriosis, dysmenorrhea and other menstruation-associated symptoms. Personal preference to avoid menstruation has become a common reason for use of the new formulations,[69] especially amongst teenagers.[70] Please see prescribing information for details of use and side-effect profile. At present the exact efficacy is unknown and there is no available data at this time concerning the long-term effects of menstrual suppression on a woman's overall health. There exists concern in the medical field that increasing the amount of hormones typically taken by a woman may have an adverse effect on her long-term health, but there is no data to confirm or disprove this.

---

69. A Edelman, MF Gallo, JT Jensen, MD Nichols and DA Grimes, 'Continuous or extended cycle vs. cyclic use of combined hormonal contraceptives for contraception', *Cochrane Database of Systematic Reviews*, issue 3, 2005.

70. KL Gerschultz, GS Sucato, TR Hennon, PJ Murray and MA Gold, 'Extended cycling of combined hormonal contraceptives in adolescents: Physician views and prescribing practices', *Journal of Adolescent Health*, vol. 40, no. 2, February 2007, pp. 151-7.

Whatever you decide with your spouse on this matter, do not use the pill if the conscience of either of you forbids it. Everything that does not come from faith is sin (Rom 14:23b). This implies that an action performed against the voice of an informed conscience can never be right.

(iii) Progestin-only injections

The most commonly used progestin-only injectables are DMPA (medroxyprogesterone acetate; e.g. *Depo-Provera, Depo, Megestron, Petogen*) and NET-EN (norethisterone enanthate; e.g. *Noristerat, Syngestal*). They are packaged in the form of an injection that is given regularly (3-monthly for DMPA and 2-monthly for NET-EN for greatest effectiveness). They are usually given into the muscle, and from there the hormone is slowly released into the bloodstream. (A newer formulation of DMPA called *depo-subQ provera 104*, or *DMPA-SC*, is injected under the skin and has similar effects.)

These contraceptives mainly work by suppressing ovulation (so there is no egg), and they also thicken cervical mucus (to slow down the sperm) and make the endometrial lining thinner. The dose of progestin used reliably suppresses ovulation, so there is never an egg available to be fertilized. As there is no embryo created, the other mechanisms of action do not contribute to the contraceptive effect. Just because they are capable of blocking implantation does not mean these drugs ever have to use this back-up mechanism. They are therefore ethically acceptable, so long as they are injected on time. They can be used in breastfeeding from 6 weeks after childbirth. They have increased effectiveness compared to other medications because you don't have to remember to take a pill every day. Failure rate is 0.3%-3.0%.

For doctors

In these drugs, progestin suppresses ovulation through the hypothalamic-pituitary-ovarian axis, controlling LH and FSH release so the ovum does not mature. To ensure suppression of ovulation it is important that the injection period is never exceeded. It is possible for minimal follicular activity to occur towards the end of the injection period in some women. For extra confidence that ovulation is suppressed, you could offer injections more frequently—for example, every 10 weeks for DMPA

---

instead of the usual 12.[71]

As there is no research into the residual effects of hormonal contraceptives when they are stopped, it is impossible to tell whether post-fertilization effects can occur while ovulation is being re-established. To avoid any risk for those who wish to avoid them, it is recommended that a couple use a barrier method of contraception until after the woman's first period after stopping Depo-Provera.[72]

(iv) Combined injectable contraceptive

Monthly injectables, also called CICs, contain the two hormones—a progestin and an oestrogen—similar to the oral contraceptive pill. This makes them different from DMPA and NET-EN, which contain progestin only. Two common combinations are medroxyprogesterone acetate (MPA)/estradiol cypionate (*Ciclofem, Ciclofemina, Cyclofem, Cyclo-Provera, Feminena, Lunella, Lunelle, Novafem*) and norethisterone enanthate (NET-EN)/estradiol valerate (*Mesigyna, Norigynon*). They work primarily by preventing the release of eggs from the ovaries (ovulation). There are few long-term studies for monthly injectables, but researchers assume they are similar to the OCP in effect. This means that the ethics for using this formulation will be similar to that of the OCP (see above). Injections need to be given regularly every 28-30 days. Failure rate is 0.05%-3%.

For doctors

As there is no research into the residual effects of hormonal contraceptives when they are stopped, it is impossible to tell whether post-fertilization effects are possible while ovulation is being re-established. To avoid any risk for those who wish to avoid them, it is recommended that a couple use a barrier method of contraception until after the woman's first period after stopping monthly injectables.

---

71. Guillebaud, *Contraception*, op. cit., p. 13.
72. ibid.

(v) Progestin-only pill (POP)

This is a pill that contains only a low dose of progestin (levonorgestrel or norethisterone). It is also called the mini-pill (because it is a low dose), or by its brand name: *Femulen, Micronor, Microval, Noriday, Neogest, Norgeston*. It is often prescribed for breastfeeding women (starting 6 weeks after the birth) as it does not contain oestrogen, which can reduce milk production. It may also be recommended for older women who smoke, as taking oestrogen greatly increases the risk of developing a blood clot in this group.

POPs appear to work by thickening cervical mucus so that the sperm cannot get through and inhibiting ovulation so there is no egg (both pre-fertilization effects), and by making the endometrium hostile to an embryo (a post-fertilization effect). When used alone (without breastfeeding), the low dose of progestin makes it unreliable in terms of suppressing ovulation, with estimated ovulation rates with 'typical' use averaging at about 50%. It is also not guaranteed to block all the sperm from getting through. This means that it will be possible for a sperm and egg to unite and create an embryo that may not be able to implant in the endometrium, because the POP may have made the lining of the uterus too thin to allow the embryo to implant and develop normally. Therefore, as it will sometimes work post-fertilization if used alone, it will be an unethical choice for Christians under these circumstances. When used alone, failure rate ranges from 0.3%-8.0%.

The POP is more successful in suppressing ovulation when combined with breastfeeding, provided it is taken conscientiously (at the same time every day). The timing is important because the contraceptive action decreases rapidly after 24 hours. Under these conditions, failure rate ranges from 0.1%-3.0%. Suppression of ovulation would make this contraceptive ethically acceptable. As weaning begins, the risk of breakthrough ovulation and therefore use of the post-fertilization anti-implantation mechanism increases. As soon as the baby starts getting nutrition from somewhere other than breastfeeding, the woman should use different or additional (barrier) contraception. (See lactation amenorrhoea method, below, or progestin-only injectables, above, for alternatives for breastfeeding women.)

For doctors

Research on POPs has been limited. It is thought that when they do interfere with ovulation, POPs work by suppressing the mid-cycle peak of LH and FSH.[73] It is critical that POPs be taken at the same time every day to be maximally effective. A formulation of the POP using desogestrel 75 mcg (Cerazette) is more reliable in suppressing ovulation than older forms (with evidence of 97% anovulation), and the manufacturers of Cerazette now advertise the flexibility of a 12-hour 'missed pill' window that is similar to OCPs.[74] Cerazette is not available in all countries.

If a woman menstruates regularly while taking a POP, it is unlikely that her ovulation has been suppressed. While no bleeding may indicate ovarian suppression, it may also indicate pregnancy.

As there is no research into the residual effects of hormonal contraceptives when they are stopped, it is impossible to tell whether post-fertilization effects are possible while ovulation is being re-established. To avoid any risks for those who wish to avoid them, it is recommended that a couple use a barrier method of contraception until after the woman's second period after stopping the POP.[75]

(vi) Implants

Implants (*Implanon, Jadelle, Zarin, Femplant*) are small plastic rods or capsules that are usually inserted under the skin of the inner arm by a healthcare worker. They continuously release a progestin at a very slow rate. They work by thickening cervical mucus (to prevent the sperm from getting through) and suppressing ovulation (so there is no egg). They also cause some changes to the endometrium (but less than other progestogen-containing contraceptives). Implants are similar to the POP in the way they work, but they have a much lower pregnancy rate because compliance is not a problem (you don't have to remember to take a pill every day). Etonogestrel (*Implanon*) implants are so effective in suppressing ovulation that it is fair to say they operate prior to

---

73. D Shoupe and SL Kjos (eds), *The Handbook of Contraception*, Humana Press, Totowa, 2006, p. 67.

74. Organon Laboratories Limited, Cerazette home page, Organon Laboratories, Hertfordshire, 2010 (viewed 19 October 2011): www.cerazette.co.uk/160/HCP-home

75. Hotonu, op. cit., p. 21.

fertilization. Just because they are capable of affecting implantation in the endometrium does not mean they ever have to use this back-up mechanism. This makes them an ethical choice. There are other types of implants that release the hormone levonorgestrel (e.g. *Jadelle, Norplant II, Sino-implant II sold as Zarin, Femplant*), which are less reliable in their suppression of ovulation and so would not constitute an ethical choice. Implants need to be replaced after a period of 3 (etonogestrel) or 4 (levonorgestrel) years. Implants are considered the most reliable contraceptive method; failure rate is only 0.05%-0.05%. The pregnancy rate associated with the use of *Implanon* is very low (fewer than one in 1000 over 3 years).

For doctors

Studies show that ovulation may occur towards the end of the 3-year period, so if a woman wanted extra reassurance that ovulation would be avoided you could consider replacing Implanon *every 2½ years instead of the usual 3 years.*[76]

There is no research into the residual effects of hormonal contraceptives when they are stopped. In the case of Implanon, *we cannot be sure whether it continues to act partially after ovulation has returned. We do know that* Implanon *has less impact on the thinning of the endometrium than other progesterone-only contraceptives, and so is unlikely to interfere with implantation by this effect. However, if your patient wants to be sure to avoid any post-fertilization action, she should use a barrier method of contraception until after her second period after the* Implanon *is removed.*[77]

(vii) Combined patch

The combined patch (*Evra, Ortho Evra*) is a small adhesive plastic patch worn on the skin that continually releases two hormones, a progestin (norelgestromin) and an oestrogen (ethinylestradiol), through the skin into the bloodstream. The patch is replaced once a week for 3 weeks and then no

---

76. HJ Bennink, 'The pharmacokinetics and pharmacodynamics of Implanon, a single-rod etonogestrel contraceptive implant', *European Journal of Contraception and Reproductive Health Care*, vol. 5, supp. 2, September 2000, pp. 12-20.
77. Hotonu, op. cit., p. 38.

patch is worn for a 4th week at which time a withdrawal bleed takes place, and then you start again with a new patch. Method of action and ethical challenges are similar to the OCP (see above). Failure rate is 0.3%-8.0%.

For doctors

At the time of writing, Evra has been associated with potentially life-threatening complications that should be considered when prescribing contraceptives. The incidence of complications is greater with Evra than with a typical OCP, due to the proportionally greater percentage of oestrogen the woman is exposed to by the topical route.[78] Evra is not available in all countries.

For increased effectiveness of ovulatory suppression you could advise using patches continuously for 2 or 3 cycles (6-9 weeks), followed by a shorter rest interval (4-6 days).[79]

(viii) Combined vaginal ring

The combined vaginal ring (*NuvaRing*) is a small flexible vaginal ring about 5 cm in diameter that you insert vaginally once a month. It contains hormones similar to those in the OCP (oestrogen/ethinylestradiol and progesterone/etonogestrel). The hormones are absorbed into the bloodstream through the lining of the vagina. It is inserted at the beginning of a menstrual cycle and removed after 21 days, allowing the withdrawal bleed, and then a new ring is inserted after a 7-day break. Method of action is similar to the OCP. For the ethical challenges, please review the OCP section above. Experience is limited but failure rate appears to be 0.3%-8.0%.

For doctors

As with the combined patch, it is possible to increase confidence that ovulation has been suppressed by using 3 or 4 rings in a row without a break.[80]

---

78.   Janssen Pharmaceuticals, *Important Safety Information*, Ortho Evra product information, Janssen Pharmaceuticals, Titusville, 2011 (viewed 19 October 2011): www.orthoevra.com/isi.html

79.   Guillebaud, *Contraception*, op. cit., p. 271.

80.   ibid.

b. Barrier contraceptives

Physical barriers placed between the sperm and egg always work before fertilization because they prevent the embryo from being formed. This makes them all ethically permissible for Christians. *To be reliable, devices need to be in good condition and used according to directions.* Several alternatives are available.

(i) Male condom

The male condom looks like a balloon before you blow it up. It is a mechanical barrier made of latex, polyurethane or natural membrane. It fits over the husband's erect penis and prevents fertilization by stopping semen and therefore sperm before, during and after intercourse. Failure rate is 2%-15%. Problems with condom failure can be caused by manufacturing defects but are more often due to incorrect use. For instance, latex condoms should not be used with oil-based lubricants such as baby oil or petroleum jelly (*Vaseline*) because they can damage the latex. While using spermicide with a condom would seem likely to increase contraceptive protection, it has never actually been proven to do so. Some condoms are manufactured with a spermicide coating anyway.

(ii) Female condom

These are generally known by their brand names: for example, *Care, Reality, Femidom*. A female condom consists of a pouch made of thin polyurethane or latex with flexible rings on both sides. It fits loosely inside the woman's vagina and prevents fertilization by stopping sperm from entering the cervix. Failure rate is 5%-21%.

(iii) Diaphragms, cervical caps and the sponge

These are barriers made of soft rubber or latex, or polyurethane foam (the sponge), which are inserted into the vagina before sex to cover the cervix. The diaphragm is a shallow, dome-shaped cup with flexible rim, which also covers part of the vagina; the cervical cap and the sponge are designed to fit over the cervix only. Use with spermicide (see below) is recommended to improve effectiveness. They come in different sizes and need to be fitted by a trained provider, but are then inserted by the wife when needed. They work by stopping the sperm from entering the cervix, and the spermicide kills or disables the sperm. Failure rate is 6%-16% for diaphragms used with spermicide. Failure rate for cervical caps is different depending on whether a woman has previously given birth (26%-29%) or not (9%-16%). This difference is thought to be related to whether the couple is just delaying pregnancy or trying to avoid it altogether, which influences how careful they try to be. The sponge has a failure rate of 9%-32%. Note that it has been reported that use of vaginal barriers is associated with Toxic Shock Syndrome, a rare but potentially fatal illness.[81]

(iv) Spermicides

Spermicides are creams, jellies, gels, pressurized foam or pessaries (tablets) that are inserted deep in the vagina, near the cervix, before sex. They are designed to break the membrane of sperm cells, which either slows their movement or kills the sperm. This stops the sperm from meeting the egg and so avoids fertilization. The most common spermicide is nonoxynol-9 (*Gynol II*), which causes damage to the vaginal wall when used frequently. Spermicides need to be applied each time you have sex—for example, if you have sex more than once in an evening, you need to reapply the spermicide each time. Alone, spermicides are considered less effective than if used with a barrier method: failure rate is 18%-29%. This is a bit misleading, because you are always meant to use them with a barrier method. Foams and sponges are the most reliable.

New non-toxic spermicides are currently being developed, as well as spermicidal microbicide gels (*BufferGel*, *PRO2000 gel*), which aim to provide dual protection against pregnancy and sexually transmitted infections (including HIV). These gels act by making the vagina more acidic so that both sperm and infections are unable to survive. It is applied in the vagina before sex, and in trials has been used with a diaphragm. If this product became available it would be ethically permissible, as it would act before fertilization.

c. Intrauterine devices

Intrauterine devices (IUDs, also known as *coils*—the shape of early IUDs) are small, usually T-shaped devices that are inserted into the uterus through the vagina and cervix by a healthcare provider. They can stay in place for a number of years, depending on the type. Almost all types of IUD have one or two threads tied to them that hang through the cervix into the vagina. Even though they have been around for a long time, the contraceptive effect is not completely understood. All IUDs appear to induce an inflammatory reaction that changes the chemical

---

81. Hotonu, op. cit., p. 16.

climate of the entire genital tract. This is a result of the body recognizing that the IUD is foreign, and trying to destroy it. In humans, the cells that are produced to do this flow out of the uterus into the fallopian tubes. The main outcome of this is thought to be a reduction in the rate of fertilization.[82] This means the common belief that IUDs work mainly by stopping an embryo from implanting in the wall of the uterus is incorrect.[83] But while we cannot be sure exactly how they work, we do know that it is possible for the sperm to reach the egg when there is an IUD in place, because occasionally a case of ectopic pregnancy (pregnancy where the embryo implants in the fallopian tube) occurs with this method. This means there can be a post-fertilization effect that makes this method ethically unacceptable.

There are two types of IUD with frames: inert (or copper-bearing) IUDs, and hormonal IUDs, which release progestogen. There are also two frameless (implantable) types of IUD: copper-bearing and hormone-releasing.

(i) Inert and copper-bearing IUD

Most non-hormonal IUDs contain copper, which increases the toxicity for sperm and egg. (Some may also contain silver, which has a similar effect to copper.) This, along with the chemical changes in the reproductive tract, damages the egg and sperm before they meet, reducing the rate of embryo production. But if an embryo *is* created, the altered environment means that its chance of survival becomes worse as it approaches the uterus.[84] Although they mainly act before fertilization, there is definite evidence that inert and copper IUDs can work after fertilization.[85] This means that they are not ethically acceptable as a form of contraception

---

82.   ME Ortiz, HB Croxatto and CW Bardin, 'Mechanisms of action of intrauterine devices', *Obstetrical and Gynaecological Survey*, vol. 51, no. 12, December 1996, pp. 42S-51S.

83.   ME Ortiz and HB Croxatto, 'Copper-T intrauterine device and levonorgestrel intrauterine system: biological bases of their mechanism of action', *Contraception*, vol. 75, no. 6, supplement, June 2007, pp. S16-30.

84.   YC Smart, IS Fraser, RL Clancy, TK Roberts and AW Cripps, 'Early pregnancy factor as a monitor for fertilization in women wearing intrauterine devices', *Fertility and Sterility*, vol. 37, no. 2, February 1982, pp. 201-4, cited in JB Stanford and RT Mikolajczyk, 'Mechanisms of action of intrauterine devices: update and estimation of postfertilization effects', *American Journal of Obstetrics and Gynecology*, vol. 187, no. 6, December 2002, pp. 1699-708.

85.   L Videla-Riviero, JJ Etchepareborda and E Kesseru, 'Early chorionic activity in women bearing inert IUD, copper IUD and levonorgestrel-releasing IUD', *Contraception*, vol. 36, no. 2, August 1987, pp. 217-26.

for those who value human life from the time it is created. Failure rate (copper-bearing IUD) is 0.6%-0.8%. The copper IUD is sometimes used after unprotected intercourse for emergency contraception (see below).

(ii) Hormonal IUD (*Mirena*)

These IUDs are impregnated with a hormone, levonorgestrel, which is similar to the hormone progesterone. In some places they are distinguished from copper IUDs by being called 'intrauterine systems' (IUS). They have some systemic effects such as thickening cervical mucus (inhibiting sperm movement through the cervix) and reducing the thickness of the endometrial lining. Despite the addition of hormones, there is evidence that not all women who use a progestin IUD have unfavourable cervical mucus, and for most women the dosage is insufficient to suppress ovulation.[86] The main effect is local. The IUS causes damage to both sperm and eggs, interfering with the way they function and reducing survival, and so decreasing the rate of fertilization. It also lowers the chance of survival for any embryo that might be formed in the fallopian tube before it gets to the uterus. This last mechanism operates after fertilization,[87] making the IUS an unethical choice for contraception. Failure rate is 0.2%-0.2%.

d. Fertility awareness

Fertility awareness methods involve teaching a woman to recognize when she is fertile, or able to become pregnant. Couples use this information to time unprotected intercourse. There are no ethical objections to this method of contraception.

(i) Natural family planning (NFP)

NFP (also called 'periodic abstinence') is an umbrella term for many different types of fertility awareness methods. By identifying on which days the woman can become pregnant, a couple can avoid pregnancy by either abstaining from vaginal intercourse or using another method of ethical contraception (usually a condom or other barrier method) on those days. The aim of each method is to reduce the number of days of abstinence in each menstrual cycle as far as possible without risking

---

86. I Barbosa, O Bakos, S Olsson, V Odlind and EDB Johansson, 'Ovarian function during use of a levonorgestrel-releasing IUD', *Contraception*, vol. 42, no. 1, July 1990, pp. 51-66.

87. Stanford and Mikolajczyk, loc. cit.; also see Ortiz and Croxatto, 'Copper-T intrauterine device', loc. cit.

conception. There are several methods available, and fertility indicators can be used alone or in combination to identify the fertile period. Use of more than one indicator is more effective.

Methods of telling when a woman is fertile include the following:

- **Calendar-based** methods involve keeping track of days of the menstrual cycle (e.g. the calendar method, standard days method and calendar rhythm method).
- **Cervical secretions** can be observed for changes around the time of ovulation (e.g. ovulation [Billings] method).
- **Basal body temperature** (BBT) or body temperature on waking can be measured through the month. It goes up after ovulation (e.g. two day method, BBT method, temperature method).
- **Sympto-thermal** method or **multiple index** method uses all the available indicators of fertility to indicate infertile and fertile phases of the month.

Using these methods, a woman can learn to assess her fertility without the use of a computerized device.

Computerized fertility monitors are also available, which may track basal body temperatures, hormonal levels in urine, changes in electrical resistance of a woman's saliva, or a mixture of these symptoms. For example, *Persona* detects luteinising hormone and oestrogen (the hormones that control your cycle), and the *WinBOM Charting System* can be used with the Billings method. *Lady-Comp* is a variation of the rhythm method, as is *CycleBeads*. These are meant to identify the days on which you are at significant risk of becoming pregnant, and on which you should avoid intercourse if prevention of pregnancy is intended.

This technique will not suit every couple. You must be highly motivated to stay aware of the woman's body cycle and keep track of the days, and both husband and wife must be committed to the program. The fertile window is usually 8 days, and vaginal intercourse should be avoided during that time. We are instructed in 1 Corinthians 7:5 that abstinence within marriage is to be undertaken only by mutual consent. However, though it sometimes causes stress, many couples have reported that this style of contraception has increased intimacy and strengthened their marriage as they share responsibility for contraception. Some have reported that the periodic abstinence has kept their sex life fresh and entertaining. And this contraceptive is free and always available!

The Roman Catholic Church approves of NFP while opposing use of other 'artificial' contraceptives (such as those listed above).[88] While NFP does differ in terms of equipment required, the intention is the same (to avoid pregnancy), and deliberate action is still taken to prevent fertilization with the outcome of (hopefully) avoiding pregnancy. Accordingly, I do not consider NFP to be superior in ethical terms to other ethically permissible methods described in this chapter.[89]

There's an old joke: "What do you call a couple who uses the rhythm method? Parents!" But this is no longer necessarily the case. Failure rate of NFP is 3%-25%. Pregnancy rates will vary for different types of fertility methods, with calendar/rhythm methods used alone being the least reliable. One German study found NFP to have a failure rate as low as 0.3%, which is similar to the OCP.[90] It depends on the users and the regularity of the woman's cycle. NFP needs to be taught by a trained instructor and used carefully to be this reliable.[91]

(ii) Lactation amenorrhoea method

The lactational amenorrhoea method (LAM) is the strategic use of breastfeeding as a contraceptive method. Breastfeeding normally results in amenorrhoea (no menstruation). This reflects a delay in the return of fertility after giving birth, which is mainly due to the baby's suckling (of the mother's nipples) blocking ovulation through hormone release. The length of this delay cannot be reliably predicted or detected. With LAM, a new mother uses frequent breastfeeding without supplementary feeds for the first 6 months as a way of preventing pregnancy. When used properly, so long as bleeding has not returned, LAM is more reliable as

---

88. See Paul VI, op. cit., paragraph 16.

89. An alternative argument is given to support the permissibility of NFP alone as a contraceptive. This is that by timing intercourse to coincide with a non-fertile period, it allows a couple to exercise birth control and at the same time respect the potential for procreation, as it is not present in a way to be violated. The marriage relationship is thought to be strengthened by abstinence in this instance. For elaboration of this argument, see JE Smith in 'Contraception: A Symposium', op. cit., pp. 27-9.

90. CMM Pyper and J Knight, 'Fertility awareness methods of family planning: The physiological background, methodology and effectiveness of fertility awareness methods', *Journal of Family Planning and Reproductive Health Care*, vol. 27, no. 2, April 2001, pp. 103-9.

91. Further information is available from the Australian Council of Natural Family Planning (www.acnfp.com.au) and FertilityCare centres (www.fertilitycare.com.au). See also The Natural Family Planning Information Site (www.nfpsite.aldred.org) if you are in the United States or Fertility UK (www.fertilityuk.org) if you are in Britain. Many other organizations can be contacted via the internet.

a contraceptive than the mini-pill (failure rate is 0.9%-2.0% compared to 0.3%-8.0%).[92] The technique can be learnt through centres that teach natural family planning. It needs to be followed carefully, but does not involve periods of abstinence. Extended LAM (more than 6 months) is less effective.

e. Male contraceptives

When some women describe what they want as a male contraceptive, it looks something like a pregnant man in labour. I don't think that's coming anytime soon! However, there are other developments on the horizon.

(i) Male hormonal contraceptives

This type of contraceptive is still at the research trial stage. It involves giving hormones to men in order to reduce sperm production, and is given as an injection, an implant, patches or pills.[93] If it did reliably remove sperm from the ejaculate then it would be an ethical choice of contraceptive, as that would make fertilization impossible. (You need both the egg and the sperm for fertilization to take place.)

(ii) Contraceptive vaccine

A class of contraceptives based on immunocontraception is being investigated. Theoretically, the vaccine acts against a chemical involved in fertilization in the body, stopping it from functioning normally. If this product were available it would be ethically permissible, as it would not cause the loss of an embryo.

(iii) Other methods

Other strategies aimed at reducing sperm production (spermatogenesis) and/or function are in the pipeline. These include techniques such as heating the testes and blocking the vas deferens (the tube that carries the sperm from the testis) with plugs, traditional Chinese medicine plant *Tripterygium wilfordii* and other medications such as *Adjudin*, enzyme inhibitors and even blood pressure medicine.[94] If the contraceptive

---

92. J Trussell, 'Contraceptive efficacy', loc. cit.

93. J Schieszer, 'Male birth control pill soon a reality', *Msnbc.com*, New York, 1 October 2003 (viewed 19 October 2011): www.msnbc.msn.com/id/3543478/

94. Those interested in such developments can visit websites such as MaleContraceptives. org.

is aimed entirely at blocking sperm production or function, it will be ethically permissible as it will always act before the embryo is formed.

f. Other methods

(i) Coitus interruptus (withdrawal method)

The withdrawal method is really self-explanatory. It involves the husband withdrawing his penis from his wife's vagina before ejaculating outside the vagina. He keeps his semen away from her external genitalia. It works by keeping the sperm outside the woman's body, so fertilization cannot occur. As mentioned above, it has a long history and is the only contraceptive method explicitly mentioned in the Bible. It is more effective than using no contraceptive technique, but challenges in its timing can cause anxiety between couples attempting to avoid conception. It requires a high degree of self-control if it is to be done properly. It therefore has the potential to reduce the pleasure of the marital act, and we know from Scripture that pleasure is an important aspect of marital sex.

However, it is free, is always available, does not cause weight gain, and is known to be acceptable to many married couples. There are no specific ethical objections to its use. The decision to use this method should be based on mutual preference. Failure rate is 4.0%-27.0%. It is possible to fail even if the withdrawal is properly timed, because the pre-ejaculate (fluid that comes out of the penis before the semen) can sometimes contain sperm.[95] Effectiveness can be increased with the use of spermicide.

(ii) Abstinence

Abstaining from vaginal intercourse is the most reliable way to avoid pregnancy in a fertile woman. But is it a contraceptive method that Christians should use?

Some writers see a justification for abstinence in Old Testament regulations. Sexual intercourse was to be avoided during menstruation (Lev 15:24, 18:19, 20:18), after childbirth (Lev 12:1-8), and by men before special missions (Exod 19:15; 1 Sam 21:4-5)—though in the Leviticus passages it was not forbidden completely. These practices would not have been intended as a form of birth control, since by avoiding intercourse at the time of menstruation the couple would be more likely to come together immediately after this period of abstinence, at a time when

---

95. Guillebaud, *Contraception*, op. cit., p. 44.

the woman is more likely to be fertile. This would act in a way directly opposite to contraception. The restrictions on men are not specified, but do not suggest an extended time (less than 3 days in the Exodus passage). Furthermore, these passages are not placed in the context of a discussion of sexual relationships within marriage.

The Bible teaches that sexual intimacy is to be the norm within marriage:

> The husband should give to his wife her conjugal rights, and
> likewise the wife to her husband... Do not deprive one another,
> except perhaps by agreement for a limited time, that you may devote
> yourselves to prayer; but then come together again, so that Satan
> may not tempt you because of your lack of self-control. (1 Cor 7:3-5)

Within marriage, abstinence should be practised only for specified time periods, by mutual agreement for the purpose of prayer. Then the couple should resume sexual relations due to the moral danger that abstinence represents. The apostle certainly does not encourage total abstinence, since that would encourage the temptation to immorality—which, according to Paul, is the opposite of what sexual relations in marriage are intended to do.

According to the Bible, married couples are to engage in regular sexual intercourse. Abstinence is not a long-term birth-control method that should be used by married Christian couples.

(iii) Abortion (surgical, RU-486)

Of the estimated 208 million pregnancies that occurred worldwide in 2008, 33 million (16%) resulted in unintended births and 41 million ended in induced abortions (20%).[96] The Guttmacher Institute sees unintended pregnancy as one of the main drivers of abortion. Modern society's belief that procreation does not have to result from sexual relations has meant that some couples see abortion as a way of 'avoiding' pregnancy.

Several methods of abortion are available depending on the stage of pregnancy. Induced abortions include surgical procedures and/or the use of medications such as RU-486. RU-486 is not a contraceptive. It was specifically designed to cause abortions. All forms of induced abortion

---

96. S Singh, D Wulf, R Hussain, A Bankole and G Sedgh, *Abortion Worldwide*, Guttmacher Institute, New York, 2009, p. 39.

are ethically wrong to use as *contraceptives*, as they directly lead to the death of an unborn child. While it is possible for a late-term abortion to accidentally result in a live birth, this is never intended; and in early pregnancy, abortion is uniformly fatal for the unborn child. We do not have definitive data regarding how many woman use abortion as a means of contraception. It is possible that women who have more than one abortion may be using it this way. For example, the only state in Australia that collects complete data on abortions is South Australia. In that state for the year 2008, of the 5,101 women who had terminations of pregnancy, 1,860 (36.5%) had had a previous termination.[97]

(iv) Ormeloxifene

Also known as centchroman, or trade names *Saheli*, *Novex-DS*, *Centron* and *Sevista*, ormeloxifene is a selective oestrogen receptor modulator (SERM), a class of medication that acts on the oestrogen receptor. It is a non-hormonal, non-steroidal oral contraceptive that is taken once per week (after the first 16 weeks, when it is advised to be taken twice weekly). It causes disruption in the menstrual cycle between ovulation and the development of the uterine lining, although its exact mode of action is not really known. It may delay ovulation, and seems to cause the lining of the uterus to build more slowly than usual. At the same time, if an embryo is formed ormeloxifene makes it travel more quickly through the fallopian tubes than normal. It is thought that this combination of factors creates an environment where, if an embryo forms, implantation is impossible.[98] This means that ormeloxifene will not be an ethical choice for those who value human life from the time of fertilization. Failure rate (estimated from clinical trials) is probably around 2%-9%.

g. Permanent contraception

Sterilization as a means of contraception involves a surgical procedure that intends to prevent pregnancy on a permanent basis by physically blocking the egg and sperm from coming into contact with each other. It is clearly a true contraceptive that prevents fertilization, and in that

---

97. A Chan, J Scott, A-M Nguyen and L Sage, *Pregnancy Outcome in South Australia 2008*, Pregnancy Outcome Unit, SA Health, Government of SA, Adelaide, 2009, p. 62. For a detailed discussion of abortion in other contexts, see chapter 7.
98. MM Singh, 'Centchroman, a selective estrogen receptor modulator, as a contraceptive and for the management of hormone-related clinical disorders', *Medicinal Research Reviews*, vol. 21, no. 4, July 2001, pp. 302-47.

sense is ethically acceptable.

However, we need to think about whether it is consistent with biblical teaching to permanently terminate a person's fertility. Sterilization is seen as a convenient form of contraception for those couples who do not expect to desire more children. But therein lies the problem. We might not expect it, but we can't predict what is in store for any of us. Even if you don't want more children now, consideration should be given to future changes of situation, such as the death of a child or spouse, which may lead you to want more children after all. Young widows are instructed to remarry and have children in 1 Timothy 5:14. The decision to be sterilized potentially robs your future spouse of the opportunity to have children with you.

A study of over 11,000 women in the United States found that 5.9%-20.3% regretted sterilization. The largest score was for women 30 years of age or younger at the time of sterilization.[99]

While some methods are potentially reversible, it is technically difficult to reverse sterilization and can never be guaranteed. Even when it is reversed, the fertility rate isn't 100%. It is not the intention at the time the surgery is performed to make it reversible. (If you wanted reversible contraception you would use one of the methods above that is reliably reversible.)

Traditional arguments against sterilization tend to focus on the morality of purposely setting aside a bodily function or removing part of the body. Is this a proper way to treat the body as a "temple of the Holy Spirit" (1 Cor 6:19-20)? As previously mentioned, passages such as Deuteronomy 23:1, where those emasculated by cutting are forbidden from entering the assembly of the Lord, are thought to refer to a prohibition of Canaanite cultic practices. Jesus' discussion about eunuchs in Matthew 19:10-12 is addressing the idea of not marrying, rather than celibacy in marriage, and points out that only those "to whom it is given" can receive this teaching. Neither passage is a discussion of contraception.

If we consider sterilization in the context of stewardship of the body, we might question whether surgical removal of part of the body is permissible for reasons of convenience, especially when safe and reliable alternatives exist. However, we can also use this as an argument

---

99.   S Hillis, PA Marchbanks, LR Tylor and HB Peterson, 'Poststerilization regret: findings from the United States Collaborative Review of Sterilization', *Obstetrics and Gynaecology*, vol. 93, no. 6, June 1999, p. 889-95.

for sterilization, since it may be good stewardship for some individuals (such as a woman whose body is not fit to carry another pregnancy to term) to ensure that future pregnancy is impossible.

A further argument against sterilization suggests that it makes one unable to fulfil the command of Genesis 1:28. But we have already discussed that this verse cannot represent a universal requirement to reproduce.

If we accept that there is a place for contraception at all, on the grounds that sexual intercourse has a unitive function that can operate independently of the procreative function, then it's hard to see an objection to this particular form of contraception. It is reasonable to think that a couple may get to the point of believing they have as many children as they can responsibly provide for, and their desire to avoid the condemnation of 1 Timothy 5:8 (that "if anyone does not provide for his relatives, and especially for members of his household, he has denied the faith and is worse than an unbeliever") leads them to consider sterilization. Furthermore, we know that fertility for women is never lifelong, as God has built into the female body a sterilization of sorts through the normal process of menopause.

If we understand the underlying theology of responsibility in relationships, we can distinguish good and evil motives for sterilization. There won't be a general 'yes' or 'no' to sterilization; it will depend on each individual case. But the irreversibility of the procedure demands careful consideration, especially if you are in a younger age group.

If the motivation for sterilization is convenience and the desire to separate contraception from sex, or to avoid the necessity of daily tablet-taking, you could consider the use of a longer-term reversible contraceptive (such as *Implanon*) as an alternative.

If a couple decides to proceed with sterilization then unless there are other reasons for the woman to undergo surgery (for example, she needs to have a hysterectomy for fibroids anyway), it is preferable for the man to undergo a vasectomy. It is cheaper and safer than female sterilization. Because of its permanent nature, it is important that the person undergoing sterilization is fully aware of the consequences and consents freely to the operation.

(i) Female sterilization

There are two main ways to remove the reproductive capacity of women, both usually carried out under general anaesthetic. Failure rate overall is 0.5%-0.5%. (Failure of tubal occlusion can occur years after surgery.)

- **Tubal occlusion:** Tubal occlusion ('tying the tubes') involves blocking or removing part of the fallopian tubes so that the egg cannot reach the reproductive tract. This can be achieved by placing a band or clip over each fallopian tube, or electrically burning the tubes. Alternatively, the mid-part of each tube can be surgically removed. A newer technique called *Essure* involves placing tiny coils into each fallopian tube that promote the growth of scar tissue, which in turn blocks the tubes. This can be performed without general anaesthesia.
- **Hysterectomy:** Hysterectomy is the surgical removal of the uterus. While this is extremely effective as a form of sterilization, the operation is too risky to be performed for this purpose only.

(ii) Male sterilization

Vasectomy is the most common form of male sterilization. It is usually done under local anaesthetic, and involves cutting the vas deferens (the tubes that carry the sperm from the testes where they are made), so that no sperm enters the normal ejaculate. It involves a minor surgical procedure that removes a small part of the vas deferens or blocks it another way. It may not be fully effective for 3 months after the operation (and occasionally even longer), during which time an alternative form of contraception should be used. The man is considered sterile when his semen contains no sperm. (You can easily have a test to check.) Overall failure rate of male sterilization is 0.1%-0.15%.

(iii) Sterilization for non-contraceptive reasons

- **Therapeutic sterilization:** This is performed when a woman's life or health is threatened by future pregnancy—for example, the removal of a damaged uterus. If there is a clear medical indication, sterilization in this situation is ethically justified as a necessary medical treatment, with the primary motivation being the preservation of health.
- **Eugenic sterilization:** The eugenics movement of the first half of last century championed the sterilization of people not thought fit to contribute to the human gene pool. It received government support in many countries, including Australia. In some parts of the United States, laws were passed providing for compulsory sterilization of 'misfits' including rapists, drunkards, epileptics and the insane. While these laws have since been repealed, the idea

that some people should not be allowed to reproduce is still voiced. There are reports of disabled women and girls being sterilized without their consent in Australia with some eugenic motivation.[100] Following Hurricane Katrina, Member of the Louisiana State Legislature John La Bruzzo proposed paying poor women US$1000 to be sterilized, to limit the numbers on welfare rolls.[101] While he said his plan would be voluntary and would include incentives for men (to avoid gender discrimination), it also included incentives for college-educated, higher-income people to have more children. "What I'm really studying is any and all possibilities that we can reduce the number of people that are going from generational welfare to generational welfare," he said.

The idea behind eugenics—that only humans with certain preferred characteristics should be born—is opposed to the biblical teaching that all humans are made in the image of God and are therefore valuable, regardless of their personal capabilities.

- **Punitive sterilization:** Punitive sterilization, such as castration, has been advocated as a punishment for criminals guilty of sexual crimes. Recently there has been discussion in a major medical journal regarding the pros and cons of surgical or chemical castration of convicted sex offenders. Those in favour (so long as the prisoner consents) mention the benefit offenders report from being released from sexual preoccupation, and being able to participate in psychological treatment programs they were previously too distracted to join. Those opposed question whether true consent is possible if the alternative is lifelong imprisonment, and also challenge whether it is ethical for doctors to act in the best interests of society rather than the best interests of their patients.[102]
- **Sterilization of the mentally disabled:** Sterilization of the mentally disabled (usually of females) can be motivated by desire for contraception or to save the person involved from the distress

---

100. L Dowse, 'Moving forward or losing ground? The sterilization of women and girls with disabilities in Australia', paper presented to the Disabled People's International (DPI) World Summit, Winnipeg, 8-10 September 2004.

101. M Waller, 'LaBruzzo considering plan to pay poor women $1,000 to have tubes tied', *Times-Picayune*, 23 September 2008.

102. D Grubin and A Beech, 'Chemical castration for sex offenders', *British Medical Journal*, vol. 340, no. 7744, 27 February 2010, c74; and subsequent correspondence.

associated with menstruation. This is a controversial topic that at times has had eugenic overtones (see above). In 2010, an Australian court considered the case of an 11-year-old girl, 'Angela', who had severe intellectual disability and seizures that were provoked by heavy menstruation despite her medication.

Discussion of how best to support the sexuality of a mentally disabled person is beyond the scope of this book, but should be multi-faceted and involve precautions to avoid abuse. Research consistently finds that rates of sexual assault of people with a disability are much higher than the general population. Despite evidence that approximately 20% of Australian women and 6% of men will experience sexual violence in their lifetime,[103] there is no standard national data collection that includes the experiences of women with a disability. A study of Victoria Police data indicates that just over a quarter of all sexual assault victims were identified as having a disability. Of this group, 130 (15.6%) had a psychiatric disability or mental health issue and 49 (5.9%) had an intellectual disability.[104] These data indicate that adults with a psychiatric and/or intellectual disability in particular are over-represented as victims of reported sexual assault, representing just 2.2% and 0.8% of the Australian population generally.[105] This would indicate a need for policy reform for those at risk of such abuse, rather than their sterilization.

Sterilization of the mentally disabled on grounds that the offspring would be disabled is not justified. We know that mentally retarded individuals will not necessarily give birth to retarded children, and discrimination on the grounds of ability is contrary to the biblical teaching that all individuals are made in the image of God and therefore deserving of respect.

To remove without consent someone's ability to reproduce is a violation of human dignity. Such a procedure should be performed

---

103. Australian Bureau of Statistics (ABS), *Personal Safety Survey Australia*, ABS cat. no. 4906.0, reissued edn, ABS, Belconnen, 2006.

104. Statewide Steering Committee to Reduce Sexual Assault, *Study of Reported Rapes in Victoria 2000-2003*, summary research report, Office of Women's Policy, Department for Victorian Communities, Melbourne, July 2006, p. 16.

105. Australian Institute of Health and Welfare (AIHW), *Disability and Disability Services in Australia*, AIHW cat. no. DIS 43, AIHW, Canberra, January 2006, p. 4.

without consent only if there is a serious threat to the life of the person concerned, as in the case above. Due to variation in degrees of retardation and levels of competence, each case should be considered individually. The option of long-term reversible contraception such as *Implanon* or *Depo-Provera* (which may also stop bleeding) should be considered as an alternative.

h. Emergency contraception (the 'morning-after pill')

In Christian marriage, the couple should think about contraception in advance of needing it so that decisions can be made thoughtfully. Emergency contraception will not be needed very often. However, since by definition you will not be expecting to use it, it helps to understand how 'emergency contraception' works, just in case.

Traditionally, those hoping to prevent conception after having unprotected sex might have tried douching. It is still tried today, often with water and spermicide. This is not a reliable form of contraception. Neither is douching with Coca-Cola (another favourite). Sperm have been detected in cervical mucous on their way to the uterus within 90 seconds of ejaculation. Douching only reaches the vagina, so by the time it is done it is usually too late.

A more common occurrence these days is for general practitioners and pharmacists to be approached by women requesting the 'morning-after pill' (MAP). This usually follows condom malfunction or unprotected intercourse during the previous 24 hours, and has been promoted as form of 'retrospective contraception'. The common label of 'morning-after pill' is misleading, as some types work up to 120 hours after unprotected sex. Our society regards use of emergency contraception (EC) as a responsible course to follow if an unplanned pregnancy is unwanted.

There are several forms of EC available. The first is a copper IUD inserted soon after intercourse. The others are pills, listed below. Effectiveness varies, but none are 100% effective.

(i) Copper IUD

When a copper IUD is inserted into the uterus immediately after intercourse, up to 5 days after ovulation, it is very effective in preventing pregnancy. If ovulation has occurred at the time of insertion, the copper IUD works mainly by blocking implantation.[106] If ovulation has not

---

106. Guillebaud, *Contraception*, op. cit., p. 460.

occurred at the time of inserting the IUD, it will act in a similar way to long-term use, which (as noted above) is primarily by toxicity for sperm but also involves effects after fertilization. Therefore this method is unethical regardless of when it is administered.

(ii) Levonorgestrel

It is not known exactly how levonorgestrel (*Postinor-2*, *Levonelle*, *NorLevo*, *Plan B*, *Plan B One-Step*, *Next Choice*) works in the emergency situation. If it is taken before the LH surge (which triggers ovulation), it will usually inhibit ovulation and probably thicken cervical mucus. If taken after ovulation, it is less clear. There is little evidence to suggest a direct anti-implantation effect. If it is not administered in time to block ovulation, it is likely to fail.[107]

It is difficult to be prescriptive about ethics when the exact method of action is unknown. There would be no doubt of the morality of using this medication if the woman were known to be pre-ovulatory in the monthly cycle at the time of use (see below), because there would be no egg available for fertilization. After ovulation there is no point in taking it, due to the side effects of the medication and the likelihood of failure. If there is an embryo in place at the time, it is likely to stay there.

(iii) Ulipristal acetate

Ulipristal acetate is a more recent morning-after pill, usually known by its brand name: *ella*, *ellaOne*. It blocks the action of the hormone progesterone. When taken immediately before ovulation is to occur, *ella* postpones follicular rupture (release of the egg). The likely primary mechanism of action is therefore inhibition or delay of ovulation; however, according to the manufacturer, alterations to the endometrium that may affect implantation may also contribute to efficacy.[108] The dose is one tablet taken as soon as possible, up to 120 hours (5 days) after unprotected intercourse. It is not available in all countries.

If ulipristal is taken before ovulation it would be an ethical choice, as no egg would be released and therefore no fertilization would occur. However, if taken after ovulation, it is possible (given the current state

---

107. ibid.

108. HRA Pharma, *Annex I: Summary of Product Characteristics*, *EllaOne* manufacturer's information, HRA Pharma, Paris, 2012, p. 6 (viewed 18 June 2012): www.hra-pharma.com/downloads/emea-SPC-ellaOne.pdf

of knowledge) that if an embryo were created it would be unable to implant in the uterus. Ulipristal would therefore be an unethical choice. See below for how to determine the timing of ovulation in this situation.

For doctors

According to the manufacturer, ulipristal acetate is an orally active, synthetic progesterone agonist/antagonist. It reversibly blocks the progesterone receptor in its target tissues (uterus, cervix, ovaries, hypothalamus) and acts as a potent anti-progestational agent. Studies have shown that when compared with levonorgestrel, ulipristal was no less effective in preventing pregnancies when administered within 72 hours of unprotected intercourse, but was more effective when administered later (within 72-120 hours). Meta-analysis suggests that ulipristal may be more effective than levonorgestrel from day one and throughout the entire 5-day period following unprotected sexual intercourse.[109]

(iv) The combined hormone (Yuzpe) method

The Yuzpe method involves a high dose of a combined pill that contains both oestrogen and progesterone. When given within 72 hours of unprotected intercourse, if ovulation has not yet occurred it may be suppressed or delayed by the intervention. If ovulation *has* occurred, the Yuzpe method normally causes shedding of the endometrium and if an embryo already exists it will be lost in the menstrual flow.

Women who use the Yuzpe method are at risk of causing an early abortion if they are unaware of where they are in their ovulatory cycle at the time (which is usually the case). However, if they did know where they were in their cycle, they could take the medication to suppress or delay ovulation so that the egg would not be available for fertilization, and so reduce the likelihood of pregnancy. This would be a true pre-fertilization contraceptive effect.

(v) RU-486 (mifepristone)

RU-486 (mifepristone) was developed specifically to cause medical

---

109. K McKeage and JD Croxtall, 'Ulipristal acetate: A review of its use in emergency contraception', *Drugs*, vol. 71, no. 7, 7 May 2011, pp. 935-45.

abortions. It is sometimes called the 'morning-after pill' but in fact it is not a contraceptive. Some authors have suggested that it should be used as an emergency contraceptive.[110]

Determining the timing of ovulation in the emergency setting

Pro-life doctors have developed a protocol that allows review of the hormone levels (oestrogen and progesterone) in the woman presenting after unprotected intercourse. These tests show where she is in her ovulatory cycle, which allows the doctor to determine whether she is in a potentially fertile phase and assess whether she really is at risk of pregnancy. As a result, doctors can reassure those women who are in one of the infertile phases that they do not need any 'treatment', and so will not be exposed to the significant side effects of these drugs. If she is in the period of possible fertility prior to ovulation, it is possible that one of the morning-after pill regimes may be able to delay ovulation long enough to prevent fertilization without harming a pregnancy if it has already begun. If ovulation has occurred or is imminent, emergency contraception could be operating by causing an abortion, and will therefore be unethical.[111] Note that there are contraindications to the use of some of these methods, which should be checked with a doctor before use.

In cases of rape

In the case of rape, care of the woman in crisis needs to be multi-dimensional, and this cannot be fully addressed in this book. The ovarian hormone tests mentioned above will give valuable information to the woman regarding her risk of pregnancy. There has been little research done on the effect of abortion after rape, but some studies suggest that women who continue a pregnancy following rape do better than those who abort.[112]

Heather Gemmen, who wrote about her experience of rape, describes

---

110. See chapter 7 for more information.

111. For details on the protocol of ovarian hormone testing and non-abortifacient emergency contraception, see N Tonti-Filippini and M Walsh, 'Postcoital intervention: From fear of pregnancy to rape crisis', *National Catholic Bioethics Quarterly*, vol. 4, no. 2, Summer 2004, pp. 275-88.

112. S Ewing, *Women and Abortion: An evidence based review*, Women's Forum Australia, Brisbane, 2005, p. 12.

her experience in the hospital that night.[113] Her doctor gave her a hormone tablet that, he said, "changes the environment of the uterus so the egg cannot implant". After clarifying that the pill would stop an *embryo* from implanting, and that this represented early abortion, she was nevertheless encouraged to take it. She wrote, "Death does not seem so gruesome or final when you are holding it in your hand in the form of a tiny pink pill".

A woman in this situation is incredibly vulnerable emotionally, and it is easy to see how she could be persuaded to act against her conscience. The immediate offer of non-abortifacient (non-abortion causing) contraception, if applicable, can avoid risking any further trauma resulting from her guilt about complicity in abortion. Such procedures attempt to delay ovulation beyond the time the rapist's sperm would be able to survive, so reducing the chance of pregnancy. This is ethically appropriate, and it is important the woman involved is told so. (Read Heather's inspiring story to see what happened next.)[114]

The chapter on abortion contains further discussion of what should be done in this situation. It should be noted that in the case of rape, it is accepted in orthodox Catholic theology that attempted postponement of ovulation by taking hormonal contraceptives is legitimate, as the goods of marriage do not exist in this circumstance (so they cannot be destroyed by the use of contraception).[115]

For doctors and pharmacists

Health professionals can find themselves in a difficult situation when a patient requests a type of contraceptive that the health professional thinks is unethical. Provision of emergency contraception can raise particularly difficult ethical questions for those health professionals who are expected to provide this legal alternative to patients who request it. It is especially stressful if the woman is extremely anxious (which is not unusual).

Some doctors have found it helpful to place a discreet sign in the waiting room advising patients before the consultation that only contraceptives acting before fertilization will be available.

---

113. H Gemmen, *Startling Beauty*, Life Journey, Colorado Springs, 2004.
114. ibid.
115. Tonti-Filippini and Walsh, op. cit., p. 11.

Few jurisdictions oppose doctors' right of conscience on this issue. Pharmacists may find it more difficult, especially if they are not senior staff in the pharmacy. It may be possible to reach an agreement with other staff not to have to provide contraceptives that you oppose on moral grounds. At present in my state of NSW, there is no legal requirement for pharmacists to stock any particular therapeutic device or treatment. Check the legalities for your jurisdiction. Australian Pharmacist John Wilks has not stocked oral contraceptives or condoms for many years. He chooses not to stock the MAP on medical grounds, because it breaches his duty of care consistent with the Pharmaceutical Society of Australia's Code of Ethics, principles 1.1 and 1.2.[116]

Regardless of your approach to emergency contraception and its provision, it is important to take this opportunity to sympathetically counsel the woman who presents. Apart from the protocol to assess fertilization risk (above), important issues to raise include the availability of support for the victims of rape or incest, and the need for future contraception so this situation does not rise again.

This is an opportunity for you to explore the woman's (and possibly man's) attitude towards keeping a pregnancy (either as the primary move or after possible EC failure), as it is possible that no-one else will raise this as a possibility. Being aware of support services for pregnant women in your area will allow you to provide practical assistance to those who initially see early abortion as their only choice, even if that is not what they really want.

Sometimes it is only when we take a stand that others start to think more carefully about their choices.

---

116. For full details of Dr Wilks's stance, see J Wilks, 'Why this pharmacy does not sell the "morning-after" pill', *Lifeissues.net*, 18 February 2004 (viewed 11 June 2012): www.lifeissues. net/writers/wilks/wilks_05map.html

Summary

In summary, then, we have the following categorization of available contraceptives:

Ethically acceptable	Caution needed (see text)	Ethically unacceptable
• Progestin-only injections (DMPA, NET-EN) • *Implanon* implant • Fertility awareness methods: natural family planning and lactation amenorrhoea method • Barrier methods: cap, condom, diaphragm, sponge, spermicide • Withdrawal method	• Oral contraceptive pill • Progestin-only oral pill (mini-pill) • Combined injectable contraceptive • Combined vaginal ring • Combined patch • Abstinence • Sterilization • Emergency contraception (morning-after pills)	• *Jadelle, Norplant* implant • Ormeloxifene • Intrauterine devices and systems (IUDs and IUSs) • Abortion (including RU-486)

We learn from this chapter that the easy availability of reversible contraception has reduced the tolerance for unplanned pregnancy. The societal expectation is now that failure of contraception, or even failure to use contraception, is appropriately dealt with by elective abortion. But is that what women really want?

Abortion

Warning: This chapter contains information that will be disturbing for some people because abortion involves the killing of vulnerable human beings.

IF ANY WOMAN EVER truly desires an abortion, I imagine it must be rare.

Shawn Carney, campaign director for 40 Days for Life, describes how awkward he felt during his first experience of praying outside an abortion clinic: *...then a woman came out of the clinic, and I looked up and our eyes met. And she just kind of looked at me in utter despair and sadness, and I knew we were both sharing this moment, both knowing she had just aborted her child.*[1]

Yet we know from the World Health Organization (WHO) that about one in 5 pregnancies worldwide end in abortion. That works out at around 42 million in 2003, down from nearly 46 million in 1995.[2] How can we explain this paradox? Why do so many women have abortions?

Pressure for easily available legal abortion grew as a result of easily available contraception, and the subsequent public perception that sex and child-bearing no longer had to go together. Once this idea caught hold,

---

1.   S Carney, Campaign Director of 40 Days for Life, quoted in A Johnson and C Lambert, *Unplanned*, Tyndale, Carol Stream, 2010, p. 255.
2.   Guttmacher Institute and World Health Organization (WHO), *In Brief: Facts on Induced Abortion Worldwide*, Guttmacher Institute and WHO, New York and Geneva, December 2009.

tolerance for enduring an unwanted pregnancy withered even when the pregnancy was due to contraceptive failure or a failure to use contraception at all. Legalization of abortion on demand was the predictable next step in the control of fertility—the so-called 'right to choose'.[3]

What is abortion?

Abortion is the premature expulsion from the uterus of the products of conception. In technical terms, abortions may be *spontaneous* (meaning that they occur from natural causes—these are often called *miscarriages*) or *induced*, where someone deliberately causes the abortion. In this chapter, I am discussing induced abortion only—that is, the deliberate ending of a pregnancy so that it does not progress to birth. This is what I am referring to here when I use the word 'abortion'. I think this is the common understanding of the word, and I am conscious that using the term for those suffering miscarriage can be offensive to some people.

History

Abortion has a long history, with evidence of its practice found in ancient Egyptian papyri.[4] In fact, while our society thinks quite differently about the killing of a child in the womb (which is legal and socially acceptable) from that of one who is already born (which is a shocking crime, particularly if committed by the parents), this was not the case in the Graeco-Roman world in the centuries leading up to the birth of Christ. During that time both abortion and infanticide (the killing of infants) were commonplace, with little differentiation between the two. There were some restrictions on each practice, but each was widely accepted nonetheless.

Infanticide involved the murder of abnormal, weak, or just plain unwanted infants, usually by drowning or suffocation. In Greece it was permitted, although in Athens a child was protected from the 10th day after birth and in Thebes infanticide was a capital offence. In Rome, infanticide of newborns was legal so long as the father approved.[5]

---

3. In her famous 'A Defense of Abortion' (*Philosophy and Public Affairs*, vol. 1, no. 1, Fall 1971, pp. 47-66), Judith Jarvis Thompson specifically denies parental responsibility for a child conceived accidentally.

4. JM Riddle, *Contraception and Abortion from the Ancient World to the Renaissance*, Harvard University Press, Cambridge, 1992, p. 8.

5. JT Noonan, *Contraception*, Mentor-Omega Press, New York, 1965, p. 112.

Soranus of Ephesus, who practised medicine in Rome between 98 and 138 AD, gave instructions in his *Gynecology* on "how to recognize the newborn that is worth rearing". He excluded the weak, premature and physically deformed.[6] Available evidence suggests that childhood death was not associated with the same formal recognition as the death of an adult.[7] The significance of this is not fully understood—it is hard to believe that parents at that time would feel significantly different from bereaved parents today.[8]

Of course, if the early Graeco Romans accepted the killing of infants then they were unlikely to give much consideration to an embryo in the womb. In early Roman law, according to Plutarch, Romulus permitted a husband to divorce his wife for using "medicine in regard to children".[9] The Greek word for 'medicine', *pharmakeia*, can also be translated as 'magic' or 'drugs'—terms that were interchangeable as far as the Graeco Romans were concerned. When used in relation to children, the term *pharmakeia* meant abortifacients (medicines that cause abortions)—although it was sometimes difficult to distinguish between those medicines that caused early abortions and those that were merely contraceptives (a difficulty that still exists today).

Abortion was tolerated and could be performed for similar purposes to infanticide (e.g. limiting family size), but there were also important differences. Obviously there was no prenatal screening, so abortions were never performed because of disability. Soranus approved of abortion for maternal health reasons, but not to hide pregnancies arising from adultery or to allow a woman to keep her figure. He describes two schools of thinking: those of his persuasion, and those who opposed abortion completely.[10] Like infanticide, legal abortion required the consent of the husband, with exile as punishment for the lawbreaker. In Greece, Aristotle approved of abortion as a means of population control in the crowded city-states but only "before sense and life have

---

6.   Soranus, *Gynecology* 2.6, trans. O Temkin et al., John Hopkins Press, Baltimore, 1991, pp. 79-80.

7.   DA Jones, *The Soul of the Embryo*, Continuum, London, 2004, p. 36.

8.   Academic theories suggesting that parental affection in previous times generally differed significantly from today are discussed in J Boswell, *The Kindness of Strangers*, University of Chicago Press, Chicago, 1988, pp. 36ff. While there are no doubt parents in every age who lack affection for their offspring, these theories are still controversial.

9.   Noonan, op. cit., p. 41.

10.   Soranus, *Gynecology* 1.19, op. cit., pp. 62ff.

begun; what may or may not be lawfully done in these cases depends on the question of life and sensation".[11] Abortion was certainly not easily available, according to these texts.

Another difference between infanticide and abortion lay in the implications for the expectant mother. Various methods of abortion were practiced in antiquity, but none were particularly safe for the woman involved. Maternal death occurred frequently. Known abortion techniques include a blow to the abdomen, vigorous movement, 'womb-binding' (tying a cloth tightly around the abdomen), abortion-inducing drugs that were either drunk or used as pessaries, and surgical techniques (which seem to have been a last resort—this is understandable in a time when sterilized instruments and effective anaesthesia were unknown).

From the first century, Roman writers began to criticize abortion. This is likely due not so much to Christian influence but to concern about declining birthrates amongst the Roman nobility.[12] The most significant Greek text opposing abortion is the oath attributed to the ancient Greek physician Hippocrates (c460-377 BC). Still quoted by doctors today, it contains the promise: "I will not give a fatal draught to anyone if I am asked, nor will I suggest any such thing, Neither will I give a woman means to procure an abortion."[13]

The reason for this opposition to abortion is unclear. It is unlikely to come from a belief that life begins at conception. In the Hippocratic Oath, abortifacients were described as 'destructive' (*phthorion*) rather than 'deadly' (*thanasimon*—the term used in the prohibition of assisted suicide in the same paragraph), so avoiding homicide was not the reason.[14] There are ancient references praising Hippocrates for identifying the need to protect "future life still in doubt", but this does not necessarily mean the unborn infant was seen as a human person before birth.

Soranus explained in his *Gynecology* that some doctors were reluctant to prescribe abortifacients because "it is the specific task of medicine to guard and preserve what has been engendered by nature".[15] This suggests

11.   Aristotle, *Politics* 7.16.1335b, in *The Complete Works of Aristotle: The Revised Oxford Translation*, vol. 2, ed. J Barnes, Princeton University Press, Princeton, 1984, p. 2119.
12.   See my brief history of contraception in chapter 6.
13.   GER Lloyd (ed.), J Chadwick and WN Mann (trans.), *Hippocratic Writings*, Penguin, London, 1978, p. 67.
14.   Jones, op. cit., pp. 39-41.
15.   Soranus, op. cit., p. 63.

a desire to promote maternal health and assist natural processes rather than cause ill health, which facilitating abortion would have done. Indeed, Soranus was the first to seek to develop effective contraceptives as an alternative to abortion, noting that "it is safer to prevent conception from taking place than to destroy the fetus".[16]

Meanwhile in Jerusalem, the Jewish attitude to abortion and infanticide was clearly different from the Graeco-Roman attitude. The importance of children permeates the Old Testament. Population growth was seen as a blessing from God in response to his command to "Be fruitful and multiply and fill the earth and subdue it" (Gen 1:28). Israel's genealogies in Genesis carefully trace the line of inheritance from Adam and Eve through to the twelve tribes of Israel. God's promise to Abraham to make his offspring as numerous as the stars of heaven (Gen 15:5) was fulfilled by the time Israel arrived at the border of the Holy Land (Deut 1:10), and his promise to bless all families of the earth (Gen 12:3) is fulfilled at the beginning of the New Testament with the birth of Jesus Christ. We also know from the Scriptures that 'deformed' babies were allowed to live (Acts 3:2). So there is no evidence in the Bible of the Jews practicing abortion or infanticide in order to limit their families. Indeed, the promise for the man who feared the Lord was that "Your wife will be like a fruitful vine within your house; your children will be like olive shoots around your table" (Ps 128:3), and the ultimate blessing was to live to "see your children's children" (Ps 128:6).

The Jews did, however, have infanticide forced upon them. While they were living as slaves in Egypt, Pharaoh attempted to control their numbers by telling their midwives to kill all male Hebrew children at birth (Exod 1:16). The Hebrews equated infanticide with homicide, so the midwives disobeyed Pharaoh out of their fear of God. Pharaoh then told his people to throw every newborn Hebrew boy into the river (v. 22). Infanticide was a terrible atrocity often committed by Israelite enemies, dashing little children to pieces and ripping open pregnant women (2 Kgs 8:12; Hos 13:16).

The only regular infanticide practiced by Jews was the sacrifice of children to pagan gods such as Molech (2 Kgs 23:10; Jer 32:35),[17] Baal (Jer 19:4-5) and others (2 Kgs 17:31). But it was prohibited in Mosaic

---

16.   ibid.
17.   2 Chronicles 28:3 and 33:6 also probably refer to the same practice.

Law (Lev 18:21, 20:2-5; Deut 18:10) and deemed an abomination by the prophets Jeremiah (32:35) and Ezekiel (23:36-9).[18]

For healthcare workers

The allegiance of the midwives in Exodus to God rather than to secular authority is an interesting lesson to us today. They were rewarded for their actions. I once had to resign from a job in a private hospital in London because I refused to assist in abortions—but then I got another job. I can't remember if it paid better, but it was certainly more interesting. But even if God does not reward us in this lifetime, we know that he will in the life to come (Matt 5:11-12).

Awkward questions

Three Old Testament passages deserve a closer look at this point, because they raise seemingly awkward questions about God's character when it comes to caring for children. The first is Leviticus 26, where God pronounces various punishments for disobedience to him. One of these is that "You shall eat the flesh of your sons, and you shall eat the flesh of your daughters" (v. 29). This curse is graphically repeated in Deuteronomy 28:53-57.[19] I expect many Israelites at the time would have had difficulty believing it would ever come to such a thing. But it did. During a siege in Samaria, a severe famine resulted in astronomical food prices. The Israelites were driven to desperate measures, including the murder and cannibalism of their own children (2 Kgs 6:24-29). What kind of God brings this on his own people?

But God didn't bring this on the Israelites; they brought it on themselves. The passages in Leviticus 26 and Deuteronomy 28 are conditional—there is nothing inevitable about them. The whole point of these warnings was to alert Israel to the consequences of their behaviour so they could avoid punishment. Only persistent rebellion against God would bring about these awful outcomes. Yahweh had warned them— and now they were suffering under his judgement. Our choices matter.

Two more passages need mentioning. In Genesis 22, God commands

---

18. The focus of the prohibition is that it represents idolatry, which is dishonouring to God (Deut 12:29-31).

19. See also Jeremiah 19:9; Lamentations 2:20; Ezekiel 5:10.

Abraham to sacrifice his only son, Isaac—a command that Abraham seems willing to obey (although the angel of the Lord stops him at the very last minute and provides him with a ram as an alternative sacrifice). In Judges 11, the triumphant Israelite warrior Jephthah kills his only daughter to fulfil a vow he has made to the Lord.[20] And the faith of both men is commended in Hebrews 11. How can this be?

Moral law is not defied in either case, as the firstborn always belongs to the Lord (Exod 13:2). But both passages are difficult, and commentators differ in interpretation. Abraham's story may represent the idea that one person's sacrifice can benefit all people. Jephthah's story may demonstrate that God is able to use Jephthah to fulfil his purposes despite Jephthah's very poor understanding of God's character (i.e. that unlike foreign gods, God does not delight in human sacrifice). The point of both stories for us is that these are examples of faith—complete trust—that may at times be very costly. This trust is what we are to emulate.

While there are no specific references to abortion in the Hebrew Scriptures, Jewish commentators have looked at Genesis 9:6 in the context of abortion. Two readings of the passage are possible depending on the meaning of the Hebrew preposition (either 'by' or 'in'):

a) Whoever sheds the blood of man, by a man shall that person's blood be shed;

b) Whoever sheds the blood of a man in a man, that man's blood shall be shed.

Read as (b), the passage is a prohibition of abortion, classifying abortion as murder (a capital offence). The Talmud explains it thus: "Who is this 'man in man'? It refers to the fetus in the mother's womb."[21] However, as bioethicist David Jones explains, the Jews thought the commandment referred only to the Gentiles because it was given to Noah (i.e. before God's covenant with the Jewish people). And the standard Greek version of the Scriptures, the Septuagint (LXX), did not leave the anti-abortion interpretation open—so the Christians didn't take any notice of it either.[22] Jones describes the tension in the Talmud view: while abortion

---

20. The vow is made when Jephthah says to the Lord, "If you will give the Ammonites into my hand, then whatever comes out from the door of my house to meet me when I return in peace from the Ammonites shall be the LORD's, and I will offer it up for a burnt offering" (11:30). It was his daughter.

21. R Yishmael, *Babylonian Talmud Sanhedrin* 57b, cited in Jones, op. cit., p. 45.

22. Jones, op. cit., p. 46. For further further discussion of Old Testament Scripture addressing the moral status of the embryo, see chapter 3.

was often seen as comparable to murder, at times there was less clarity (although it was always a serious crime against God). The only explicit permission for abortion found in the rabbinic tradition related to the forcible extraction of the infant to save the mother's life.[23] In contrast, infanticide was clearly seen as murder from the moment of birth.

Jesus affirmed the importance of children demonstrated in the Old Testament. He likened the welcoming of children to the welcoming of Christ himself (Matt 18:5; Mark 9:36-37), rebuking his disciples for trying to keep them away (Matt 19:13-15; Mark 10:13-16; Luke 18:15-17). The terms used by Matthew, *paidion* and *paidia* ('child' and 'children'), are used for children aged from earliest infancy to 12 years; while Luke uses the word *brephē* ('babies'), the same Greek word he uses to refer to the unborn John the Baptist in Luke 1:41 and 44. The disciples may have thought children incapable of a relationship with Jesus, but these passages show us that even those we consider mentally incompetent (young children) were able to receive his blessing and were important to him. We should embrace them likewise.

Although there are no explicit references to abortion in the New Testament, the term *pharmake-ia*[*-us*] (use[r] of medicines that can cause abortions) does appear in lists of sinful acts (translated as 'sorcery' in Galatians 5:19-21 and 'sorcerers' in Revelation 21:8 and 22:15).

Church teachings

The early church attitude to abortion grew out of this background. It was initially influenced more by the Jewish tradition than by the surrounding pagan nations, but in the absence of direct biblical guidance it has developed over time, often in response to the surrounding culture.

The *Didache* is the earliest Christian text to mention abortion. Thought to have been written in the first century AD, it reflects the early ethical position: "You shall not kill a child by abortion nor kill it after it is born".[24] Early Christians did not just oppose the practices of abortion and infanticide—they also provided practical alternatives. Rescuing orphans and foundlings (young children abandoned by their parents) was seen as a Christian duty. Parents seeking to abandon their babies often left them at churches, which took a major role in overseeing the care of abandoned

---

23. *Misnah, Oholot* 7.6, cited in Jones, op. cit., pp. 53-4.
24. *Didache* (or *Teaching of the Twelve Apostles*) 2.2, cited in Jones, op. cit., p. 57.

children from at least the 4th century, often arranging for the foundlings to be brought up in Christian homes.

Over the next couple of centuries, records documenting this prohibition were plentiful as Christians—in particular Tertullian—sought to persuade the Roman authorities that Christianity did not undermine community morals and did not, as was spitefully rumoured, practice child sacrifice. Sadly, as is still the case, Christians then did not always practise what they preached. Many Christians were criticized for procuring abortions at the time. Because of this the church continued to emphasize the dehumanizing qualities of abortion, accusing those who obtained abortions of attacking not only the child but also the institution of marriage. Abortion was worse than murder because one's own flesh and blood was involved. Athenagoras of Athens warned that the guilty would "have to give an account to God".[25]

This occurred at a time when the early church was grappling with the threat of coming judgement, and with the ongoing repentance that Jesus demands of his people. While all sin is forgiven when a person first trusts Christ, the reality is that Christians keep on sinning. How was the church to handle ongoing sin in people who were washed clean by the blood of Christ? And so in order to deal with what was going on, yet without giving the impression that abortion was acceptable, the church allowed acts of penance as a means of forgiveness and reconciliation for those who had disobeyed. This way they were forgiven according to biblical direction (1 John 1:5-9), but at the same time Christian discipline was upheld.

The earliest record we have of the penance required for abortion comes from a church synod in Spain in 305 AD. A Christian who committed adultery, became pregnant and then had an abortion would not be allowed to receive communion again, even on her deathbed; and a woman preparing to become a Christian who committed the same sin would be barred from baptism until the end of her life.[26] These are very severe penalties, reflecting the seriousness with which abortion was viewed. This penalty was later reduced to ten years' exclusion, after the Emperor Constantine made Christianity the state religion of Rome in 313 AD.[27] Pope Innocent I, commenting around 400 AD, stated that this revision was more tempered with mercy than the earlier penalty, but that "even the more severe practice

---

25. Athenagoras, *A Plea for Christians* 35:6, cited in Jones, op. cit., p. 60.
26. Council of Elvira, *Canon 63* and *Canon 68*, cited in Jones, op. cit., p. 62.
27. Council of Ancrya, *Canon 21*, cited in Jones, op. cit., p. 63.

of the past, by imposing penance, was offering a path of hope and salvation and not abandoning the repentant sinner altogether."[28]

But the most authoritative statements, which still inform canon law in the Orthodox Church to this day, were those of the Sixth Ecumenical Council of Trullo in 692 (canons 2 and 91). These dictated that abortion was homicide, and that those giving drugs to procure an abortion were also guilty of murder.[29]

Modern abortion law

As early as the 13th century, English law prohibited abortion after the time of 'quickening'.[30] But a revival of interest in Roman law during the Renaissance encouraged the Stoic view that the fetus became a legal person only after birth, and so by the beginning of the 19th century, the attitude of English law towards abortion had once again changed so that no charge of killing could arise until after the child was born. This meant that for British subjects and American citizens, abortion producing a live birth and subsequent death of the child was regarded as homicide, while abortion leading to stillbirth was a 'great misprision' (not homicide but still a very serious offence), especially after quickening. But the legal status of abortion prior to quickening was debated, although even where it was not a criminal offence, it was still considered unlawful. However, difficulty in prosecuting abortion cases led to a situation where the law failed to deter a growing trend.

In the 1800s, both England and the newly independent United States enacted statutes restricting abortion. Attitudes to abortion and legislative changes occurred at similar times and in similar ways in the United Kingdom, United States and Australia.

United Kingdom

The first legislative change was Lord Ellenborough's Act of 1803, which made it a capital offence to administer poisons after quickening with the intention of causing abortion, once again giving legal significance to

---

28. Innocent I, *Letter to Exuperius*, ibid.
29. A detailed history of the church's attitude to abortion can be found in Jones, op. cit., chapters 5, 12 and 13. I highly recommend this book to those interested in the topic.
30. 'Quickening' is when the mother first feels the baby moving, usually beginning around 18-20 weeks gestation. This reference to quickening may reflect the medieval distinction between abortion before and after the soul was thought to enter the body. This in turn is a reference to Aristotle's understanding of embryology.

the unborn child. Subsequent laws gradually removed the reference to quickening and reduced the punishment for abortion to three years (1837). In 1861, the maximum term was raised to life imprisonment. In 1929, abortion of a *viable* fetus was specifically prohibited (to close a loophole). But though the acts of 1861 and 1929 remain in force, community desire to reduce illegal 'backyard' abortions (generally considered to be dangerous) was strong enough by 1966 to lead to radical abortion law reform.

Feminists in particular argued that abortion was inevitable because men kept pressuring women, making them pregnant when they could not manage a child. Since it was inevitable, the only practical solution to the risks of abortion was to make it safe and freely available. This led to a mental shift from seeing abortion as something that harmed a woman and her child, to something that was necessary to free a woman from difficult circumstances. At this point, the reframing of abortion as an act of compassion attracted some Christians to campaign for its legalization, which was a complete reversal of the traditional position of the church. This caused a split in the Christian lobby, as many Christians remained at the forefront of opposition to abortion. Note the problems caused when we determine matters by focusing only on our intentions (which in this case were good) rather than the morality of the act involved (terminating the life of an innocent unborn child).

The Abortion Act 1967 defines the statuary framework on which current mainland United Kingdom (England, Scotland and Wales but not Northern Ireland) abortion law is based. This legislation allows termination of pregnancy by registered medical practitioners under the following conditions:

- when an abortion would cause less damage to a woman's physical or mental health, or her child(ren)'s physical or mental health, than continuing with the pregnancy
- when a woman's health or life is gravely threatened by continuing with the pregnancy
- when the fetus is likely to be born with severe physical or mental abnormalities.[31]

---

31. This clause developed as a result of the thalidomide tragedy. The drug was developed in the 1950s for treatment of morning sickness, but was subsequently found to cause severe birth defects if taken during pregnancy. Over 10,000 children were born with congenital abnormalities, especially phocomelia (stunted limb growth). There was much public sympathy for those women affected. See BA Berkowitz, 'Development and Regulation of Drugs', in BG Katzung, S Masters and A Trevor (eds), *Basic and Clinical Pharmacology*, 11th edn, McGraw-Hill, New York, 2009, pp. 67-75.

The abortion must be carried out in a hospital or specialized licensed clinic. Two doctors need to agree that the conditions are met except in the event of an emergency, when an abortion can be performed without a second doctor's agreement.[32] The passing of the Human Fertilisation and Embryology Act 1990 reduced the abortion limit from 28 to 24 weeks on the grounds that 24 weeks was the current limit of viability (i.e. the earliest stage at which a child had survived outside the womb)— although it still allows abortions after 24 weeks if there is a grave risk to the life of the woman, evidence of severe abnormality, or risk of grave physical and mental injury to the woman.

Under these laws, the father of the child has no rights to give or refuse consent for abortion (coercion will be discussed below).

Today, at least one third of British women will have had an abortion by the time they reach the age of 45. Over 98% of induced abortions in Britain are undertaken because of risk to the mental or physical health of the woman or her children under the regulations listed above (common interpretations making it a conveniently broad category).[33] In 2008, 202,158 abortions were performed in England and Wales, representing 22.8% of all pregnancies. 91% of these abortions were funded by the NHS.[34]

United States

In the United States, abortion law is worked out state by state. Before 1820, the United States followed British common law (abortion after quickening was an offence). The first American abortion law was enacted in Connecticut in 1821, mirroring the common law example (and similarly, the reference to quickening was dropped later on grounds of being unscientific). In 1860, Connecticut introduced a law that clarified the woman's liability and also banned advertising or provision of abortifacients. By 1880, there were anti-abortion statutes in most states.

While doctors in the United Kingdom had supported anti-abortion legislation, doctors in the United States were even more active. In

---

32. The Royal College of Obstetricians and Gynaecologists recommended removing the requirement for the second authorization in their 2011 guidelines.

33. Royal College of Obstetricians and Gynaecologists (RCOG), *The Care of Women Requesting Induced Abortion*, Evidence-based Clinical Guideline no. 7, rev. edn, RCOG Press, London, November 2011.

34. Department of Health, *Abortion Statistics, England and Wales: 2008*, statistical bulletin 2009/01, Department of Health, London, May 2009.

1857, an American physician called Horatio Robinson Storer launched a campaign to limit abortion. This led to an 1859 American Medical Association resolution opposing abortion on grounds that the role of the physician was concern for the life and health of both the mother and (especially) the unborn child.

Interestingly, at this stage the feminists were in favour of anti-abortion legislation. They saw women being oppressed by men who made them pregnant and then pressured them, or abandoned them, to the risk and guilt of abortion. Their concern was less for the unborn child than for the cause of the situation the woman found herself in. Most feminist spokeswomen called for prohibition of abortion, but also equality and respect for women and their right to refuse unwanted sexual advances. 'Voluntary motherhood' was advocated, primarily through sexual abstinence.

Several factors came together to bring about the abortion rights rhetoric of the 20th century. First was the emphasis on autonomy—the right to choose for oneself, which was developed in the writings of philosophers such as John Locke (1632-1704) and Jean Jacques Rousseau (1712-78). The American and French revolutions were also expressions of this idea of personal liberty. Second, the writings of English economist Thomas Malthus (1766-1834) popularized the idea that overpopulation led to poverty. Although he was personally against contraception and abortion, it was his idea that first led to the promotion of contraception and then, as I have already suggested, the corollary of abortion as society lost interest in tolerating unwanted pregnancy.

The first generation of birth-controllers included Marie Stopes.[35] It is interesting that her organization eventually promoted abortion (when contraception failed) not only for population control but also for 'racial progress'—encouraging those with 'superior' qualities to breed and preventing the 'inferior' (i.e. mentally ill) from having children. Sterilization programs in several countries in the 1930s (Nazi Germany, Sweden and the United States) led to the practice of aborting children solely because they had some form of disability—echoing the Graeco-Roman practice of abandoning 'defective' children.[36]

In the 1920s a new feminist movement began with leaders such as Stella Browne, who promoted abortion as an element of women's

---

35. Jones, op. cit., p. 203. Marie Stopes is now the company name of an international abortion provider.
36. More on this in chapter 8.

emancipation. Abortion was seen not as a violent act towards a mother and her unborn child, but as a social necessity for the liberation of women from poverty, unemployment, abandonment, physical and sexual abuse, exploitation and discrimination. Even though the slogan 'Every child a wanted child' was popular (coined by those in favour of abortion), in the big picture of abortion the humanity of the child was essentially disregarded. To deserve protection, a child had to be 'wanted'. Those who spoke against this idea were criticized for not caring enough about the woman involved (and this is still the case, even now).

Illegal abortion by this time was not necessarily unsafe (due to the introduction of antibiotics and improved understanding of surgical techniques), but the risks fell primarily on poor women who could not pay good surgeons.

By the 1960s, the pro-abortion (pro-choice) movement was widespread, and some state legislatures began reforming abortion law. But it was the 1973 Supreme Court decision in *Roe v. Wade* that struck down anti-abortion legislation across the country, arguing that the Constitution contained a right to abortion.[37] This right to abortion is based on a right to privacy—the right to decide on matters that do not harm others—thereby implying that the embryo is not a human being with human rights. According to the ruling in this case, abortion cannot be restricted in the first trimester; second-trimester abortions can only be restricted on grounds of the mother's health; and third-trimester abortions (after viability) can be allowed when necessary to preserve the mother's life or health. Obviously, the definition of 'health' becomes quite important in defining the scope of the ruling. Another case decided at the same time, *Doe v. Bolton*, defined maternal health so broadly ("all factors—physical, emotional, psychological, familial, and the woman's age—relevant to the wellbeing of the patient")[38] that abortion became available essentially on demand. It is interesting that the anonymous 'Jane Roe' of *Roe v. Wade*, Norma McCorvey, has since become a Christian and deeply regrets taking part in the action. She has tried to get the decision overturned.[39]

Late-term abortions (partial-birth abortions) were prohibited in the

---

37. *Roe v. Wade* (1973) 410 US 113.
38. *Doe v. Bolton* (1973) 410 US 179 at 192.
39. C Overington, 'Roe v Roe: a woman's change of heart', *Sydney Morning Herald*, 21 June 2003, p. 34.

Partial-Birth Abortion Ban Act of 2003, and this ruling was upheld in the 2007 Supreme Court decision *Gonzalez v. Carhart*.[40]

Despite the federal law, individual states can limit the practice of abortion, or create 'trigger laws' (laws that would make abortion illegal within the first and second trimesters, but could only take effect if *Roe v. Wade* were overturned by the United States Supreme Court). Indeed, there has been a recent increase in the number of state-based restrictions, including limitations on insurance coverage, targeted regulation of abortion clinics, ultrasound requirements, and mandatory counseling and waiting periods.

As in the United Kingdom, the father of the child has no rights to give or refuse consent to abortion.

Abortion remains a controversial subject in the United States. This *should* be the case, although I do not believe that violence in retaliation for the facilitation of abortion is ever justified. We are called to hate the sin and love the sinner (John 8:1-11).

Abortion statistics in the United States are collected by the government's Centers for Disease Control and Prevention (CDC) and also by the Guttmacher Institute, which is Planned Parenthood's special research affiliate monitoring trends in the abortion industry.[41] States report data voluntarily to the CDC for inclusion in its annual Abortion Surveillance Report. The CDC ordinarily develops its annual report on the basis of data received from 52 central health agencies (50 states plus New York City and the District of Columbia). The Guttmacher Institute gets its numbers from direct surveys of abortionists. There is no national requirement for data submission or reporting, so data—especially for the CDC—is incomplete. It is calculated that in 2008, 1.2 million American women obtained abortions, producing a rate of 19.6 abortions per 1,000 women of reproductive age. This is virtually unchanged from 2005, when the abortion rate was 19.4 abortions per 1,000 women 15-44 years. At current rates, around one third of American women will have an abortion in their lifetime.[42]

The racial distribution of abortion is interesting: the abortion rate for black women (33.9 per 1,000 women) is more than three times the

---

40. *Gonzales v. Carhart* (2007) 550 US 124.
41. Planned Parenthood is the largest abortion provider in the United States.
42. Guttmacher Institute, *In Brief: Facts on Induced Abortion in the United States*, Guttmacher Institute, New York, August 2011.

rate for white women (10.8 per 1,000 women). The abortion rate for women of other races, including Hispanic and Native American, is 18.3 per 1,000 women.[43] I remember an anti-abortion campaign in New York in 2010 showing a picture of an African-American child and proclaiming that "the most dangerous place for an African-American is in the womb". I heard soon after that the child model's mother had asked for the advertisements to be removed, as she did not agree with the message of the poster. Sadly, it seems some people took it as a criticism of African-Americans instead of the way it was intended—as a show of concern for their children and a plea for the mothers to explore their options.[44]

The legal situation in Australia

Abortion law in Australia is decided on a state-by-state basis; laws across the country at the time of writing are quite inconsistent. Until 1901, when Australia became a federation, Australia followed the English law— specifically, the *Offences Against the Person Act 1861*, which prohibited abortion or supplying the means for abortion and carried a maximum penalty of life imprisonment. The wording of the Australian provisions establishing the crime of *unlawful* abortion, directly based on this Act, indicates that there will be circumstances in which involvement in an abortion is *not* unlawful, and therefore not a crime.

The legal test for when an abortion is not unlawful is different in each state and territory of Australia. Until the late 1960s and early 1970s, there were no Australian judicial or statutory explanations of when involvement in an abortion would constitute the crime of unlawful abortion, although the 1930s English case of *R v. Bourne* gave some guidance. In that case, regarding an abortion Dr Bourne performed for a 14-year-old girl who had been raped, the judge ruled that if "the probable consequence of the continuance of the pregnancy will be to make the woman a *physical or mental wreck*", then an abortion represented "preserving the life of the woman" and was therefore lawful.[45] Justification for abortion was further extended by other cases to include preserving physical health (1948)

---

43. K Pazol, SB Gamble, WY Parker, DA Cook, SB Zane, S Hamdan and Centers for Disease Control and Prevention (CDC), 'Abortion Surveillance—United States, 2006', *MMWR Surveillance Summaries*, vol. 58, no. SS-8, 27 November 2009, pp. 1-35.

44. J Swaine, 'Anti-abortion billboard in New York sparks off furious row', *Telegraph*, 24 February 2011.

45. *R v. Bourne* (1938) 3 All ER 615 at 619.

and mental health (1958). Abortions for 'therapeutic' reasons therefore became more common, as these court cases broadened the definition so that it could pretty well cover any social or personal reason that might arise for avoiding pregnancy. This continues to be the case today.

At the time of writing, abortion has been decriminalized in the Australian Capital Territory, the Northern Territory and Victoria, but it remains a crime in the other states (however, there are 'provisions' so that if you are Australian you don't need to travel far to get abortion on demand—and probably with a government rebate). Late-term abortion (abortion after 20 weeks) can involve laws regarding child destruction, which exist in some form in every state except Victoria.[46] For abortions performed from 20 weeks on, there is a legal requirement to register the birth even if the child is stillborn.

As in the United States and the United Kingdom, the father of the child has no rights regarding giving or withholding consent for abortion.

We don't know the exact number of abortions performed each year in Australia because only South Australia collects detailed information. In the other states and territories, there is no official record of the abortion if the government (Medicare) rebate isn't claimed and/or the procedure isn't done in a public hospital. Research shows that this may be the case for up to one third of abortions.[47] According to the Australian Department of Health and Ageing, probably around 90,000 abortions are performed every year in Australia.[48] If 90,000 abortions are performed in Australia every year, this works out as one abortion for every 2.8 births.[49] One in three Australian women will have an abortion in their lifetime.

---

46. Child destruction is an unlawful intentional act causing the death of a child who is capable of being born alive. The law was introduced to criminalize the killing of a child *during* its birth, as this is technically neither abortion nor homicide. It therefore applies only to later terminations of pregnancy that are judged to be 'unlawful'.

47. C Nickson, AMA Smith and JM Shelley, 'Intention to claim a Medicare rebate among women receiving private Victorian pregnancy termination services', *Australia and New Zealand Journal of Public Health*, vol. 28, no. 2, April 2004, pp. 120-3.

48. This was the estimate given by Senator Patterson in her response to Senator Boswell's question in 2005. See Australia, Senate 2005, *Debates*, vol. S14, p. 69. A parliamentary review that year explained the impossibility of accurately assessing abortion numbers but noted the range of 70,000-100,000/year given in public debate. See Department of Parliamentary Services, *How Many Abortions are There in Australia?*, report prepared by A Pratt, A Biggs and L Buckmaster, Parliamentary Library Research Brief no. 9, 2004-05, Canberra, 14 February 2005.

49. According to the Australian Bureau of Statistics. This number does not include early abortions as a result of the 'morning-after pill' (see chapter 6).

Ethics of abortion

So—*legally*—abortion is permissible in many countries. But ethics and law are not the same thing. While we would hope that ethics influence the laws we create, there is no longer much moral consensus in our pluralist community. As mentioned in chapter 5, this means it is not always *your* morality that is considered when laws are debated and enacted. And so it is possible for something to be legal but not ethically permissible for Christians.

To make it even more confusing, Christians today do not always agree on the matter of abortion. Some continue to argue that abortion represents the taking of a human life. Others see it as a compassionate response to a woman in a difficult situation—although this response has only been voiced since the middle of the 20th century. As we have already seen, until then the church had consistently opposed abortion.

The ethics of abortion have traditionally been argued from two opposing positions:

- **Pro-life:** People who hold this position generally maintain that every person has a right to life. They argue that human fetuses and embryos are human persons and therefore have a right to life. Even though the mother has a right to decide what happens to her body, the child's right to life is stronger than the right of its mother to control her body. It acknowledges the humanity of both the mother and the child and seeks to protect the lives of both whenever possible. This pro-life position is my position.
- **Pro-choice:** Those who hold this view argue that a woman should have control over her body, which includes her fertility and the choice to continue or terminate a pregnancy. This entails the guarantee of *reproductive rights*, which include access to sexual education, contraception, fertility treatments, and safe and legal abortion. The humanity of the fetus is not necessarily denied, but it is seen as less important than the autonomy of the mother.

Websites abound that list the arguments for abortion with varying degrees of sophistication, but here is a summary of the main arguments in serious debate. I have also provided a response to each argument.[50]

---

50. This section is influenced by FJ Beckwith's elegant response to the main arguments for abortion. See FJ Beckwith, 'Personal Bodily Rights, Abortion, and Unplugging the Violinist', *International Philosophical Quarterly*, vol. 32, no. 1, March 1992, pp. 105-18.

1. Argument for a woman's right over her own body

This argument says that a woman has a right to control her own body, so she has a right to undergo an abortion for any reason she chooses.

Response: First, the being within the pregnant woman's body is not *part* of her body. It is a genetically distinct organism; it may have a different blood group from the mother, or a different gender. It has directed its own development since the time of fertilization. Although the being is *attached* to the mother from approximately ten days' gestation onwards, it is not a *part* of the mother. Furthermore, there is no reason for the mother's rights to automatically trump the fetus's rights. Even if a right to control one's body does exist, it is not an absolute right. Many laws exist to prevent us from using our bodies in any way we want (e.g. laws to restrict suicide). This first argument only works if you presume that the embryo is not a human being.

2. Argument from the danger of 'backyard abortions'

This argument says that if abortion is made illegal, desperate women will still seek it anyway, and an unsafe 'backyard abortion' industry will re-emerge. Thus, legalized abortion is said to be necessary in order to prevent maternal deaths from backyard abortions.

Response: First, we might point out that this is not a valid argument if abortion is in fact the wrongful killing of a human being. That people will seek abortions anyway, and risk injury in doing so, is no justification for legalizing the practice—just as people will steal anyway, even though it is illegal, and often suffer injury, loss or imprisonment as a result.

More significantly, the evidence simply doesn't support the myth of the dangerous backyard abortionist. The Australian Bureau of Statistics data shows that the maternal death rate from abortion fell significantly from approximately 100 deaths every year in the 1930s to one death in 1969, the year *prior* to the first legal abortion clinic opening in Australia. This improvement was mainly due to the introduction of antibiotics in the 1940s—a finding reflected in many countries.

A definitive 2012 study in Chile found that illegal abortion is not associated with increased maternal mortality.[51]

---

51.   E Koch, J Thorp, M Bravo, S Gatica, CX Romero, H Aguilera and I Ahlers, 'Women's education level, maternal health facilities, abortion legislation and maternal deaths: A natural experiment in Chile from 1957 to 2007', *PLoS ONE*, vol. 7, no. 5, 4 May 2012, e36613.

3. Argument from abortion being safer than childbirth

Based on the notion that we are never morally obliged to risk our own lives to save the life of another, this argument says that the pregnant woman has no moral obligation to carry her unborn offspring to term, regardless of whether or not it is fully human. And because abortion is statistically less dangerous than childbirth (as some claim), it is argued that a woman cannot be obliged to give birth to an unwanted child. This argument also implies that a mother's obligations to her child are voluntary, not obligatory—that is, the mother has no special obligations towards her own child.

Response: Overall, is abortion safer than carrying a child to birth? This is not as easy to answer as you might think. Death caused by pregnancy (maternal mortality) is defined in the *International Classification of Diseases* (ICD-10) as "the death of a woman while pregnant or within 42 days of termination of pregnancy, irrespective of the duration and site of the pregnancy, from any cause related to or aggravated by the pregnancy or its management but not from accidental or incidental causes".[52] Because this definition captures both abortions and live births some countries pool the data, making it impossible to see the difference between the two groups. But a 2004 study looking at the population of Finland over 14 years found that the death rate of women following a birth (28.2/100,000) was lower than the death rate following an induced abortion (83.1/100,000), which suggests that childbirth may actually be safer than abortion.[53]

This argument ignores the idea of partiality—that there *is* a special relationship between mothers and their babies. Parents are indeed expected to perform self-sacrificing acts for their children even if not for anyone else. Furthermore, an obligation does not have to be voluntary to be binding. We assume that all children have a natural right to their parents' care, which is demonstrated by laws requiring payment of child support and prohibiting child abuse.

If you recognize the humanity of the unborn child, it can be difficult

---

52. WHO, *International Statistical Classification of Diseases and Related Health Problems*, 10th revision, WHO, Geneva, 1992, cited in C Ronsmans and WJ Graham, 'Maternal mortality: who, when, where, and why', *Lancet*, vol. 368, no. 9542, 30 September 2006, p. 1190.

53. M Gissler, C Berg, MH Bouvier-Colle and P Buekens, 'Pregnancy-associated mortality after birth, spontaneous abortion, or induced abortion in Finland, 1987-2000', *American Journal of Obstetrics and Gynecology*, vol. 190, no. 2, February 2004, pp. 422-7.

to understand the commitment that some lobbyists have to protecting abortion rights. Yet the push continues. There have been attempts within the United Nations to register abortion as a basic human right (under the euphemism of 'rights to sexual and reproductive health'), which would create an obligation for all member states. Pressure is being put to bear on countries that 'deprive' their citizens of this so-called human right. This has been countered by the launching of a document in 2011 called the San Jose Articles, which were written to clarify that there is no 'right to abortion' enshrined in international law. The document was signed by international experts in law, medicine and public policy.[54]

But there are also non-government organizations such as Amnesty International that while not promoting abortion as a human right in itself, nonetheless see its selected availability as necessary to address effectively the consequences of widespread sexual violence targeting women and girls. They want abortion to be available for the Mexican eight-year-old who is pregnant because she was raped. They also oppose the laws in countries such as El Salvador (whose constitution protects life from the time of conception without exception) that prevent a woman with an ectopic pregnancy (a life-threatening condition, and one of the few situations in which I believe abortion is morally justified) from receiving medical care.[55]

The WHO has reported that legal restrictions on abortion do not affect its frequency, but they do affect its safety. It found that 48% of all abortions worldwide are unsafe, accounting for 70,000 maternal deaths per year and leading to approximately 220,000 children losing their mothers to abortion-related death every year. The WHO provides examples of unsafe abortion methods, including drinking turpentine, bleach or tea made with livestock manure; placing foreign bodies such as a coat hanger or chicken bone into the uterus; and jumping from a roof.[56]

I give these facts not to argue the case for legal abortion but to explain why I can understand the anger that some women feel, even if we do not

---

54. This is an excellent initiative. My one concern is its failure to articulate the (admittedly rare) circumstance of abortion being necessary to preserve the life of the mother when the baby has no hope of survival (e.g. ectopic pregnancy). See *San Jose Articles*, San Jose, 25 March 2011 (viewed 23 November 2011): www.sanjosearticles.org

55. Amnesty International, 'Protecting the human rights of women', *Human Rights Defender*, vol. 19, no. 3, 21 September 2010, pp. 8-9.

56. Guttmacher Institute and WHO, *In Brief: Facts on Induced Abortion Worldwide*, loc. cit.

agree as to when abortion is ethically permissible. In this fallen world there will always be hard cases. While we need to maintain our own integrity, we also need to be careful how we judge those with whom we disagree.[57] We should also, however, remember that 'hard cases make bad law'. Indeed, the Chile study has shown that it is education, not legal abortion, which will ultimately improve maternal health.[58]

The arguments I have summarized above obviously do not apply everywhere. Why does the push for abortion remain so strong in more developed countries? Is it really just about competing rights of mother and child? Or is there something else driving it?

Abortion is big business. The abortionist profits, as well as the owners of the clinics. The regular supply of fetal cells, tissue and organs has led, unintentionally, to the establishment of businesses that use this substrate to develop research, pharmaceutical products and cosmetics.[59]

While it is not clear whether abortion in the West is primarily a commercial enterprise or not, the ethical position that underlies the modern justification for continuing current laws will always be in conflict with the Christian position. Those who support the laws allowing easy access to abortion focus on a woman's autonomy, equality and 'right' to self-determination. These will always be at odds with the position that respects human life at all its stages, and seeks to love God and one's neighbour as oneself.

However we got here, though, current Western abortion laws—allowing what is essentially abortion on demand up to the time of delivery—are the most liberal that have ever existed in recorded human history.

The Christian position

Many books have been written on abortion, but the things I think we need to consider in order to think through the ethics of abortion include the following:

- We need to consider what kind of thing the embryo/fetus is. Is it the kind of thing that it is wrong to kill?
- We need to find out what happens during an abortion. What is

---

57. The WHO attributes the abortion problem to unintended pregnancy, which is a complex problem it is attempting to address.
58. Koch et al., loc. cit.
59. See appendix II for further details.

intended as the end result? Is the death of the child deliberate or accidental?

- We need to consider what makes a woman choose to have an abortion. Does the situation involved make a difference, ethically?
- Finally, we need to decide how we make an ethical choice. Is abortion always wrong?

1. What kind of thing is a fetus? Is it the kind of thing that it is wrong to kill?

In chapters 2 and 3 I argued that the developing human in the womb deserves to be treated with respect and protected by the law from the time of fertilization (although this is not absolute—exceptions are discussed below). It is interesting to look at the human fetal development table in chapter 2 and realize that abortion is still legal for a normal baby in Australia at 20 weeks, in the United Kingdom at 24 weeks, and in the United States right up until birth. Look at how much development has already taken place at these gestations. Thankfully, the humanity of the developing child is no longer contested in informed ethical debate. With regard to the human embryo/fetus, it is no longer an argument of whether we are dealing with humans; it is now a matter of how we are going to treat them.

In the past, abortion debates focused on the 'right to life' of the unborn child. More recently, as awareness of the negative effects on the women involved has grown, it is the danger to the mother that has dominated community discussion. While this is an important consideration, for Christians the humanity of the unborn child will remain the major moral argument against abortion.

2. Abortion procedures: What does abortion involve?

Induced abortion is divided into *medical abortion*, where a drug is used to end the pregnancy, and *surgical abortion*, where instruments are used to remove the fetus from the womb. The procedure used depends on the stage of the pregnancy, the woman's medical history and preferences, the clinical judgement and experience of the practitioner, and local availability of resources. Obviously the surgical method requires an operation, while the medical method may involve a few trips to the doctor.

Normally during pregnancy the cervix is tightly closed to keep the pregnancy in place. When labour starts, the cervix opens or 'dilates' to allow the fetus through. Obviously the later in the pregnancy you are, the larger the fetus, and the more challenging it will be to get it out of the uterus through the cervix. Below is an outline of what is involved in each procedure. It does not contain full details of methods, side effects or complications. **This information may distress some readers.**

Medical abortion
RU-486 (mifepristone)
RU-486 was specifically designed to terminate a pregnancy. It is usually used in the first trimester, although in some places it is used throughout pregnancy. Up to 7-9 weeks gestation it may be possible to perform the abortion at home,[60] although after 9 weeks it would usually be done in a hospital. It is also known by its chemical name, mifepristone, and is usually used with misoprostol, a prostaglandin, in medical abortion. While its action is not fully understood, it is clear that mifepristone's main action is blocking the chemical receptor sites normally used by the hormone progesterone in the uterus. This interrupts the functioning of the placenta so it produces less progesterone.[61] Progesterone is needed to sustain the pregnancy. Reduced levels of progesterone lead to degeneration of the endometrium (uterine lining), cervical softening and dilatation, and release of natural prostaglandins as well as an increase in the sensitivity of the uterus muscles to the contracting effects of prostaglandins. Mifepristone therefore indirectly causes the woman's body to shut down the preparation of the uterus for the pregnancy and disrupts development of the embryo or fetus.[62]

As a result, in combination with misoprostol, labour is initiated and the developing embryo/fetus is expelled from the woman's body with the uterine lining. Women are usually aware of when this occurs, and may recognize the fetus in the tissue discharge. Fetuses aborted after 20 weeks may show signs of life after abortion, and in a 2007 medical journal doctors were advised to consider giving intra-amniotic digoxin

---

60. TD Ngo, MH Park, H Shakur and C Free, 'Comparative effectiveness, safety and acceptability of medical abortion at home and in a clinic: a systematic review', *Bulletin of the World Health Organization*, vol. 89, no. 5, May 2011, pp. 360-70.

61. Mifepristone-induced endometrial breakdown leads to trophoblast detachment, resulting in decreased production of human chorionic gonadotropin (hCG) and a withdrawal of support from the corpus luteum. Pregnancy is dependent on progesterone production by the corpus luteum for the first 9 weeks of gestation, until the placenta can take over.

62. MA Fritz and L Speroff, *Clinical Gynecologic Endocrinology and Infertility*, 7th edn, Lippincott Williams and Wilkins, Philadelphia, 2005, p. 852.

or potassium chloride into the fetal heart to stop it before the abortion begins and ensure the aborted child is dead on delivery.[63] According to the Royal Australian and New Zealand College of Obstetricians and Gynaecologists (RANZCOG), mifepristone plus misoprostol is the preferred regimen for medical abortion, and it seems to be the most common medical abortion in those places where it is legally available.[64] Its use in Australia is currently subject to approval of the Therapeutic Goods Administration.

For doctors

The WHO has approved the use of mifepristone 200 microgram tablets in combination with mifepristone "for termination of pregnancy (where legally permitted and culturally acceptable), on the Complementary List (added in 2005)".[65] In 2011, the WHO approved the use of mifepristone for prevention of post-partum haemorrhage when oxytocin is not available.[66] This comes from good intentions, as post-partum haemorrhage is a significant cause of maternal death. However, there is concern that it may lead to self-administered abortions, especially since the organization that sought the drug's approval, Gynuity Health Projects, has advocated the use of the drug without medical supervision.[67] Medical abortion without professional supervision can be dangerous.

Prostaglandins alone

Prostaglandins stimulate uterine contractions and soften the cervix. The procedure is similar to RU-486 use, with abortion occurring a couple of days after the administration of the drugs.

---

63.   PC Ho, PD Blumenthal, K Gemzell-Danielsson, R Gómez Ponce de León, S Mittal and OS Tang, 'Misoprostol for the termination of pregnancy with a live fetus at 13 to 26 weeks', *International Journal of Gynecology and Obstetrics*, vol. 99, supp. 2, December 2007, pp. S178-81.
64.   Royal Australian and New Zealand College of Obstetricians and Gynaecologists (RANZCOG), *Termination of Pregnancy*, RANZCOG, Melbourne, November 2005.
65.   WHO, *Unedited Report of the 18th Expert Committee on the Selection and Use of Essential Medicines*, WHO, Accra, 21-25 March 2011, p. 88.
66.   ibid.
67.   S Yanow, *The Best Defense is a Good Offense: Misoprostol, Abortion, and the Law*, report for Gynuity Health Projects and the Reproductive Health Technologies Project, New York, August 2009.

Methotrexate

Methotrexate can also be used with prostaglandins. Methotrexate is a drug used as chemotherapy for cancer or for treatment of immune disease. It was originally designed to attack fast-growing cells (like cancer cells) by blocking the folic acid that is needed for cell division. It works in abortion by inhibiting the rapid growth of the tissue that develops into the placenta (the trophoblast), which is the 'support system' for the embryo, providing oxygen and nutrients from the mother's blood and disposing of waste. This in turn inhibits the implantation process and causes suppression of the hCG hormone, which is needed to sustain progesterone levels. Progesterone is needed to prevent breakdown of the uterine lining that is needed to support the pregnancy. The result of these effects is that within a few days or weeks of receiving the methotrexate injection, the placenta stops functioning and the embryo stops developing. Misoprostol causes the cervix to soften and the uterus to contract, resulting in the expulsion of the uterine contents.

Methotrexate can be used for treatment of ectopic pregnancy, which is ethically permissible.[68]

Surgical abortion

This type of abortion is more common than medical abortion, and is most often performed between 6-12 weeks gestation. It is used in conjunction with priming of the cervix (recommended for all abortions after 10 weeks or, in some places, where the woman is less than 18 years old). There are two common methods of priming the cervix. One method involves inserting a substance into the cervix that will absorb moisture and expand to open the cervix (usually a type of seaweed called laminaria, but synthetic osmotic dilators are also used). Alternatively, prostaglandins such as misoprostol or gemeprost are used, and there is evidence that mifepristone could also be used for this purpose.[69]

The procedures used in early abortion are also used for some other conditions, including treatment following spontaneous miscarriage. Use of the procedures for a non-abortion purpose is ethically permissible.[70]

---

68. See 'Ethics of abortion' section, above.
69. RANZCOG, op. cit., p. 8.
70. See chapter 16.

Suction curettage/Vacuum curettage
This is the most common procedure, used in the first trimester and up to 14-15 weeks gestation. The procedure involves dilating the cervix by inserting metal rods of increasing size through the *os* (the opening in the cervix that leads to the uterus), and then inserting a plastic tube through the cervix into the uterus. The fetus and placenta are sucked out using a high-power vacuum. The walls of the uterus are then scraped with a curette to ensure that everything has been fully removed. The procedure is performed under local or general anaesthetic.

Manual vacuum aspiration
This method is less common and also used in the first trimester, especially before 7 weeks. A tube, narrower than the electric suction used in conventional curettage, is inserted into the uterus. The procedure lasts a bit longer and has a lower failure rate than suction curettage, but is otherwise quite similar. Interestingly, the American College of Obstetricians and Gynecologists (ACOG) call it 'menstrual aspiration', which makes it sound like you weren't even really pregnant![71]

Dilation (dilatation) and curettage (D&C)
This method of abortion has been used since the late 19th century. It is used for gestation up to 12 weeks and is similar to suction curettage, except that instead of vacuuming the contents of the uterus, they are scraped out with a curette shaped like a loop. D&C requires heavy sedation or general anaesthesia and has higher risks of complication than suction procedures, so it is becoming less common as a method of abortion. According to the WHO, "D&C is an obsolete method of surgical abortion and should be replaced by vacuum aspiration and/or medical methods".[72]

This procedure shouldn't be confused with D&C used to treat other problems such as irregular menstrual bleeding and miscarriage.

Dilation and evacuation (D&E)
After 14-15 weeks, dilation and evacuation is often used. Cervical priming is recommended after 10 weeks. The cervix is dilated manually with rods

---

71.   ACOG, *Induced Abortion*, FAQ043, ACOG, Washington DC, October 2011 (viewed 16 November 2011): www.acog.org/~/media/For%20Patients/faq043.pdf
72.   WHO, *Safe Abortion: Technical and Policy Guidance for Health Systems*, 2nd edn, WHO, Geneva, 2012, p. 31.

and then instruments are used to crush and remove the fetus piecemeal. A combination of forceps, suction and curettage is often used. Sometimes the fetus will be delivered intact if sufficient cervical dilatation has occurred. Drugs that promote uterine contraction may be used. The procedure will be performed under local or general anaesthetic.[73]

Later second- and third-trimester abortions

Although medical abortion is available in the second trimester in some places, there is evidence that women prefer surgical abortion at this stage if they have a choice.[74] In later pregnancy, abortions are usually performed by inducing labour first. Several methods are used to commence labour. Inserting prostaglandins into the vagina is the most common method, and is generally preferred over instillation methods, which have largely been abandoned because of the risk of complications. Oxytocin (a hormone) is also sometimes given. As labour begins, the uterus contracts and the abortion usually occurs within 12-24 hours.

To avoid the accidental birth of a child who is old enough to survive outside the womb once it is born, and to shorten the time the abortion takes, the fetus is often killed with an injection of potassium into its heart with or without an injection of digoxin before the delivery. This causes a cardiac arrest (the fetus's heart stops). Another method of ensuring fetal demise is an intra-amniotic injection of a small amount of hypertonic saline used in conjunction with vaginal prostaglandin.[75] The birth of a live child does sometimes occur,[76] testified to by mothers who heard their babies cry. One can only assume what happens next.

> Gianna Jessen's mother was seven-and-a-half months pregnant when it was decided to abort the fetus she was carrying. A saline solution was injected into Gianna's mother's womb, which doctors thought would kill the fetus within hours. This time, most unusually, the procedure failed and Gianna was born alive, thanks in part to a shocked nurse. She was so taken aback by Gianna's live delivery that

---

73.   RANZCOG, op. cit., p. 14.

74.   T Kelly, J Suddes, D Howel, J Hewison and S Robson, 'Comparing medical versus surgical termination of pregnancy at 13-20 weeks of gestation: a randomised controlled trial', *BJOG: An International Journal of Obstetrics and Gynaecology*, vol. 117, no. 12, November 2010, pp. 1512-20.

75.   AH Goroll and AG Mulley, *Primary Care Medicine*, 6th edn, Lippincott Williams and Wilkins, Philadelphia, 2009, p. 893.

76.   IL Craft and BD Musa, 'Hypertonic solutions to induce abortion', *British Medical Journal*, vol. 2, no. 5752, 3 April 1971, p. 49.

she summoned an ambulance to whisk her from the abortion clinic to the hospital…

Gianna, a committed Christian, is opposed to abortion. She has cerebral palsy as a direct result of the procedure carried out on her in the womb. *The saline solution injected into the mother is to burn the baby, which gulps it in the womb*, she said. *But after being literally burned alive for 18 hours I was delivered live. It says on my records that I was born after a saline abortion.*

I was not expected to be delivered live but fortunately for me the abortionist was not in the clinic when I arrived alive instead of dead…

Ann Furedi, chief executive of the British Pregnancy Advisory Service, said it was important to remember that late abortions, like that of Gianna's mother, are uncommon. "These stories are extremely distressing. But the point we would always make is that these very late abortion at times when there is a potential for life are very few and far between.

"And there is very clear guidance to make sure this sort of thing does not happen."[77]

Instillation abortion

This method of abortion was first developed in 1934 by Romanian obstetrician Eugen Aburel. It is most frequently used between 16-24 weeks gestation, when enough fluid has accumulated in the amniotic fluid sac surrounding the fetus to permit the technique. These days, this type of abortion technique is not commonly used due to complications for the mother. Instillation abortion is performed by first dilating the cervix, then inserting a needle through the abdomen or the vagina into the amniotic sac, which encloses the fetus in the womb. Amniotic fluid is withdrawn and replaced with a solution of chemicals such as hypertonic saline, hyperosmolar urea or prostaglandin (prostaglandins are usually given with a hyperosmolar agent). The fetus breathes in, swallowing the chemicals, which usually leads to death. Hypertonic saline also has a corrosive effect on the fetal tissues.[78] The chemicals induce uterine

---

77.   J Elliot, 'I survived an abortion attempt', *BBC News*, 6 December 2005 (viewed 25 October 2011): http://news.bbc.co.uk/2/hi/health/4500022.stm

78.   RS Galen, P Chauhan, H Wietzner and C Navarro, 'Fetal pathology and mechanism of fetal death in saline-induced abortion: A study of 143 gestations and critical review of the literature', *American Journal of Obstetrics and Gynecology*, vol. 120, no. 3, 1974, p. 347.

contractions, which precipitate labour and lead to expulsion of the fetus. Sometimes a dilation and curettage procedure will be necessary to remove any remaining tissue. According to the CDC, intrauterine instillation accounted for only 0.1% of reported abortions in the USA in 2007.[79]

Intact dilation and extraction

After 16 weeks gestation, abortions can be performed by intact dilation and extraction (IDX; also called intrauterine cranial decompression). Labour is induced and the cervix is primed to dilate, usually over the course of several days. Next, the doctor rotates the fetus to a breech position (head under the woman's ribs). The body of the fetus is drawn out of the uterus feet first, until only the head remains inside the uterus. The doctor can then use an instrument to puncture the base of the skull, which collapses the fetal head. Typically the contents of the fetal head are then partially suctioned out, which results in the death of the fetus and reduces the size of the fetal head enough to allow it to pass through the cervix. (The baby may have been killed already by cardiac injection.) The dead and otherwise intact fetus is then removed from the woman's body. IDX is sometimes called 'partial-birth abortion'.

Hysterotomy and hysterectomy

Hysterotomy involves removing the fetus from the uterus using an approach through the abdominal wall. It is rarely used as the first method of abortion due to the increased risk to the mother. Hysterectomy involves removing the uterus itself. These two methods are sometimes used for late terminations if an abortion has failed and other methods such as D&E cannot be used due to an abnormality in the uterus. Hysterectomy is occasionally needed to control complications of abortion. These procedures would usually only be performed as a last resort.

Short-term complications of abortion

It is extraordinary to read in a 1989 article in the *British Medical Journal* that "early abortion is a safe operation and in most cases has no adverse

---

79. K Pazol, SB Zane, WY Parker, LR Hall, SB Gamble, S Hamdan, C Berg, DA Cook and CDC, 'Abortion Surveillance—United States, 2007', *MMWR Surveillance Summaries*, vol. 60, no. SS-1, 25 February 2011, p. 24 (Table 11).

sequelae, either mental or physical".[80] Subsequent correspondence identified that the reason for this perceived lack of problems was a technicality (complications had to be officially reported within 7 days, and most were detected later). Still, this attitude has been pervasive in both medical and community circles. The reality is quite different, as many women have discovered to their dismay.

In any abortion, complications include pain, bleeding (occasionally requiring transfusion), infection and (rarely) uterine rupture. Both approaches (medical and surgical) may be accompanied by short-term emotional distress, and the continuation of the pregnancy is also listed as a possible 'complication'. In addition to this, medical abortion can be associated with side effects of the medication used—side effects such as nausea, vomiting, diarrhoea, fever and chills. A minority of women will need surgery to complete the abortion. At least three deaths have occurred from mifepristone use for medical abortion.[81] In a surgical abortion, there may also be damage to the cervix or uterus itself; and any surgical procedure involves the risk of death, with mortality rate < 1 in 100,000.[82] The drugs used to start labour may cause side effects such as fever, nausea, vomiting, and diarrhoea, but less often than in medical abortions. The stage of pregnancy and the procedure used influence how often these problems occur, with fewer complications for earlier abortions.

Long-term complications of abortion
Future reproductive outcomes
Current research suggests that in countries where abortion is legal, it has no long-term effects on a woman's reproduction with regard to future fertility or risk of ectopic pregnancy. There is a small risk of subsequent preterm delivery.[83] Results are mixed regarding whether abortion increases the future risk of placenta praevia or miscarriage.[84] More research is needed to clarify these risks.

---

80. D Munday, C Francome and W Savage, 'Twenty one years of legal abortion', *British Medical Journal*, vol. 298, no. 6682, 6 May 1989, pp. 1231-4.

81. PG Stubblefield, S Carr-Ellis and L Borgatta, 'Methods for induced abortion', *Obstetrics and Gynecology*, vol. 104, no. 1, July 2004, pp. 174-85.

82. J Herndon, LT Strauss, S Whitehead, WY Parker, L Bartlett, S Zane and CDC, 'Abortion surveillance—United States, 1998', *MMWR Surveillance Summaries*, vol. 51, no. SS-3, 7 June 2002, pp 1-32.

83. RCOG, op. cit., pp. 44-5.

84. RANZCOG, op. cit., p. 26.

Breast cancer

There has been much discussion regarding a link between breast cancer and induced abortion. Some early studies that suggested the possibility had technical errors; more recent research has established there is no causal relationship between abortion and an increased risk of breast cancer.[85]

Post-Abortion Syndrome

With regard to psychological problems following abortion, there has been ongoing debate for decades now regarding whether 'Post-Abortion Syndrome' (PAS) exists. PAS has become the term that describes a woman's psychological response to abortion: long-lasting and recurring sadness, depression, anger or guilt; preoccupation with the aborted child and what it would have looked like; flashbacks of the abortion experience and nightmares related to it; low self-image, feelings of 'craziness', anxiety, discomfort being around babies; anniversaries of both the operation and the would-have-been birthdays noted each year.[86] Substance use, suicide and self-harm are also reported following abortion.[87] As a theory promoted by the anti-abortion movement, it has been viewed with skepticism by many commentators, especially because up until recently there was no strong evidence that abortion actually caused psychological problems. Studies on the topic generally showed that only a small number of women exhibited severe negative psychological responses to abortion, and it tended to be associated with psychological or other problems that were present before the abortion. Even when there was clear evidence of problems after abortion, causality was still questioned.[88] The usual conclusion was that it was due to the circumstances of the particular woman at the time of the abortion, rather than the abortion itself.[89]

This was always difficult to understand for those of us who had

---

85. RCOG, op. cit., pp. 42-3.

86. E Lee and A Gilchrist, 'Abortion psychological sequelae: the debate and the research', paper presented to the Pro-Choice Forum conference 'Issues in pregnancy counselling: What do women need and want?', Oxford, May 1997.

87. DM Fergusson, LJ Horwood and EM Ridder, 'Abortion in young women and subsequent mental health', *Journal of Child Psychology and Psychiatry*, vol. 47, no. 1, January 2006, pp. 16-24.

88. For example, Gissler et al., loc. cit.

89. This is the view held by RCOG and commentators such as Lee and Gilchrist, loc. cit.

counselled women who relived the horror of the abortion years after it had occurred. We knew PAS existed, but the data did not measure up. Melinda Tankard Reist describes the hundreds of women "emotionally disabled by unrecognized and unrelieved grief" who have told her about their abortion experiences.[90] These women found the telling their stories cathartic, and she was encouraged to document this material:

> So many feelings and emotions, locked in the secret hallways of my heart and mind! But it helps knowing that I'm not the only one going through all this. (Cassie)[91]

Still, many women feel they cannot share their pain with anyone:

> I have paid the ultimate price. I have to live with myself… The worst part of the pain is there's no-one to share it with… but… not a day goes by when I don't think about it. I can't believe I did it, I wish I could change everything and go back… I will never be forgiven for what I did. (Anonymous)[92]

While the existence of this disorder was denied, many women did not receive the help they needed to recover, emotionally or spiritually. And there was no reason for counsellors to warn women of the risk of post-abortion grief:

> In 1998 an Australian woman sued her doctor for not warning her of the risk of depression she experienced after an abortion in 1990. It was settled out of court.[93]

Much confusion in the research was due to the polarization of those expressing the alternative views (either claiming that abortion always, or never, had psychological effects), and inadequate follow-up time (proponents argue it can take up to 10 years or even longer for PAS to manifest).[94] But also it was the result of a failure to separate two closely related questions:

1. Is unwanted pregnancy terminated by abortion an adverse life event that leads to increased risks of mental health problems in

---

90. M Tankard Reist, *Giving Sorrow Words*, Duffy and Snellgrove, Potts Point, 2000, p. 1.
91. Quoted in Tankard Reist, ibid., p. 4.
92. Quoted in Tankard Reist, ibid., p. 13.
93. S Vale, 'GPs need to advise on risks of abortion', *Australian Doctor*, 13 November 1998.
94. Women Hurt by Abortion, 'Post-abortion syndrome. Does it exist?' *Australian Doctor*, 4 September 1998, p. 32.

those women exposed to the event?

2. Are any adverse consequences of unwanted pregnancy terminated by abortion greater or lesser than the adverse consequences of unwanted pregnancy continued to birth?

A 2008 study has clarified the two and shown that mental disorder is 30% higher in those who have had abortions.[95] A further study in 2009 has shown that this is associated with a negative reaction to abortion, but not to whether the abortion was considered to be the right decision.[96] As the authors of both studies note, these findings are not consistent with either the pro-life position that abortion has devastating effects on women's health, nor the pro-choice position that legal abortion is risk-free. Rather, it shows that unwanted pregnancy terminated by abortion is an event that causes significant distress in some, but not all, women. Even authors who are unhappy to agree with the results now acknowledge that some women do experience mental health problems following abortion, and that these experiences need to be "recognized, validated, and understood".[97] Thankfully it is now recommended that women be warned of this possible complication.[98] Hopefully this will result in further research and the development of screening procedures to identify and help those affected.

It was also reported that unwanted pregnancy that was not terminated but proceeded to birth was not associated with a significant increase in mental health problems; and that abortion did not reduce the risks of mental health problems in women with unwanted pregnancy. This has important legal implications for those jurisdictions where legal abortion can be justified on the grounds that proceeding with the pregnancy represents a greater risk to a woman's mental health than ending it (e.g. Britain, New Zealand and parts of Australia).

---

95. DM Fergusson, LJ Horwood and JM Boden, 'Abortion and mental health disorders: evidence from a 30-year longitudinal study', *British Journal of Psychiatry*, vol. 193, no. 6, December 2008, pp. 444-51.
96. DM Fergusson, LJ Horwood and JM Boden, 'Reactions to abortion and subsequent mental health', *British Journal of Psychiatry*, vol. 195, no. 5, November 2009, pp. 420-6.
97. B Major, M Appelbaum, L Beckman, MA Dutton, NF Russo and C West, 'Abortion and mental health: evaluating the evidence', *American Psychologist*, vol. 64, no. 9, December 2009, pp. 863-90.
98. RCOG, op. cit., p. 39.

Since then, despite more studies that deny the mental health risk,[99] a 2011 meta-analysis of 22 published studies with data on 877,181 participants—163,381 of whom had experienced an abortion—found that women who had undergone an abortion had an 81% risk of increased mental health problems, and nearly 10% of those problems were directly attributable to abortion. The author of this study criticized the methods used by previous researchers who came to the opposite conclusion.[100] This raises the possibility that the law that was intended to reduce risks of mental health problems in women with unwanted pregnancy may in fact increase mental health risks. This suggests a need for further research and perhaps a need to review the legislation involved.

For doctors

The term 'post-abortion syndrome' was first used in 1981 by Vincent Rue, a psychologist and trauma specialist, during his testimony before American Congress. He used the term to describe post-traumatic stress disorder (PTSD) symptoms he had observed as a response to the stress of abortion. PAS was subsequently popularized and widely used by pro-life advocates to describe a broad range of adverse emotional reactions that they attribute to abortion (see above). Attempts have been made to have PAS defined as a form of PTSD. In order for abortion-related distress to be classified as PTSD in the American Psychiatric Association's Diagnostic and Statistical Manual of Mental Disorders *(DSM-IV-TR), the abortion would need to be classified as a traumatic event experienced or witnessed by the woman "that involved actual or threatened death or serious injury, or a threat to the physical integrity of self or others" (criterion A1).*[101] *Currently there is no formal recognition of PAS as an actual diagnosis or condition, and it is not included in the DSM-IV-TR or in the WHO's* International Classification of Diseases

---

99. National Collaborating Centre for Mental Health, *Induced Abortion and Mental Health*, Academy of Medical Royal Colleges, London, December 2011, cited in RCOG, op. cit., p. 99; Major et al., loc. cit.

100. PK Coleman, 'Abortion and mental health: quantitative synthesis and analysis of research published 1995-2009', *British Journal of Psychiatry*, vol. 199, no. 3, September 2011, pp. 180-6.

101. For full diagnostic criteria, see American Psychiatric Association, *Diagnostic and Statistical Manual for Mental Disorders*, 4th edn, text revision, American Psychiatric Association, Washington DC, 2000, pp. 467-8.

(ICD-10) list of psychiatric conditions. Some pro-choice advocates have argued that efforts to popularize the term 'post-abortion syndrome' are simply a tactic used by pro-life advocates for political purposes. Research keywords for this topic include 'abortion and mental health', 'psychological responses to abortion', 'emotional reactions to abortion', and similar. The Royal College of Psychiatrists has recommended that women contemplating abortion should be advised of mental health risks.[102]

Psychological effects of medical abortion

I am not aware of any long-term studies on the psychological effects of medical (RU-486) abortion. There is anecdotal evidence of the shock women feel when they see their aborted child (possibly fully formed) in the toilet bowl or on the shower floor, leading to ongoing memories of their encounter. The abortion can happen at home if there is a delayed response to the prostaglandin given on day two. Also, counsellors often discuss how women feel more responsible for their abortion when they suffer over a longer period to achieve it. (Bleeding after mifepristone administration averages 9-15 days but can continue for up to around 70 days).[103] Some women say they feel it is right that they suffer. Time will tell what long-term psychological effects this has.

Despite the inherent dangers known to exist for the mother with elective abortion, these are not ethical objections (although the need to fully inform those contemplating abortion of possible complications is an ethical issue). The ethical basis for opposing abortion lies in the injustice done to the innocent child who is killed during the procedure.

Fathers hurt too

Australian novelist Peter Carey has written about the deep sadness he feels for his lost children—his grief over babies lost through abortion

---

102. Royal College of Psychiatrists, *Position Statement on Women's Mental Health in Relation to Induced Abortion*, Royal College of Psychiatrists, London, 14 March 2008.
103. RANZCOG, op. cit., p. 17.

and subsequent miscarriages (due to damage to his first wife's cervix during the abortion procedures); "children a long time dead". He writes that he had been unable to give names to the lost children—his way of holding the grief at bay—and that he allowed their ashes to be placed in an unmarked niche in a wall. *I wish only that we had honoured those children with a plaque, a name. I will always wish that, forever.*[104]

The 'atonement' or 'replacement' child

This is the term for children born following an abortion, where the pregnancy is consciously chosen to compensate for the lost child. *I needed to show the world I was a life-giver, not a baby killer*, said Belinda, who had had four abortions.[105]

Fetal pain relief

In April 2010, the state of Nebraska in the United States banned abortions at and after 20 weeks. The Pain-Capable Unborn Child Protection Act is based on research that tells us fetuses can feel pain at 20 weeks, and possibly as early as 17 weeks. And according to the testimony of paediatrician Kanwaljeet Anand, who has been studying infant pain for 25 years, unborn infants may feel pain more keenly than those already born.[106] Abortion advocates are concerned that discussion of fetal analgesia 'humanizes' the fetus and is being used to oppose legal abortion.

The legislation is expected to be challenged in the courts, but meanwhile, it has inspired eight other states (Alabama, Idaho, Indiana, Georgia, Kansas, Ohio, Louisiana and Oklahoma) to also ban most abortions after five months.[107]

> **For doctors**
>
> *The underlying research for this legislation has been challenged by researchers who suggest that the legislation is based on what is only*

---

104. P Carey, 'My lasting wish', *Australian Magazine*, 14-15 October 1994.

105. Quoted in Tankard Reist, op. cit., p. 42.

106. M Earley, 'Seeing is believing: The humanity of the fetus', radio program episode, *Breakpoint*, Breakpoint Prison Fellowship, Lansdowne, 27 April 2010.

107. More than 80 restrictions aimed at reducing access to abortion were approved in United States state legislatures in 2011. Other measures included expansion of counselling requirements and tougher regulations for clinics. See D Crary and T Ross, 'More states crack down on late-term abortions', *Boston.com*, 24 July 2011 (viewed 6 November 2011): http://articles.boston.com/2011-07-24/news/29810324_1_late-term-abortion-providers-ban-abortions

a theory. A review article published in 2005 concluded that evidence regarding the capacity for fetal pain is limited but indicates that fetal perception of pain is unlikely before the third trimester.[108] This conclusion was based on the presumption that conscious cortical processing is necessary for pain perception, and that EEG evidence suggests the necessary brain connections required for the fetal perception of pain (the establishment of the thalamocortical connections) do not exist before 29-30 weeks. A working party of the Royal College of Obstetricians and Gynaecologists (RCOG) reported in 2010 that intact nerve connections between the cortex and the periphery of the brain are not present before 24 weeks.[109]

However, while Kanwaljeet Anand acknowledges that the cerebral cortex is not fully developed in the fetus until late in gestation, he notes that what is up and running is a structure called the subplate zone, which some believe may be capable of processing pain signals. A kind of holding station for developing neurons that eventually merge into the mature cerebral cortex, the subplate zone becomes operational at about 17 weeks.[110] In other words, the fetus's undeveloped state may not preclude it from feeling pain. In fact, its immature physiology may well make it more sensitive to pain, not less—the body's mechanisms for inhibiting pain and making it more bearable do not become active until after birth.[111]

Anand's findings are confirmed by Nicholas Fisk, fetal medicine specialist and director of the University of Queensland Centre for Clinical Research in Australia. He showed that the fetus mounts significant stress, hormonal and circulatory changes in response to invasive diagnostic and therapeutic procedures from 18-20 weeks.[112] He also showed that these changes are reduced once analgesia is given (he injected fentanyl

108.   SJ Lee, HJP Ralston, EA Drey, JC Partridge and MA Rosen, 'Fetal pain: A systematic multidisciplinary review of the evidence', *Journal of the American Medical Association*, vol. 294, no. 8, 24/31 August 2005, pp. 947-54.

109.   RCOG, *Fetal Awareness, Report of a working party*, RCOG Press, London, March 2010.

110.   KJS Anand and PR Hickey, 'Pain and its effects in the human neonate and fetus', *New England Journal of Medicine*, vol. 317, no. 21, 19 November 1987, pp. 1321-9.

111.   AM Paul, 'The first ache', *Times Magazine*, 10 February 2008.

112.   RP Smith, R Gitau, V Glover and NM Fisk, 'Pain and stress in the human fetus', *European Journal of Obstetrics and Gynecology and Reproductive Biology*, vol. 92, no. 1, September 2000, pp. 161-5.

into fetuses requiring blood transfusion).[113] *Perinatal stress may have long-term neurodevelopmental implications.*[114] *Since it is possible that the fetus is aware of pain from around 20 weeks, he and co-researcher Vivette Glover have long suggested that we should err on the safe side and provide analgesia to fetuses during procedures and terminations from mid-gestation (since we can't ask the patient if it hurts).*[115]

David Mellor, the founding director of the Animal Welfare Science and Bioethics Center at Massey University in New Zealand, suggests that this does not take into account the special environment of the fetus. He found biochemicals produced by the placenta and fetus that have a sedating and even an anaesthetizing effect on the fetus (both equine and human).[116] *Furthermore, some authors note that even if we can demonstrate the presence of anatomical structures responsible for pain impulses in fetuses, we cannot be sure that it means they perceive pain as we do.*[117]

Anaesthesia has long been used for the fetus as well as the mother in intrauterine surgery by using drugs that cross the placenta. Parenteral opioids may also be administered to the fetus. Even though the practice commenced when withdrawal responses to noxious stimuli were observed, administration of anaesthesia and analgesia may serve purposes unrelated to reduction of fetal pain, including inhibition of fetal movement, prevention of fetal hormonal stress responses, and induction of uterine atony. It does not always reflect a belief that the fetus will experience pain during the procedure.[118]

So what of abortion? Is it valid to suggest that the fetus feels pain from 20 weeks and so requires pain relief in all procedures, including termination of pregnancy?

In 1997 the RCOG suggested that practitioners who undertake diagnostic or therapeutic surgical procedures upon the fetus at or

---

113.   NM Fisk, R Gitau, JM Teixeira, X Giannakoulopoulos, AD Cameron and VA Glover, 'Effect of direct fetal opioid analgesia on fetal hormonal and hemodynamic stress response to intrauterine needling', *Anesthesiology*, vol. 95, no. 4, October 2001, pp. 828-35.

114.   Anand and Hickey, loc. cit.

115.   V Glover and NM Fisk, 'Do fetuses feel pain? We don't know; better to err on the safe side from mid-gestation', *British Medical Journal*, vol. 313, no. 7060, 28 September 1996, p. 796.

116.   DJ Mellor, TJ Diesch, AJ Gunn and L Bennet, 'The importance of "awareness" for understanding fetal pain', *Brain Research Reviews*, vol. 49, no. 3, November 2005, pp. 455-71.

117.   Glover and Fisk, loc. cit.

118.   Lee et al., 'Fetal pain', loc. cit.

> *after 24 weeks gestation consider the requirements for fetal analgesia and sedation; and that practitioners who undertake termination of pregnancy at 24 weeks or later should consider the requirements for feticide or fetal analgesia and sedation.*[119]
>
> *The authors of the 2005 review disagree. They write that there is inadequate evidence available to assess the effectiveness of fetal anaesthetic or analgesic techniques. Similarly, limited or no data exist on the safety of such techniques for pregnant women in the context of abortion. They note that general anaesthesia for the mother increases the risk of the abortion for the mother, as well as the cost.*[120] *It is not a straightforward issue of 'erring on the safe side', since some animal research suggests there may be a risk of long-term developmental damage to the fetus when given opioids.*[121] *I read of one commentator who dismissed the whole problem by saying that if it was risks for the future we were worrying about, it was simple in the case of abortion. An aborted fetus has no future.*

The final word comes from a research review of fetal pain by the Medical Research Council in the United Kingdom.[122] Basically, we don't really know when or how the fetus feels pain. But there is enough evidence to suspect there is a need for more attention to be given to how we treat developing humans. Does this mean the baby needs analgesia during childbirth, just like mum? I'm not sure. More research is needed.

There are no illustrations for this chapter. Those who would like more detail regarding how abortions are performed can use a search engine on the internet using the names of the procedures above. Be warned that this is an extremely unpleasant topic to research. The trauma personally experienced by abortion providers has been documented. Daleiden and Shields write:

---

119. Medical Research Council (MRC), *Report of the MRC Expert Group on Fetal Pain*, MRC, London, 28 August 2001, p. 1.
120. Lee et al., 'Fetal pain', op. cit.
121. MRC, loc. cit.
122. MRC, loc. cit.

Especially in abortions performed far enough along in gestation that the fetus is recognizably a tiny baby, this intimacy exacts an emotional toll, stirring sentiments for which doctors, nurses, and aides are sometimes unprepared. Most apparently have managed to reconcile their belief in the right to abortion with their revulsion at dying and dead fetuses, but a noteworthy number have found the conflict unbearable and have defected to the pro-life cause.[123]

One particularly famous abortion provider who changed his mind is Dr Bernard Nathanson, who by his own estimate performed more than 60,000 abortions, including one on his own child. After leaving his profession to spend time trying to repeal abortion laws in America, he produced a documentary called *The Silent Scream* (1984). It shows an actual abortion on ultrasound, where the 12-week-old fetus pathetically tries to escape the instrument that will terminate its life. Even now, this disturbing movie can be found on YouTube. Parental guidance is recommended.

It was seeing an abortion on ultrasound that made former Planned Parenthood clinic director Abby Johnson decide to change her allegiance. The image of a 13-week-old fetus reminded her of her own daughter's ultrasound. Its futile twisting and struggling haunted her:

> It wasn't just tissue, just cells. That was a human baby—fighting for life! A battle that was lost in the blink of an eye.[124]

In summary, elective abortion involves the deliberate killing of a human embryo or fetus during termination of pregnancy. Obviously it will be a distressing and often painful procedure. This leads us to our next question.

3. What makes a woman choose to have an abortion? Does her situation make a difference, ethically?

What are the circumstances in which the decision is made to end a pregnancy? Most abortions are performed on healthy mothers and babies. However, unplanned pregnancy is not the simple cause of abortion. A significant number of women are ambivalent about their pregnancies and the abortion decision, and this ambivalence may last

---

123. D Daleiden and JA Shields, 'Mugged by ultrasound: Why so many abortion workers have turned pro-life', *Weekly Standard*, vol. 15, no. 18, 25 January 2010.
124. Johnson and Lambert, op. cit., pp. 6-7.

a long time.[125] I have certainly found this as a doctor—women, and less often men, who years afterwards can tell you what age their aborted child would have been had they lived. They wonder what the child would have looked like. A substantial number of women undergo abortion while being morally opposed to it. Their decisions are influenced by their circumstances and the people around them. Evidence suggests that most women consider abortion because they believe that they are not free to pursue motherhood, or because they lack the emotional and financial support they need to cope with a having a baby. Abortion is strongly associated with domestic violence and abuse of women.[126] Many women are unaware of the potential psychological harm associated with abortion, and afterwards express anger that they weren't informed.

Even in the democratic West, it can be hard to access accurate abortion statistics. In Australia, currently the only state that collects information regarding the reasons for abortion is South Australia. For the year 2006 these were the official reasons given for elective (non-emergency) abortions:[127]

Reason given for abortion	Number	Percentage
Specified medical condition	16	0.3
Serious handicap of fetus	141	2.9
Mental health of woman	4,727	96.7
Pre-existing psychiatric disorder	4	0.1
Assault on person (e.g. rape or incest)	1	0.0
Total	4,889	100%

We see that the difficult cases—fetal abnormality and rape—motivate relatively few abortions compared with the vague 'mental health of woman' category. We won't really know what is going on until more states start collecting detailed data. However, even now when you look more closely, the picture is not so straightforward. An Australian research project in 1995 asked 20 women what they considered while deciding to

---

125. S Ewing, *Women and Abortion*, Women's Forum Australia, Brisbane, 2005.
126. ibid.
127. South Australia, Parliament 2000, *Annual Report of the South Australian Abortion Reporting Committee 2007*, Parl. Paper 90, Adelaide, p. 7.

have an abortion (they were questioned at an abortion clinic).[128] The list of important factors, from most to least considered, is as follows:

- pregnancy would jeopardize future
- could not cope
- my right to choose
- know termination of pregnancy is safe and simple
- can't afford a baby
- pregnancy has no real form yet
- know other women who aborted and did well
- don't want others to know I'm pregnant
- important others would suffer
- would be a single mother
- worried would not be a good mother
- relationship unstable or new
- partner could not cope, too young
- not enough support
- scared of childbirth
- others say I should terminate
- relationship at risk if continue
- coped well with previous termination
- health would suffer
- don't ever want (more) children
- too old
- result of forced sex
- worried about health of pregnancy
- not want others to know I had sex

It is obvious that lack of support, lack of confidence and coercion play an important part in the choice to abort. And this research was done by a group that supports abortion.

This is a topic that deserves much more attention than I can give it here, but suffice to say that abortion tends to be a difficult and distressing choice for most of the women involved. Indeed, many of these women would say they didn't have a choice, because the option to keep the baby didn't seem to exist for them. While pressure from male partners

---

128. S Allanson and J Ashbury, 'The abortion decision: reasons and ambivalence', *Journal of Psychosomatic Obstetrics and Gynecology*, vol. 16, no. 3, 1995, pp. 123-36.

is known to play a significant part in choosing abortion,[129] fathers who want the child to live have no legal rights over the decision at all.

It is important to identify whether abortions are sometimes necessary to preserve a woman's life and health.[130] There have been reports in the past that therapeutic abortion of wanted pregnancies has occurred to relieve severe morning sickness (hyperemesis gravidarum).[131] This was thought to be exacerbated by an unwillingness in physicians to prescribe drugs to stop nausea and vomiting in pregnancy (in case it would hurt the baby). This excuse has been firmly refuted in the literature.

Late-term abortions (over 20 weeks) are often justified on the basis of being necessary to preserve a woman's life and health. However, the research suggests that most late-term abortions are just regular abortions performed late because of delayed diagnosis of pregnancy. The most common reasons are failure to recognize the pregnancy, and delays in arranging the abortion. Interestingly, a 2007 study found that 41% of women questioned had delayed the abortion due to indecision.[132] But regardless of why they are late, they are done for similar reasons to early abortions: relationship problems, young or old maternal age, education or financial concerns. Former abortionist Mary Davenport, of the American Association of Pro-Life Obstetricians and Gynaecologists, questions the necessity of late abortion on grounds of risk to maternal health:

> The very fact that the baby of an ill mother is viable raises the question of why, indeed, it is necessary to perform an abortion to end the pregnancy. With any serious maternal health problem, termination of pregnancy can be accomplished by inducing labour or performing a caesarean section, saving both mother and baby.[133]

---

129.   AN Broen, T Moum, AS Bödtker and Ö Ekeberg, 'Reasons for induced abortion and their relation to women's emotional distress: A prospective, two-year follow-up study', *General Hospital Psychiatry*, vol. 27, no. 1, January 2005, pp. 36-43.

130.   This is the justification for abortion in the third trimester given by the United States Supreme Court in *Roe v. Wade* (1973).

131.   P Mazzota, L Magee and G Koren, 'Therapeutic abortions due to severe morning sickness: Unacceptable combination', *Canadian Family Physician*, vol. 43, June 1997, pp. 1055-7.

132.   R Ingham, E Lee, S Clements and N Stone, 'Reasons for second-trimester abortions in England and Wales', *Reproductive Health Matters*, vol. 16, no. 31, supp. 1, May 2008, pp. 18-29.

133.   ML Davenport, *Is Late-term Abortion Ever Necessary?* American Association of Pro-Life Obstetricians and Gynecologists, Holland MI, June 2009 (viewed 6 November 2011): www.aaplog.org/american-issues-2/late-term-abortion/is-late-term-abortion-ever-necessary/

The point she is making is that in late-term abortion, the baby is often old enough to survive outside the womb (viable). If that is the case, why is the mother aborting? Why not just have an early delivery? Davenport describes the argument for late-term abortion on grounds of maternal health, particularly after viability, as a great deception.

However, there are some conditions where an abortion may be necessary to save a mother's life. Sometimes the decision to end the pregnancy will be straightforward medically and ethically, although obviously still difficult emotionally. Consider these situations where the baby is not sufficiently mature to survive outside the womb:

- Early ectopic pregnancy ('tubal' pregnancy) means the baby has started growing somewhere other than the uterus (usually the fallopian tube), which is inadequate to support the pregnancy. Internal bleeding is a common complication that can lead to death.
- Severe eclampsia (high blood pressure) is another situation where the woman is at risk of dying if she does not receive treatment.

Sadly, treatment of these conditions at present involves termination of the pregnancy. This is not because the woman's life is more valuable. It is ethically justified because the child has no chance of survival whether you try to save the mother's life or not (it cannot survive outside the womb, and it cannot survive if it stays in the womb and the mother dies). The best outcome possible in this situation is that the mother's life is preserved.

More complicated are the decisions where the woman's health and the baby's chances are more evenly balanced. Even in these conditions it may be possible to delay delivery until the baby is old enough to survive if the mother so desires. Each case will be judged on its own merits, but saving the mother's life will be the priority for the obstetrician. If abortion is recommended, it is always worth getting a second opinion from a doctor who specializes in maternal fetal medicine.

For doctors

Maternal mortality is greater than 20% in the setting of late pregnancy for pulmonary hypertension (Eisenmenger's syndrome), Marfan's syndrome with aortic root involvement, complicated coarctation of the aorta, and, possibly, peripartum cardiomyopathy with residual dysfunction.[134] These conditions are rare. Their importance lies in the way they have been used to justify abortion on maternal morbidity grounds. While there is a long list of conditions that may occur during pregnancy and threaten the mother's health, including preeclampsia, cancer and heart disease, it is always worth exploring whether treatment is possible while the pregnancy continues either to term or viability. Maternal fetal medicine specialists will be a great help in such situations.

There will occasionally be cases where a mother's refusal of treatment for herself may lead to the child's death, as it will be unsafe to deliver. Thankfully such cases are rare. This will be ethically challenging and will need to be reviewed on a case-by-case basis. In most Western countries, it is not possible to insist that a mentally competent patient is denied the right to refuse treatment.

As mentioned above, recent research shows that difficult situations such as fetal abnormality and rape motivate relatively few abortions. But abortion for fetal abnormality is a growing trend as we improve methods of detection.[135]

Abortion following IVF

About 80 British women abort their IVF babies every year. Apparently most are within weeks of the embryo transfer, after the mother has had a change of heart. 749 babies have been aborted in this setting over the 19 years in which statistics have been collected.[136]

Selective/fetal/pregnancy reduction

Selective reduction is a procedure used to 'manage' the problem of multiple gestation. It involves the termination of one or more, but not all, of the fetuses. This was originally done to increase the likelihood that the surviving child may develop in a healthy way, as risks (such as premature delivery) increase with every extra baby. It is now also done to spare parents the stress of having to look after twins.[137] The reduction

---

134.   TM Goodwin, 'Medicalizing Abortion Decisions', *First Things*, March 1996, pp. 33-6. This article discusses several case studies of women who were incorrectly told they needed abortions for medical indications.

135.   See chapters 8 and 9.

136.   M Davis, 'IVF babies aborted', *Sunday Express*, 26 June 2011.

137.   R Padawer, 'The two-minus-one pregnancy', *New York Times Magazine*, 10 August 2011.

procedure is generally carried out during the first trimester of pregnancy. The most common method is to inject potassium chloride into the fetal heart, which makes it stop beating. Generally, the fetal material is reabsorbed into the woman's body. Miscarriage rate after the procedure (of the remaining child/ren) is around 5%-10%.[138]

While the motive for this intervention is a good one (wanting a healthy child), the action itself is not. This is how Gary justified it: *You start thinking to yourself, Oh God, am I killing this child?* But then he was told that it was not an abortion; it was a reduction. *You're reducing the pregnancy to make sure you have a greater chance of a healthy child,* he told me. *If you're going to bring a child into this world, you have an obligation to take care of that child to the best of your abilities.* See how easy it is to justify your actions just by changing terminology and focusing on consequences? This procedure is unethical for those who wish to protect life from the time of fertilization, as it involves the intentional killing of unborn children and perhaps the manslaughter of the children who are not targeted for death but are lost through miscarriage.

In November 2011, a tragedy occurred in Melbourne, Australia, which received worldwide news coverage. A woman who was pregnant with twins was told at 32 weeks that one of the twins had significant heart problems. She was advised to abort the child. The affected child would have had to have years of operations if he survived at all.

It was decided to abort the single twin by selective reduction. After a careful study of the two babies under ultrasound, the sonographer gave the healthy twin the lethal injection by mistake. When the mistake was noticed, the other twin was also aborted by emergency caesarean section.[139] The woman's distress can only be imagined. However, it is interesting to reflect that only the death of the 'wanted' normal twin made the story newsworthy.[140]

---

138. KL Armour and LC Callister, 'Prevention of triplets and high order multiples: Trends in reproductive medicine', *Journal of Perinatal and Neonatal Nursing,* vol. 19, no. 2, April/June 2005, pp. 103-11. See also A Antsaklis, AP Souka, G Daskalakis, N Papantoniou, P Koutra, Y Kavalakis and S Mesogitis, 'Pregnancy outcome after multifetal pregnancy reduction', *Journal of Maternal-Fetal and Neonatal Medicine,* vol. 16, no. 1, 2004, pp. 27-31.

139. S Drill, 'Medical bungle at Royal Women's Hospital kills healthy fetus', *Herald Sun,* 24 November 2011.

140. For an alternative way to have managed this case, see case 1 in chapter 9.

4. How should Christians make ethical decisions about abortion?

Now that we have our information, what do we do with it? Is abortion always wrong? In chapter 5 we looked at a model for ethical Christian decision-making. We will now work through that model to examine the question of abortion.[141]

Motivation

Christians will be motivated by virtues like compassion, but unlike their pro-abortion neighbours, will act in ways that protect vulnerable human life as far as possible. It can be confusing to realize that those on both sides of the abortion debate share the motivation of compassion. How can this be? It is due to the meaning of 'motivation'. Motivation will *prompt* us to act, but it will not *inform the content* of our actions.

Intention

In the context of abortion, our intentions will always be to protect the lives of both mother and child as far as is possible.

Action

Our actions will correspond with our intentions to protect human life. We will not disobey the guidance of Scripture in our attempts to reach our intended goal. In the case of abortion, we have seen that it involves the deliberate killing of an unborn child. Biblical commands represent absolute values; there are some things we should never do, whatever the consequences. By this argument most cases of abortion will be wrong—both performing the abortion as well as having it.

But what if our good intentions and actions lead to bad consequences? Consider this scenario: a mother develops a serious medical problem (e.g. acute heart failure) in the third trimester, and early labour is induced in an attempt to save the life of both mother and child. Despite every effort to save him, the baby dies because of complications of premature delivery. In this case the intention was morally good (to save both lives) and the action was morally acceptable (an appropriate medical intervention so the heart failure could be treated). But the outcome troubles us.

---

141. Note that abortion was used as the example in chapter 5, so please revisit 'Responding to alternative ethical theories' in that chapter for a more detailed discussion.

Consequences

We are judged only according to those things for which we are responsible, and not those things that are out of our control. If we aim for a good outcome—for example, in the case I just mentioned, a live mother and a premature but live infant—yet a bad outcome intervenes through circumstances beyond our control, we are not morally liable.

For doctors

This is not to say that we should not make the best prediction we can regarding the outcome; in medical scenarios we can usually make an educated guess regarding the impact of our intervention. But as humans we have limited foresight. (Though we would be negligent if we had made a treatment error and did not try to fix it as soon as possible.) I know that philosophers have spent time discussing whether we can know if good or bad outcomes are intended in medicine, but in my experience, doctors know what they are intending to achieve when they are treating patients. And God certainly knows our hearts (Rom 2:16).

Rights of conscience

In light of recent political activity around the world to remove the right of conscientious objection for doctors who oppose abortion, we also need to consider whether referring a patient for abortion is morally wrong for the Christian. For example, legislation passed in 2008 in the Australian state of Victoria decriminalized termination of pregnancy and removed the right of conscientious objection for doctors and nurses to avoid any involvement in the act of abortion.

Whether a doctor is morally complicit in an action will depend on several factors. Firstly, have you any role in the causation of the act? Is the woman's desire for an abortion influenced by your role? It is easy to make sure you do not have a role in causation of the wrong act, by gently counselling the woman involved regarding alternatives to this path of action. Listen to her so that you understand her concerns. Direct her to explore the options, such as practical support for those who feel they cannot cope. If the child has a problem, the woman could speak to those who spend time with the disabled, such as support associations. They can explain what is available to help parents living with disabled children and what it actually looks like. Sometimes what we imagine is worse than what actually is the case. Allow time for your patient to reflect in ways that your colleagues do not allow time for. If the husband or partner is with her, include him in all your discussions. Even if the woman says she knows what is involved, it is necessary to check that her knowledge is correct in order to ensure proper informed consent.

Secondly, are you facilitating the morally wrong act directly? Are you making the abortion happen? This second question is interesting. By referring a woman for abortion are you helping her achieve her morally wrong aim? If you were the only possible referrer you may perhaps prevent the abortion by being obstructive, but in many cases a referral is not even formally required. However, agreeing immediately to her request may appear to give her choice some kind of legitimacy that may reinforce her decision—hence the benefit of taking the time to counsel. You may be the only person she meets who discusses the option of keeping the child. It would be tragic to miss the opportunity. Some healthcare workers believe that referral constitutes complicity and merely distances you from a morally wrong act rather than making you a value-neutral service provider. If you are convicted that referral does constitute complicity at this point, you should not go against your conscience (Rom 14:23).

Thirdly, does your action perpetuate the moral wrong? Does your referral increase the likelihood of it happening again? This is difficult to determine. With regard to refusal to refer, apart from the unlikely possibility of obstructing access to abortion (above), it is possible that by making a stand and sensitively explaining your point of view to the woman involved and others, you may persuade her to think differently about abortion in future. This may alter her behaviour. By going ahead and referring a patient for abortion at her request, as suggested above, you infer that this is a legitimate therapeutic pathway to take. This may also impact on future behaviour. Once again, we must each decide prayerfully what we believe is correct action.

But as I discuss this issue with those who work in this field, I realize it's not so straightforward. Some Christians do not see referral for abortion as morally equivalent to performing the procedure themselves. They believe there are some moral arguments for referral. There are professional obligations to do good and not harm, to uphold 'duty of care' and ensure patient safety even if care is transferred to another doctor. You may have an ongoing relationship with the patient whether you like it or not, and you may not want to damage it. Remember that your non-

Christian patients do not have the indwelling Holy Spirit who convicts them of sin (John 16:8-11), and we should not judge them.

In this case of referral, the doctor is motivated by care for the patient. If you have gently explored all options and the woman persists in her request, you may direct her ultimately to those who will perform a termination. And this you will grieve. But who knows what will happen as you continue on the path together, where you may have the opportunity to offer support in the aftermath of the termination; where you can help her make sure this never happens again. You do not necessarily condone her choice. Modern medical practice requires that we respect the autonomy of our mentally competent patients even when we do not agree with their choices.

This does not, however, mean that the patient has a right to make the doctor violate their conscience. There are ethical arguments both for and against referral, and committed Christians exist at both ends of the spectrum.

It is important that pro-life doctors work in the area of obstetrics to be salt and light in this specialty. There is also a need for all healthcare workers to show interest in public policy so that rights of conscience are not further eroded.

At times God may call us to take a stand against unjust laws and suffer the consequences. This will be between each individual and God. We must continue to pray for wisdom as modern medicine continues to move away from life-preserving Hippocratic medicine.

We have considered that the way to best live out kingdom values may be by being creative in considering what therapeutic options are available to us. This is easier to think through when we reflect on specific examples. Obviously when involved with anyone facing the challenges of an unwanted pregnancy, you will need considerable sensitivity in discussing the issues with them. In the following examples I will just discuss the basic approach.

Case 1: A university student requests abortion after finding out she is pregnant; it's just not a good time for her to have a baby

In this case there is no medical indication for terminating the pregnancy.

However, if we are going to urge a woman to continue what may be an unwanted pregnancy, we will need to provide practical alternatives.

A national survey in the United States in 1991 found that of 65 babies abandoned at birth, eight died. In 1998 the number jumped to 105 abandoned babies, and 33 were found dead. As a result of increasing infant abandonment and infanticide, the majority of state legislatures have enacted safe haven laws. Beginning in Texas in 1999, 'Baby Moses laws' have been introduced as an incentive for mothers in crisis to safely relinquish their babies to designated locations where the babies are protected and provided with medical care until a permanent home is found. These laws generally allow the parent to remain anonymous and to be shielded from prosecution for abandonment or neglect in exchange for surrendering the baby to a safe haven.[142]

A service was introduced in Austria in 2001 that allows women to give birth in hospital secretly so the baby can be offered for adoption. The service allows the mother to give birth free of charge and without stating her identity. She can then disappear without fear of prosecution, and the child is kept safe for adoption. Another initiative in Austria that allows ➥

There are three possible alternatives for a woman with an unwanted pregnancy: abortion, adoption, and keeping the baby.

It is easy to understand why some young women see abortion as a quick fix when they find themselves unexpectedly pregnant. It is often presented as an uncomplicated and safe procedure; a simple matter of removing the 'tissue' that is causing the problems and voilà—your life is back on track.

Do we need to encourage women to put their children up for adoption more often? There are always good families wanting to adopt. This option allows the mother to continue on her life journey without the responsibility of caring for a child. Interestingly, one reason women don't give up their babies for adoption is that it would make them feel like a bad mother. Instead they choose abortion… which doesn't?

However, in some places the pressure to keep the child despite the difficulties is the reason adoption is uncommon. This can vary according to peer pressure. Many workers in the adoption field saw the 'Juno effect' after a movie depicting a teen adopting out her baby became a hit. The social influences that have changed attitudes

---

142. US Department of Health and Human Services, *Infant Safe Haven Laws: Summary of State Laws*, Child Welfare Information Gateway, Washington DC, 2010.

to adoption are complex.

However, if women are choosing abortion due to insufficient support, then being pro-life involves much more than being anti-abortion. If we really are serious about reducing the abortion rate then we need to show pregnant women a realistic, practical, reliable, available alternative to termination. The needs of a woman in this situation aren't hard to work out. Apart from spiritual, emotional and psychological encouragement, it is possible she may need a place to stay if those close to her disagree with her choice. She may need other practical assistance—the single mother's pension usually isn't available until after the birth in those countries where it exists, and many women are unable to keep working until then. How will she

mothers to leave their babies in a 'baby nest' at hospitals was also introduced to prevent deaths among abandoned babies.[143]

Amritsar's 'cradle scheme', as with many others in India, was established in 2008 to save unwanted babies. Mothers are able to anonymously leave newborns in a wicker basket at the Red Cross headquarters. In this part of northern India, gender discrimination has meant that the overwhelming majority of abandoned babies are girls. In some parts of the state, female babies are killed because they are considered by many to have lower economic, social and religious value than sons.[144]

manage to live with no income? This in itself is one reason some young women feel unable to cope with keeping the baby. They need clothes for the newborn, nursery furniture—all the paraphernalia of babies. This might be a good church project if there is a refuge for young pregnant girls near you. And everyone can do with a few meals dropped off when they have a new baby to manage.

Within the church we also need to think about creating an environment where single women are commended for keeping their babies and where single mothers are particularly supported. It has been suggested that the low rate of single mothers in our churches may not reflect sexual purity so much as the belief that proof you've been sexually active needs to be avoided at all costs. According to the Guttmacher Institute, two thirds of

143. Agence France Presse, 'Service aids women in secret births, adoptions', *Australian Doctor*, 8 June 2001.

144. M Wade, 'India's boy craze: From the cradle to a grave future', *Sydney Morning Herald*, 23 October 2010.

women in the United States who have abortions identify themselves as Christian.[145] We need to develop a culture where those brave repentant girls who take responsibility for an unborn child are forgiven for their mistakes and praised for their choice and given all the help a sister would expect from her family at such a time. Mary the mother of Jesus was a young unwed mother in a culture where it was far less acceptable than in ours.

Why is an unplanned pregnancy so often seen as a woman's problem? Apart from the obvious reason, it is often because the child's father refuses to stand by the mother. Christians need to take the lead in recognizing the importance of male responsibility and support, and commending those who live it out.

The take-home message is this: if we want to dissuade women from choosing abortion, we need to make sure there *is* a choice available, and one that they find out about before it is too late. The right to choose abortion has been won; the right to choose the opposite too often appears absent.

For healthcare professionals

In many countries it is possible to arrange sessions of non-directive pregnancy support counselling by eligible practitioners for any woman concerned about a pregnancy. Partners may also attend. The provider may be a GP, psychologist, social worker or mental health nurse. In Australia there is a government (Medicare) rebate for such counselling. The organization Real Choices Australia can you put you in touch with local services. In the United Kingdom, organizations such as CareConfidential can provide support. In North America, there are many pro-life organizations such as Care Net, Heartbeat International and Birthright International. Healthcare professionals should familiarize themselves with the relevant organizations in their area so they can

---

145. Almost three quarters of women obtaining abortions in 2008 reported a religious affiliation. The largest proportion was Protestant (37%), and most of the rest said that they were Catholic (28%) or that they had no religious affiliation (27%). One in five abortion patients identified themselves as born-again, evangelical, charismatic or fundamentalist. See RK Jones, LB Finer and S Singh, *Characteristics of US abortion patients*, 2008, Guttmacher Institute, New York, May 2010.

make suggestions if asked. Christians in the relevant professions should think about training for this kind of work. Training in counselling aims to prevent bias in the provision of information and facilitate the patient's own decision-making rather than attempt to give them solutions.

Case 2: A 27-year-old woman wants an abortion for a pregnancy that is the result of a sexual assault

Rape is an extremely traumatic experience for women. Care of the woman in crisis needs to be multi-dimensional, and this cannot be fully addressed here.

The pregnancy rate following rape is unclear. While many authors cite around 5%, it is well known that rape is under-reported so it is very hard to know exactly. Certainly it is uncommon. However, that is no comfort to the rape victim who discovers she is pregnant.

In the case of rape, the wrongdoer is the rapist. He is the one who should be punished. The child conceived in the rape is innocent. While the woman involved has been wronged, abortion means that further injustice is perpetrated by punishing the innocent child. The Bible teaches the idea of personal accountability where punishment is concerned. In Deuteronomy 24:16 God commands that "Fathers shall not be put to death because of their children, nor shall children be put to death because of their fathers. Each one shall be put to death for his own sin". Wronging the unborn child does not make right the violation of the mother.

Furthermore, rape does not change the moral significance of the unborn child, and therefore it is not a justification for abortion. The unborn child is still a human being made in the image of God who should not be killed (Exod 20:13).

There has been little research done on the effect of abortion after rape. There is no evidence that abortion helps the woman recover from her ordeal, and some evidence that it may have an overall negative effect.[146] One study found that none of the women subjects who continued a pregnancy following rape regretted their choice.[147] Obviously the woman

---

146. Ewing, op cit., p. 12.

147. DC Reardon, J Makimaa and A Sobie (eds.), *Victims and Victors*, Acorn Books, Brunswick, 2000.

who makes such a choice will need an enormous amount of spiritual, emotional and practical support. This is a challenge for the church.

Case 3: A 38-year-old woman is 11 weeks pregnant when she is found to have breast cancer; she is told her best chance of survival requires that she undergo chemotherapy after having an abortion

As mentioned previously, abortion on genuine grounds of maternal health is in reality a very small number. Most medical 'indications' for abortion (such as cancer and severe autoimmune disease) can be managed during pregnancy. In this actual case, chemotherapy (adriamycin and cytoxan) was given during pregnancy with no ill effects for the child and no increased cancer risk to the mother.

If the unborn child were viable at the stage where risk to maternal health developed, early induction of pregnancy or caesarean section would be appropriate. Should the fetus's viability be in question when the mother's life is at risk, it is still ethically appropriate to attempt early delivery as it means the mother's life will be saved and an attempt is also made to save the baby. If the mother dies, the baby will not survive anyway. Occasionally the mother will be able to be kept alive on life support until viability is reached (e.g. with brain injury).

While this may sound straightforward, it is not always easy to determine viability. While babies *have* survived from as early as 22 weeks gestation, this is rare (which is why it gets into the news).[148] Survival rate at 23 weeks is 30%, at 24 weeks is 60% and at 25 weeks is 80%; and the survivors will most likely have substantial health problems and disability. It is not always a question of the gestation either. Survival among infants with a birth weight of less than 500g is rare. This is a difficult assessment that needs to be made on an individual basis.

Experienced Christian neonatologist Professor John Wyatt of the United Kingdom has watched many tiny frail bodies in his care struggle desperately for life. He has noted, "Treating babies with respect does not mean that we are obliged to provide intensive treatment in every conceivable condition, to attempt to prolong life even when there

---

148. A Florida IVF baby who was born at 21 weeks and 6 days survived and was released from hospital with an 'excellent' prognosis in February 2007. She overcame many medical problems to reach that point. See A Cable, 'The tiniest survivor: How the "miracle" baby born two weeks before the legal abortion limit clung to life against all odds', *Daily Mail*, 22 May 2008.

is no prospect of recovery".[149] Those of us who care for the dying are familiar with the idea that we think in terms of whether a treatment is worthwhile—not whether a life is worthwhile. Every human life is precious. But as a baby's chance of survival decreases, the importance of the health of the mother increases in our equation as we decide what needs to be done.

For doctors

Research suggests that improvements in survival and reductions in morbidity for babies born between 23-25 weeks may have reached a limit. The above figures come from tertiary nurseries in the United States and the United Kingdom, however mortality rates are known to vary among neonatal intensive care units even when similar care practices are in place. Local statistics are therefore preferred when counselling patients. Most units would resuscitate some babies at 23 weeks and most at 24 weeks, depending on the child's condition at birth. Preterm infants are at risk for specific diseases related to the immaturity of the body's organs and influenced by the cause and circumstances of the preterm birth. Basically, the frequency of short-term major morbidity increases as the gestational age decreases, especially under 30 weeks. Long-term problems such as chronic lung disease, cerebral palsy, vision and hearing impairment, and reduced cognitive and motor performance are especially increased in those born under 26 weeks. In a 2005 United Kingdom study, 78% of 308 survivors born at less than 25 weeks were followed and almost all of them had some kind of disability at the age of 6 years. Having said that, according to some experts, healthcare workers regularly overestimate the likelihood and severity of neurologic morbidity in preterm infants.[150] It is a difficult and distressing call to make, and expert opinion is recommended.

The take-home message is that maternal illness can often be treated while the pregnancy continues, and abortion should be the last resort.

---

149.   J Wyatt, *Matters of Life and Death*, 2nd edn, IVP, Leicester, 2009, p. 183.

150.   JD Iams and R Romero, 'Preterm Birth', in SG Gabbe, JR Niebyl and JL Simpson (eds), *Obstetrics*, 5th edn, Churchill Livingstone, Philadelphia, 2007, pp. 668-712.

However, the woman in case 3 above had to shop around to find a doctor who was willing to treat her while she continued her pregnancy.

According to Planned Parenthood, "everyone had the right to choose when or whether to have a child… every child should be wanted and loved, and… women should be in charge of their own destinies".[151]

Case 4: Abortion for fetal abnormality

As previously mentioned, this is a growing trend in our community. For further discussion of this complex topic, see chapter 9.

I have been discussing right and wrong from a Christian perspective. As we live in a world where elective abortion is almost universally socially acceptable, there will be many around us who will make choices with which we will not agree. While I advocate encouraging a couple to continue with a pregnancy they do not want, I am conscious that this is an act one cannot demand of another even if we think it is the right thing to do. And so my last suggestion is that whatever our friends or patients may decide, we endeavour to maintain our relationships with them so that we may be able to support them in the grief that ensues, and be witnesses to a loving God who forgives the repentant sinner.

I finish this chapter with the words of Pope John Paul II:

> I would now like to say a special word to women who have had an abortion. The Church is aware of the many factors which may have influenced your decision, and she does not doubt that in many cases it was a painful and even shattering decision. The wound in your heart may not yet have healed. Certainly what happened was and remains terribly wrong. But do not give in to discouragement and do not lose hope. Try rather to understand what happened and face it honestly. If you have not already done so, give yourselves over with humility and trust to repentance.[152]

---

151.   Johnson and Lambert, op. cit., p. 42.

152.   Encyclical of John Paul II, *Evangelium Vitae: On the Value and Inviolability of Human Life*, Rome, 25 March 1995, paragraph 99.

Screening in normal pregnancy

T HERE WAS A TIME, now long gone, when pregnancy was a natural process that did not involve doctors and hospitals, ultrasounds and blood tests. Modern pregnancy is a technical affair, partly because we have discovered ways to keep the mother and baby safer during pregnancy and childbirth, and partly because we think we can control pregnancy to make sure we get the outcome we want. (It would be cynical to suggest it has anything to do with the fact that an obstetrician can be sued for malpractice up to 20 years after a birth.)

It is customary and right to want what is best for our offspring and to hope for a healthy child to be born. Love for the baby will usually mean that a mother will do her best to follow dietary and lifestyle advice to maximize her own health and the health of the child she is carrying. And by embracing modern medicine, we increase the likelihood of the best possible outcome through routine tests that aim to make sure we do all we can to keep mother and baby well. This is positive.

However, we now have an antenatal process that involves an increasing number of tests that not only check that the baby is *healthy*, but also that it is *normal*. These additional tests are slowly being adopted as part of routine antenatal care in industrialized countries, and there is no sign of the trend slowing down. This has occurred with virtually no community discussion as to whether this is the way we want pregnancy to be managed. Sometimes these tests for normality are done without the mother even realizing she is undergoing that kind of test. How can this be done, and what is the outcome of this change in direction?

Before we examine some of these more contentious issues, it is worth understanding the great benefits of good antenatal care in industrialized nations, and the nature of birth abnormalities. When we compare pregnancy outcomes for both mother and baby with those of developing nations, we soon realize that any improvement in obstetric care is a great blessing for which we should be truly thankful.

It can come as a shock to realize that, even today, pregnancy is not a risk-free enterprise. Over her lifetime, the risk of a woman dying as a result of pregnancy or childbirth is about 1 in 6 in the poorest parts of the world, compared to about 1 in 30,000 in northern Europe. Such a discrepancy poses a huge challenge to the United Nations in meeting the fifth Millennium Development Goal of reducing maternal mortality by 75% between 1990 and 2015.[1]

The global maternal mortality rate (MMR) decreased from 422 per 100,000 live births in 1980 to 320 in 1990 and 251 in 2008. More than 50% of all maternal deaths occurred in only 6 countries in 2008 (India, Nigeria, Pakistan, Afghanistan, Ethiopia and the Democratic Republic of the Congo).[2] Most deaths occurred around the time of the delivery.

However, this apparent improvement in MMR looks very different if we look at countries individually. In 2008, MMR was as follows:[3]

Country	MMR in 2008 (per 100,000 live births)	Country	MMR in 2008 (per 100,000 live births)
Australia	5[4]	France	10
Sweden	5	Singapore	16
Ireland	6	United States	17
Canada	7	Saudi Arabia	28

---

1.   C Ronsmans and WJ Graham, 'Maternal mortality: who, when, where, and why', *Lancet*, vol. 368, no. 9542, 30 September 2006, pp. 1189-1200.

2.   MC Hogan, KJ Foreman, M Naghavi, SY Ahn, M Wang, SM Makela, AD Lopez, R Lozano and CJL Murray, 'Maternal mortality for 181 countries, 1980-2008: a systematic analysis of progress towards Millennium Development Goal 5', *Lancet*, vol. 375, no. 9726, 8 May 2010, pp. 1609-23.

3.   ibid.

4.   In Australia, leading direct causes of maternal death were amniotic fluid embolism, thromboembolism and hypertension. Leading indirect causes of maternal death were cardiac disease, psychiatric-related causes and non-obstetric haemorrhage. See EA Sullivan, B Hall and JF King, *Maternal Deaths in Australia 2003-2005*, Maternal deaths series no. 3, cat. no. PER 42, AIHW, Canberra, 2008.

Germany	7	Ukraine	30
Japan	7	China	40
New Zealand	8	Fiji	85
United Kingdom	8	Afghanistan	1575
Denmark	9		

Congenital abnormalities (birth defects)

There have always been children born with abnormalities. Research suggests that 2%-4% of all children born worldwide have major congenital abnormalities. In Australia, not all conditions at birth are reported and recorded, but national reports suggest that an average of 1.6% of all children born in Australia have major congenital abnormalities.[5] Common abnormalities include hypospadias (an abnormality of the penis where the urethra opens on the underside), trisomy 21 (Down syndrome) and neural tube defects such as spina bifida.[6] A higher rate of congenital anomalies has been reported for births among Indigenous women compared to non-Indigenous women (356 per 10,000 births compared to 308 per 10,000 births).[7] These numbers are not static. In about 60% of cases, the cause of the congenital anomaly is unknown and is probably multifactorial.[8]

Data is being collected more carefully now as governments try to reduce the incidence of newborns affected by congenital abnormalities. Some initiatives involve prevention, such as encouraging women who are attempting to get pregnant to take folic acid tablets to prevent neural tube defects and congenital heart defects, and introducing the mandatory fortification of bread flour with folic acid. These are welcome interventions.

But in cases where we have no preventative strategy, the focus is now on prenatal diagnosis; the trouble is that we can now screen for more problems than there are treatments. This has led to a much more troubling outcome where abortion has become the dominant 'solution'

---

5.   S Abeywardana and EA Sullivan, *Congenital Anomalies in Australia 2002-2003*, Birth anomalies series no. 3, cat. no. PER 41, AIHW, Canberra, 2008.

6.   ibid., p. vi.

7.   ibid.

8.   F Al-Yaman, M Bryant and H Sargeant, *Australia's Children: Their Health and Wellbeing 2002*, AIHW cat. no. PHE 36, AIHW, Canberra, 2002, p. 103.

for these problems. Screening has now reached the point where even if we have do have a cure, it is still not enough; over 90% of pregnancies found to have abnormalities present proceed to termination. It seems as if the whole modern reproductive industry is aimed at making sure that only normal babies come to term.

What are we to do? Those couples who value human life from fertilization and who do not want to abort their child will need to become familiar with standard screening tests in pregnancy in order to decide which ones are desirable (to maximize health in the mother and baby) and which ones are not. If they are not prepared to terminate a pregnancy, they will have to ask whether there is any point in having tests to identify problems that can only be managed by termination.

Let's look first at the standard antenatal tests and their purpose, before moving on to discuss genetic testing and screening. (This chapter is not intended to be a comprehensive guide to medical care in pregnancy.)

What are the standard tests for a normal pregnancy?

The Royal Australian and New Zealand College of Obstetricians and Gynaecologists (RANZCOG) has a standard protocol for antenatal testing.[9] The initial tests are recommended before the woman becomes pregnant, because some intervention is best done at that stage. All of these recommended tests aim to improve outcomes for the mother and baby.

1. Pre-pregnancy clinical assessment

a. Rubella (German measles) immunity status

Rubella is a highly contagious, though usually mild, viral disease. Those affected may have a transient rash and enlarged lymph nodes (and occasionally more serious problems), but half the people affected have no symptoms at all; it is hard to know who has had it. Consequently, it is necessary to confirm previous infection by looking for protective

9.   The Royal Australian and New Zealand College of Obstetricians and Gynaecologists (RANZCOG), *Pre-pregnancy Counselling and Routine Antenatal Assessment in the Absence of Pregnancy Complications (C-Obs-3)*, College statement, RANZCOG, Melbourne, November 2009 (viewed 19 December 2011): www.ranzcog.edu.au/component/content/article/503-c-obs/283-pre-pregnancy-counselling-routine-antenatal-assessment-c-obs-3.html

levels of antibodies in the blood.[10] Although it is a mild illness when it occurs in adults, if a woman contracts a rubella infection in the first 8-10 weeks of pregnancy, it can infect the baby, resulting in congenital rubella syndrome (CRS) in 90% of affected pregnancies.[11] CRS causes multiple defects in the baby, including intellectual disabilities, cataracts, deafness, heart abnormalities, restricted growth and inflammatory lesions of the brain, liver, lungs and bone marrow. Infection of the baby after 8 weeks of pregnancy commonly results in deafness and progressive blindness.[12] It is rare for the baby to be damaged if the infection occurs after 10 weeks of pregnancy, although it has been reported after 20 weeks of gestation.[13]

There is no treatment for the disease. Prevention is the best strategy, and since the rubella vaccine was introduced, rubella infection (including congenital rubella) has fallen by 99.6%.[14] It is recommended that women of child-bearing age who are found to have no evidence of previous infection should be vaccinated (and avoid conception for one month after the injection), and be checked 8 weeks after vaccination to make sure they are covered. All women are advised to check their rubella levels before every planned pregnancy, regardless of any previous results.[15] Even when a pregnant woman has been vaccinated, it is still best to avoid people who have had rubella or been exposed to it, for 6 weeks from the time of the exposure.[16]

---

10. DL Heymann (ed.), 'Rubella (German Measles), Congenital Rubella (Congenital Rubella Syndrome)', in *Control of Communicable Diseases Manual*, 19th edn, American Public Health Association, Washington DC, 2008, pp. 529-34; S Reef, S Redd, E Abernathy and J Icenogle, 'Rubella', in Centers for Disease Control and Prevention (CDC), *Manual for the Surveillance of Vaccine-Preventable Disease*, 4th edn, CDC, Atlanta, 2008, chapter 14; CDC, *Epidemiology and Prevention of Vaccine-Preventable Diseases*, 12th edn, eds W Atkinson, S Wolfe and J Hamborsky, Public Health Foundation, Washington DC, 2011, pp. 275-89.

11. S Reef and S Redd, 'Congenital Rubella Syndrome', in CDC, *Manual for the Surveillance of Vaccine-Preventable Disease*, op. cit., chapter 15.

12. Heymann (ed.), loc. cit.

13. SA Plotkin and S Reef, 'Rubella vaccine', in SA Plotkin, WA Orenstein and PA Offit (eds), *Vaccines*, 5th edn, Saunders, Philadelphia, 2008, pp. 735-72.

14. LE Riley, 'Measles, mumps, varicella and parvovirus', in DK James, PJ Steer, CP Weiner and B Gonik (eds), *High Risk Pregnancy*, 3rd edn, Saunders, Philadelphia, 2006, pp. 636-8.

15. Plotkin and Reef, loc. cit.

16. Australian Government Department of Health and Ageing (AGDHA), 'Rubella', in *The Australian Immunisation Handbook*, section 3.19, 9th edn, Office of Health Protection, Canberra, 2008.

b. Varicella (chicken pox) immunity status

This test is recommended if the woman's immunity status is unknown and she does not know if she has had chicken pox. Varicella is another highly contagious viral infection. Once you've had it, it may reactivate later as herpes zoster (shingles). Varicella is usually a mild childhood disease, but in adults or in any person with lowered immunity it becomes a severe disease and may even be fatal. Varicella infection in pregnancy may result in congenital varicella syndrome, which can cause skin scarring, limb defects, eye abnormalities and malformations of the baby's neurological system. Unlike rubella (which is a risk only in the first trimester), there is a greater risk of the baby being damaged if maternal infection occurs in the second trimester, while intrauterine exposure during the third trimester poses the greatest risk of developing shingles in infancy.[17] Because of these serious potential dangers for the baby, a non-immune mother should be vaccinated before pregnancy to avoid infection during pregnancy.[18]

c. Cervical (Pap) smear

The cervical or Pap smear—named after Dr George Papanicolaou—is used to check for changes in the cervix (the neck of the womb) at the top of the vagina.[19] This is done to look for abnormalities that might develop into cervical cancer in the future. It is recommended that all pregnant women be offered a cervical smear if they have not had one performed within the previous two years (for women with no history of abnormal changes), or within the time specified for follow up (for women who have had abnormal changes in the past). If abnormal changes are found at screening, further tests will be done to see if treatment is needed.[20]

---

17.   CDC, *Epidemiology and Prevention of Vaccine-Preventable Diseases*, op. cit., pp. 301-24; M Marin, D Güris, SS Chaves, S Schmid, JF Seward and CDC, 'Prevention of varicella: Recommendations of the Advisory Committee on Immunization Practices (ACIP), *MMWR Recommendations and Reports*, vol. 56, no. RR-4, 22 June 2007, pp. 1-40.

18.   AGDHA, 'Varicella', in *The Australian Immunisation Handbook*, section 3.24, op. cit.

19.   GN Papanicolaou and HF Traut, 'The diagnostic value of vaginal smears in carcinoma of the uterus', *American Journal of Obstetrics and Gynecology*, vol. 42, no. 2, August 1941, pp. 193-206.

20.   AGDHA, *National Cervical Screening Program*, AGDHA, Canberra, 2009 (viewed 19 December 2011): www.health.gov.au/internet/screening/publishing.nsf/Content/ncsp-policies; National Health and Medical Research Council (NHMRC), *Screening to Prevent Cervical Cancer: Guidelines for the Management of Asymptomatic Women with Screen Detected Abnormalities*, NHMRC, Canberra, 2005.

2. The first antenatal visit in pregnancy

If the tests listed above have not been done just before the pregnancy, they should be done at the first antenatal visit (although vaccination should be postponed until after delivery if women are found to have had no previous exposure.)[21]

The following investigations are recommended as screening tests, to see if there are any relevant medical problems the doctor needs to know about to keep the mother and baby safe. By detecting disease before it causes symptoms, treatment can be started early to avoid, or minimize, complications for either mother or child. The doctor will take a detailed history and examine the mother at this time, and extra tests may be considered depending on the woman's medical history, her family history and whether she has been exposed to other infections that could cause harm to the baby. Most of the extra tests are blood tests and all are recommended to make the pregnancy safer.

In its principles of screening, the World Health Organization (WHO) expects that tests used for screening will: detect a disease when it is still asymptomatic; have a high sensitivity and specificity (few false positives and false negatives);[22] have an available treatment for the condition and evidence of an improved outcome with treatment; have acceptability among the general population; and be cost efficient.[23] The tests in this section all achieve these screening goals.

a. Full blood count

A full blood count (FBC)[24] is a very common test in medicine and it assesses the general health of the mother. An FBC not only tests for abnormalities of the blood, but it can also give an indication of disease present in other organs. It is repeated at 28 weeks of pregnancy. A full blood count includes the following:

- Measurement of haemoglobin (which carries oxygen) in the blood. If anaemia is detected, further investigation is warranted to

---

21. LE Riley, *Rubella in Pregnancy*, UpToDate, Waltham MA, 7 June 2010 (viewed 19 December 2011): www.uptodate.com/contents/rubella-in-pregnancy (subscription based)

22. A false negative test result indicates no abnormality when there really is one; a false positive result indicates an abnormality when there really isn't one.

23. JMG Wilson and G Jungner, 'Principles and Practice of screening for disease', *WHO Chronicle*, vol. 22, no. 11, 1968, p. 473.

24. Also known as full blood examination (FBE), complete blood count (CBC), blood cell profile, blood count, haemogram.

discover the cause. Anaemia can make women tired and faint, and can put them at increased risk of infection and maternal mortality. Iron deficiency anaemia in pregnancy is a risk factor for preterm delivery and subsequent low birth weight, and possibly for inferior neonatal health. (Iron supplementation for pregnant women who are not iron deficient is controversial.)[25]

- Close analysis of red blood cells; this also helps to diagnose the cause of anaemia, if it is present.
- Measurement of white blood cells (WBCs). These are an important part of the body's immune system, which fights infection.
- Measurement of platelets in the blood. Platelets are part of the blood clotting system of the body.[26]

b. Blood group and antibody screen

This screening determines the mother's blood group and detects the presence of antibodies. This is done at the first visit for all women, and then again at 28 weeks for Rhesus (Rh) negative women only, to check for 'public antibodies'.[27] It is used, in particular, to identify those that have potential for causing a reaction in the baby's blood at birth, known as haemolytic disease of the newborn (HDN).[28] Commonly, the mother is stimulated to produce these antibodies through blood transfusion, bleeding associated with delivery, trauma, miscarriage, induced abortion, ectopic pregnancy or invasive obstetric procedures. Any fetal red blood cells that cross the placenta into the mother's bloodstream and are incompatible with the maternal blood group have the potential to stimulate the mother to produce antibodies against the baby's red blood cells. These antibodies can then cross the placenta into the baby's bloodstream and begin to attack the baby's red blood cells, which can result in the fetus becoming anaemic, with potentially disastrous consequences such as neurologic injury or death. It is most commonly an issue of incompatibility between the (Rh negative) mother's blood

25. J Strong, 'Anaemia and white blood cell disorders', in James et al. (eds), op. cit., pp. 867-9; IR Mabry-Hernandez, 'Screening for iron deficiency anemia—including iron supplementation for children and pregnant women', American Family Physician, vol. 79, no. 10, 15 May 2009, pp. 897-8.
26. RANZCOG, loc. cit.
27. Rhesus status is part of your blood type.
28. L Dean, Blood Groups and Red Cell Antigens, National Center for Biotechnology Information, Bethesda, 2005, chapter 4.

and the (Rh positive) baby's. In order to prevent the development of these destructive antibodies in the mother, Rh-negative women may require the administration of RhD-Ig antibodies both during pregnancy and after delivery.[29]

c. Syphilis serology

Syphilis is an infectious disease caused by the bacterium *treponema pallidum*. It is a treatable disease primarily transmitted through direct sexual contact, although it can also be transmitted from mother to child via the placenta during pregnancy and during childbirth. Pregnant women with untreated early syphilis can transmit the infection to their baby, resulting in miscarriage, stillbirth (25% of pregnancies), neonatal death (14% of pregnancies), premature birth, low birth weight or congenitally infected infants.[30]

All women should be tested once for syphilis during the first trimester of each pregnancy. Women at risk of acquiring (or reacquiring) syphilis should have a further test in the third trimester (preferably at 28-30 weeks) and at delivery. Untreated maternal infection in the first trimester is more likely to affect the baby. The infected mother can be treated with antibiotics appropriate to the stage of syphilis infection and thus avoid effects on the baby.[31]

d. Midstream urine (MSU)

Due to the body changes that occur during pregnancy, up to 10% of pregnant women develop bacteria in the urine. This can be confirmed in urine specimens. The primary complication of this condition is cystitis (bladder infection). If left untreated, this may cause an infection of the kidneys (pyelonephritis) in 25%-30% of cases.[32] There is an association

---

29. ibid.
30. World Health Organization (WHO), *Sexually Transmitted Infections*, fact sheet no. 110, WHO, Geneva, August 2011 (viewed 19 December 2011): www.who.int/mediacentre/factsheets/fs110/en; Western Australian Department of Health, *Guidelines for Managing Sexually Transmitted Infections*, section 2.7.9, WA Health, Shenton Park, 2010 (viewed 19 December 2011): www.silverbook.health.wa.gov.au/Default.asp?PublicationID=1&SectionID=148
31. A Daley and L Gilbert, 'Treponema pallidum (Syphilis)', in P Palasanthiran, M Starr and C Jones (eds), *Management of Perinatal Infections*, Australasian Society for Infectious Disease (ASID), Sydney, 2002, pp. 42-4.
32. EK Johnson and JS Wolf Jr, *Urinary Tract Infections in Pregnancy*, WebMD, New York, 2011 (viewed 19 December 2011): http://emedicine.medscape.com/article/452604-overview

between pyelonephritis and low birth weight, prematurity and death in the baby.[33] Antibiotic treatment can significantly reduce the risk of these complications.[34]

e. Human immunodeficiency virus (HIV)

The *human immunodeficiency virus* (HIV) causes acquired immune deficiency syndrome (AIDS) by infecting and damaging helper T cells, which are an important part of the body's defences against infection. Internationally, HIV/AIDS remains a leading cause of illness and death in pregnancy. Mother-to-child transmission is the most common cause of HIV infection in children worldwide. Infection can occur during pregnancy, during labour and delivery, and during breastfeeding, and it is almost entirely preventable. Treatment of the mother through medication (antiretroviral therapy), delivery by caesarean section, and the avoidance of breastfeeding reduces the rate of transmission to the child from around up to 45% to less than 5%.[35]

The Centers for Disease Control and Prevention (CDC) in the United States recommend that HIV testing be part of the routine screening for all pregnant women because reproductive-aged women make up the fastest-growing group with new HIV infections, usually acquired through sexual contact. The recommendation is for testing at the beginning of pregnancy and again at 28 weeks, regardless of perceived risk.[36] Screening for HIV is not routine in all Australian states, despite the recommendations of both the national HIV testing policy and RANZCOG that all pregnant women should be offered HIV screening at the first antenatal visit.[37] Informed

---

33. RL Sweet and RS Gibbs, *Infectious Diseases of the Female Genital Tract*, 5th edn, Lippincott Williams and Wilkins, Philadelphia, 2009, p. 256.

34. TM Hooton, *Urinary Tract Infections and Asymptomatic Bacteriuria in Pregnancy*, UpToDate, Waltham MA, 21 May 2012 (viewed 25 June 2012): www.uptodate.com/contents/urinary-tract-infections-and-asymptomatic-bacteriuria-in-pregnancy (subscription based)

35. WHO, *Mother-to-Child Transmission of HIV*, WHO, Geneva, 2011 (viewed 19 December 2011): www.who.int/hiv/topics/mtct/en

36. DH Watts, 'Human immunodeficiency virus', in James et al. (eds), op. cit., pp. 620-21.

37. Joint Ministerial Advisory Committee on AIDS, Sexual Health and Hepatitis and Intergovernmental Commmittee on AIDS, Hepatitis and Related Diseases HIV Testing Policy Steering Group, *National HIV Testing Policy 2006*, F Bowden and K Stewart (chairs), AGDHA, Canberra, 2006; ML Giles, A Pedrana, C Jones, S Garland, M Hellard and SR Lewin, 'Antenatal screening practice for infectious diseases by general practitioners in Australia', *Australian and New Zealand Journal of Obstetrics and Gynaecology*, vol. 49, no. 1, February 2009, pp. 39-44.

consent ideally should be obtained from the woman prior to appropriate counselling and testing.[38]

f. Hepatitis B serology

Hepatitis B (HBV) is also a blood-borne viral infection, and is symptomatic in 30%-50% of adults.[39] There are more than 350 million HBV carriers worldwide, of whom one million die annually from liver disease.[40] Mothers with chronic infection (carriers) have higher rates of preterm deliveries, premature rupture of membranes, placental abruption, labour induction and caesarean deliveries, and there is a greater risk of death, congenital malformations and low birth weight in their newborns.[41]

It is critical to identify HBV carriers because of the opportunity to provide almost complete protection against infection to the baby. Transmission of HBV from infected mother to newborn usually occurs at, or around, the time of birth. Around 90% of babies infected as newborns, although usually remaining asymptomatic, develop chronic HBV infection and are capable of transmitting the disease for years, or for life. Significantly, more than 25% of these infants develop chronic active hepatitis B and up to 25% die prematurely. Prevention of transmission from a carrier mother to her child can be achieved by adjusting labour management (no fetal scalp electrode, no fetal blood sampling), routinely giving newborns immunoglobulin as soon as possible after birth, and beginning a course of vaccination.[42]

g. Hepatitis C serology

As with hepatitis B infection, infection with hepatitis C virus (HCV) has implications for both mother's and baby's health. Chronic infection

---

38. BM Branson, HH Handsfield, MA Lampe, RS Janssen, AW Taylor, SB Lyss, JE Clark and CDC, 'Revised recommendations for HIV testing of adults, adolescents, and pregnant women in health-care settings', *MMWR Recommendations and Reports*, vol. 55, no. RR-14, 22 September 2006, pp. 1-17.

39. Heymann (ed.), 'Hepatitis viral', in *Control of Communicable Diseases Manual*, op. cit., pp. 295-7.

40. A Mellor, 'Routine antenatal screening', *Obstetrics and Gynaecology Magazine*, vol. 11, no. 2, Winter 2009, pp. 13-15.

41. A Safir, A Levy, E Sikuler and E Sheiner, 'Maternal hepatitis B virus or hepatitis C virus carrier status as an independent risk factor for adverse perinatal outcome', *Liver International*, vol. 30, no. 5, May 2010, pp. 765-70.

42. AGDHA, 'Hepatitis B', in *The Australian Immunisation Handbook*, section 3.6, op. cit.; CR MacIntyre, 'Hepatitis B vaccine: risks and benefits of universal neonatal vaccination', *Journal of Paediatrics and Child Health*, vol. 37, no. 3, June 2001, pp. 215-17.

can result in the development of liver cirrhosis, or liver cancer, later in life.[43] The risk of an infected mother passing on hepatitis C to her baby during pregnancy and birth is related to the amount of virus in her blood. At present no drug therapies can be recommended to reduce the risk of mother-to-child transmission. Unlike HBV infection, no specific intervention at the time of delivery has been shown to reduce the risk of transmission to the baby.[44]

Advice varies regarding whether all pregnant women should have hepatitis C screening in pregnancy.[45]

h. Routine antenatal ultrasound

The place of ultrasound is controversial.[46] In Australia, it is recommended that all women be offered an obstetric ultrasound prior to 20 weeks in order to facilitate a safe delivery. This replaces the x-ray that used to be done (x-rays can be dangerous for the unborn).

During the first trimester—defined as the first 13 weeks of pregnancy— an ultrasound is often performed between 8-11 weeks gestation to check how many weeks pregnant the woman is, usually measuring crown-rump length (CRL). It is also used to check for placental position, multiple pregnancy and the baby's growth and development.[47] The main aim of these observations is to make sure that the baby will be born without problems and, as such, it is a reasonable thing to do (for example, sometimes there may be reason why a caesarean is safer than a vaginal delivery).

Note that we are discussing *routine* antenatal screening here, which should be done when everything appears to be normal. If a specific problem is identified, the benefit versus risk ratio changes, and it may be safest for extra ultrasounds to be done to check that the baby is safe.

However, in their guidelines on routine ultrasound in low-risk

---

43. Heymann (ed.), 'Hepatitis viral', loc. cit.
44. Hepatitis C Subcommittee of the Ministerial Advisory Committee on AIDS, Sexual Health and Hepatitis and Blood Borne Virus and Sexually Transmissible Infections Subcommittee of the Australian Population Health Development Committee, *National Hepatitis C Testing Policy*, AGDHA, Canberra, May 2007.
45. RANZCOG, loc cit.; Giles et al., loc. cit.; Hepatitis C Subcommittee and Blood Borne Virus and STIs Subcommittee, loc. cit.
46. SJ Buckley, 'Ultrasound: not so safe and sound', *Nexus*, vol. 9, no. 6, October-November 2002.
47. RANZCOG, loc. cit.

pregnancy, the American College of Obstetricians and Gynecologists (ACOG) concludes:

> In a population of women with low-risk pregnancies, neither a reduction in perinatal morbidity (harm to babies around the time of birth) and mortality (death) nor a lower rate of unnecessary interventions can be expected from routine diagnostic ultrasound. Thus ultrasound should be performed for specific indications in low-risk pregnancy.[48]

Current research suggests that screening by ultrasound in early pregnancy improves the early detection of multiple pregnancies and improves estimates of how many weeks pregnant the woman is, but does not reduce adverse outcomes for babies.[49]

Other ways in which ultrasound is used are documented below.

i. Gestational diabetes (GDM)

It is recommended that all pregnant women be screened for gestational diabetes (diabetes of pregnancy).[50] Blood screening is generally performed at 26-28 weeks of gestation, or at any stage if symptoms develop. The Glucose Challenge Test (GCT) is performed, followed by the Fasting Glucose Tolerance Test if the GCT is abnormal.[51]

Primary outcomes of GDM include serious perinatal complications (such as death, shoulder dystocia, bone fracture and nerve palsy), admission to the neonatal nursery, jaundice requiring phototherapy, induction of labour, caesarean birth, and maternal anxiety and depression. Treatment of GDM reduces serious perinatal morbidity and may also improve the woman's health-related quality of life.[52]

---

48. American College of Obstetricians and Gynecologists (ACOG), *Routine Ultrasound in Low-Risk Pregnancy*, practice pattern no. 5, ACOG, Washington DC, August 1997.

49. M Whitworth, L Bricker, JP Neilson and T Dowswell, 'Ultrasound for fetal assessment in early pregnancy', *Cochrane Database of Systematic Reviews 2010*, no. 4, 14 April 2010.

50. NW Cheung, JN Oats and HD McIntyre, 'Australian carbohydrate intolerance study in pregnant women: implications for the management of gestational diabetes', *Australian and New Zealand Journal of Obstetrics and Gynaecology*, vol. 45, no. 6, December 2005, pp. 484-5.

51. RANZCOG, *Diagnosis of Gestational Diabetes Mellitus (C-Obs 7)*, College statement, RANZCOG, Melbourne, November 2011 (viewed 19 December 2011): www.ranzcog.edu. au/component/content/article/503-c-obs/417--diagnosis-of-gestational-diabetes-mellitus-c-obs-7.html

52. CA Crowther, JE Hiller, JR Moss, AJ McPhee, WS Jeffries and JS Robinson, 'Effect of treatment of gestational diabetes mellitus on pregnancy outcomes', *New England Journal of Medicine*, vol. 352, no. 24, 16 June 2005, pp. 2477-86.

j. Group B streptococcal disease (GBS)

GBS bacteria are recognized as a major cause of serious newborn infection. About one in 2000 newborn babies have GBS bacterial infections, usually presenting at birth or within 24-48 hours of birth. The baby contracts the infection from the asymptomatic mother during labour and delivery.[53] It is recommended that prenatal screening be performed at 35-37 weeks of gestation.[54] Preventative antibiotics are commonly given to 'at risk' women during labour to reduce the incidence of this disease.[55]

k. Other tests

Other tests that can be considered for women who have risk factors, but which are not included in routine screening, include:
- testing for vitamin D deficiency
- screening for abnormalities of haemoglobin, such as thalassaemia
- checking blood for exposure to cytomegalovirus (CMV) and toxoplasmosis viral infections
- checking for chlamydia infection
- testing thyroid function.

Summary

All the tests listed above are recommended in a normal pregnancy to maximize health outcomes for mother and child. As a result of these tests:
- treating the infection can prevent intrauterine infection (syphilis)
- immunization can avoid the infection (rubella)
- treating the infection can prevent complications (urinary tract infection)
- treating the deficit can prevent complications (anaemia)
- changing aspects of care can avoid infection of the baby (HBV).

---

53. Heymann (ed.), 'Group B Streptococcal Sepsis of the Newborn', in *Control of Communicable Diseases Manual*, op. cit., pp. 585-7.

54. RANZCOG, *Screening and Treatment for Group B Streptococcus in Pregnancy (C-Obs 19)*, College statement, RANZCOG, Melbourne, July 2011 (viewed 19 December 2011): www.ranzcog.edu.au/component/content/article/503-c-obs/414--screening-and-treatment-for-group-b-streptococcus-in-pregnancy-c-obs-19.html

55. A Ohlsson and VS Shah, 'Intrapartum antibiotics for known maternal Group B streptococcal colonization', *Cochrane Database of Systematic Reviews 2009*, no. 3, 8 July 2009; SM Garland and M Starr, 'Streptococcus, group B', in Palasanthiran et al. (eds), op. cit., pp. 36-8.

There are no ethical problems with this approach. It is an appropriate use of medical knowledge to identify and manage any health problems before they have a negative impact on the pregnancy. These screening tests meet the requirements of the WHO guidelines.

Prenatal genetic testing

In a world where we are used to being in control of all areas of our lives, there have been moves to influence pregnancy outcomes to make sure we have perfect babies. But there's a problem: there is no test that guarantees a healthy, normal baby.

Screening during pregnancy is done to assess the *risk factors* associated with having a baby with a chromosomal (genetic) or structural abnormality. Particularly if a woman is over 35 years old or has a family history of a genetic disease (i.e. one that is passed down through families), she may seek or be offered prenatal genetic testing for the baby.

Prenatal screening early in the pregnancy can sometimes be presented to women as routine, rather than as a choice (which in fact it is). Some doctors may not explain the screening fully because they feel uncomfortable asking women what they will do if the baby has an abnormality (e.g. "Do you want to terminate the pregnancy?"), while many doctors think early testing is beneficial as it allows couples with affected pregnancies to have more time to decide what to do. Research has shown, though, that many couples are not aware of the purpose for screening and its limitations, and so are unprepared when they receive bad news about the baby.[56]

All screening tests have limitations. They do not definitely show whether a baby *will* have a problem, nor do they identify every pregnancy that *does* have a problem (i.e. they can give a false negative test result); and they may identify an unaffected pregnancy as being at risk when in fact there isn't a problem (i.e. they can give a false positive test result).[57] Most babies assessed as having an increased risk will be normal and

56. J Garcia, L Bricker, J Henderson, M Martin, M Mugford, J Nielson and T Roberts, 'Women's views of pregnancy ultrasound: A systematic review', *Birth*, vol. 29, no. 4, December 2002, p. 225-50.
57. As mentioned earlier, a false negative test result indicates no abnormality when there really is one; a false positive result indicates an abnormality when there really isn't one.

healthy.[58] These are not precise tests.

Another concern with this testing is that we can test for a lot more problems than we have treatments, and often the only way to 'solve' the problem of an abnormality is termination of the pregnancy.[59] Genetic testing should always be preceded by counselling; this allows the parents to decide which tests, if any, are best for mother and child. Different tests are done depending on the stage of the pregnancy.

I do not want to imply that all women walk ignorantly into prenatal screening without any idea of what they are doing. For some it is an active decision. Connie, who has a family history of a bleeding disorder, said: *It's easy to say you shouldn't screen if your family isn't affected by genetic disease, but if you are, why would you leave something like this completely to chance?* If you think this world is all there is, it's a completely understandable choice.

One test is an exception, in that it claims to give a definite result—the newly developed test that determines the fetal gender as early as 7 weeks (though it is more reliable later on). This test analyses DNA found in the mother's blood and may be used to identify gender-linked genetic disorders, in order to terminate affected pregnancies early.[60]

Once a risk is identified with these tests, only affected couples are offered further *diagnostic* tests, because the diagnosis of problems involves tests that carry a risk of miscarriage even if the baby is completely normal. Counselling should be offered here, too. If an

58.   C Gaff, J Newstead and M Saleh, 'Testing and Pregnancy', in Genetics Education in Medicine Consortium, *Genetics in Family Medicine*, Biotechnology Australia, Canberra, 2007.

59.   WHO, *Sickle-cell Disease and Other Haemoglobin Disorders*, fact sheet no. 308, WHO, Geneva, January 2011 (viewed 19 December 2011): www.who.int/mediacentre/factsheets/fs308/en; E Dormandy, M Gulliford, S Bryan, TE Roberts, M Calnan, K Atkin, J Karnon, J Logan, F Kavalier, HJ Harris, TA Johnston, EN Anionwu, V Tsianakas, P Jones and TM Marteauik, 'Effectiveness of earlier antenatal screening for sickle cell disease and thalassaemia in primary care: cluster randomised trial', *British Medical Journal*, vol. 341, no. 7779, 30 October 2010, c5132; V Tsianakas, M Calnan, K Atkin, E Dormandy and TM Marteau, 'Offering antenatal sickle cell and thalassaemia screening to pregnant women in primary care: a qualitative study of GPs' experiences', *British Journal of General Practice*, vol. 60, no. 580, November 2010, pp. 822-8.

60.   SA Devaney, GE Palomaki, JA Scott and DW Bianchi, 'Noninvasive fetal sex determination using cell-free fetal DNA: A systematic review and meta-analysis', *Journal of the American Medical Association*, vol. 306, no. 6, 10 August 2011, pp. 627-36.

abnormality is diagnosed, a couple needs time to consider the diagnosis and make decisions. The tests may be used to plan the management of the pregnancy and delivery, to prepare for the care of a child with special needs, to plan for the adoption of the baby, or to enable parents to decide whether they want to continue with the pregnancy.[61]

The WHO's principles of screening should be followed for these screening tests as well.

Let's see how these tests measure up. A discussion of the ethics of these tests will follow an outline of what is involved.[62]

1. First trimester

a. Obstetric first-trimester ultrasound scan

As explained above, RANZCOG recommends that all women should be offered an obstetric ultrasound before 20 weeks of gestation to check that the baby will be born without problems. This is an ethical and responsible thing to do within our current technological abilities, but it is not what is being discussed here. Because the best time to date the pregnancy and check the number of babies is between 8-12 weeks, a first-trimester scan is often done for these reasons. But a practice has developed where other features of the baby may be examined at the same time, to look for abnormalities.

b. Nuchal translucency (NT) screening test

This is an ultrasound that examines a fluid-filled space at the back of a baby's neck (described as nuchal translucency) and measures its depth. This test is normally carried out between 11½-13½ weeks. Marketing claims the test finds "all chromosome anomalies", especially trisomies 13, 18 and 21 (Down syndrome).[63] Trisomies 13 and 18 are usually associated with structural anomalies found at the morphology scan (18-20 weeks).

The NT test examines the collection of fluid within the skin at the back of the fetal neck observed between 10-14 weeks gestation. The NT peaks at 12-13 weeks and often disappears by 15 weeks. An increased NT (greater than 3 mm at 10-12 weeks) was first shown to be associated with

---

61. D Tapon, 'Prenatal testing for Down syndrome: comparison of screening practices in the UK and USA', *Journal of Genetic Counseling*, vol. 19, no. 2, April 2010, pp. 112-30.
62. For an introduction to genetics, see the beginning of appendix III.
63. Pregnancies with the other autosomal trisomies do not survive.

Down syndrome in 1989.[64] Using a standardized protocol by appropriately trained staff, the detection rate for Down syndrome is up to 82% (being the probability of a probability). But there is a 1 in 20 chance that you will get a false positive result—that is, that the test will indicate a risk of Down syndrome when in fact the baby is normal (there is *always* a risk of Down syndrome until a direct gene test proves otherwise).[65] This can be pretty stressful, as it cannot be confirmed either way at this stage of the pregnancy. Ultrasound scanning is a user-dependent test, and a review of NT scan operators found that 45% of them were not performing it accurately.[66]

If the NT scan is performed alone without a blood test (see below), about 75% of babies who have Down syndrome will receive an increased risk result, so about 25% of Down syndrome babies will be missed. A 2005 study suggested that NT is insufficiently effective to justify doing it alone.[67]

Some studies show that pregnant women in industrialized countries expect to have the NT scan routinely, often with little understanding of what it means.[68]

c. First-trimester serum screening (FTSS)

In addition to ultrasound examination, blood tests can be used in the first trimester to identify babies with an increased likelihood of having

---

64. M Bronshtein, S Rottem, N Yoffe and Z Blumenfeld, 'First-trimester and early second-trimester diagnosis of nuchal cystic hygroma by transvaginal sonography: diverse prognosis of the septated from the nonseptated lesion', *American Journal of Obstetrics and Gynecology*, vol. 161, no. 1, July 1989, pp. 78-82.

65. RJM Snijders, EA Thom, JM Zachary, LD Platt, N Greene, LG Jackson, RE Sabbagha, K Filkins, RK Silver, WA Hogge, NA Ginsberg, S Beverly, P Morgan, K Blum, P Chilis, LM Hill, J Hecker and RJ Wapner, 'First-trimester trisomy screening: nuchal translucency measurement training and quality assurance to correct and unify technique', *Ultrasound in Obstetrics and Gynecology*, vol. 19, no. 4, 1 April 2002, pp. 353-9.

66. DL Nisbet, AC Robertson, PJ Schluter, AC McLennan and JA Hyett, 'Auditing ultrasound assessment of fetal nuchal translucency thickness: A review of Australian national data 2002-2008', *Australia and New Zealand Journal of Obstetrics and Gynaecology*, vol. 50, no. 5, 2010, pp. 450-5.

67. NJ Wald, C Rodeck, AK Hackshaw and A Rudnicka, 'SURUSS in perspective', *Seminars in Perinatology*, vol. 29, no. 4, August 2005, pp. 225-35.

68. H Gottfredsdóttir, J Sandall and K Björnsdóttir, '"This is just what you do when you are pregnant": a qualitative study of prospective parents in Iceland who accept nuchal translucency screening', *Midwifery*, vol. 25, no. 6, December 2009, pp. 711-20.

a chromosomal or structural abnormality. (These tests are not always available and may only be done in conjunction with the NT scan.) The levels of specific proteins in the mother's blood are measured.[69] These test results are combined with the result of the NT scan and the mother's age to provide information about the risk of chromosomal abnormalities.[70] They can also give the doctor information about increased risk of obstetric complications.[71]

For chromosomal anomalies, a low risk is considered to be less than 1 in 300, however the risk is still there; 'low risk' should not be confused with 'no risk'. About 5% of the women who have this test (1 in 20) as well as the NT scan will receive an increased risk result, but it is important to realize that most of these babies will not have a problem with their chromosomes.[72]

Other techniques to detect chromosomal abnormalities that have been recommended, but are not routine, include the ultrasound examination of the nasal bone and measurement of blood flow in the heart and the

---

69.   Some more technical details: FTSS measures pregnancy associated placental protein-A (PAPP-A) and maternal serum free beta subunit human chorionic gonadotropin (free β-hCG). PAPP-A is a protein produced by both the embryo and placenta during pregnancy. Whereas elevated levels of this marker are not associated with adverse obstetric outcomes, low levels are associated with spontaneous fetal loss at less than 24 weeks gestation, low birth weight, preeclampsia, gestational hypertension, preterm birth and stillbirth, preterm premature rupture of membranes and placental abruption.

Free β-hCG is a glycoprotein hormone produced during pregnancy by the developing embryo and later by the placenta. Low maternal serum levels of free β-hCG during the first trimester are associated with low birth weight and miscarriage.

An increased serum level of free β-hCG with decreased PAPP-A indicates an increased risk of trisomy 21, whereas low levels of both analytes indicate increased risk of trisomy 18. The combination of maternal age with the first-trimester markers NT, PAPP-A and free β-hCG increases the detection rate of trisomy 21 to around 80%-90%. The combined first-trimester screen (scan plus bloods) has a diagnosis rate of 90% and a false positive rate of 5%.

70.   KH Nicolaides, 'Screening for fetal aneuploidies at 11 to 13 weeks', *Prenatal Diagnosis*, vol. 31, no. 1, January 2011, pp. 7-15.

71.   L Dugoff, JC Hobbins, FD Malone, TF Porter, D Luthy, CH Comstock, G Hankins, RL Berkowitz, I Merkatz, SD Craigo, IE Timor-Tritsch, SR Carr, HM Wolfe, J Vidaver and ME D'Alton, 'First-trimester maternal serum PAPP-A and free-beta subunit human chorionic gonadotropin concentrations and nuchal translucency are associated with obstetric complications: A population-based screening study (The FASTER Trial)', *American Journal of Obstetrics and Gynecology*, vol. 191, no. 4, 2004, pp. 1446-51.

72.   K Barlow-Stewart and G Parasivam (eds), *The Australasian Genetics Resource Book*, 8th edn, The Centre for Genetics Education, St Leonards, 2007.

liver (for increased detection of Down syndrome).[73]

In October 2011, a new blood test was released that checks fetal DNA in the mother's blood to detect Down syndrome. A published study indicates this test has a lower false negative rate than previously available tests (it picked up 98.6% of children with Down syndrome in the study), and a false positive rate of only 0.2% (it gave a result of Down syndrome for 0.2% of the children who were normal).[74] The test's authors see this as an advantage as it means fewer women will need to have the invasive tests (see below) that currently are required to definitely diagnose the syndrome. The test can be used as early as 10 weeks into a pregnancy and will cost about US$1900, although it will be considerably less if health insurers decide to cover it. At the time of writing, it has not been approved by the FDA.

Neural tube defects occur in about one in 800 babies. The risk is increased if there is a family history of neural tube defects, or the mother has insulin-dependent diabetes or is taking medicine for epilepsy. The most common types are anencephaly (the brain is undeveloped and the baby cannot survive long after birth) and spina bifida (an opening on the baby's spine that exposes the spinal cord and can cause paralysis and other problems.)

Surgery during pregnancy to ➥

2. Second trimester

a. Second-trimester screening scan/fetal anomaly ultrasound/morphology scan

The second-trimester screening ultrasound, usually performed between 18-20 weeks gestation, is a major tool used to screen for abnormalities in the baby. As it is not invasive, it carries no added risk of miscarriage.

This scan is used primarily for diagnosing fetal structural anomalies such as neural tube defects (abnormalities of the spinal cord or brain) and cardiac, gastrointestinal, musculoskeletal, urinary tract and

---

73. KO Kagan, I Staboulidou, J Cruz, D Wright and KH Nicolaides, 'Two-stage first-trimester screening for trisomy 21 by ultrasound assessment and biochemical testing', *Ultrasound in Obstetrics and Gynecology*, vol. 36, no. 5, November 2010, pp. 542-7; N Maiz and KH Nicolaides, 'Ductus venosus in the first trimester: contribution to screening of chromosomal, cardiac defects and monochorionic twin complications', *Fetal Diagnosis and Therapy*, vol. 28, no. 2, August 2010, pp. 65-71.

74. GE Palomaki, EM Kloza, GM Lambert-Messerlian, JE Haddow, LM Neveux, M Ehrich, D van den Boom, AT Bombard, C Deciu, WW Grody, SF Nelson and JA Canick, 'DNA sequencing of maternal plasma to detect Down syndrome: An international clinical validation study', *Genetics in Medicine*, vol. 13, no. 11, November 2011, pp. 913-20.

central nervous system defects in the second trimester.[75]

Scanning has become a rite of passage for pregnant women in most developed countries. In Australia, it is estimated that 99% of babies are scanned at least once in pregnancy, usually as a routine prenatal ultrasound at 4-5 months. In the United States, where this cost is borne privately or by an insurer, around 70% of pregnant women have a scan, and in European countries it is estimated that 98% of pregnant women have an ultrasound, usually once in each trimester (third) of pregnancy.[79]

cure spina bifida was first performed successfully in 1998. Mrs Kipfmiller was 23 weeks pregnant when surgeons lifted her son, Noah, out of her womb to close the opening over the spinal cord.[76] A 2011 study showed that spina bifida babies who are operated on in the womb have better outcomes than babies operated on after birth.[77] However, the mothers don't do as well. Research is progressing to find a less invasive way to correct the abnormality.[78]

It's worth asking whether the main reason scans are scheduled is to allow parents a last-minute check to see if there is anything wrong with the baby, so that if they decide to terminate the pregnancy, they can do so before the 20-22 week cut-off (depending on your country) when it will need to be registered formally as a birth.

Some people are concerned about the frequency with which ultrasound is being used in pregnancy. An American study—looking at ultrasound operators' knowledge regarding safety aspects of diagnostic ultrasound during pregnancy—found that ultrasound end users are poorly informed about the safety issues of using ultrasound during pregnancy.[80] Choices

---

75. FM Ndumbe, O Navti, VN Chilaka and JC Konje, 'Prenatal diagnosis in the first trimester of pregnancy', *Obstetrical and Gynecological Survey*, vol. 63, no. 5, May 2008, pp. 317-28.

76. 'Surgery on baby in womb cures spina bifida', *Sydney Morning Herald*, 23 November 1998.

77. NS Adzick, EA Thom, CY Spong, JW Brock III, PK Burrows, MP Johnson, LJ Howell, JA Farrell, ME Dabrowiak, LN Sutton, N Gupta, NB Tulipan, ME D'Alton and DL Farmer, 'A randomized trial of prenatal versus postnatal repair of myelomeningocele', *New England Journal of Medicine*, vol. 364, no. 11, 17 March 2011, pp. 993-1004.

78. Coping with the news that there is something wrong with your baby is discussed in chapter 9.

79. SJ Buckley, 'Ultrasound Scans—Cause for Concern?' *Kindred*, vol. 24, December 2007-February 2008, pp. 12-23.

80. E Sheiner, I Shoham-Vardi and JS Abramowicz, 'What do clinical users know regarding safety of ultrasound during pregnancy?', *Journal of Ultrasound in Medicine*, vol. 26, no. 3, March 2007, pp. 319-25.

in medicine should balance risk and benefit. A review paper examining the use of ultrasound in pregnancy found that:

> Routine ultrasound in early pregnancy appears to enable better gestational age assessment, earlier detection of multiple pregnancies and earlier detection of clinically unsuspected fetal malformation at a time when termination of pregnancy is possible. However, the benefits for other substantive outcomes are less clear.[81]

This ultrasound should be distinguished from the commercial 3D and 4D entertainment ultrasounds, which are currently not recommended either.[82]

b. Second-trimester blood screening

The second-trimester blood screening test is usually done at the 15-18 week stage. It involves the measurement of three special proteins produced during pregnancy, and is sometimes known as the 'triple test' or, if an extra one is measured, the 'quadruple (quad) test'.[83] It is also

---

81. JP Neilson, 'Ultrasound for fetal assessment in early pregnancy', *Cochrane Database of Systematic Reviews 1998*, no. 4, 26 October 1998 (reprinted in *Cochrane Library*, no. 4, 2007).
82. SE Simonsen, DW Branch and NC Rose, 'The complexity of fetal imaging: reconciling clinical care with patient entertainment', *Obstetrics and Gynecology*, vol. 112, no. 6, December 2008, pp. 1351-4.
83. Some more technical details: second-trimester maternal serum screening involves measurement of alphafetoprotein (AFP), free beta or total human chorionic gonadotropin (free β-hCG or total hCG) and unconjugated estriol (uE3), together sometimes known as the 'triple test' or, if it includes inhibin A, the 'quadruple (quad) test'.

AFP is a normal fetal protein that can also be detected in maternal serum. Normally, serum concentrations rise until the third trimester and then fall to non-pregnant concentrations at delivery. The concentration of AFP in both the amniotic fluid and the mother's serum also rises with a fetal neural tube defect in 80% of affected fetuses (spina bifida), with a false positive rate of 3%, in the second trimester (see R Harris, 'Regular review: Maternal serum alphafetoprotein in pregnancy and the prevention of birth defect', *British Medical Journal*, vol. 280, no. 6225, 17 May 1980, pp. 1199-1202). There are several other causes for such a rise, including other fetal malformations, multiple pregnancy, threatened abortion and intrauterine death, but the most common reason for an abnormal AFP level is an inaccurate estimated gestational age. Higher levels of maternal serum AFP appear to correlate with a higher incidence of poor pregnancy outcome, such as intrauterine growth restriction, haemorrhage, gestational hypertension, spontaneous preterm labour and delivery, and perinatal morbidity.

Unlike in the first trimester, higher levels of free β-hCG or total hCG in the second trimester are correlated with a higher frequency of perinatal complications such as gestational hypertension, preterm labour or delivery, and stillbirth.

Unconjugated estriol (uE3) is an oestrogen only made by the placenta, and low (sometimes undetectable) maternal serum levels are associated with fetal chromosomal abnormalities, structural anomalies (anencephaly), fetal death and a number of fetal metabolic disorders.

Inhibin A is also a second-trimester marker made by the placenta. High serum levels are associated with triploidy (69 chromosomes in each cell) or the loss of one twin in the first trimester (see KM Goodwin, PJ Sweeney, GM Lambert-Messerlian and JA Canick, 'High maternal serum inhibin A levels following the loss of one fetus in a twin pregnancy', *Prenatal Diagnosis*, vol. 20, no. 12, December 2000, pp. 1015-7).

called the 'maternal serum test', or, as one brochure described it, "a blood test to determine the risk of certain problems in your pregnancy". No wonder people are unclear about the purpose of these tests.

This test is not diagnostic—that is, it does not identify the presence of specific conditions but it indicates if there is an increased likelihood of them. An increased risk means that the test result gives you a risk of greater than 1 in 300. A reduced risk means there is less than a 1 in 300 chance of a birth defect.

The levels of the proteins in the blood, combined with the mother's age and other factors, can allow the doctor to estimate the risk of the baby having a problem with a chromosomal abnormality (the wrong number of chromosomes, for example) or having a neural tube defect (problems with the development of the spine [spina bifida] or brain [anencephaly]).

Every pregnant woman faces the possibility of having a baby with a chromosomal problem or a neural tube defect. This blood test tries to estimate that risk more clearly. Most babies with a neural tube defect will be identified using this blood test alone. Maternal blood screening plus the 19-week ultrasound can identify spina bifida in 95% of cases and anencephaly in 100% of cases.

About 5% of tests will give an increased risk result, and most of these babies will not have a chromosome problem. Down syndrome occurs in about one in every 700 babies. About 60% of babies who have Down syndrome will have an abnormal result, so about 40% of them will be missed using this test alone. There also are other birth defects that will not be detected using these tests.[84]

Evaluating these tests
Although it would seem reasonable to expect that using both the first- and second-trimester screening tests would increase the chances of detecting a fetal abnormality, this is not recommended; the false positive rate increases, making it more likely that the mother will be offered more invasive diagnostic procedures, thereby increasing the risk of the spontaneous loss of an unaffected (normal) baby.

Confused? I should think so.[85] So let's compare these second-trimester screening tests with the WHO guidelines for such tests (above).

---

84. Barlow-Stewart and Parasivam, loc. cit.
85. See appendix III for more information about genetic test results.

- **Can they detect disease in the asymptomatic stage?** Yes and no, although the baby will continue to survive in the womb with most abnormalities.
- **Do the tests have high sensitivity and specificity?** If there is such a test, it isn't being used here! There are so many false negatives and false positives, I am surprised these tests are used so widely.[86]
- **Are there available treatments for the conditions?** For some, yes. Spina bifida can be treated with surgery while the baby is still in the mother's womb, and other problems can be treated after birth; these things are worth identifying so that what can be done *is* done. Sometimes it means the doctor will monitor the pregnancy more carefully, but for most problems this is not the case; hence the association with abortion. In my experience, abortion is now sometimes chosen even for curable problems. I have a paediatrician friend who says she hasn't seen a case of club foot (which may not even need surgery for correction) in at least 20 years. (There are regional variations.)
- **Is there evidence of improved outcome with treatment?** If babies are treated and not aborted, then usually, yes.
- **Are the tests acceptable to the population?** Who knows? This program of weeding out the less-than-perfect babies has not been widely debated in our community and, as already mentioned, many of the women presenting for tests don't realize what they are for.
- **Are they cost efficient?** Does it save money to abort the abnormal babies? A 1992 study in the United Kingdom concluded that the cost of antenatal screening to 'avoid' the birth of one baby with Down syndrome was £38,000, but the cost of lifetime care was estimated at £120,000. The study concluded that the screening was therefore "cost effective", and recommended that screening be made available throughout the country.[87] In 2007, an Australian paper quoted three studies that came to a similar conclusion.[88]

86. P Wieacker and J Steinhard, 'The prenatal diagnosis of genetic diseases', *Deutsches Ärzteblatt International*, vol. 107, no. 48, 3 December 2010, pp. 857-62.

87. NJ Wald, A Kennard, JW Densem, HS Cuckle, T Chard and L Butler, 'Antenatal maternal serum screening for Down's syndrome: results of a demonstration project', *British Medical Journal*, vol. 305, no. 6850, 15 August 1992, pp. 391-4.

88. MD Coory, T Roselli and HJ Carroll, 'Antenatal care implications of population-based trends in Down syndrome birth rates by rurality and antenatal care provider, Queensland, 1990-2004', *Medical Journal of Australia*, vol. 186, no. 5, 5 March 2007, pp. 230-4.

And in an article in *Nature* magazine, the head of Stanford's Center for Law and Biosciences, Hank Greely, said that he estimates the number of genetic tests performed on unborn babies in the United States will jump within 5 years from the current 100,000 to over 3 million, and that abortions will be viewed as a way to prevent money being spent on "high-cost children"—because who really wants "to bring a child into the world who will suffer and cause their family undue burden and emotional and financial hardship?"[89]

According to the WHO screening guidelines then, these tests should not be used as screening tools. They give unreliable results for conditions we cannot cure, and so they have normalized the termination of pregnancy when babies are not 'perfect' enough. The whole point of screening is to improve the health of the population; instead, this screening promotes eugenics.

Prenatal diagnostic tests

Prenatal diagnostic testing gives parents reliable information about whether their baby has a genetic problem. While everyone hopes for a healthy baby, sometimes there are serious problems with physical or mental development. Women who have been shown to be at increased risk of having a baby with a fetal abnormality are offered diagnostic testing. It is important that the parents receive counselling before deciding whether they want this test. Their decision may be influenced by concerns about the risk of miscarriage (caused by the test), not wanting to know prior to the birth whether there is a problem, and whether termination of the pregnancy is acceptable to the family.[90] Even if parents receive counselling, it's not always easy. Gail remembers: *It was a hard decision because the risk of miscarriage was the same as the risk of Down syndrome. If I had a miscarriage when there was nothing wrong with the baby, it would have been a terrible result.* Research shows that women undergoing tests like amniocentesis often feel ambivalent about

---

89.   H Greely, 'Get ready for the flood of fetal gene screening', *Nature*, vol. 469, no. 7330, 20 January 2011, pp. 289-91, cited in K Hawkins, 'Wrong to use prenatal genetic testing to push for abortion', *Lifenews.com*, 5 April 2011 (viewed 30 June 2012): www.lifenews. com/2011/04/05/wrong-to-use-prenatal-genetic-testing-to-push-for-abortion/
90.   Gaff et al., loc. cit.

the test, and that counselling can help to clarify their decision-making.[91]

Both chorionic villus sampling (CVS) and amniocentesis (discussed further below) are invasive sampling procedures. They both collect cells that are used for chromosome analysis or, in specific cases, for DNA or biochemical analysis, to diagnose a specific genetic condition. Non-invasive genetic testing is under development, such as the maternal blood tests that look at fetal DNA (see above).[92]

Those who consider undergoing these tests should seek specialist counselling from a genetics service. This will provide the information they need to decide whether they want to go ahead, and support them as they consider what is involved. The Centre for Genetics Education gives reasons for seeking specialist counselling, which include:

- there is a family history of genetic disease (a disease that runs in the family) and a couple is worried that the baby will develop the condition
- a previous child has a serious medical problem
- the mother is in her mid-thirties or older
- the couple are blood relatives
- the prenatal screening tests have given an increased risk result.[93]

In a small number of cases, the three tests mentioned below will indicate that the baby has, or will develop, a problem. This is obviously a devastating event for parents.[94] While you might think that counselling would be mandatory in each stage of this process, in many centres it is not.

1. Chorionic villus sampling (CVS)

Chorionic villus sampling involves the collection of tissue from the chorionic villus, which is the substance lining the uterus that develops into the placenta. The cells of the chorion are similar to the baby's cells, so by taking a sample the baby's genetic make-up can be examined. A fine needle is inserted through the abdominal wall or, less commonly, via the vagina.

---

91. JC Sapp, SC Hull, S Duffer, S Zornetzer, E Sutton, TM Marteau and BB Biesecker, 'Ambivalence toward undergoing invasive prenatal testing: an exploration of its origins', *Prenatal Diagnosis*, vol. 30, no. 1, January 2010, pp. 77-82.

92. CA Hyland, GJ Gardener, H Davies, M Ahvenainen, RL Flower, D Irwin, JM Morris, CM Ward and JA Hyett, 'Evaluation of non-invasive prenatal *RHD* genotyping of the fetus', *Medical Journal of Australia*, vol. 191, no. 1, 6 July 2009, pp. 21-5.

93. Barlow-Stewart and Parasivam, loc. cit.

94. Subsequent management is discussed in chapter 9. For further explanation of genetics, see appendix III.

Continuous ultrasound monitoring is used to guide the operator so that the baby is protected. CVS is usually performed between 11-13 weeks gestation. However, there is a 1% risk it will not be accurate because of contamination of the sample with maternal cells, or because of the placenta cells being slightly different from the baby's. In these cases, it may need to be repeated. Complications associated with CVS include cramping, vaginal bleeding and a <1% risk of miscarriage.[95] Its role in the subsequent development of preeclampsia (a serious, potentially life-threatening condition developing in late pregnancy, characterized by a sudden rise in blood pressure) is still being debated.[96] If CVS is performed prior to 10 weeks gestation, there is a risk of procedure-related limb defects.[97]

CVS is a diagnostic test, so it can indicate reliably whether or not the baby has certain problems, but it does not check for all possible diseases.

2. Amniocentesis

Amniocentesis involves the collection of a small sample (around 15 ml) of the amniotic fluid around the fetus using a fine needle and ultrasound guidance. From this fluid, fetal cells are extracted and then grown. The procedure is usually performed at 15-20 weeks gestation and is associated with a 1% miscarriage risk. Early amniocentesis (performed between 9-14 weeks gestation) is not safe.[98] As with CVS, amniocentesis can give a definite result for some, but not all, genetic abnormalities in the baby.

Due to the high rate of false positive results for the earlier tests, many women undergoing amniocentesis and CVS will not be carrying a Down syndrome child. However, with the miscarriage risk of these tests, it has been estimated that for every 660 Down syndrome children that are detected and terminated in England and Wales each year, 400

---

95. A Tabor and Z Alfirevic, 'Update on procedure-related risks for prenatal diagnosis techniques', *Fetal Diagnosis and Therapy*, vol. 27, no. 1, January 2010, pp. 1-7; Z Alfirevic, K Sundberg and S Brigham, 'Amniocentesis and chorionic villus sampling for prenatal diagnosis', *Cochrane Database of Systematic Reviews 2003*, no. 3, 21 July 2003 (reprinted in *Cochrane Library*, no. 4, 2007).

96. WA Grobman, M Auger, LP Shulman and S Elias, 'The association between chorionic villus sampling and preeclampsia', *Prenatal Diagnosis*, vol. 29, no. 8, August 2009, pp. 800-803; A Khalil, R Akolekar, P Pandya, A Syngelaki and K Nicolaides, 'Chorionic villus sampling at 11 to 13 weeks of gestation and hypertensive disorders in pregnancy', *Obstetrics and Gynecology*, vol. 116, no. 2, part 1, August 2010, pp. 374-80.

97. H Firth, 'Chorion villus sampling and limb deficiency—cause or coincidence?', *Prenatal Diagnosis*, vol. 17, no. 13, Deceber 1997, pp. 1313-30.

98. Alfirevic et al., 'Amniocentesis and chorionic villus sampling', loc. cit.

> Hospital ethicist Robert Orr tells the sad story of a couple who decided to abort their 20-week fetus after Down syndrome had been diagnosed by amniocentesis. The baby was born alive and pronounced dead sixteen minutes later. Nurses reported that the father examined the baby closely and said, I thought he was going to be abnormal.[101]

children without Down syndrome die as well.[99] While there was reaction against the suggestion that these figures demonstrated a need to withdraw screening completely, it was admitted that "There is clearly an urgent need for wider medical and public debate about screening".[100]

CVS and amniocentesis results require a complete analysis of the chromosomes (karyotype), which usually takes 1-3 weeks. FISH[102] has hastened the result return time to 48-72 hours. Uncultured amniotic fluid can also be used to determine levels of a protein (AFP) that is present in open neural tube defects.

3. Cordocentesis/fetal blood sampling

If the results of the amniocentesis are unclear or a quick result is needed, cordocentesis may be recommended. It can be used to diagnose infection as well as some genetic conditions. A needle is passed into the umbilical cord using ultrasound for guidance. There is a miscarriage risk of around 2%, or even higher if there are other problems with the pregnancy. This test is not done very often.[103]

Ethical issues

When you realize that many of these screening tests need to be done early in a 'normal' pregnancy, you can understand why it is that general practitioners often order them before the mother has had her first visit with an obstetrician. However, this means the doctor ordering the test may not have specialist knowledge of the conditions being tested for,

99. F Buckley and SJ Buckley, 'Wrongful deaths and rightful lives—screening for Down syndrome', Down Syndrome Research and Practice, vol. 12, no. 2, October 2008, pp. 79-86.
100. P Summerfield, 'Prenatal screening for Down's syndrome: balanced debate needed', Lancet, vol. 373, no. 9665, 28 February 2009, p. 722.
101. RD Orr, Medical Ethics and the Faith Factor, Eerdmans, Grand Rapids, 2009, p. 419.
102. FISH (fluorescence in situ hybridization) is a technique used to detect specific features in DNA on chromosomes.
103. Tabor and Alfirevic, loc. cit.

and may not be able to explain fully what is involved.[104] Research shows that not all women are fully informed before testing[105] and there is sometimes a lack of dialogue about sensitive topics such as disability and termination.[106] This problem needs to be addressed. It is possible there will be time pressure, and it may be difficult to provide comprehensive genetic counselling in a busy general practice;[107] these are difficult issues to raise with someone who has just found out they are pregnant. Hence the continued ignorance of what these tests are for.

However, this is a violation of the informed consent process, which demands we know what and why procedures are being carried out on our bodies, before we agree to participate.

Comprehensive counselling allows parents to know what a test is for and what risks may be involved, which will help them decide whether they want to go ahead with it. Counselling will also help them mentally prepare in case the test result is bad. If an abnormality is detected, an experienced counsellor can tell them whether it is a condition that can be corrected during, or soon after, the pregnancy. If they decide to continue the pregnancy with an untreatable disorder, they can obtain information about their baby's condition that will help them to plan for raising a child with a disability or illness. Counselling also enables the doctor to know whether closer monitoring of the pregnancy is required.

It occurs to me that one problem with increasing public awareness of available screening may be the effect it has on bonding between parents and child. If the parents know they can screen for abnormalities and abort the imperfect baby, will they consciously, or unconsciously, hold back affection until they know whether they will carry the pregnancy to term? Abortion would potentially be easier if they felt less attached to their baby.

---

104. HJ Harris, 'The primary care perspective of quality in clinical genetics service—United Kingdom as an example', in U Kristoffersson, J Schmidtke and JJ Cassiman (eds), *Quality Issues In Clinical Genetic Services*, Springer, London, 2010, pp. 75-82.

105. HJ Rowe, JRW Fisher and JA Quinlivan, 'Are pregnant Australian women well informed about prenatal genetic screening? A systematic investigation using Multidimensional Measure of Informed Choice', *Australian and New Zealand Journal of Obstetricians and Gynaecologists*, vol. 46, no. 5, October 2006, pp. 433-9.

106. JM Hodgson, LH Gillam, MA Sahhar and SA Metcalfe, '"Testing times, challenging choices": An Australian study of prenatal genetic counseling', *Journal of Genetic Counseling*, vol. 19, no. 1, February 2010, pp. 22-37.

107. C Nagle, S Lewis, B Meiser, J Gunn, J Halliday and R Bell, 'Exploring general practitioners' experience of informing women about prenatal screening tests for foetal abnormalities: A qualitative focus group study', *BMC Health Services Research*, vol. 8, no. 114, 28 May 2008.

I think this would be an unhelpful result and may further reduce the ability of parents to love their children unconditionally as our Father in heaven loves us. We should be careful not to allow the easy availability of abortion to reduce our sense of responsibility for our offspring.

Prenatal screening for the purpose of detecting abnormalities in the baby, with a view to abortion, is not ethical for those who want to protect all human life. While extra tests may be done at times to see if a pregnancy needs to be monitored more closely—some parents would like to screen 'just so they know'—the only definitive tests are CVS and amniocentesis (and cordocentesis), which carry a risk of miscarriage. It has been argued that it is difficult to justify these investigations (and the risk to the child) merely to satisfy your curiosity. However, there is an argument for the tests in that they may also enable doctors to plan closer monitoring of the 'at risk' babies, whether it be Down syndrome or not. In the case of chromosomal abnormalities that are incompatible with life, palliative care plans can then be put in place.

Nonetheless, undertaking these tests can make things harder. British neonatologist John Wyatt has noted that, in his experience, the knowledge gained from fetal screening when the baby is impaired does not so much help parents to prepare psychologically, as lead them to wait for the birth with increasing anxiety and distress. He is concerned that this damages the normal relationship between parents and child; instead of spending the pregnancy learning to love the developing baby unconditionally, parents are wondering how the child will measure up.[108]

Biblical teaching is clear on this subject: killing innocent human beings is wrong (Exod 20:13).[109]

In Australia in 2002-2003, 63.6% of fetuses diagnosed with Down syndrome, and about 76% of fetuses affected with neural tube defects, were either aborted or died in the womb.[110] Screening is now more widespread and so the relative number of babies aborted will have increased since then. It is now standard for all pregnancies to be screened for Down syndrome in many industrialized countries, with the unspoken expectation that abnormal babies will be aborted. Recent research on screening for Down syndrome is working on new ways to

---

108. J Wyatt, *Matters of Life and Death*, 2nd edn, IVP, Leicester, 2009, p. 174.
109. The arguments for and against abortion are examined in chapter 7. A discussion about responding to disability is found in chapter 9.
110. Abeywardana and Sullivan, loc. cit.

screen during fetal life that are cheaper and more efficient. Over 350 articles have been written on this subject in the medical literature in just the last five years.[111]

Down syndrome

Down syndrome, or trisomy 21, is one of the most common chromosomal abnormalities in live born children. It is caused by a failure of the chromosomes to separate properly during production of the mother's eggs (usually) or during cell division early in development, resulting in three copies of chromosome 21 in all, or some, of the baby's cells.[112] The parents do not pass it on—they would usually have normal chromosomes. Children with Down syndrome have varied abilities dependent on heredity and early upbringing. The extra genetic material in the additional chromosome 21 causes them to have a number of common physical characteristics that give them their distinctive appearance. A child with Down syndrome is generally delayed in reaching developmental milestones (such as sitting, crawling, walking, talking, toileting, etc.) but, as the Down Syndrome Society of South Australia reports on its website, "For most children with Down syndrome the future is brighter today than it might have been only a short while ago. Educational and medical techniques have made, and continue to make, great advances in helping children with Down syndrome lead a life of dignity, meaning and independence."[113] The Stanford University School of Medicine Down Syndrome Research Center is among several units that have been exploring the condition and they have had promising results in animal trials using medication to improve memory.[114] In 2002-2003,

---

111.   M Hill, *Trisomy 21*, UNSW Embryology Wiki, Sydney, 29 May 2012 (viewed 2 July 2012): http://embryology.med.unsw.edu.au/Defect/page21.htm.

112.   3%-4% of trisomy 21 is due to a 'balanced' translocation of chromosome 21 on to another chromosome (usually chromosome 14). When this occurs, the parent with the balanced translocation has the normal amount of genetic material, but it is distributed unevenly so that during production of the egg (or sperm), there is an uneven distribution resulting in trisomy at fertilization.

113.   Down Syndrome Society of South Australia (DSSSA), *About DS: General Overview*, DSSSA, Greenacres, 2006 (viewed 20 December 2011): www.downssa.asn.au/about_ds/what.php

114.   S Heyn, 'Pharmacotherapy improves cognitive performance in a Down syndrome mouse model', *News and Views*, vol. 9, 2007 (viewed 20 December 2011): http://dsresearch.stanford.edu/community/archive_issue_09.html

Down syndrome affected 11.1 in every 10,000 live births, but after early detection and terminations of pregnancy were included, the estimated actual rate for trisomy 21 was 26.3 per 10,000 pregnancies.

A 2011 study from the Children's Hospital in Boston interviewed over 2000 parents of Down syndrome children and found that "The overwhelming majority of parents surveyed report that they are happy with their decision to have their child with DS and indicate that their sons and daughters are great sources of love and pride".[115] Interestingly, 79% of parents felt their outlook on life was more positive because of their child, only 5% felt embarrassed by them and only 4% regretted having them. Similarly, nearly all siblings regarded their relationship with a brother or sister with Down syndrome as positive and enhancing. Of older siblings, 88% felt that the experience had made them better people.[116]

Neuroscientist Dr Alberto Costa is conducting the first human trial on ways to improve memory in Down syndrome, but he has noticed a reduction in available research funding since a blood test to screen for Down syndrome in pregnancy has been in development. In 2011, research into Down syndrome—a condition affecting 300,000 to 400,000 people in the United States—received US$22 million, while cystic fibrosis research—affecting about 30,000 (one tenth the number of people who have Down syndrome)—received US$68 million. "The geneticists expect Down syndrome to disappear," Costa says, "so why fund treatments?"[117]

Soon it is expected that all pregnancies will be screened for cystic fibrosis (CF), a hereditary condition that leads to thickened secretions by the glands of the body. It is one of the most common life-shortening genetic diseases in the Western world. Although it cannot be cured, with today's improved treatment most people with CF are able to lead reasonably normal and productive lives. Currently, babies are screened for CF at

---

115.   BG Skotko, SP Levine and R Goldstein, 'Having a son or daughter with Down syndrome: Perspectives from mothers and fathers', *American Journal of Medical Genetics Part A*, vol. 155, no. 10, October 2011, pp. 2335-47.

116.   ibid.

117.   D Hurley, 'A drug for Down syndrome', *New York Times Magazine*, 29 July 2011.

birth in many countries, including Australia. This is morally good, as it allows all children with CF to receive treatment early. However, screening early in the pregnancy is intended to prevent these children being born.

Kits are now available which allow parents to test to see if they are carriers of the CF gene. Parents who find that they are *both* carriers—and thus at risk of having a CF-affected child—are offered genetic screening in pregnancy.

Cystic fibrosis (CF)

CF is a chronic disease due to a defective gene that causes the body to produce unusually thick, sticky mucus. The mucus clogs the lungs, which leads to life-threatening lung infections, and obstructs the pancreas by stopping natural enzymes from helping the body break down and absorb food.

The CF gene is inherited as an autosomal recessive mutation, meaning that if two carriers have a child, there is a 1 in 4 chance that it will be affected by CF. While in the 1960s children with CF survived on average for less than one year, improvement in treatment has greatly improved the outlook for them. Most children with CF are fairly healthy until they reach adulthood. They are able to participate in most activities and should be able to attend school. Many young adults with CF are able to complete their education and find employment.[118] In the United States, the average life expectancy in 2009 for people with CF was in the mid-thirties,[119] and in Canada it was 48.1 in 2010.[120] Much research is being done aimed at seeking a cure.

Although CF affects only 1 in 2500 Caucasian babies born, 1 in 25 people of European descent are carriers with no symptoms of the disease.

---

118. PubMed Health, 'Cystic fibrosis', *A.D.A.M. Medical Encyclopedia*, PubMed Health, Bethesda, 1 May 2011 (viewed 20 December 2011): www.ncbi.nlm.nih.gov/pubmedhealth/PMH0001167/

119. Cystic Fibrosis Foundation, *What is the Life Expectancy for People Who Have CF (in the United States)?*, Cystic Fibrosis Foundation, Bethesda, 8 May 2011 (viewed 1 July 2011): www.cff.org/aboutcf/faqs/#What_is_the_life_expectancy_for_people_who_have_CF_(in_the_United_States)?

120. Canadian CF Patient Data Registry Working Group, *Canadian Cystic Fibrosis Patient Data Registry Report 2010*, Cystic Fibrosis Canada, Toronto, 2010, p. 3.

> *The customer information in the 'carrier testing kit' warns that while some people know they are at risk of being a carrier because of family history, over 85% of children born with CF do not have a known family history of the disease.*[121]
>
> *There are two types of screening tests for CF because it can be caused by many different types of genetic mutation. The basic model (checking the F508del gene) will detect 79% of carriers, and by testing both parents, 90% of 'at risk' couples are detected. The deluxe test (checking the 32 most common CF mutations) detects about 90% of carriers.*[122]

Eugenics

Eugenics is "the science of improving a population by controlled breeding so as to increase the occurrence of desirable heritable characteristics" (*Oxford English Dictionary*). Are we witnessing, in prenatal screening, a form of population 'improvement' that makes sure we stop any 'faulty products' from being born?

There have been court cases assessing 'wrongful birth' in many countries now; parents have regularly sued for the cost of caring for a disabled child. (Sometimes these suits are an attempt to pay for care costs in a society that underfunds support for the disabled.)

There was a new development in 2000 when a French court agreed that a child had a 'right not to be born'. This was in the case of Nicholas Perruche, who had been born deaf, partly blind and brain-damaged from a rubella infection (his parents had already been compensated in 1997). His mother had asked her doctor to check if she had rubella at the time of her pregnancy because she wanted to abort rather than risk having a disabled child. Her doctor made a mistake.

Then, in 2001, a French court agreed again that a child had a 'right not to be born' when they awarded damages to a boy with Down syndrome. His mother would have aborted him if she'd known he had the condition, but her doctor also made a mistake. As a result, medical insurance premiums rose and French doctors protested until the French

---

121. Genea, *Before Getting Pregnant*, Genea, Sydney, 2011 (viewed 2 July 2012): www.geneagenetics.com.au/Before-getting-pregnant
122. ibid.

Parliament introduced legislation protecting them from being sued every time a prenatal screening test gave an unreliable result.

How do you test whether a life is worth living? I would have thought it was more a metaphysical question than a legal one, and I know some judges who agree with me. However, others seem to think it is better to be dead than disabled. Ethicist Julian Savulescu has suggested that:

> ...if a child is born with afflictions so severe and a life so miserable that he or she would be considered better off dead, then a claim could reasonably be made on the child's behalf that he or she was harmed by being born. Nicholas Perruche may have such a life, but Down syndrome is not generally so severe as to make life not worth living.[123]

He notes that many people describe a happy and worthwhile life for those with Down syndrome. His test of whether a life is worth living is this: would life-prolonging medical treatment be administered if this child developed a life-threatening condition? I would say that this does not measure whether the life is worth living so much as whether *he* thinks the life is worth living.

In fact, Savulescu would contend that even if a parent can claim damages (because they would have aborted the child if they'd known), a child has no legitimate claim because they have benefited from the mistake—the benefit of having a life of one's own. Against this, the parents can have great harm done to them if they have a child that they cannot "accommodate into their lives" (his words) whether disabled or not. Therefore, Savulescu sees these court cases as further justification for procreative autonomy—the right of the parents to decide whether or not and when to have children, and the right to be given information so they can decide about their pregnancy options: "Children have a profound impact on their parents' lives. For this reason, people should retain control over their reproduction."[124] Other supporters of prenatal screening agree.

Discoverer of the DNA molecule, James Watson, suggests: "Reproductive decisions should be made by women... If you could just say, 'My

---

123. J Savulescu and M Spriggs, 'Is there ever a "right not to be born"?' *Australian Medicine*, vol. 14, no. 6, 1 April 2002, p. 8.

124. ibid.

baby's not going to have asthma', wouldn't that be nice?"[125] One doctor told me I would be negligent if I were looking after a pregnant woman and did not let her know that these prenatal screening tests existed. "It doesn't mean that everyone has to have them," he said, "but they must be given enough information to allow them to decide for themselves." I agree—informed consent is very important in medicine.

Susan, who had watched her brother die from muscular dystrophy at 13 years of age, said, *Women who have decided to make the decision to terminate will make it on their own moral beliefs, and they're not going to change. This sort of option will give them a choice not to terminate the pregnancy.* She underwent CVS and all was well.

You can understand the fear that some parents will have for their children, having seen the suffering of a loved one. I am not trying to play down the seriousness of congenital disease and the challenge it represents for the parents. I am trying to look at this situation from the perspective of the child. The arguments above are considering the child's right to life on the basis of what suits the parents, and I would like parents to know what they're getting into if they decide to have these tests. I don't expect everyone to agree with me, but my point is that the issue of informed consent for prenatal screening is still a big problem.

Many health professionals are aware that the consent process is often unsatisfactory. In 2007, British ultrasound specialist Hylton Meire said, "Women are being referred for amniocentesis on the basis of a very flimsy test. And I think they need to understand just how inaccurate it can be."[126] At the time, he calculated that in the United Kingdom as many as 3200 women a year would lose a normal child because of miscarriage following CVS or amniocentesis. Obstetrician Andrew McLennan commented, "It's not a eugenics project or euthanasia. It's simply about offering every woman the choice to have further testing if the scan is abnormal."[127]

However, it's not just a problem in the United Kingdom. In many places, prenatal screening tests are routine or require a proactive 'opt-

---

125.   JD Watson in 'A Conversation with James D Watson', interview with J Rennie, *Scientific American*, April 2003, p.69.

126.   L Hall, 'Healthy babies "at risk": UK doctor questions Down test', *Sun-Herald*, 26 August 2007, p. 22.

127.   ibid.

out' notification (partly due to time constraints), thus increasing the use of the tests at the expense of informed choice.[128] An observer in the United States wrote, "Pregnant women rarely know what their blood is being tested for, or that the results may lead to painful dilemmas involving disability and abortion". And yet, in response to a proposed toughening up of consent laws in California, he said, "If the new laws result in one woman shunning screening, or the avoidable birth of a severely disabled child, the state and its people will be the losers".[129]

Inherent in all these supportive comments is the idea that some lives are not worth living. You could say that simply existing is in the created child's best interests, as life is a basic good, but the argument we are hearing is that it is only good if you are normal, healthy and wanted by your parents.

I would like to make several points here. The argument for reproductive autonomy ignores the fact that the best way to avoid having children you don't want is to avoid sexual intercourse in the first place (though I realize this idea is immediately rejected in our self-gratifying society). Supporters of

Ultrasound technology is improving all the time, and it is possible that this contributes to some of the false positive results. With each improvement, more structures are visible in the baby, and there have been cases where abortion has been recommended for 'abnormalities' that were subsequently found to be normal structures that had just never been seen before with inferior machines.

As a student, I was present at the post-mortem examination after a mistaken diagnosis of porencephaly (abnormal cavities in the brain) led to the decision to abort a baby. The 'malformation' on the 18-week ultrasound was found to represent receding cysts in the choroid plexus. The baby was completely normal. Subsequent review of the scans by five senior ultrasonographers at the time found that all agreed with the diagnosis of porencephaly. It was only when they were more familiar with the higher resolution scans that they realized their mistake. A lot of diagnoses by inexperienced operators are changed when they are reviewed at specialist centres.

---

128. J Searle, 'Fearing the worst—why do pregnant women feel "at risk"?', *Australian and New Zealand Journal of Obstetrics and Gynaecology*, vol. 36, no. 3, August 1996, pp. 279-86.
129. P Billings, 'Stem cell research: Dangerous territory?' *New Scientist*, vol. 2576, November 2006.

reproductive autonomy are ignoring the fact that when pregnancy occurs, the child already exists; hence the convenience of the 'personhood' debate—because if it isn't human, it doesn't matter what you do with it. But I would argue that the question is not about whether you want a particular child; it is about whether you want to kill it. What conditions are considered adequate grounds for abortion after screening? Where is society heading?

Well, for a start, in many places completely healthy babies are aborted simply because they are not the preferred gender. One paediatrician wrote:

> Formerly, imperfections warranting termination were those
> incompatible with life, but things have changed and I have observed
> terminations for a range of treatable conditions, for example,
> gastroschisis (85% expected survival)... low meningocoele
> (probably walk unaided)... dysplastic changes in one kidney
> (which might never have caused any trouble), and even cleft lip.
> There seems to be at best a commitment to perfection these days;
> at worst, an intolerance of interference with personal aspirations.
> Just how much disease parents will be able to accept in their baby is
> unknown, but I fear a new Eugenics based on the New Genetics.[130]

Some paediatric surgeons are concerned that expertise they have gained in treating congenital abnormalities may not be passed on to their trainees; because so many affected children are being aborted, surgeons do not always have an opportunity to demonstrate the techniques. Extrapolating from there, those children not aborted will receive poorer quality treatment as a result of diminished expertise, and poorer community support as the parents and children are ostracized for the child's (avoidable) existence. For diseases such as spina bifida, complications of Down syndrome and congenital heart disease, there are many surgical solutions for problems that are now considered grounds for abortion.

Disability groups and feminist supporters fear that when physicians encourage the abortion of fetuses with diseases or disabilities, they are fostering intolerance of the less-than-perfect people who have already been born. How will this make us think of them? How will it make them

---

130. J Whitehall, 'The challenge of the new genetics', *Luke's Journal*, December 1996.

think of themselves? Anecdotal evidence gives cause for concern: in one study of 73 parents-to-be undergoing prenatal screening, 30% said they thought screening might encourage negative attitudes toward the disabled; and 50% thought that mothers of disabled children would be blamed for their failure to undergo screening or have abortions.[131] Disability groups are also concerned that fewer resources will be allocated for research and the treatment of congenital abnormalities, if these abnormalities become a feature of a less educated, less socioeconomically mobile class who are less able to access antenatal services that include prenatal screening.

American educator Charlotte Spinkston is concerned that when a disability is discovered through prenatal screening, termination of the pregnancy is often the only option offered as a first response. In her experience, far too many women are told of other options only after they have told health professionals of their decision not to abort. She says:

> It is important that a range of available options be offered to families
> who receive diagnoses of disability in utero before they decide
> (when it is feasible to do so). It is crucial for families to be informed
> of community-based family information and support services as well
> as hospital-based services as soon as possible.[132]

So how do we know which lives are worth living and which ones are not? There are many disabled people who wish someone would ask them. Disability advocate Harriet Johnson writes:

> The social-science literature suggests that the public in general, and
> physicians in particular, tend to underestimate the quality of life of
> disabled people, compared with our own assessments of our lives.
> The case for assisted suicide [read abortion] rests on stereotypes that
> our lives are inherently so bad that it is entirely rational if we want
> to die.[133]

She insists that the presence or absence of a disability doesn't predict

---

131.   E Kristol, 'Picture perfect: the politics of prenatal testing', *First Things*, vol. 32, April 1993, pp. 17-24.
132.   C Spinkston, 'He giveth more grace', *Leadership Perspectives in Developmental Disability*, vol. 3, no. 1.
133.   HM Johnson, 'Unspeakable conversations', *New York Times Magazine*, 16 February 2003.

quality of life, and she is concerned that children with disabilities are being killed because parents prefer normal babies: "I have trouble with basing life-and-death decisions on market considerations when the market is structured by prejudice".[134]

> The experience of Dutch doctors practicing euthanasia on disabled newborns was published in 2005. These doctors developed the Groningen protocol, which aims to set the standard for doctors wishing to relieve "unbearable suffering" in severely impaired newborns.[136]

One study found that because most women have a lot of confidence in their doctors and rely on their advice, what may seem to be consumer demand is actually just medical dominance of antenatal care.[135] Unfortunately, the medicalization of pregnancy is a topic beyond the scope of this book.

I will leave it to you to decide whether you think there is a eugenics agenda here.

Disability in the Western world

Society has often singled out the disabled. In antiquity, children identified as weak or disabled were commonly abandoned and not considered worth rearing, with Aristotle approving it as an excuse for infanticide (no ultrasounds back then, therefore no chance to abort). The Judaeo-Christian culture, as recorded in the Bible, was more inclusive at times, with biblical records of the disabled living with their families: Mephibosheth, son of Jonathan, was crippled in both feet. King David showed kindness to him for Jonathan's sake and he always ate at the king's table (2 Samuel 9). However, the disabled were portrayed as helpless (2 Sam 5:6-8) and the deformed were excluded from the priesthood (Lev 21:17-23).[137]

According to Jayne Clapton and Jennifer Fitzgerald, the history

---

134. ibid.
135. Searle, loc. cit.
136. The protocol was introduced in two medical journals: see E Verhagen and PJJ Sauer, 'The Groningen protocol: Euthanasia in severely ill newborns', *New England Journal of Medicine*, vol. 352, no. 10, 10 March 2005, pp. 959-62; and AAE Verhagen and PJJ Sauer, 'End-of-life decisions in newborns: An approach from the Netherlands', *Pediatrics*, vol. 116, no. 3, September 2005, pp. 736-39.
137. Further discussion of the biblical understanding of disability is found in chapter 9.

of disability in the West has been characterized by the progressive development of several models of disability: the religious model, the medical/genetic model, and the rights-based model. These models influence how we respond to the disabled. Yet even though the models have changed over time, one thing about them remains constant—the idea of 'otherness'.[138]

In the agrarian societies of pre-industrialization, when people lived by the seasons and the pace was less pressured, people perceived to have limitations often lived with their families. They were given tasks within their capabilities, but which helped the family as a whole to function. They were accommodated within the patterns of daily life. Others, though, could not stay with their families. Some were ostracized and their survival was threatened, because of a popular conception that such people were monsters and therefore unworthy of human status. Some became homeless and dislocated for other reasons such as poverty or shame. Mental illness was not understood and was often ascribed to evil forces. Religious communities responded to these groups of people in various ways, including seeking cures through

Joseph Carey Merrick (1862-1890), also known as John Merrick, was an English man who was lame and had severe deformities, making his speech difficult to understand. Unable to find employment, he arranged to be exhibited as a human curiosity named the Elephant Man. He was visited by a surgeon named Frederick Treves, who invited Merrick to be examined and photographed. He was found to be sensitive and of normal intelligence and became well-known in London society after he went to live at the London Hospital. The official cause of his death was asphyxia, although Treves, who dissected the body, said that Merrick had died of a dislocated neck. He believed that Merrick—who had to sleep sitting up because of the weight of his head—had been attempting to sleep lying down, to 'be like other people'.

His body is still preserved in the Royal London Hospital Museum. In 2001, it was proposed that Merrick had suffered from a combination of neurofibromatosis type I and Proteus syndrome. DNA tests conducted on his hair and bones have proved inconclusive.

---

138.   J Clapton and J Fitzgerald, *The History of Disability: A History of 'Otherness'*, Renaissance Universal, London, 2011 (viewed 20 December 2011): www.ru.org/human-rights/the-history-of-disability-a-history-of-otherness.html

exorcisms, purging, rituals and so on, or providing care, hospitality and service as acts of mercy and Christian duty to 'needy strangers'.

Our Western society is not comfortable with disability.

In the post-industrial era, disability in Western society has been regarded as an individual affliction described in medical terms. The *person* is disabled—he has the problem, not society, and he has to deal with it. However, in a youth-obsessed, death-denying culture, disability is seen as a failure and those who suffer from disability are looked down upon. They are 'impaired'. Society does not adequately support their needs, and so they become 'handicapped'—not from the disability so much as the society that is unwilling to fully accommodate them.

While the campaign for 'the rights of the disabled' has brought some additional entitlements to people with disability, it has not significantly altered the way in which disability is viewed and so, despite changes in the law and some improvement in facilities for the disabled, some people's lives have not necessarily changed for the better. In fact, new developments in genetic technology and reproductive technology threaten to further separate the person with the disability. With our increasing understanding of genetics, we seem to be expanding the population of the disabled to include people who have abnormal chromosomes, even if no abnormality has been physically expressed. They too are suffering discrimination, and even elimination, due to their impaired genes. Ironically, by demanding their 'rights', the disabled may be accentuating their 'otherness', thus affirming the assumption that they are a separate group.

Some people have suggested that it is not fair to expect society to pay the medical costs of disabled children when they could have been aborted. Colleagues of mine have come across cases of families who have been refused health insurance for their newborn child because their child's disability was a 'previously known condition': the suggestion is that parents who do not screen their children and abort the defective samples are the negligent ones. What was initially presented as a parent's choice in the name of freedom (i.e. prenatal screening) is becoming an obligation.

Will society become less tolerant of the disabled if fewer of them are born? Would it be better for a child to have no life at all? This is what one contributor to the Human Genome Project, Grant Sutherland, has suggested:

> Anyone who's born (with a disability) that we have to deal with, we
> have to deal with with compassion, with understanding. But if we
> can prevent the birth of handicapped individuals, then I think that
> society will be better off.[139]

The disability lobby condemned his remarks. Of course, society *would* be better off if no-one was ever afflicted with disease. But that will not be possible in this world. Anyone who dreams of a world without disability is doing just that: dreaming.

Perhaps we would all be better off if we regarded disability as part of a spectrum on which we all are placed—a dynamic spectrum that we could all move along, in different directions, as life and health have an impact on our lives. If we live in a fallen world, we have to expect some difficulties. According to the United Nations, around 10% of the world's population (or 650 million) is living with disability—the world's largest minority.[140] More people will become disabled after birth than before birth.[141] On average, in countries with life spans exceeding 70 years, 8 years (or 11.5%) of a person's life will be affected by disability. Numbers will increase as the population ages.[142] This, too, is acknowledged in the Bible, with the frailty of old age portrayed for heroes such as Israel (Jacob), who lost his eyesight (Gen 48:10), and David, who could not keep himself warm (1 Kgs 1:1).

I work in the area of palliative care, which involves care of those with life-threatening illness. My patients often tell me that they don't want to be a burden, but we will all be a burden at some time in our lives, from the first nappy change onwards. We are our brother's keeper. It is normal to be disabled or dependent at times; this is part of what it means to live in a fallen world. It is only in the new creation that our bodies will be imperishable (1 Cor 15:42-44).

This idea informs the work of the WHO. *The International Classification of Functioning, Disability and Health* (ICF) is a classification of

---

139. S Dow, 'Don't play God with our lives, plead disabled', *Sun-Herald*, 25 February 2001, p. 54.

140. United Nations Secretariat for the Convention on the Rights of Persons with Disabilities (SCRPD), *Fact Sheet on Persons with Disabilities*, SCRPD, New York, 2006 (viewed 20 December 2011): www.un.org/disabilities/default.asp?id=18

141. Australian Bureau of Statistics (ABS), *Disability, Ageing and Carers, Australia: Summary of Findings*, ABS cat. no. 4430.0, ABS, Belconnen, 2003.

142. SCRPD, loc. cit.

health and health-related domains that casts new light on the notions of 'health' and 'disability'. It acknowledges that every human being can experience a decrease in health and thereby experience some degree of disability. Disability is not something that only happens to a minority of human beings. The ICF thus 'mainstreams' the experience of disability and recognizes it as a universal human experience. By shifting the focus from what caused the disease to how it affects the way we live, it places all health conditions on an equal footing, allowing them to be compared using a common measure for both health and disability.[143]

This, then, is what it means to be human.

143. WHO, *Towards a Common Language for Functioning, Disability and Health ICF*, WHO, Geneva, 2002, pp. 2-3 (viewed 20 December 2011): www.who.int/classifications/icf/training/icfbeginnersguide.pdf

When there is
something wrong

T HEY ARE THE WORDS you never want to hear. During your ultrasound, the sonographer or doctor looks up at you with a worried expression and says, "I think there may be something wrong". Or as your child is finally born and you reach for your baby, you notice that the midwife looks worried. Faye says, *By the time they told me, I knew something was wrong. When he looked at me and said he was so sorry, I just started crying. I couldn't even tell (my husband on the phone) what was wrong. I couldn't even think. I didn't know what to do.* When your baby is found to have an abnormality, everything changes.

Parents experience many feelings at such a time. There will be shock and bewilderment, and many feel guilty because they feel they are in some way responsible for what has happened. Some are angry because it seems so unfair. Others are ashamed that there is something wrong with their child, and do not want anyone to know. And so there may be silence, stigma and taboos that mean they can't even talk about it. Inevitably, there is unbelievable sadness.

During one of my pregnancies I was told that our baby might develop some problems, and it was recommended that I have an abortion. My doctor knew me well enough not to spend a whole lot of time on it, but all of a sudden our lives seemed out of our control. At no time did my husband and I consider abortion, but boy, did we pray! We prayed that God would give us the strength to cope with whatever happened, but we also prayed for a healthy baby. All parents have expectations and hopes for their children and it is difficult when these are threatened. I have never been so aware of God's sovereignty as during that pregnancy.

Birth defects are a major cause of suffering and death in young children, causing significant emotional and financial cost for the families involved. With the advent of widespread prenatal screening for congenital abnormalities, more parents than ever are finding themselves in the unbearable situation of hearing that there is something wrong with their child and there is no treatment available to fix it, not even in this modern day and age. As I found out, the medical recommendation for an unborn child who has something wrong can often be to terminate the pregnancy.

But do we have to? Are there options? How should Christians respond when they discover their child has a disability? In his experience, neonatologist John Wyatt has discovered that in an abnormal pregnancy there is nearly always an alternative better than abortion.[1] Another neonatologist, John Whitehall, in his experience has found two factors that compound the misery for patients who proceed to abortion. First, the abnormality in the baby often seems worse in the mind than to the eye; second, the burden of guilt and grief in the mind from the abortion may be heavier than bearing the disability in the child.

Whitehall recalls:

> It is terrible to watch people concluding that a lesion in the unborn baby is too great to bear, then to witness them bonding with a corpse not nearly as disfigured as imagined and later to hear of repeated visits to the social workers. To one poor mother, the cleft lip turned out to be insignificant in the overall beauty of the now lifeless face. That baby was dressed and undressed almost daily (a little suit of blue, as I recall)… For months, the mother rang the hospital seeking reassurance.[2]

Grief can return to parents on birthdays and upon catching sight of a child living with the condition for which theirs was terminated.

How can we help those who find themselves confronted with a diagnosis of fetal abnormality? How can we help them avoid this aching regret?

I think there are two areas that need to be addressed: what are the biblical principles that help us think about disability, and what are the practical things that help? In this chapter, I will explore these questions

1. J Wyatt, *Matters of Life and Death*, 2nd edn, IVP, Leicester, 2009, p. 177.
2. J Whitehall, 'The challenge of the new genetics', *Luke's Journal*, December 1996.

and also look at our response as a society to the disabled who live among us.

Theology

How can it happen that an almighty and loving God allows an unborn baby to develop an abnormality? Is it an accident? Are the parents being punished? The Bible teaches us that God reigns in the universe and that his will is the final cause of all things. The chance that a pregnancy will end in miscarriage is 1 in 4; the chance of a baby being born with an abnormality of some kind is 1 in 30; and the chance of a baby being born with a serious physical or intellectual handicap is 1 in 50.[3] How can this be? Can God allow this to happen?

Yes, he can: "I form light and create darkness, I make wellbeing and create calamity, I am the LORD, who does all these things" (Isa 45:7). Furthermore, although we are still made in the image of God, this image has been corrupted through the Fall and now we all live in a broken world where bad things happen, people get sick, and ultimately, we all die. We groan along with the creation as we long for a new and liberated creation (Rom 8:22-23). Yet the Lord remains sovereign.

In our study of Psalm 139 (in chapter 3), we have seen how carefully God makes us. He doesn't make mistakes. When Moses tried to get out of speaking to Pharaoh, and he told God he did not have the skill, God replied, "Who has made man's mouth? Who makes him mute, or deaf, or seeing, or blind? Is it not I, the LORD?" (Exod 4:11). This is unexpected. You get the feeling that you may be looking at the issue of disability the wrong way.

Old Testament scholar Kirk Patston has had personal and professional experience of disability. He wrote an insightful passage about a Creator who allows the inexplicable to appear in this world:

> When the Lord addressed Job he… spoke of his rights and powers as Creator, urging Job to think about the wild and wonderfully diverse world he created. The world includes creatures like ostriches, of whom the Lord says:

---

3.   D Challis, *Prenatal Diagnosis and Screening*, BGD 1-2AS, Medical Faculty, University of NSW, Sydney, 2006.

> She lays her eggs on the ground
> > and lets them warm in the sand,
> unmindful that a foot may crush them,
> > that some wild animal may trample them.
> She treats her young harshly,
> > As if they were not hers;
> She cares not that her labour was in vain,
> > For God did not endow her with wisdom
> Or give her a share of good sense.
> > Yet when she spreads her feathers to run,
> She laughs at horse and rider. (Job 39:14-18)

In this passage and the ones that surround it, God seems to be delighting in his own capacity to create diversity, even if it seems inefficient or puzzling from a human point of view. I find this liberating when I want to see disability as an unfair tragedy or to see my children or myself as victims in a random, cruel game. There is One who stands behind disability who knows what he is doing.[4]

He adds that when it comes to being wise, we are all disabled.

We can find this hard to accept because we are so conditioned by our society that it is difficult to truly believe disability is meant to be part of this world. We are used to having what we want, when we want it. No-one plans to have a disabled baby. How do we adjust to this unexpected news? How can we find the faith to hold on to our God?

Sarah Williams, who was told that her unborn child would probably die at birth, refused an abortion but then pondered with her husband how they could cope with the remainder of a difficult pregnancy and then watch their daughter die. *Principles, however sound they might be, were simply not enough to give us the capacity to go on. They stopped short, leaving a great wide chasm of pain.* She believes that God himself spoke to her in her distress: *Here is a sick and dying child. Will you love it for me and care for it until it dies?*[5] It is only through God's grace that such sacrifice is possible.

It can help to go back to basics and consider the suffering Saviour hanging from a cross:

---

4. K Patston, 'Introduction to disability', in K Hurley (ed.), *Take Heart*, Blue Bottle Books, Sydney, 2008, p. 9.

5. SC Williams, *The Shaming of the Strong*, Kingsway, Eastbourne, 2005, p. 30.

...a man of sorrows, and acquainted with grief...
he was pierced for our transgressions;
    he was crushed for our iniquities;
upon him was the chastisement that brought us peace,
    and with his wounds we are healed. (Isa 53:3, 5)

But remembering Jesus does not mean that we will not grieve our losses. Sometimes all we can say is, "I believe; help my unbelief!" (Mark 9:24).

In the Old Testament, deformed humans were not permitted to present sacrifices to God (Lev 21:17-23), and deformed animals were not to be sacrificed (Lev 22:18-25). Patston notes that, since the sacrificial system was concerned with sin and atonement, this practice set up an implicit connection between disability and sin.[6] Furthermore, when the prophets wished to condemn behaviour, they often used 'disability rhetoric', imagining the audience as blind and deaf (e.g. Isa 42:18-20, 43:8), thus further reinforcing the link between sin and disability.[7]

Of course, Jesus has replaced the sacrificial system with his own sinless death in our place. During his life on earth, he broke the Mosaic taboos regarding the treatment of the 'other', for example by touching lepers (Matt 8:3) and the dead (Matt 9:25). Furthermore, he denied the close link between sin and disability when he healed a man born blind (John 9:1-7) and, in fact, specifically included the disabled in his vision of the kingdom of God as a great banquet (Luke 14:21). It is interesting that he himself was depicted in prophecy as unattractive to men and carrying infirmity (Isa 53:2-4). God's own divine power is made perfect in weakness (2 Cor 12:9).

This is the God who sacrificed himself on a cross to save us, who loved us and sent his Son as an atoning sacrifice for our sins. This is the God who loves us so much that he does not leave us as we are, but allows us to grow to maturity through suffering (Jas 1:2-4). How do you know you've had an encounter with God? Ask Jacob—you limp (Gen 32:24-31).

We have already discussed (in chapter 3) the doctrine of man made in the image of God (Gen 1:27). Man's dignity is not based on his abilities or his characteristics, but is derived from the God in whose

---

6.   He also notes that baldness, gender, species, and so on were also points of discrimination, with no clear explanation, so it is possible that exclusion of the disabled was just a teaching device to emphasise the holy 'otherness' of God.

7.   K Patston, 'God's inefficient creation: a fresh look at disability in the Old Testament', *Case Magazine*, vol. 21, 2009, pp. 16-21.

image he is made. In biblical thought, as each human life has unique dignity because of the divine image, so each life has an incalculable and incommensurable value. Each human being is an irreplaceable masterpiece of God's creation. Each child is a gift of God to its parents. How can we say some are gifts while others should never be born? God does not make mistakes.

Furthermore, as the people of God, we are aware of a glorious future awaiting us after this life—so glorious that "the sufferings of this present time are not worth comparing with the glory that is to be revealed to us. For the creation waits with eager longing for the revealing of the sons of God" (Rom 8:18-19). In the new earth, there will be no more suffering (Rev 21:4).

Stanley Hauerwas questions why it is that we try so hard in this life to avoid suffering altogether. While not suggesting that every form of pain and suffering should be viewed as good, he considers what sort of people we should be:

> ...so that certain forms of suffering are not denied but accepted as part and parcel of our existence as moral agents. In viewing our life narrowly as a matter of purposes and accomplishments, we may miss our actual need for suffering, even apparently purposeless or actively destructive suffering. The issue is not whether retarded children can serve a human good, but whether we should be the kind of people, the kind of parents and community, that can receive, even welcome, them into our midst in a manner that allows them to flourish.[8]

He further suggests that "We rightly try to avoid unnecessary suffering, but it also seems that we are never quite what we should be until we recognize the necessity and inevitability of suffering in our lives".[9] We live in a society where individuality and self-possession are valued. But are humans really like that? Hauerwas argues that the reason the disabled are so profoundly threatening to us is because not only do they seem to accept they are not self-sufficient, but also "they expose our own fear of

---

8. S Hauerwas, *The Hauerwas Reader*, ed. J Berkman and M Cartwright, Duke University Press, London, 2001, p. 564. NB: Although Hauerwas uses the term 'retarded', his arguments apply to any disabled person.

9. ibid., pp. 564-5.

weakness and dependence on others".[10] In fact, the disabled offer us an opportunity to remember how dependent we really are on the suffering God of the cross.[11]

But this teaching may be too hard for parents at the time of diagnosis.

Support during a time of crisis

When parents learn that their child has a problem or is at risk of developmental impairment, they are thrown into turmoil. This is a paralyzing experience. During the period of indecision, those in the supporting role need to acknowledge that it's really, really hard.

Jonathan Morris, a maternal-fetal medicine specialist who has counselled many parents in this situation, stresses that during this crisis, parents need time—time to talk, time to make decisions. Time is needed to adjust to the anxiety that every parent feels when their child is found to have something wrong with them. They need to deal with disappointed dreams—dreams each of us has as we (rightly) hope for the wellbeing of our children. Anger is not uncommon. Grief and waves of sadness can wash over them. Where there is a definite diagnosis, doctors can outline all the available options, but if the diagnosis is indefinite then it will be harder.

Parents also need *information* about their child's situation. Wide consultation to get a variety of views is important. It works best if they can talk to someone with whom they already have a relationship. Annette says, *I spoke to my doctors, but I wanted to talk about it to others too. I found it very difficult when people didn't refer to it—it was the biggest single decision I had to make and as such I wanted interest and concern, whatever it was. I didn't want it just to be ignored.*

Parents need to spend time gathering information *before* making decisions. Medical input regarding the options is important. Often those who make the initial diagnosis have a limited understanding of the precise lifelong implications of that diagnosis. Parents need accurate information about what is known about the problem, what treatment options are available, and what can be expected throughout the pregnancy and after the birth. Such information can only be obtained from a wide range of medical and paramedical experts.

---

10. ibid., p. 556.
11. ibid.

It is also important to put parents in touch with people who know what's really involved in having a child with the same diagnosis—people who have had a similarly affected child and so have firsthand knowledge. This can be done through linkage with individuals or by contacting a patient support group. *Talking it through with people who had experience of what was involved were the most valuable discussions*, remembers Will.

Patient support groups can function face-to-face or online. Different resources will be available according to which disease is the focus, and where parents live. Parents may need assistance to know which disease organization is relevant to their child's diagnosis; rarer diseases are generally under the umbrella of a more common but related disease. As well as giving social and emotional support, these organizations usually have information regarding what practical and financial resources are available in the community.[12]

It can be extremely liberating to talk to someone who has been in the same place and understands what it is like. Because of the prejudice against the disabled, some people just can't even picture what life would look like with a disabled child in the family, and often are reassured by an opportunity to talk to a parent who is familiar with the lifestyle. Those who have had the experience often express their surprise at the joys involved. *There's no way I would ever want to change her*, said Senator Sue Boyce of her daughter, who has Down syndrome. She regrets the increase in abortions for children with this genetic variation: *It is my view that the world is a much poorer place without people with Down syndrome.*[13]

A 2011 publication reported on 284 interviews with people affected by Down syndrome, conducted in order to collect information to pass on to expectant parents. The people with Down syndrome encouraged parents to love their babies with Down syndrome, mentioning that their own lives were good. They further encouraged healthcare professionals to value them, emphasizing that they share hopes and dreams similar to people without Down syndrome. Overall, the overwhelming majority of people with Down syndrome surveyed indicated they live happy and

---

12.   C Newell, 'Finding a patient support group', *Australian Prescriber*, vol. 27, no. 1, 2004, pp. 19-21.

13.   T Dick, 'Life enriched by care', *Sydney Morning Herald*, 7 June 2008.

fulfilling lives.[14]

Even if life is hard for parents caring for a disabled child, it does not mean they regret the opportunity to have the experience. Susan Riggs's son, Hugo, was born with Pelizaeus-Merzbacher disease, which left him severely physically and intellectually disabled. He was expected to die in early childhood. *I believe these kids are sent to you for a reason, and a life's a life whether it's one trapped in a body like his or one that runs riot like his two sisters.* Her husband, Ben, agrees: *I don't view Hugo as anything other than my first son and I'm very attached to him.* Ben has spent many hours holding Hugo, preparing as best as he can for his son's death.[15]

Research supports the benefits of making these links with those who have firsthand experience:

> Surveys of women undergoing amniocentesis have shown that 62% say they would abort for sex-chromosome abnormalities, and 57% for blindness or paralysis of the legs. Yet only 20% of parents who have children with cystic fibrosis would consider abortion for CF. Clearly, having a personal relationship with an afflicted individual can summon up a host of nurturing instincts that do not come into play in a theoretical deliberation. It is interesting to note that these same parents of children with CF would be far more willing to abort for disorders they had no personal experience with. A similar pattern has been reported in parents of children with Down syndrome.[16]

Sometimes the parents need to be given the *vocabulary* to talk about what is happening. For example, what do you say to your other children? They will know something is wrong even if you say nothing. Be aware that they may feel responsible. Talk to them at their level of understanding, and listen to them to discover their questions. And again, how do you tell the mothers at school that your baby will die when it is born? How do you deal with all the well-wishers when you know your baby will not be normal? How do you cope with all the people who go quiet when they

---

14. BG Skotko, SP Levine and R Goldstein, 'Self-perceptions from people with Down Syndrome', *American Journal of Medical Genetics Part A*, vol. 155, no. 10, October 2011, pp. 2360-9.

15. B Kontominas, 'Making every minute count', *Sydney Morning Herald*, 28 June 2008.

16. E Kristol, 'Picture perfect: The politics of prenatal testing', *First Things*, April 1993, pp. 17-24.

hear the news? Normally when a couple find they are having a baby, everyone is happy for them and congratulations pour in. *When you have a disabled baby, no-one calls.*

Support services are often attached to hospital units and may be able to provide support and counselling during this stage. It is very important that anyone involved with counselling does not put pressure on the couple either to keep or abort the baby. The parents are the ones who will have to live with this decision, and they have to know why they made the choice they did. Don and his partner found out that their baby had a problem that meant that she would die at birth. They were offered an abortion. *It is undoubtedly the most difficult thing and decision I have ever made in my life, the reason being that I could not see any clear-cut right or wrong, and it was really only the two of us who could make the decision.* Giving the parents time limits is a form of coercion that should be avoided. Even though many people aim to have an abortion before the point at which the baby's birth and death needs to be recorded (often 20 weeks, though it depends on where you are), it is more important to make sure you make the right decision than try to meet any deadlines. This is an important decision and there is no rush. It's a matter of life or death.

For doctors

Some researchers have expressed concern that if too many doctors suppress their own moral judgements regarding prenatal diagnosis and the decision to abort (in support of the 'official' commitment to non-directive patient counselling), then open debate between professionals working in morally contested fields will not be encouraged. They are concerned that this approach runs the risk of these fields being staffed by people with homogeneous moral views. This lack of diversity could lead to a lack of critical analysis and debate among staff about the ethos of, and standards of care within, their unit. These researchers suggest that this kind of debate not only helps to sustain high standards but, in addition, also helps to ensure that a humane (and not simply technical) service is provided for women and their families.[17]

---

17. B Farsides, C Williams and P Alderson, 'Aiming towards "moral equilibrium": health care professionals' views on working within the morally contested field of antenatal screening', *Journal of Medical Ethics*, vol. 30, no. 5, October 2004, pp. 505-9.

Choices

The options for the parents to consider are whether they will:

- abort the baby
- continue the pregnancy and prepare to take care of the baby
- look into palliative care if the baby is not expected to live long
- give the baby up for adoption.

If the parents decide to keep the baby then they will need ongoing physical, emotional and spiritual support. Caring for a disabled child is challenging. Nadia says, *I kept asking myself why. I will never have an answer. But I feel that I learnt to rely on God more to get me through.*[18]

You can pray for them, but don't tell them that God would only let this happen to a strong Christian—it takes away their freedom to tell you how hard it is sometimes.

Abortion for fetal abnormality

Many couples make the decision to abort a baby after they find out that there is an abnormality. This suggests that regardless of whether the parents want *a* baby, they have decided they don't want *this* baby.

Some liberal feminists reject the argument that antenatal screening expresses prejudice towards disability.[19] In particular, they argue that research into why women abort after a 'positive'[20] prenatal diagnosis is complex, and that it is wrong to read desires and intent into the actions of individual women.[21] This is not to say there are no selfish or prejudiced women who abort simply because they do not like disabled people, or because they find it difficult to envisage fitting a disabled child into their lifestyle. However, these feminists argue that to deny the right to abortion because of fears of eugenics denies women the opportunity to abort because of inadequate governmental support systems.[22] Christians would not agree with this thinking, and even some feminists who are

---

18. Discussion of living with disability is beyond the scope of this book.

19. MA Baily, 'Why I had amniocentesis', in E Parens and A Asch (eds), *Prenatal Testing and Disability Rights*, Georgetown University Press, Washington DC, 2000, pp. 64-71.

20. In medicine, a 'positive' result means the abnormality was detected. A 'negative' result means it wasn't detected.

21. A Brookes, 'Women's voices: Prenatal diagnosis and care for the disabled', *Health Care Analysis*, vol. 9, no. 2, 2001, pp. 133-50.

22. J McLaughlin, 'Screening networks: Shared agendas in feminist and disability movement challenges to antenatal screening and abortion', *Disability and Society*, vol. 18, no. 3, 2003, pp. 297-310.

staunchly pro-choice oppose abortion for defect:

> As Harvard University's Ruth Hubbard has explained, "It is one thing to abort when we don't want to be pregnant and quite another to want a baby, but to decide to abort this particular fetus we are carrying in hopes of coming up with a 'better' one next time".[23]

We do well to hesitate in judging the motives of those who choose abortion. Aborting a previously desired child because of birth defects is rarely done easily or happily, and for many it is a difficult decision full of regret and pain.[24] However, as in all scenarios where abortion is considered, it is important that in this situation the parents are informed that they *can* choose to *keep* the baby.

Julie says, *No-one actually said I had to end the pregnancy, but you know that's what the experts think is best.* Kay, on the other hand, was absolutely opposed to abortion and kept refusing to agree. *It was so hard, everyone seemed to think I was crazy, and I had to keep saying it over and over. But once I was in the antenatal section, the doctors were much more supportive and they were much more encouraging about what would happen. Even the percentages changed.* How many parents wish they could have kept their child, and how many didn't realize it was a feasible option?

Alison Brookes discovered three factors that influence women's decisions about whether to undertake prenatal diagnosis, as well as their use of the information made available by testing: the level of care a child will require, the level of care a woman feels confident to provide, and the level of care available for children with genetic conditions.[25]

In one way, the routine nature of antenatal testing can give parents a false sense of security. With all the tests offered, it is all too easy for prospective parents to forget that illness can befall a baby at any time during pregnancy and delivery, and after birth, and that the majority of birth defects are undetectable and unpreventable. It is well known that despite counselling, parents often take a negative prenatal screen test to mean there is nothing wrong with the child. Consequently, if the baby is found to have a problem late in pregnancy, or at birth, it may be all

---

23. Kristol, loc. cit.
24. R Rapp, 'Refusing prenatal diagnosis: The meanings of bioscience in a multicultural world', *Science, Technology and Human Values*, vol. 23, no. 1, January 1998, pp. 45-70.
25. Brookes, loc. cit.

the more difficult for them to handle. Remember, there is no test that guarantees a healthy baby.

Deciding to terminate the pregnancy

There are different procedures in different places, and parents will need to ask questions, wherever they are, if they decide to end the pregnancy. They need to know the facts about the termination procedure itself, the inherent risks of having it (or not having it), their choices, the delivery method for the baby, time spent with the baby after delivery, legal requirements (postmortem, birth/death certificates, funeral arrangements), who can stay with them, and what they can expect afterwards.[26] They will need to know about the various options for collecting memories of the baby, and the emotional challenges that can be expected.[27]

Cases

I will look now at two hypothetical cases, in order to consider the options beyond abortion when a parent discovers in prenatal screening that their child has an abnormality. I will differentiate between *lethal* (incompatible with life) and *non-lethal* birth defects.

Case 1: A 31-year-old woman and her husband are told after her 18-week scan that the baby has anencephaly (congenital absence of the brain), a condition that is incompatible with life.

At first glance, it might appear that termination of pregnancy is the quickest and easiest way to help parents recover from the grief of finding that their child has a serious abnormality. However, research suggests this may not be the case. The decision to abort for genetic abnormality may have a more negative impact than abortion for non-medical reasons.[28] While abortion is sometimes presented as the only option when a fetus is diagnosed with a life-limiting condition, I would suggest that a perinatal hospice is a better option. In this scenario, the pregnancy is continued while plans are made for palliative care (comfort care) for the child

---

26. Adapted from Support after Fetal Diagnosis of Abnormality (SAFDA), *Diagnosis of Abnormality in an Unborn Baby*, Northern Sydney and Central Coast NSW Health, Gosford, August 2006.
27. See chapter 11 for more information on these matters.
28. Royal Australian and New Zealand College of Obstetricians and Gynaecologists, *Termination of Pregnancy*, RANZCOG, Melbourne, November 2005, p. 26.

at the time of birth. If one considers life in the context of eternity, 9 months instead of 90 years is of little significance. Continuing pregnancy is consistent with allowing life to be realized to its full—albeit only until birth in this case.

What will this look like?[29]

During the pregnancy

Sadly, I have had some experience supporting families in this situation. They need a lot of encouragement. From professionals they need accurate information and good communication. Specialist antenatal units are great if one is available. The family will need emotional support and the parents may want to record the pregnancy in some way, such as through a journal or through photographs.

It was weird, harrowing, to move through the months of the pregnancy knowing that the baby will die. I have heard of one couple who really enjoyed the pregnancy as the special time of their baby's life—but we found it very challenging. At times, I wondered if abortion would have been a less protracted affair, even though we are glad we didn't take that option.

At the time of delivery

The pregnancy is continued until labour begins and birth occurs normally, in a supportive and comfortable setting.[30] It is helpful to have detailed discussions in advance so that the time between the birth and death of the child is used well. In my experience, parents who pursue this option have had the consolation of knowing they did all they could for their child as long as they were able, and the subsequent funerals have been a powerful witness to the value of human life.

Case 2: A 42-year-old woman is told that it is highly possible her fourth child will be born with Down syndrome.

When a non-lethal birth defect is diagnosed, parents face the challenge of life with a disabled child.

First, as a mother who was advised on grounds of fetal abnormality to abort a daughter who was subsequently born healthy, my first response is

---

29. In all of this it's important to remember that even when careful planning is done, the unexpected may occur in childbirth.

30. Sometimes labour needs to be induced, either because the hormonal triggers from the child are absent, or because the mother needs to deliver before labour occurs naturally, for her own health.

to remember the false positive rate! Sometimes doctors can get it wrong.

Second, we know that some birth defects regarded as indications for abortion can be treated successfully in the womb or after birth. The confusion in our society about the value of unborn human life is highlighted by the fact that—hypothetically speaking—in one operating theatre a 22-week-old child can be treated for a birth defect (such as hypoplastic left heart) with intrauterine surgery (surgery in the womb), while in the next operating theatre a 22-week-old child can be aborted because of exactly the same problem. Some evidence suggests that surgery performed in the womb may give better results than surgery after birth,[31] however, what can be treated this way is limited because maternal outcomes are not as good.[32]

Third, we know that many families with a disabled child have indeed been able to manage, and they—and many disabled adults—would assert that these lives can be worthwhile and satisfying.

During the pregnancy
It can be helpful to spend time during the pregnancy understanding more about what will happen at and after the birth. If the child is expected to need medical care, it may be possible to meet those who will be involved beforehand. Will the hospital be able to provide the appropriate care, or will a transfer be necessary? When will the baby be able to come home? It's difficult to prepare parents before the birth of any baby, but information will help. Non-judgemental support will be needed before and after the birth.

Education may be needed to help parents understand what the disability entails. For example, Down syndrome is often considered an indication for abortion, and without counselling, many parents would not be aware

31. NS Adzick, EA Thom, CY Spong, JW Brock III, PK Burrows, MP Johnson, LJ Howell, JA Farrell, ME Dabrowiak, LN Sutton, N Gupta, NB Tulipan, ME D'Alton and DL Farmer, 'A randomized trial of prenatal versus postnatal repair of myelomeningocele', *New England Journal of Medicine*, vol. 364, no. 11, 17 March 2011, pp. 993-1004.
32. E Danzer and NS Adzick, 'Fetal surgery for myelomeningocele: patient selection, perioperative management and outcomes', *Fetal diagnosis and Therapy*, vol. 30, no. 3, November 2011, pp. 163-73.

that these children can attend school and live semi-independent lives. They tend to have happy dispositions and I am sure they are much loved by their families. Sadly, it often happens that these families struggle to get the help they need in terms of community support, and Christians should be alert to the need to improve available services.

An interesting report from the United Kingdom indicates that the number of children born with Down syndrome rose by about 15% between 2000 and 2006. According to the Down Syndrome Association, more parents now feel that life and society have improved for the people affected. Religious or pro-life beliefs were a deciding factor for only about a third of parents surveyed. Others said they had been influenced by personal acquaintance with people who had Down syndrome.[33]

> *I was born with severe spina bifida, and am confined to a wheelchair as a result. Despite my disability and the gloomy predictions made by doctors at my birth, I am now leading a very full, happy and satisfying life by any standards. I am most definitely glad to be alive. Yet, because handicapped people are now presumed by some doctors, philosophers and society in general to have the capacity only for being miserable and an economic burden on the community, most of those who would otherwise grow up to be like me are now aborted or "allowed to die" (such a comfortable euphemism) at birth.*[35]

Some of the most passionate objections to the discarding of disabled unborn babies come from those who are disabled themselves. They find it highly offensive that society should judge their lives to be not worth living.[34]

It is interesting to consider why we think that disabled children suffer. Do we really think they suffer so much from being disabled that they would be better off dead? Do we think they will suffer living in a world where they don't fit in? Or are we concerned that we will suffer because of them?

In fact, the disabled do not necessarily suffer the way we imagine *we would suffer if we were them*.[36] Those who are born disabled

---

33. M Cook, 'Down syndrome births rising in UK', *BioEdge*, 26 November 2008 (viewed 18 January 2012): www.bioedge.org/index.php/bioethics/bioethics_article/8391
34. A Asch, 'Prenatal diagnosis and selective abortion: A challenge to practice and policy', *American Journal of Public Health*, vol. 89, no. 11, November 1999, pp. 1649-57.
35. A Davis, 'Yes, the baby should live', *New Scientist*, vol. 108, no. 1480, 31 October 1985, p. 54.
36. Hauerwas, op. cit., p. 569.

may be aware that they cannot do what others do, but for someone born blind, sight is not missed in the same way that we, who are so dependent on sight, would miss it. Harriet Johnson explains:

> ...disability shapes all we are. Those disabled later in life adapt. We take constraints that no-one would choose and build rich and satisfying lives within them. We enjoy pleasures other people enjoy, and pleasures peculiarly our own. We have something the world needs.[37]

Perhaps our concern for any suffering the disabled might experience would be better directed at changing things in us and our world, than at ensuring they are never born.

Kathy McReynolds, from the Christian Institute on Disability, suggests that if the disabled do suffer, it is partly due to the marginalization and discrimination they encounter. She encourages us to discover human dignity within the brokenness of disability by acknowledging the source of human dignity: God himself, who has stamped his image on us.[38]

Perhaps our attitude towards disability and abortion is too much influenced by the way the issue is framed in our world: the language of 'personhood', competing rights, a problem to be solved by individuals, the need to justify our decisions and find reasons for allowing the disabled to be born in spite of their disability. This is not how God views the situation. The Bible teaches us to be a people who practise hospitality and provide for the needs of others. Jesus said:

> "Then the King will say to those on his right, 'Come, you who are blessed by my Father, inherit the kingdom prepared for you from the foundation of the world. For I was hungry and you gave me food, I was thirsty and you gave me drink, I was a stranger and you welcomed me, I was naked and you clothed me, I was sick and you visited me, I was in prison and you came to me.' Then the righteous will answer him, saying, 'Lord, when did we see you hungry and feed you, or thirsty and give you drink? And when did we see you a stranger and welcome you, or naked and clothe you? And when did we see you sick or in prison and visit you?' And the King will answer

37.   HM Johnson, 'Unspeakable conversations', *New York Times Magazine*, 16 February 2003.
38.   K McReynolds, 'Disability and dignity in a global context', paper presented to the Global Bioethics Conference, Chicago, 18 July 2009.

them, 'Truly, I say to you, as you did it to one of the least of these my brothers, you did it to me'." (Matt 25:34-40)

Who is more vulnerable than an unborn child?

We have been created for relationships, and God has given us Christian community. The Christian life is not intended to be one of isolation and self-containment. A problem that seems overwhelming for an individual can often be eased significantly by sharing it with a community of Christian brothers and sisters. I am encouraged when I hear of churches working together to help those caught in the dilemma of carrying an unwanted child, no matter why it is unwanted.

> In this church, when a teenager has a baby that she cannot care for, the church baptizes the baby and gives him or her to an older couple in the church that has the time and wisdom to raise the child. That way, says the pastor, the couple can raise the teenage mother along with the baby. "That", the pastor says, "is how we do it".[39]

Adoption

Some parents may not want to abort their child, but feel that they would be unable to cope with a child who has special needs. In this situation, bringing the child to term and giving him or her up for adoption may be the best solution. Once again, the parents need information as well as supportive counseling. They may feel grief as the birth approaches and the time for relinquishing the child arrives.

Our attitude to the disabled, or to any other 'unwanted' child, should be one of welcome; they give us an opportunity to express Christian hospitality. I am aware of many authors who assume that relieving suffering may necessitate the elimination of the sufferer.[40] How did we come to this?

As I write I am aware of how perverse my words will sound to some readers, but suffering is not the worst thing that can happen to you. In order to emulate our Lord Jesus, who gave himself for us, we will do what we can to ease the suffering of others, while also communicating the message, 'It's good that you are here'.

---

39. T Hamilton-Poor quoted in Hauerwas, op. cit., p. 606.
40. This has been applied not just to disability but also in the context of euthanasia.

Longer-term support

If, as we have noted above, Jesus calls us to offer hospitality to the disabled, how can we support those who join our church communities? Because disability can last a lifetime, Christian communities will need to consciously and actively plan how to continue supporting disabled brothers and sisters; it is easy to grow lax when a need is ongoing. We are all members of the one body and we can be confident that we all have a part to play in the life of the church (1 Corinthians 12).

A list generated by those living with disability included the following practical tips that are worth considering if you want to help:

- Try to understand and provide a listening ear.
- Ask for prayer points and pray in an ongoing way.
- Give spiritual support (ministers have a key role in making contact with families, answering their questions as they seek to understand their position, and making sure the church does not forget their needs).
- Provide respite (offer to give the parents a break, or pay for a qualified carer if professional expertise is required).
- Provide home help (shopping, cooking and cleaning).
- Give financial support.
- Modify your church building so that no person with a disability is excluded (this may include building ramps, installing a hearing loop, providing special care for children so parents can attend a service).
- Reach out (invite the disabled to church and show your willingness to break down barriers, and make sure church functions are inclusive).
- Start a support group for those isolated by disability.
- Care for the siblings of the disabled.
- Take on an advocacy role to improve services for the disabled.[41]

Ruth and I have been Christians all of our married life and have found that our faith is the basis for coping with Alison day to day and for hoping for a life that is ultimately joyful and everlasting. We know that our resources are limited but that God's are unlimited and we can always turn to him when life seems impossible. God doesn't solve all of our problems and grant all

---

41. Hurley, op. cit., pp. 76-7.

our reasonable desires for Alison. She has not become 'normal' or shed her shocking behaviours. But there is help from our heavenly Father and there is eternal hope in the midst of all our joys, heartaches and suffering in the present life.[42]

Sometimes we feel dreadfully sad that we cannot have a conversation with William. This is something we truly long for. When we feel deep grief in our hearts that our son doesn't relate to us in a way that we yearn for, we're actually reminded of the grief that God feels for us, his children, to relate to him as we should. He, too, longs for us to talk to him.[43]

I have spent the last two or three months feeling sad, heavy and dismayed by the idea that my child is going to struggle in life with his understanding and communication. But stopping to analyse the fears I have for him, I can see that I'm most afraid of other people's reactions to him. I'm worried that he'll be bullied, excluded, laughed at, tormented or just plain ignored. How do I know he will suffer these things? Because I know the tendency of my own heart, and I know my own sinful reactions to others who are different from me. At times, I have bullied, excluded, laughed at, tormented and just plain ignored people who were 'imperfect'. And in doing so, I have shown my own imperfections, which are far more serious, far more deadly and far more vile than any physical or mental disability could ever be. The real human imperfection is the sinful, unloving heart that each one of us carries inside.[44]

---

42. ibid., p. 15.
43. ibid., p. 21.
44. ibid., p. 18.

Infertility

Three things are never satisfied;
    four never say, "Enough":
Sheol, the barren womb,
    the land never satisfied with water,
    and the fire that never says, "Enough". (Prov 30:15b-16)

INFERTILITY IS PAINFUL, and often unexpected.

Married Christian couples usually just assume they will have children; they don't anticipate any problems, because they have never tried to have a child before. If conception becomes difficult, they then realize they have no control over what happens. They don't sleep well and sexual intimacy starts to suffer.

What makes it harder is that in many places infertility is a taboo subject, and many couples discover they can't talk about it with anyone. It becomes a very lonely experience, especially in a church full of family programs. Meanwhile, life gets put on hold. It's hard to plan ahead. The emotional pain gets worse every time menstruation recurs, confirming that there's no pregnancy in place. One doctor said, "In the past three decades, researchers have made great strides in the treatment of infertility… Yet all of that is the relatively simple part. The more difficult part is mending the broken hearts."[1]

It's very difficult for those on the outside to understand an infertile

---

1.   SL Glahn and WR Cutrer, *The Infertility Companion*, Zondervan, Grand Rapids, 2004, p. 47.

couple's level of suffering, but some sense of the pain and desperation can be gauged from the efforts they make to overcome their problem: the time and money spent, and the stress and pain of fertility treatment.

In some ways, the advent of assisted reproductive technology (ART), such as in vitro fertilization (IVF), has increased the anguish of infertile couples. The availability of these therapies forces them to decide if they want to take on the burden of treatment, and it can prolong the struggle for years. The Bible validates this emotional pain when it is compared to the insatiable natural phenomena listed at the start of this chapter.

In this chapter, I will look at infertility from both the pastoral and the medical perspectives, covering the following subjects:
- Definition of infertility
- Theology
- Infertility in a fallen world
- Options
- Biology of pregnancy
- Causes of infertility
- Medical assessment
- Treatment
- Living with infertility
- Coming to terms with infertility

Infertility: a definition

Infertility is a medical diagnosis that can be made when a couple has been having normal unprotected intercourse for a year or more without conceiving a child. It is a decrease in the ability to conceive, or 'subfertility'. This should be distinguished from *sterility*, which implies an absolute inability to achieve pregnancy. *Primary infertility* describes those who have never conceived. *Secondary infertility* is a medical diagnosis for couples who have conceived successfully in the past but are then unable to conceive. It is also used to describe couples in whom conception has occurred but the pregnancy has not progressed past 20 weeks.[2]

It is difficult to know exactly how many couples infertility affects because not everyone presents for treatment, but it is thought to be a

---

2.   A Kumar, S Ghadir, N Eskandari and AH DeCherney, 'Infertility', in AH DeCherney, L Nathan and TM Goodwin (eds), *Current Diagnosis and Treatment: Obstetrics and Gynecology*, 10th edn, McGraw-Hill Medical, New York, 2006, pp. 917-25.

problem for around 1 in 6 couples of reproductive age.

There are many reasons people want to have children—for example, to continue the family name, to make sure they have someone to look after them when they're old, or as a symbol of the marriage union. Some people respond to family expectations, some aim to help build the kingdom of God, while others don't really think about it much at all. Whatever the motivation is, theologian Karl Barth suggests that:

> In some degree they will all feel their childlessness to be a lack,
> a gap in the circle of what nature obviously intends for man, the
> absence of an important, desirable and hoped for good. And those
> who have children and know what they owe to them will not try to
> dissuade them. The more grateful they are for the gift of children, so
> much more intimately they will feel this lack with them. Parenthood
> is one of the most palpable illuminations and joys of life, and those
> to whom it is denied for different reasons have undoubtedly to bear
> the pain of loss.[3]

For me, the longing for a child was an overwhelming biological urge that is difficult to describe. I just can't imagine what it would have felt like if that urge had never been fulfilled. Infertility from any cause is an enormous hardship for a couple to bear. How are Christians to understand it?

What the Bible says

Child-bearing is a good thing. It is not wrong to want to raise a family with your spouse. Christians believe that children are a gift from God. Throughout the Bible, fertility is described as a blessing for the obedient (Deut 28:4-11) and a lifetime asset:

> Behold, children are a heritage from the LORD,
>   the fruit of the womb a reward.
> Like arrows in the hand of a warrior
>   are the children of one's youth.
> Blessed is the man
>   who fills his quiver with them! (Ps 127:3-5a)

---

3.   K Barth, 'Parents and Children', in *Church Dogmatics*, vol. III.4, GW Bromiley and TF Torrence (eds), T and T Clark, London and New York, 2010, pp. 265-6.

By contrast, infertility is often seen as a curse from God. Deuteronomy 28 presents the opposite of fertility as not just barrenness, but also mayhem and exile. This passage anticipates the sacking of Jerusalem and the Babylonian exile in 587 BC, prophesying "cursed" offspring (v. 18) and exile with loss of children:

> "Your sons and your daughters shall be given to another people,
> while your eyes look on and fail with longing for them all day long,
> but you shall be helpless." (v. 32)

> "You shall father sons and daughters, but they shall not be yours, for
> they shall go into captivity." (v. 41)

Even the unimaginable cannibalism that eventuated as besieged Jerusalem starved is mentioned (vv. 53-57). Later in the chapter, the Lord again threatens to punish disobedience with barrenness:

> "Whereas you were as numerous as the stars of heaven, you shall
> be left few in number, because you did not obey the voice of the
> LORD your God. And as the LORD took delight in doing you good and
> multiplying you, so the LORD will take delight in bringing ruin upon
> you and destroying you. And you shall be plucked off the land that
> you are entering to take possession of it." (vv. 62-63)

We also see a connection between infertility and punishment from God when wives commit adultery (Num 5:11-28), and when adultery is committed between an aunt and nephew, or brother-in-law and sister-in-law (Lev 20:20-21).

Because of these and other passages, infertile men and women often search their hearts seeking reasons for God 'punishing' them—indeed, as do Christians who are suffering in other ways (through sickness, or the death of a child, etc.). There is an important balance to be maintained in dealing with these feelings.

At one level, we are right to realize that all the sickness, suffering and trouble of our world is a consequence of the Fall, of God's judgement against human rebellion and sin. Every time we see or experience any kind of suffering, evil or injustice, it should remind us that this is a broken, sinful and judged world—a world in need of remaking. It should prompt us to remember that we ourselves are sinful and in need of forgiveness. And it should make us long for the new creation where there will be no "mourning nor crying nor pain any more, for the former things have passed away" (Rev 21:4). Infertility is one of these signs of the world's brokenness, and the heartbreak and agony that it causes are real.

And yet on the other hand, we shouldn't conclude that because we are suffering from infertility, it means God is punishing *us*, personally and specifically, for a particular sin that we have committed. Suffering and trouble in this world are not connected with our personal sins in a neat one-to-one correspondence like this. This is the message of Job, whose 'comforters' were convinced, quite wrongly, that Job's terrible suffering must be God's direct punishment against a particular sin or sins that Job had committed.

This is also the message of John 9 and the man born blind. The disciples asked Jesus, "Rabbi, who sinned, this man or his parents, that he was born blind?" (v. 2). But Jesus reminded his disciples that we can't make a simple direct connection between suffering and sin: "It was not that this man sinned, or his parents, but that the works of God might be displayed in him" (v. 3). In the purposes of God, there was a reason for the man's blindness, but it was not his sin or his parents'.

We also know by the example of Elizabeth, John the Baptist's mother, that infertility is not necessarily due to sin. We are told that both she and her husband, Zechariah, were "righteous before God, walking blamelessly in all the commandments and statutes of the Lord. But they had no child, because Elizabeth was barren..." (Luke 1:6-7).

Indeed, Elizabeth's story is one of many instances in the Bible where God 'opens the womb' of the barren woman and blesses her with a child. Sarah, the wife of Abraham, was blessed in her old age with the first child of the promise (Genesis 15-21). In the next generation, "Isaac prayed to the LORD for his wife, because she was barren. And the LORD granted his prayer, and Rebekah his wife conceived" (Gen 25:21). Then again in Jacob's family: "When the LORD saw that Leah was hated, he opened her womb, but Rachel was barren" (Gen 29:31). Eventually God remembered Rachel and opened her womb as well (Gen 30:22-24). God was closely involved with the early generations of Abraham's offspring.

The mother of Samson was also sterile until the angel of the LORD told her she would conceive a son who would bring the deliverance of Israel from the hands of the Philistines (Judg 13:2-24). Hannah wept and prayed for a child who she promised to commit to the Lord's service, and her prayer was answered in the birth of Samuel, destined to be Israel's prophet, anointing both Saul and David as kings over Israel (1 Sam 1:11-20).

However, just as we shouldn't conclude that infertility is a particular punishment on us from God, nor should we conclude that God is bound to bless us with fertility if we are obedient, godly Christians. God worked in the lives of these particular women in the Bible for special purposes that apply to them alone. We cannot claim promises that were made to others in specific contexts that we do not share.

But there is no doubt that God is sovereign over fertility, just as he is over everything in our world. Eve acknowledged this at the birth of Cain, when she said, "I have gotten a man with the help of the LORD" (Gen 4:1). Sarah (or Sarai, at this point) acknowledged that it was God who had prevented her having children (Gen 16:2). As in all things, God is in charge.

I remember being particularly conscious of this when I was pregnant. We were not technically infertile ourselves, but as we started trying for a baby, we were in touch with a lot of couples who were. I knew I could not take becoming—or staying—pregnant for granted. I think this helped me a great deal.

When we start thinking about building a family our expectations about parenting are often very strong. We have such high hopes. But this means that for some of us there is a long way to fall.

Is this perhaps a problem in the way we teach young couples about marriage and family? Should we start teaching young people more clearly that children are a gift we should not take for granted? It's important to strike a balance. Of course, we will continue to value marriage as the right place for the begetting and raising of children, but we also need to recognize with humility that God may have other purposes for our particular marriage.

Nowhere in the Bible does God promise that we will all have children. He hears all our prayers (Ps 65:2)—but sometimes he answers slowly, and sometimes the answer is "No". The apostle Paul tells the story of how God gave him a thorn in his flesh (although we are not sure what the physical ailment was): "Three times I pleaded with the Lord about this, that it should leave me. But he said to me, 'My grace is sufficient for you, for my power is made perfect in weakness'" (2 Cor 12:8-9a).

The Bible does not answer all the questions we have about infertility. But it does help us understand the character of our God. We live in a fallen world and our bodies are subject to decay. But that is not the end of the story.

I don't want to minimize the pain of longing for a child who never arrives. But when we look at what God does promise, we realize that he will never leave us alone (Heb 13:5). He sent his Son to share our human life, with all its weakness and pain (Heb 2:17). We know that Jesus can sympathize with the deepest of our hurts.

God may choose to open a barren womb (as he did for the women above), but ultimately, whether or not we have children is in his hands. It can be difficult to think this way when you are in the midst of a storm. For those suffering with infertility, my prayer is:

> …that according to the riches of his glory he may grant you to be strengthened with power through his Spirit in your inner being, so that Christ may dwell in your hearts through faith—that you, being rooted and grounded in love, may have strength to comprehend with all the saints what is the breadth and length and height and depth, and to know the love of Christ that surpasses knowledge, that you may be filled with all the fullness of God. Now to him who is able to do far more abundantly than all that we ask or think, according to the power at work within us, to him be glory in the church and in Christ Jesus throughout all generations, forever and ever. Amen. (Eph 3:16-21)

Infertility in a fallen world

The number of infertility clinic visits is increasing. Why is this?

It is partly because more women are leaving child-bearing until after 35 years of age. In the United States, according to data from the National Center for Health Statistics and the Census Bureau, in 1990, teenagers had a higher share of all births (13%) than women aged 35 years and older (9%). In 2008, the reverse was true—10% of births were to teenagers, compared with 14% to women aged 35 years and older.[4] In Australia, around 21% of women giving birth were aged 35 or over in 2006, up from 15% in 1997.[5] In the United Kingdom, the Office for National Statistics reports show that fertility rates for women aged 35-39 and 40-44 increased in 2009 by 1.0% and 2.4%, respectively. This continues the trend of the last two decades, during which the number of

---

4.   G Livingston and D Cohn, *The New Demography of American Motherhood*, Pew Research Center, Washington DC, 19 August 2010 (viewed 6 January 2012): www.pewsocialtrends.org/files/2010/10/754-new-demography-of-motherhood.pdf

5.   Australian Institute of Health and Welfare (AIHW), *More Births to Older Mother Trend Still Continuing*, media release, AIHW, Canberra, 9 December 2008.

live births to mothers aged 40 and over has nearly trebled, from 9,336 in 1989 to 26,976 in 2009.[6]

In some cases, couples delay child-bearing until their careers are established and they are financially stable; easily available, reversible contraception has made this possible. The number of celebrities conceiving after the age of 35 years has perpetuated a myth that the biological clock can be ignored and child-bearing can safely be delayed. When we read about these celebrities, what is often not mentioned is that many have used eggs donated by younger women (which can be difficult and expensive to acquire). The number of older women who have tried, and failed, to conceive in their forties is usually not in the news at all. Some women find it difficult to find a partner who wants to have children. United States economist Sylvia Ann Hewlett surveyed more than 1,000 professional women and discovered that 42% were still childless after age 40, and only 14% had ever explicitly renounced motherhood as a goal.[7] While women generally know that their fertility reduces over time, many do not know when. Hewlett found that nearly 9 out of 10 young women were confident they could get pregnant in their forties.[8]

In fact, a woman's fertility begins to decline at age 27. With regard to fertility there is only one message in the medical media: women are urged *not* to delay having children.

Other factors that account for increased fertility problems are the social phenomena of multiple sexual partners, and the consequent transmission of infectious disease and development of pelvic inflammatory disease and other problems that can damage the reproductive system.

The popular media sends contradictory messages to women about fertility. On the one hand, it's considered liberating for women to not let a man get in the way of personal development; but more recently, celebrity babies in the media are reinforcing the 'old-fashioned' view that the role of women is to get married and have babies—like the 1950s, with edgier clothes.

This whole way of thinking seems to define a woman by her relationships—whereas the Bible legitimizes both singleness and mother-

---

6.   Office for National Statistics (ONS), *Births and Deaths in England and Wales 2009*, statistical bulletin, ONS, Newport, 21 July 2010.

7.   SA Hewlett, *Creating a Life*, Miramax, New York, 2002.

8.   ibid.

hood for women, and our value does not depend on which we embrace. Furthermore, if we do invest too much significance in being a parent when considering our fundamental identity, the pain of infertility and childlessness is heightened even more. As Christians, we need to find our identity in Christ. The church should be the source of significant bonds of love and affection, providing opportunities to love and serve others. We should not regard it as a place that serves families, and thus a place to be avoided when we don't fit the criteria for entry. As Christians, we need to be careful to avoid the insidious influence of public opinion (Rom 12:2).

Approximately 13% of women are diagnosed with infertility (7%-28% depending on age), and this has remained stable for the past 40 years. Ethnicity or race appears to have little effect, but primary infertility has increased while secondary infertility has decreased, probably due to the delayed child-bearing trend. Sterility affects 1%-2% of couples.[9] In normal fertile couples having frequent unprotected intercourse (i.e. making love every 2-3 days throughout your cycle), there is around an 85% chance of conceiving within one year.

Is there a *right* to have a child?

In community discussions about access to assisted reproductive technology (ART), we often hear talk about the 'right' to have a child. Does such a right exist? Many would say so—but it is difficult to see a basis for it. In legal terms, there are jurisdictions that make sure access to medical therapies like ART is available to everyone, but, as I have previously mentioned, 'rights talk' can confuse needs with wants.[10]

To establish a genuine 'right to reproduce' requires an argument to support the claim that having a child is a *need* rather than a want. The World Health Organization (WHO) has defined 'health' as "a state of complete physical, mental, and social well-being and not merely the absence of disease or infirmity".[11] With this in mind, proponents of this

---

9. Kumar et al., loc. cit.
10. The ethics of human rights are discussed in chapter 5.
11. Preamble to the Constitution of the World Health Organization (WHO) as signed on 22 July 1946 by the representatives of 61 states, and entered into force on 7 April 1948. See WHO Interim Commission, 'Proceedings and final acts of the International Health Conference held in New York from 19 June to 22 July 1946', *Official Records of the World Health Organization*, no. 2, June 1948, p. 100. The definition has not been amended since 1948.

view therefore argue that:

- the strength of the desire to reproduce is biological in nature and requires the satisfaction of that desire if we are to live fulfilled lives
- infertility is a disease we are compelled to treat to allow for physical wellbeing
- it is not the role of governments to regulate private sexual relationships
- there are laws in many places that protect the right to marry and have a family (including the United Nations' Universal Declaration of Human Rights).12

Response:

1. The physical impossibility for some people to bear a child (sterility) suggests that reproduction cannot be a 'right', because no-one has the power to make it possible for everyone.
2. While we can argue about whether infertility is the disease or the underlying problem is the disease, the question then is, "Who is responsible for providing treatment?" Is *all* healthcare a right, or just basic healthcare? What does this include? A universal right would mean it should be provided to people in every country.
3. It's a fact that governments have long regulated private sexual relationships—by prohibiting incest and paedophilia, and by restricting polygamy and polyandry, for instance.
4. While there are laws allowing adults to marry and have families, these are considered to be negative rights that prevent interference by the state, rather than positive rights that oblige the state to assist the infertile with every treatment available.

I think it is difficult to argue that reproduction is a universal human right rather than a want. Regardless, 'rights talk' is not biblical. We have already seen that children are a gift from God—a privilege. But we are not all given the same gifts.

---

12. Arguments listed are taken from L Frith, 'Reproductive Technologies, Overview', in R Chadwick (ed.), *Encyclopedia of Applied Ethics*, vol. 3, Academic Press, San Diego, 1998, pp. 817-28.

What are the options for a Christian couple who might be infertile?

Couples trying to come to terms with the idea that they may be infertile are incredibly vulnerable. They can easily commence a treatment that promises a child without stopping to think what it involves. Dr David Knight, a fertility doctor in Sydney, is well aware of the competing interests in an IVF clinic:

> People are so desperate to have a child. I could get them to do almost anything. And that is a very scary and very powerful position to be in. And that's why we have to work hard to ensure that the couple's vulnerability is not exploited in pursuit of business objectives.[13]

This makes it particularly important that any couple in this situation seeks careful counselling in the early stages of their discussions, before anything is decided. It is ethically acceptable for Christians to seek medical help to restore the natural function of child-bearing,[14] but not all 'standard' medical therapy will be morally acceptable for those who want to protect life from its beginning.

Given that life starts at fertilization, what are the options for couples who find themselves in this position?

1. It's okay to pursue no further treatment. Some couples may be happy to accept that child-bearing is not God's current plan for them, and look to his guidance for the future. Christian ethicist Brent Waters describes marriage as not simply a means of reproductive self-fulfilment, or the parallel stories of a woman and a man, so much as a single story "whose bond shapes who they become in their life together".[15]

2. It's possible to wait. Even though infertility is diagnosed after one year of trying to become pregnant, only 85% of couples are expected to conceive in the first year. Sometimes 'infertility' is really just impatience. For those considering taking things further, however, some doctors would advise that they not wait longer than 6 months if any of the following apply:

---

13. Quoted in J Macken, "How much is (s)he worth?", *Sunday Life Sun-Herald Magazine*, 25 March 2007, pp. 18-21.
14. See chapter 16.
15. B Waters, *Reproductive Technology*, Darton, Longman and Todd, London, 2001, p. 41.

- the woman is over 35 years of age
- there is a history of amenorrhoea (no periods), oligomenorrhoea (infrequent periods) or pelvic inflammatory disease
- either partner has had treatment for cancer or a serious illness, such as diabetes or hypertension.[16]

3. The couple can seek a diagnosis to determine the cause of infertility. This can be helpful even if no further treatment is pursued, just to know what is going on. Sometimes the problem underlying the infertility can be corrected easily. However, couples need to be careful that they continue to regard infertility as a joint problem within their marriage—rather than one partner's problem—so that blame is not focused on one person. This helps marital unity.

4. Subsequent to diagnosis, couples may be offered correction of a medical problem or a recommendation to go straight to ART treatment. It is at this point that I would particularly urge Christian couples to stop, pray, collect information, think carefully and not just agree to anything that will help them achieve their desire for a baby. Gerry remembers, *We were given a 100% impossibility of falling pregnant naturally, so the process of thinking through IVF as our only solution for having our own children was a hard journey for us.* Couples should take it slowly; problems are avoided by looking ahead.[17]

5. Couples may consider adoption at any point of their journey. It helps if they have come to terms with the loss of the potential for biological offspring before exploring this option. It is possible to have a healthy, loving family without any genetic link.[18] Embryo adoption is a new option to consider.[19]

There are many known causes of infertility. The problems for secondary infertility are almost identical to those of primary infertility. To understand the problem, we need to understand the normal biology of pregnancy.

---

16. National Collaborating Centre for Women's and Children's Health (NCCWCH), *Fertility: Assessment and Treatment for People with Fertility Problems*, clinical guideline, RCOG Press, London, 2004.

17. See chapter 12 for a discussion of ART.

18. Is it really the biological link that makes a child your own? When you think of the prevalence of donated sperm and eggs in ART, it becomes clear that for a lot of people, the genetic link is not what matters. And the fact that a new family is formed through marriage between two unrelated people shows that love does not require a biological link.

19. See chapter 14.

Biology of pregnancy

The first step of pregnancy is fertilization. This requires the egg and sperm, at the correct stage of maturity, to be brought together. Next, the resulting embryo needs to be transported to the uterus at a time when the endometrium (uterus lining) is ready to support implantation and further development of the embryo. For all these events to occur in sequence requires intact reproductive systems in the man and the woman, with intercourse occurring sufficiently frequently for the sperm to arrive at the fallopian tube when an egg happens to be there (there is only a 12-24 hour window of opportunity). Even when fertilization occurs, it is estimated that over 70% of the resulting embryos are abnormal and fail to develop or implant.[20] When you think about it, it is not surprising that some people are unable to conceive. What's surprising is that anyone manages to have children at all!

Female reproduction

At puberty, a woman has around 400,000 immature eggs stored in her ovaries. When she starts menstruating in her early teens, she releases an egg every month when she ovulates. The female ovulatory cycle is explained in detail in chapter 6, but basically, in the first half of the menstrual cycle, the egg develops in the follicles of the ovaries in response to hormones. About halfway through the cycle there is a surge of oestrogen when the egg is released into the fallopian tube (ovulation), which thickens the endometrium (uterine lining).

If the egg is joined with a sperm in the fallopian tube following sexual intercourse, fertilization takes place and an embryo is formed. The embryo grows as it moves down the fallopian tube towards the uterus, and at the end of the first week it attaches to the endometrium in a process called implantation.[21] Hormones produced first by the woman's body, and then by the placenta, sustain the pregnancy until the child is born. It is not necessary for a woman to orgasm for fertilization to take place.

If the egg is not fertilized, hormone production stops and the endometrial lining (with the egg) is shed from the body in menstruation (the woman's period). This occurs monthly until a woman reaches menopause around 50 years of age.

---

20. DR Meldrum, 'Infertility and assisted reproductive technologies', in NF Hacker, JG Moore and JC Gambone (eds), *Essentials of Obstetrics and Gynecology*, 4th edn, Saunders, Philadelphia, 2004, pp. 413-21.
21. See diagram 1: Female reproductive organs in chapter 2.

Male reproduction

The male is born with two testes. Each testicle has to make and store sperm on a regular basis. Beginning at puberty, a new stock is made every 74 days in response to a surge of the hormones testosterone, gonadotropin-releasing hormone (GnRH), luteinizing hormone (LH) and follicle-stimulating hormone (FSH). The epididymis (the coiled tubes that store and carry sperm from the testes) aids in the development of the sperm and helps it to travel through the vas deferens tubes and the ejaculatory duct. As it travels, the sperm combines with secretions from the epididymis, vas deferens, seminal vesicles and the prostate (the secretions are collectively known as seminal plasma) to make semen. The seminal plasma provides nutrients for the sperm and protects them during their journey through the female reproductive tract (which is usually hostile to sperm). When the man has an orgasm during sexual intercourse, the semen travels through the urethra, out of the penis and into the woman's vagina in ejaculation. The sperm must make its way through the cervix to the uterus and into the fallopian tube. If an egg is travelling through the fallopian tube at this time, the sperm can enter the egg, resulting in fertilization. Approximately 200-500 million sperm are normally released per ejaculation.

Diagram 4: Male reproductive organs

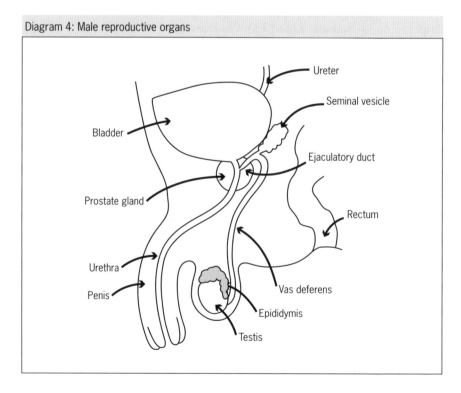

Causes of infertility

Infertility can result from problems in either spouse, or both. There are some geographical variations, but overall, a cause for the infertility can be found in 80% of cases with an even distribution of male and female factors. Male factors account for about a third, female factors for about the same number, and about 40% of cases are due to multiple factors. Estimates vary, but for 5%-30% of couples no cause is found. (The wide range is due to varying ways of defining 'no cause' in research.)

Age

A couple aged 30 with no infertility problems has an 80% chance of conceiving within 12 months; at 40, a 50% chance; at 45, a 10% chance.

Female

By the time she is 40, a woman has only a few thousand eggs left. As the eggs age, they are harder to fertilize and less likely to produce healthy embryos. There is a drop in fertility, an increase in miscarriage rate, an increase in perinatal death rate and an increase in fetal abnormality. Also, intercourse tends to decrease in frequency with age. The biological clock is real, and no advances in reproductive technology have been able to slow it down.

For doctors

Fertility is reduced because of fewer available follicles and eggs, and reduced ovarian and oocyte function. The oocyte is reduced in quality and has a thicker zona pellucida, which may interfere with fertilization. With increased age, the proportion of oocytes with metabolic errors that prevent a successful pregnancy also increases. There is evidence that the increased fetal abnormality rate with rising age is related to higher rates of aneuploidy during meiosis, or the 'dance of the chromosomes' as Robert Edwards (father of IVF) described it. With age, there is also an increased incidence of uterine disease and reduced endometrial receptivity, and a higher likelihood of other medical illnesses.

Male

Men are also putting off having children, but some of them do have that luxury. Pablo Picasso fathered a child when he was 66, and I once had a patient who had a child in his eighties. "Life doesn't stop at thirty", he told me after I finally accepted he didn't mean he'd had a *grandchild*. The effect of age on male fertility is less clear but some evidence suggests the decline parallels that in women.[22] The pregnancy rate goes down, the miscarriage rate goes up, and for those over 40 years of age, male infertility is a definite risk, with more chromosomal (genetic) abnormalities detected.[23] Slightly reduced testosterone may lead to reduced libido (sex drive), the testes become smaller and softer, there is more erectile dysfunction, and there is a reduction in normal sperm; thus the ability to conceive is reduced. Worldwide, male fertility rates are declining, and it is possible that environmental as well as genetic factors are contributing.

Lifestyle factors

You may be stuck with your age, but there are some things that you *can* modify that may affect fertility as well as the health of the baby.[24]

Anne Clark, a fertility specialist in Sydney, screened the blood of men in her reproductive clinic and found that more than a third of them had vitamin D deficiency. These men were also deficient in folate and had high levels of homocysteine (a protein associated with cell toxicity). In the couples where the man had his nutritional deficiency corrected, just over half conceived naturally or with minimal treatment.[25]

Pre-conception health

Given that several lifestyle factors are known to contribute to infertility, some doctors suggest couples spend at least three months 'cleaning up their act' before they try to get pregnant. Even though one single

---

22. S Belloc, P Cohen-Bacrie, M Benkhalifa, M Cohen-Bacrie, J De Mouzon, A Hazout and Y Ménézo, 'Effect of maternal and paternal age on pregnancy and miscarriage rates after intrauterine insemination', *Reproductive BioMedicine Online*, vol. 17, no. 3, 2008, pp. 392-7; E de La Rochebrochard and P Thonneau, 'Paternal age ≥40 years: an important risk factor for infertility', *American Journal of Obstetrics and Gynecology*, vol. 189, no. 4, October 2003, pp. 901-5.

23. NP Singh, CH Muller and RE Berger, 'Effects of age on DNA double-strand breaks and apoptosis in human sperm', *Fertility and Sterility*, vol. 80, no. 6, December 2003, pp. 1420-30.

24. K Anderson, V Nisenblat and R Norman, 'Lifestyle factors in people seeking infertility treatment—A review', *Australian and New Zealand Journal of Obstetrics and Gynaecology*, vol. 50, no. 1, February 2010, pp. 8-20. This is an excellent review with comprehensive information for those who would like to read further.

25. D Cooper, 'Ray of sunshine for infertile males', *ABC Science*, 21 October 2008 (viewed 12 January 2012): www.abc.net.au/science/articles/2008/10/21/2396765.htm. Some fertility clinics offer dietary guidelines.

problem may not cause infertility, a combination of factors can be enough to push you over the line. Men should be encouraged by the fact that though women have the eggs they were born with, men have a new batch of sperm every three months, so there is an opportunity to improve the quality. Even if IVF is planned, making lifestyle changes (for both husband and wife) can reduce the risk of miscarriage, without any ethical problems. Couples who hope to become pregnant should address these issues:

- **Diet:** A well-balanced diet is important, as it can improve fertility, reduce the risk of fetal abnormality, and increase the likelihood of a live birth. Women should take folate supplements—usually 0.4mg daily from two months prior to conception—and check with their doctor in case more is needed.[26] Women at risk should be screened for vitamin D deficiency prior to pregnancy and given vitamin D supplements if necessary; if you live somewhere with nice weather, 10-15 minutes of sun per day without sunscreen should be effective. In Australia and New Zealand, iodine (250mcg daily) for women is also recommended. Women should avoid taking vitamin A supplements and eating crustacea and liver products, before and during pregnancy, as too much can cause problems.

- **Exercise:** Undertake exercise in moderation.

- **Weight:** Abnormal weight can be associated with hormonal dysfunction. Obese women are almost three times as likely as non-obese women to have difficulty conceiving, either naturally or with ART. Weight should be lost before pregnancy, not during. Current evidence advises against conception within the first year after bariatric surgery (gastric banding etc.) due to risks of miscarriage, prematurity and fetal growth restriction.[27] There is some evidence that paternal obesity may contribute to reduced fertility.[28] Underweight women also have difficulty conceiving. People trying to conceive should aim to have a body mass index (BMI) between 20 and 25 kg/m².

26.   T Forges, P Monnier-Barbarino, JM Alberto, RM Guéant-Rodriguez, JL Daval and JL Guéant, 'Impact of folate and homocysteine metabolism on human reproductive health', *Human Reproduction Update*, vol. 13, no. 3, May/June 2007, pp. 225-38.

27.   N Andreadis and M Bowman, 'The role of the GP in managing female infertility', *Medicine Today,* vol. 12, no. 5, May 2011, pp. 16-24.

28.   AO Hammoud, M Gibson, CM Peterson, BD Hamilton and DT Carrell, 'Obesity and male reproductive potential', *Journal of Andrology*, vol. 27, no. 5, September/October 2006, pp. 619-26.

- **Smoking:** Smoking cigarettes reduces fertility—and because passive smoking causes problems as well, both man and woman should stop smoking when trying to conceive.[29] Regular marijuana use also increases the risk of infertility.[30]
- **Alcohol:** It is unclear how much alcohol is needed to affect fertility, so it is advisable for men to reduce their intake; women should consider avoiding alcohol completely.
- **Caffeine:** The association between infertility and caffeine is unclear but it is recommended that women not drink more than two cups of coffee per day while trying to conceive and during pregnancy.
- **Other factors:** There is some evidence that stress and environmental pollution may cause infertility problems. While couples are getting healthy, they should ask their GPs which tests and vaccinations are recommended before conceiving.[31]

Female factors

Ovulatory factors

Dysfunction of the ovaries (not producing eggs normally) accounts for around 40% of female factor infertility. Dysfunction can include ovarian cysts, polycystic ovarian syndrome, and other hormonal problems such as early menopause. Advanced age leads to a natural reduction in ovarian reserves.

Cervical factors

When a woman is ovulating 'fertile mucus' is usually produced, which helps the sperm to swim up through the cervix and the uterus to meet the egg in the fallopian tube. Infertility can result from problems with the mucus, such as it being too scant, too thick or hostile to the man's sperm.

Pelvic factors

Uterine factors are not commonly a cause of infertility, but they include tumours, polyps or abnormal anatomy. The role of fibroids in infertility is unclear.

---

29. MM Werler, 'Teratogen update: Smoking and reproductive outcomes', *Teratology*, vol. 55, no. 6, June 1997, pp. 382-8.
30. BA Mueller, JR Daling, NS Weiss and DE Moore, 'Recreational drug use and the risk of primary infertility', *Epidemiology*, vol. 1, no. 3, May 1990, pp. 195-200.
31. See chapter 8.

Tubal abnormalities

These are more common, usually in the form of a blockage caused by endometriosis, infection, or damage from a previous ectopic pregnancy or surgery. Endometriosis in the pelvis (having normal endometrial tissue in abnormal places) can distort the anatomy of the reproductive system, and interfere with egg quality and the subsequent development and implantation of the embryo. It appears that the extent to which fertility decreases roughly correlates with the severity of the disease.[32]

Immunological problems

While antibodies are usually protective cells that protect the body against foreign substances like bacteria, some women produce antibodies that can attack sperm, the embryo or even their own cells. This can cause infertility or recurrent pregnancy loss.

Male factors

The cause of up to 40% of male infertility is unknown.

Sperm abnormality

If sperm can't swim in a straight line it makes it hard for them to get anywhere near the egg. A low sperm count or impaired sperm function make it difficult for a sperm to fertilize an egg under normal conditions. Max didn't believe the result when he got his sperm count back. *I've been healthy all my life!* he said. He had it rechecked. Twice.

Poor sperm quality, low sperm motility (movement), semen deficiency or insufficient (or no) sperm can all cause problems. Some men have a problem where their own immune system attacks their sperm.

Other problems

Some men have ejaculatory problems. Others can have a blockage either in the epididymis or the vas deferens. Testicular cancer, infections, an extra X (female) chromosome, undescended testes, low testosterone levels and steroid use can all cause problems.

No cause found

This can be very frustrating. *I found it very hard to accept that no-one could tell us what was wrong. I still do,* said Brett. Up to two thirds of

---

32. MA Fritz and L Speroff, *Clinical Gynecologic Endocrinology and Infertility*, 7th edn, Lippincott Williams and Wilkins, Philadelphia, 2005, p. 1109.

couples in this category will conceive within three years, if they keep trying.

The menstrual cycle

As explained above, in order to conceive it is necessary for sperm to arrive at the fallopian tube just after ovulation (when an egg is released). It can be helpful for couples to learn about the phases of the menstrual cycle in order to time intercourse to coincide with peak fertility (aim for every two days just before and during the ovulatory phase). Ovulation usually occurs 14 days before the next period is due (irregular periods can make the timing more difficult). Natural family planning centres can teach couples to recognize the ovulatory phase using body temperature and cervical mucus changes. Some clinics offer 'ovulation tracking'—a more accurate way of working out when ovulation occurs by measuring hormone levels in the blood.

For doctors

Ovulation occurs in response to a surge in luteinizing hormone (LH) released by the pituitary gland as the maturing follicle and associated rise in oestrogen is detected. The surge occurs 24 hours before ovulation, so by daily measuring the LH level, ovulation can be accurately predicted. Transvaginal ultrasound is used to measure follicular diameter in order to time when the daily tests should begin.

Medical assessment

When first visiting the doctor, couples will need to talk about their past health and any factors that may be affecting their fertility. The range of causes is large and the doctor will want to narrow things down so that you do not have unnecessary tests. Both partners will need to be examined carefully. If the couple has any questions about things they have been told or have read on the internet, this is a good time to ask.

Women may be asked about their menstrual history, contraceptive measures, any prior pregnancies, surgery, infections, pap smears (and treatment if test results were abnormal), medications or exposure to toxins.

Men may be asked about any children they have fathered previously, exposure to toxins, previous surgery, infections and treatment, any medications, and whether they have had to shave less often (this can reflect hormone problems).

The doctor will also be interested in the couple's general health, family history (looking for disorders that may affect fertility), and the regularity and timing of intercourse.

Depending on what the doctor finds, the couple will probably be asked to undergo some tests at this time. These may include the following:

- **Semen analysis:** The man will be asked to provide a sample of semen for examination.[33] He will be asked to abstain from sex for several days before collecting the sample (to allow it to build up), and it will need to be at the lab within an hour of collection (so it is fresh). Semen examination includes looking carefully at the sperm to see how many are there, how they move (motility), and whether they look normal (morphology). If there are abnormalities in the first test, it is usually repeated three months later to allow the production cycle to complete. One abnormal test does not confirm a problem.

- **Blood tests:** Hormone levels in the man and the woman may be checked to ensure that normal production of hormones is occurring so that sperm and egg production is supported.

Further tests may be done to check for blockages or damage to the woman's reproductive system, and also to check for infection. These include:

- **Hysterosalpingogram (HSG) or hysterosalpingo-contrast-sonography (HyCoSy):** HSG is an x-ray that shows the inside of the womb and fallopian tubes to check for blockages. It involves the injection of fluid into the womb. HyCoSy is a similar test but it uses *transvaginal ultrasound* instead of x-ray. Ultrasound can also be used to detect anatomical abnormalities in the reproductive tract.

- **Laparoscopy:** This is explorative surgery to see if the fallopian tubes are damaged. It is likely to be recommended if there is a history of pelvic infection, ectopic pregnancy or endometriosis, or if infertility continues at 24 months.

- **Endometrial biopsy:** The lining of the uterus can be examined by taking a small sample of uterine tissue via a small catheter inserted through the cervix. It may be done with a transvaginal ultrasound to examine the endometrial thickness.

---

33. See chapter 12 for potential ethical challenges involved in collecting a semen sample.

There are no ethical problems for Christians seeking a diagnosis for their infertility in this way.[34]

The first assessment can be quite overwhelming. Deciding to present for investigation can be a very emotional time as it is an acknowledgment, even if just between the couple themselves, that they have a problem. They will often receive a large amount of information and it may be hard to take it all in. They should ask if the doctor has any written information they can take away, and if they find they have questions afterward, they should be encouraged to write them down so they can remember to ask at their next appointment.

Treatment of infertility

If any general medical problems are found—such as malfunctioning of the thyroid—these will be treated in the standard way. These days, many causes of infertility are effectively bypassed rather than treated. Some doctors may think it will be cheaper and easier to go directly to IVF rather than to spend time treating the underlying disease itself. Conditions such as endometriosis can be treated with medication or surgery, but sometimes IVF is recommended instead. Couples need to be aware of their options whenever IVF is recommended, especially if they have concerns about its use. They may need to make a point of asking about alternative treatments, because IVF is so routinely used nowadays that it may not occur to the doctor to mention other options.

This book is not a replacement for medical advice, and each doctor has a couple's personal information to guide them in a way I cannot; but here are some things to keep in mind for those who want to explore all possibilities with their doctor.[35]

In the treatment of infertility, the usual practice is to go from the least to the most invasive treatment in a stepwise manner. The treatments involved will obviously depend on the cause of infertility being addressed. The doctor involved will advise regarding the appropriate steps for each particular couple. The treatments listed here aim to correct the underlying problems causing infertility, and raise no ethical problems for Christians.[36]

---

34. The possible exception here is collecting semen, depending on the method used.
35. See chapter 12 for the ethics of IVF.
36. See chapter 16.

Where ART is part of the recommended therapy, it is marked with an asterisk (*). Where this is the case, please go to chapter 12 to read the discussion about whether there are ethical issues for that particular procedure.

Male factor infertility

Poor semen quality
Medical or surgical treatment to normalize or at least improve poor semen quality is always the first and most appropriate option, when necessary and possible. A wide range of treatments is available depending on the cause.

Intrauterine insemination (IUI)*
Mild to moderate abnormality of the sperm can be managed by preparing the semen in order to concentrate the sperm, then injecting it through the cervix into the uterus. Fertility drugs may boost sperm production.

Intracytoplasmic sperm injection (ICSI)*
ICSI involves injecting a single sperm into each egg, and is used in combination with IVF*. If necessary, the sperm can be retrieved from the testes by microsurgical epididymal sperm aspiration (MESA)* or testicular sperm aspiration (TESA)*. A minimum number of sperm are necessary. ICSI is used when there are severe abnormalities in the sperm (low numbers, low motility, poor appearance), and fertilization through standard IVF fails.

Obstructive problems
These obstructions block the passage of the sperm. They can be addressed directly through surgery, or bypassed by using MESA* or TESA* with ICSI*.

Retrograde ejaculation
This condition can be treated with medication, or urine can be treated in order to collect sperm for IUI*.

Hormone abnormalities
These abnormalities can result from genetic problems such as Klinefelter's syndrome, or they can be caused by a lesion in the pituitary or hypothalamus gland in the brain. Most of these problems can be treated with medication.

Varicocoele

This is a dilatation of scrotal veins, which is thought to impair fertility by raising the scrotal temperature. It is present in 15% of men. Treatment is controversial.

Donor sperm*

When male infertility cannot be treated, donor sperm* for insemination* or IVF* is available. This is a common practice. Donor sperm is usually frozen before injection to reduce the risk of transmission of infection to the woman.

Female factor infertility

Ovulatory problems

Ovulation can be induced in 90%-95% of patients so long as they have eggs and no serious hormonal disturbances.

The usual medication used is clomiphene citrate* (*Clomid, Milophene, Serophe*). Once ovulation is achieved, timed intercourse is recommended. Side effects are common with treatment and include hot flushes, swinging emotions, bloating and visual changes. There is a slight increase in the likelihood of twins with this treatment, and an even smaller increase in triplets. If this treatment doesn't work, or clomiphene was not indicated, ovulation may be induced using gonadotropins*, often used in conjunction with IUI*. These are given by injection and have an increased risk of side effects such as multiple pregnancy and ovarian hyperstimulation syndrome. Even though these medications can be given outside of an ART context, they are commonly used with it and so are examined from an ethical perspective in chapter 12.

Menopause or reduced number/quality of eggs

The recommended treatment in women over 42 years of age or those with inadequate eggs is to use donor eggs* from a younger woman, using IVF*.

Uterine abnormality

Some uterine abnormalities can be surgically corrected. Other women with normal ovaries, but who are unable to use their own uteruses due to abnormal shape, disease, surgical removal, or another illness which makes it unsafe for them to become pregnant, can still have genetically-related children by using IVF* with a gestational surrogate*.

Tubal factor infertility

Depending on which part of the tube is blocked, reconstructive surgery is an option; in fact, in some instances it can improve the success rate for IVF*. However, in other instances the success rate for surgery will be extremely poor. IVF* will be offered if the obstruction cannot be repaired.

Endometriosis

While IVF* is likely to help with an anatomical problem, it is less likely to help with the other aspects of infertility in endometriosis. Depending on the severity of disease, treatment options include surgery, medication and ART*.[37]

Unexplained infertility

Treatment options range from 'expectant management' (i.e. waiting), to IUI*, hormone treatment, IVF* or a combination of these. In 2008, a British study found that in couples with unexplained infertility, existing treatments such as clomifene and unstimulated intrauterine insemination are unlikely to offer superior live birth rates compared with expectant management.[38] One study suggested that early treatment with IVF (after one year) does not improve outcomes, with 60% of births after early IVF possibly resulting from natural conception that would have occurred anyway in the following two years.[39]

Some specialist clinics use preimplantation genetic diagnosis (PGD)* to screen for aneuploidy (chromosome abnormalities) in older women, recurrent miscarriage or unexplained IVF failure.[40] The abnormal embryos are discarded and only those that appear normal are transferred to the uterus. This is not an ethical choice for Christians.

---

37. Fritz and Speroff, op. cit., pp. 1114-24.
38. S Bhattacharya, K Harrild, J Mollison, S Wordsworth, C Tay, A Harrold, D McQueen, H Lyall, L Johnston, J Burrage, S Grossett, H Walton, J Lynch, A Johnstone, S Kini, A Raja and A Templeton, 'Clomifene citrate or unstimulated intrauterine insemination compared with expectant management for unexplained infertility: pragmatic randomised controlled trial', *British Medical Journal*, vol. 337, no. 7666, 16 August 2008, a716.
39. JDF Habbema, MJC Eijkemans, G Nargund, G Beets, H Leridon and ER te Velde, 'The effect of *in vitro* fertilization on birth rates in western countries', *Human Reproduction*, vol. 24, no. 6, June 2009, pp. 1414-19.
40. Fritz and Speroff, op. cit., p. 1220. See chapter 12 for further discussion.

The last resort

In the treatment of infertility, whether you are dealing with female or male factors, the last resort offered with standard treatment will be IVF* and embryo transfer* (although some doctors refer earlier).

Can Christians use alternative therapies?

Infertile couples need to be careful that their vulnerability and intense desire for a child do not make them susceptible to fraud. Alternative therapies like acupuncture and traditional Chinese medicine have helped some couples. But as with any medical treatment, Christians need to be good stewards with regard to their money, time and acceptance of God's sovereign will. Therapies relying on 'life-energy' or spiritual forces other than Christianity should be avoided. Remember that even the beast, as recorded in Revelation, could do great and miraculous signs (Rev 13:13). With any alternative medicine we should check with our doctor that it won't do any harm, but in this situation it is important to establish that there is no risk either to the woman or to the baby if a pregnancy occurs.[41]

Living with infertility

Infertility challenges self-image, sexuality and relationships. The diagnosis begins a roller-coaster ride that can continue month after month for years. Professional counselling may be needed to cope with the stresses associated with infertility. Subtle pressure may be felt from well-meaning friends and relatives. This can develop into judgemental attitudes towards couples that are assumed to be childfree by selfish choice.

Amy, who with her husband suffered from secondary infertility and had tried for more than 10 years to have a second child, was criticized for allowing her daughter to grow up without siblings. Carmel said:

> We've been pretty open about our infertility. But we've struggled to know how much to tell family while we're going through IUI cycles. The first cycle, we let family and close friends know. It was good to have people know and pray for us. But at the same time we didn't want to be talking about it heaps because conceiving is a private matter normally, so it does

---

41. For an overview of alternative therapies, see GP Stewart, WR Cutrer, TJ Demy, DP O'Mathúna, PC Cunningham, JF Kilner and LK Bevington, *Basic Questions on Alternative Medicine*, Kregel Publications, Grand Rapids, 1998.

feel strange telling people about it. And then there is the disappointment of no pregnancy and needing to tell people who are disappointed for us. I felt bad as they had their own grief about it. So we've not told people much about subsequent cycles. We've talked to a few people and it's really nice. However, family does like to know and a few have expressed disappointment that they didn't know. I'm not sure what the answer is.

Failed expectations can mean couples put pressure on themselves, which may increase stress levels further.

Stresses of infertility

With infertility comes a loss of control—loss of control over one's body, one's life. As yet another monthly period comes, the sense of failure and frustration can increase. Stress can be experienced in a number of areas.

Marital stress

Authors Sandra Glahn and William Cutrer have good advice for couples struggling with infertility; the relevant chapter in their book is subtitled, 'She wants a baby; he wants his wife back'. It reminds me of Hannah's husband, Elkanah, who said to his distressed, infertile wife, "Hannah, why do you weep? And why do you not eat? And why is your heart sad? Am I not more to you than ten sons?" (1 Sam 1:8). Some things never change.

After explaining how infertility affects men and women differently, the authors give some advice to limit the stress. Given that women often complain their husbands don't listen, the authors have found that it can be helpful for couples to agree ahead of time to limit their talk about infertility to 20-30 minutes a day. This motivates the woman to focus on the most important things she wants to communicate, and lets the man know there are limits to the amount of energy she expects him to spend focusing on infertility for that day. Most couples don't spend enough time talking to build a healthy relationship anyway, so it is good for the marriage if both of them can discuss other things (that includes you, husband!). As they communicate and the husband begins to recognize the grief triggers for the wife (pregnant women, babies) and responds, her needs are met, and he gets what he wants—a happier spouse.[42]

---

42. Glahn and Cutrer, op. cit., p. 41. This book is highly recommended for couples struggling with infertility. Note that the medical details refer to the USA care model.

Most couples report having less sex after a diagnosis of infertility. What was once pleasurable intimacy becomes 'love by the calendar'. It is important to take time for physical intimacy. Glahn and Cutrer suggest that by separating 'lovemaking sex' (where you take the time to be close) and 'baby-making sex' (where you just get the job done), couples can maintain marital intimacy despite the pressures of treatment.[43] It's worth a try. *Afterwards, it took a long time to get it back to normal*, said Lara.

Woman and men usually grieve differently. Although infertility hits both men and women with self-image challenges, these are expressed in different ways. For her, it attacks her womanhood; for him, it challenges his virility. Linda felt that her body had let her down: *Part of being a woman is being able to be a mother. I can't do what I was made to do.* I wonder if this is partly influenced by the habit we have of saying it is the wife who can't have children, even when we know it takes two. If men can perform the act, they are thought to be fertile. Consider the Bible: sure, Elizabeth was past menopause when she became pregnant, but she had been married for a long time before menopause occurred. Is it possible that Zechariah had a low sperm count (Luke 1:5-25)?

Yet it is just as difficult for men. *I felt emasculated, humiliated*, one man said of his medical assessment where he discovered he was 'undersized'. *IVF nearly wrecked our marriage.* He felt very guilty knowing that, even though his was the abnormality, most of the IVF treatment was going to be his wife's burden. *The treatment options were deeply unfair and inequitable. We've worked out that my wife had 200 injections over the course of the treatment. I had two. She suffered the hormone treatment, the scanning, the surgical collection of eggs, the psychological hell of embryo transfer and the two-week wait for a result. So that was tough, knowing that I was the reason for her pain.* He felt that during their infertility his masculinity hung in the balance. *In my head, I know infertility just happens. It does not reflect who you are as a man. But when you can't give your wife what she wants more than anything else in the world, and you know that any other man could, it's impossible not to take it personally.*[44] This is a problem that men just don't talk about—having their manhood on the line. Some research has indicated that infertile men report a 42% decrease in their level of sexual satisfaction after diagnosis.[45]

---

43. ibid., pp. 100ff.
44. J Van Tiggelen, 'Seeds of doubt', *Good Weekend*, 12 June 2004.
45. Glahn and Cutrer, op. cit., p. 113.

Even though some research suggests there is a higher rate of marital breakdown during infertility treatment, some couples find that they come through stronger and closer than ever, with the sentiment, 'If we can survive that, we can survive anything'.

Emotional stress

It is normal for men and women to feel emotional when they fear infertility. We have a reassuring example in Hannah, who wept and wouldn't eat and was so disturbed in her prayers that Eli the priest thought she was drunk (1 Sam 1:1-14). The Lord did not reprimand her for her behaviour, but "remembered her" (v. 19). By looking at the psalms, we know that God wants us to be honest with him.

One of the hardest aspects of infertility is the death of all the dreams the couple shared. It is difficult for them to see their friends having children, then yet more children, while they are struggling with daily injections. Then the teenage girl down the road gets pregnant without even trying. The process of fertility treatment can take a long time, and it may take years for the couple to finally recover from the grief. It waxes and wanes with each cycle. While everyone grieves differently, many people will find they go through some, or all, of the classic stages of grief described by Elisabeth Kübler-Ross (not necessarily in this order): denial and isolation ("this is not happening to me"), anger ("how dare God do this to me"), bargaining ("if you will just let me"), depression ("what is the point?") and acceptance ("I'm going to be okay").[46] People come to terms with their situation in their own way. Those stuck in this process may benefit from counselling to help work through it.

Spiritual stress

A common experience for those suffering from infertility is the long journey to a place where they can believe God is good and know that they still trust him. A woman familiar with the problem wrote:

> It's easy to say you trust God, but it takes a lot longer to actually mean it—and mean it to the point where you can honestly say that whatever God's will is, you are content to accept it. And while this end point is the Lord's work, you also have to work hard to get there. There is no way to circumvent or hasten the learning process.[47]

---

46. E Kübler-Ross, *On Death and Dying*, Tavistock Publications, London, 1970.
47. K Galvin, 'The joy of infertility', *Briefing*, vol. 380, 2010, pp. 16-17.

Well-meaning advice

I remember once, years ago, a friend tearfully telling me that she and her husband had just been told they would never be able to have children. I reached for her hand and said earnestly, "God must have something better in mind for you". She pulled her hand away and said, "What could be better than having your own child?" I thought about our two little girls asleep in their beds, and at that moment I couldn't think of anything to say.

There seems to be no end to the variations of saying the wrong thing when it comes to infertility. There are whole websites dedicated to listing the insensitive comments and uninvited advice that infertile patients suffer. It is hard to know where to start listing them:

- You've been married for years now—when are you going to have a baby?
- Just relax! (This is a big favourite.)
- You really need to pray about it.
- Maybe you're not doing it properly!
- What kind of underpants does your husband wear?
- I know just how you feel…
- I know someone who… then fell pregnant.
- At least you can have fun trying!
- Want kids? You can have mine!
- Don't worry—just keep trusting God.
- At least you have…
- You can always adopt.
- You think you've got problems? Well…

The problem with these sorts of comments is that, while they may be said casually or even seriously, they can be very hurtful to those on the receiving end. There are several types of comments that are common: the 'personal' comment, which is just plain rude; the 'cheer up' comment, which is inappropriate; the 'don't worry it will be fine' comment, which may not be true; the 'fix-it' comment, which won't work; the 'spiritual pep talk' comment, which is just plain irritating because they don't need reminding that God is involved. Finally, the 'trite' comment attempts to deal with the situation by minimizing the grief of the infertile. That will only make them feel worse.

Within the Christian community there will be many people with good intentions and no idea what to do or say (I can attest to that). For those wanting to help, here are some tips to consider:[48]

1. Be there for them. For me, one of the most powerful biblical examples of empathy is found in Job 2, where Job's friends decide to go and comfort him:

   > And when they saw him from a distance, they did not recognize him. And they raised their voices and wept, and they tore their robes and sprinkled dust on their heads toward heaven. And they sat with him on the ground seven days and seven nights, and no-one spoke a word to him, for they saw that his suffering was very great. (Job 2:12-13)

   Never underestimate the power of just being with someone who is suffering. It's okay to say nothing. At these times we are comforted by human presence.

2. If you do want to say something, keep it simple. "I'm sorry" can be enough. You're not being asked to fix the problem.

3. Be sensitive in the way in which you give spiritual encouragement. It is natural for Christians to want to help their brothers and sisters with biblical exhortations of the goodness of God. But this is not the time for intellectual answers. As theologian Don Carson suggests, "Doubtless it is true… that 'in all things God works for the good of those who love him' (Rom 8:28)", but it is less obvious that it should be quoted to a suffering couple:

   > If they know the Lord well, then perhaps, with time, they themselves will cite the verse with renewed faith and understanding; but it should not be thrust at them in the wrong way, or at the wrong time, or without tears, lest it seem like a bit of cheap ritual, miserable comfort, heartless proof texting.[49]

4. The warmth of touch—a handshake, a pat on the back, a hug, whatever is appropriate for your relationship—can go a long way.

5. Let your infertile friends express their honest feelings without you judging them. The Bible is full of examples of people who became angry and frustrated and expressed their grief to God, who

---

48. The practical advice in Glahn and Cutrer (op. cit.) is recommended, and has informed this section.

49. DA Carson, *How Long, O Lord?* 2nd edn, Baker Academic, Grand Rapids, 2006, pp. 97-8.

comforted them. Look at the psalms. I wonder if one of the reasons no-one talks about their infertility is the hurtful things people say to them when they try. This creates barriers and makes it difficult to offer them support; it would be good to see this change. Think carefully about the questions you could ask a childless couple, such as "Have you thought about having children?" There are ways of asking questions that are gentle, especially in the context of an ongoing relationship. Consider how to ask questions that convey interest, concern and love, that are sensitive, and that provide them with an opportunity to say as much or as little as they feel they can. The couples I have spoken with would love to be asked, but it is often the *way* they are asked that makes the difference. If they share, try to stay on the topic with them. Listen and don't change the topic just because you find it too hard. Listen and ask them what it is like for them, and this will help. Pastoral care worker Jill McGilvray suggests:

> When we listen to someone who is hurting we help to carry their burdens. If we rush in with so many words, we risk adding to it instead. Your aim is to create a comfortable space for someone, where they will feel safe to talk.[50]

6. Acknowledge their mourning. We are told to "Rejoice with those who rejoice, weep with those who weep" (Rom 12:15). This is not a time for being cheerful. Statements such as, "It must be so hard" are better than, "It's not so bad".

7. Pray for them and with them. Ask them what they want prayer for. Don't just pray for them to fall pregnant; pray they will be content, whatever the circumstances, and that they will grow in their trust in God.[51]

8. Initiate acts of kindness and don't wait to be asked. Sometimes coping with pain takes all your energy and you don't know what others can do for you, even when they ask. Take the initiative and either make a specific offer ("Can I mow your lawn?") or just go ahead and help, if you know them well enough. Drop off a meal— everyone needs to eat.

9. Be patient. Mari said, *I remember going to Bible Study for years and*

---

50. J McGilvray, *God's Love in Action*, Acorn Press, Brookvale, 2009, p. 43.
51. Galvin, loc. cit.

the only prayer point I ever had was that I wanted to have a baby. Even if it takes a long time, hanging in there with them will make a big difference to the couple.

10. Be aware of childless couples in your congregation or Bible study group and don't make assumptions about why they are childless. Ask sensitive questions of them, draw them into fellowship, and don't let their childlessness be a barrier. When mothers are together they naturally chat about their children, but what if there is a woman in their midst who has no children? What is it like for her? At church the couples with children join together and the childless couple can feel excluded. Work out how to include them and share your family—your children—with them. Break that barrier. Some couples experiencing infertility have 'church-shopped' because they have felt so excluded and odd, but when a couple is so fragile and so vulnerable, this is how they will feel. Be especially sensitive at times like Mother's Day and Father's Day. These are not happy times for everyone.

If you want to be sensitive but you're not sure how, it can help to just ask infertile friends directly what you should do. For example, it is difficult to predict how they will feel when they're around other people's children. Hayley and Andrew were asked if they wanted to come to a first birthday party, or whether they'd prefer not to come. Hayley responded, *We'd love to come—it does hurt to see our friends' families, but it hurts more to be excluded from their lives.* Judy, on the other hand, decided it was just too painful to be around children, so she stopped going to the women's Bible study and socialized with her friends who didn't have kids.

How to handle the comments if you're on the receiving end

It does help to think ahead about how you would handle some situations. You can't explain everything to everyone, so sometimes it's best to smile and move on. Try to forgive the tactless as Jesus requires, even "seventy-seven times" (Matt 18:21-22).

Online chat rooms and networking sites like Facebook have made the issue of difficult comments much harder for many people; news of a new baby travels quickly on these sites and this can be confronting for those struggling with their own fertility. Polly, undergoing fertility treatment for 4 years now, described how she felt when she read a girlfriend's post: *"Your daughter will hold your hand for a little while, but will hold your heart forever." I know she wasn't trying to hurt anyone, but it felt like she was kicking me in the gut.* She feels bombarded by pictures of pregnant abdomens and baby ultrasounds. In these situations, when it becomes too hard, it may be necessary to block your friend for a while. Polly noted, *If I was smart I just wouldn't go on Facebook any more, but then I'd lose touch with all my family and friends.* It is an ongoing dilemma.

In other ways, however, the internet can connect infertile couples to online support groups with many other people who are going through the same problems they are. It can help to ease the journey when it's shared with someone who understands. And if couples can manage to share their grief with their friends, they might be amazed by how many others have had the same experience. *It's like a club,* Amy said. *You don't realize how many members there are until you become one of them.*

Coming to terms with infertility

When I spoke to couples who had struggled with infertility, I always asked them to tell me the most important thing they would say to others in their position. Many times, the answer was, *It's okay to stop trying.*

I have seen couples go to extraordinary lengths to find the money and the energy to keep trying with IVF. The injections, the blood tests, the medical appointments, the roller-coaster each month as they wait for the pregnancy test result to see if the embryo 'stuck'. Those who opt for no treatment are also 'trying' in their own way. They may still have the monthly held breath of hope as they wonder, "Maybe this time…"

How do you know when to stop trying? Glahn and Cutrer suggest, "When it hurts more to go on than it does to quit, it's time to quit".[52] This works for some people, but not everyone would agree. At one point in Australia, ART received the government subsidy for only six cycles. When it became available for an unlimited number of cycles, while there was gratitude for the government's generosity, it also meant that many couples lost a logical 'cut-off' point that allowed them to pull out gracefully. *My wife was so obsessed she just couldn't stop,* said Paul. *How could I tell her she had to stop? But that was our marriage for 12 years. In the end, it was only when she turned 40 that we were able to talk about doing something else with our lives.* Stopping treatment can be made even harder because of the way it is described as 'giving up' or 'failing', with

---

52. Glahn and Cutrer, op. cit., p. 241.

the implicit suggestion that such couples just aren't committed enough, rather than using terms that affirm them for making a positive choice.[53] However, infertile couples really can't win, because those who *don't* stop are just as pitied, often being described as 'desperate'. Kay told me, slowly, *I wish I had been secure enough in my faith that I could look at not having children and know I could survive it.*

Couples may find it easier if they think about the stopping point before starting treatment. It is not necessarily a negative approach; it simply means taking a realistic look at success rates. How far are you prepared to go to get a baby? Are there some treatments you definitely won't try? Is there a limit to how much money you are going to spend? Is there a limit to how much of your married life you are prepared to dedicate to the quest for a biological child? Questions of Christian stewardship regarding use of time and energy should also be considered. How long should life be on hold regarding the work of the kingdom? These are significant questions. There is nothing wrong with wanting a baby, but once you want one at any cost, you have a problem. Be careful (1 Cor 10:14). When starting on the quest for a child, consider writing down your guidelines and the reasoning behind them. It may help later on.

When a couple decides to stop trying for a child—and only they can do that—it's time for them to make decisions. Although there are many paths their lives could take, the essential question for them at this point is whether they want to try building a family by other means (e.g. adoption, foster parenting). In some places there are age restrictions on who is eligible, but spiritual parenting will still be an option.

Deciding to accept one's infertility, to walk on and not look back, can be very hard and very sad. The anguish can take some couples by surprise. Grief at ending infertility treatment can last for years. *You're not just giving up IVF*, said Patsy, *You're giving up hope.* At the same time there may be some relief in knowing you can move on. There is no 'right' way to feel. *You don't stop feeling sad*, said Tina, *but it doesn't keep hurting so much.* There are many accounts of the rewarding lives Christians can lead as they seek first the kingdom of God, and childless couples will still have many joys in life—but it will not be the same.

---

53. A Woollett, 'Infertility: from "inside/out" to "outside/in"', *Feminism and Psychology*, vol. 6, no. 1, February 1996, pp. 74-8.

It may seem like more than they can bear, but we all have this promise from God: "I will never leave you nor forsake you" (Heb 13:5). God does not minimize the loss. Let him help you.

For doctors

The public misconception regarding the reduction in female fertility in a woman's late thirties and early forties is a big problem for ART clinics. Doctors need to be aware of the data and make sure they do not contribute to the anger and grief of their patients by giving them false and often poorly informed hope as to what ART can offer them.

Silent sorrow:
miscarriage and stillbirth

W HAT COULD BE WORSE than losing a child? The death of the firstborn was the last and worst of the plagues in ancient Egypt, and the Lord knew it would bring "a great cry throughout all the land of Egypt, such as there has never been, nor ever will be again" (Exod 11:6).

King David and Job expressed their grief at the loss of their children in other physical ways—David fasted, lay on the ground and wept (2 Sam 12:15-23), and Job tore his robe, shaved his head, fell on the ground and worshipped (1:13-20). Jeremiah prophesies King Herod's 'slaughter of the innocents' (Matt 2:16-18) by describing Jacob's wife, Rachel, grieving inconsolably over the lost children of Israel at the site of her tomb:

> "A voice is heard in Ramah,
>> lamentation and bitter weeping.
> Rachel is weeping for her children;
>> she refuses to be comforted for her children,
>> because they are no more." (Jer 31:15)

It is only in the new heaven and the new earth that God will wipe every tear from our eyes (Rev 7:17, 21:4).

Any type of pregnancy loss is a devastating experience for the parents. Yet it is a strange grief, because you are mourning for someone you have never met. It often goes unnoticed by others, and can become a lonely journey for those who experience it: isolated, alone, confused, and gut-wrenchingly sad. Some aspects are experienced in common but every story is unique. It is thought that one in four known pregnancies ends in loss.

Different types of pregnancy loss

Pregnancy loss can be confusing because there seem to be so many names for the same thing. There is no internationally agreed list of terms to describe many of the events in pregnancy, and some terms have persisted that were developed before ultrasound was available for accurate diagnosis. Changes in terminology have been recommended to clarify these events, which would be helpful in improving data collection and research in this important area.[1] Unexplained stillbirth in late pregnancy is the single largest cause of death in perinatal life in the Western world. The lack of understanding about what causes pregnancy loss is a problem that must be addressed.

Below, I list different types of pregnancy loss and the various names that can be used to describe them. Categories marked with an asterisk (*) are not technically the kind of pregnancy loss that would be investigated as outlined below under 'recurrent miscarriage/recurrent abortion', but as parents may have a similar response regardless of the cause of the loss, they are included here.

Miscarriage/spontaneous miscarriage/spontaneous abortion*

These terms refer to the ending of a pregnancy before 20 weeks gestation, a time when the baby is unable to survive independently. It involves the spontaneous expulsion of the baby from the womb. The loss may occur anywhere. There will usually be heavy bleeding, possibly blood clots and abdominal cramping like period pain. Sometimes there is a sudden release of fluid out of the vagina if the waters break. The cervix opens and the developing baby comes out with the blood. Sadly, there is little that can be done to prevent a miscarriage once it is underway.

It can be distressing for women who have the medical term for this—'spontaneous abortion'—written in their medical records, as non-medical people can confuse it with 'elective abortion'. This is one reason it has been suggested that the term no longer be used.

Many women miscarry without even realizing, especially in early pregnancy. They may mistake a miscarriage for a late period. The miscarriage may be *complete*, which means the uterus is emptied, or *incomplete*, which means some tissue is left in the uterus and the mother

---

1.   RG Farquharson, E Jauniaux, N Exalto and on behalf of the ESHRE Special Interest Group for Early Pregnancy (SIGEP), 'Updated and revised nomenclature for description of early pregnancy events', *Human Reproduction*, vol. 20, no. 11, November 2005, pp. 3008-11.

will need a dilation and curettage (D&C) of the uterus under general anaesthetic to remove it. There is a risk of infection if this is not done.

Stillbirth

This term refers to a baby who dies before or during birth. The WHO definition of stillbirth is a birth weight of at least 1000g or a gestational age of at least 28 weeks (third-trimester stillbirth). However, there is still no international standard to define when a baby is considered stillborn. In Sweden, babies are considered stillborn at 28 weeks. In the United Kingdom it is 24 weeks. In the United States and Australia, a baby who has passed the 20-week mark is considered stillborn, while in Norway it is at 16 weeks.[2] Most stillborn babies are delivered naturally after the mother has gone through labour, even if it is known that the baby is dead before labour starts. In many places, stillborn children need to be legally registered as a birth and a death. Approximately half of stillbirths occur prior to 28 weeks of gestation and about 20% are at, or near, term.[3]

I just felt numb when I was told [that my baby had died]. And terrified that I had to give birth, remembers Rhea.

Blighted ovum/anembryonic pregnancy/early fetal demise/ empty sac*

These terms describe a pregnancy where the egg is fertilized and implantation occurs in the uterus, but an embryo does not develop. There will be symptoms of pregnancy and there may even be an empty gestational sac in the womb on the ultrasound.

Threatened miscarriage/threatened abortion

These terms refer to any vaginal bleeding before 20 weeks. There may or may not be cramping. The cervix is closed. Spotting (losing very small amounts of blood) in early pregnancy is common. Women experiencing spotting or bleeding during pregnancy should check with their doctor or midwife to see whether there is a problem. Up to half of these women will go on to have a miscarriage, but the rest of the

---

2.   I am using the Australian definition of 20 weeks here.

3.   RM Silver, MW Varner, U Reddy, R Goldenberg, H Pinar, D Conway, R Bukowski, M Carpenter, C Hogue, M Willinger, D Dudley, G Saade and B Stoll, 'Work-up of stillbirth: a review of the evidence', *American Journal of Obstetrics and Gynecology*, vol. 196, no. 5, May 2007, pp. 433-44.

pregnancies will continue normally. Tests may be done to check what is happening. *Even when I went for the ultrasound, it was so surreal. I couldn't believe this was happening to me. This was something that would only happen to someone else*, said Jan.

Missed miscarriage/delayed miscarriage/missed abortion/intrauterine death

This occurs when the embryo or fetus has died but a miscarriage has not yet occurred. Women who experience this may not know there is a problem until they have a routine check-up.

Wendy didn't know she had miscarried the first time until she saw her doctor. He couldn't find the heartbeat. An ultrasound was done to check on the baby, but the baby had died and was still inside her. This was extremely upsetting. *How could I not know there was something wrong with my baby?*

The mother may be allowed to choose whether to have a D&C (also called an ERPC—evacuation of retained products of conception) or to wait until labour starts so she can deliver the dead baby naturally.

Recurrent miscarriage/recurrent abortion

This refers to three or more consecutive miscarriages by the same woman. It is at this point that most women would start to have tests to discover the cause.

Ectopic pregnancy*

This term denotes a pregnancy where the embryo implants outside the uterus (usually in the fallopian tube), where the baby will not survive. It is a serious situation that is potentially fatal for the mother and requires urgent treatment. An ectopic pregnancy can be especially hard to cope with when the emergency situation may prevent a woman from fully comprehending that not only is she losing the baby but also her chances of having another baby in the future may be reduced.

How common is recurrent pregnancy loss?

A 1988 study found that the total rate of early pregnancy loss after implantation, including clinically recognized spontaneous abortions, was 31%. Most of the 40 women in this study with unrecognized early pregnancy losses had normal fertility, since 95% of them subsequently became clinically pregnant within two years.[4]

Across the globe, around 3 million babies are stillborn every year—more than 8200 babies a day.[5] Although 98% of these deaths take place in low-income and middle-income countries, stillbirths also continue to affect wealthier nations, with around one in every 300 babies stillborn in high-income countries.[6] This translates to around 6500 per year in the United Kingdom and around 2000 in Australia.[7] While no accurate data is collected in the United States, it is thought to be around 26,000 every year.

An Australian study found that, on average, for every 10 women aged between 28 and 33 years who had ever been pregnant, 5 would have had a birth only, 2 would have had a loss only, and 3 would have had a birth and a loss.[8]

Causes

After a pregnancy loss, there can be an overwhelming need to find out why it happened. Many people will spend time searching the internet for answers, but there is a lot of inaccurate information out there. Check with your doctor if you have questions about information you have found. Although there are still many unknowns, some causes for pregnancy loss have been recognized. Miscarriage and stillbirth occur along a time continuum of nine months, so the conditions that can cause them do overlap.

---

4.   AJ Wilcox, CR Weinberg, JF O'Connor, DD Baird, JP Schlatterer, RE Canfield, EG Armstrong, and BC Nisula, 'Incidence of early loss of pregnancy', *New England Journal of Medicine*, vol. 319, no. 4, 28 July 1988, pp. 189-94.

5.   J Scott, 'Stillbirths: breaking the silence of a hidden grief', *Lancet*, vol. 377, no. 9775, 23 April 2011, pp. 1386-8. This article is part of a series on stillbirths (see footnote 7). For numerical comparisons in this series 'stillbirth' is defined as 28 weeks and above, so 3 million is a conservative estimate.

6.   TheLancet.com, 'Stillbirths', Elsevier, London, 14 April 2011 (viewed 13 January 2012): www.thelancet.com/series/stillbirth. This series is an excellent analysis of the global problem of stillbirths and solutions to improve it.

7.   There were 2188 fetal deaths in Australia in 2007. See PJ Laws, Z Li and EA Sullivan, *Australia's Mothers and Babies 2008*, Perinatal statistics series no. 24, cat. no. PER 50, AIHW, Canberra, November 2010.

8.   D Herbert, J Lucke and A Dobson, 'Pregnancy losses in young Australian women: Findings from the Australian longitudinal study on women's health', *Women's Health Issues*, vol. 19, no. 1, January 2009, pp. 21-9.

Miscarriage

It is still not known what causes many miscarriages, but it usually seems to be because a pregnancy is not developing normally. Most miscarriages occur in the first trimester (first 3 months of pregnancy). The most common known cause (over 50%) is genetic abnormality (abnormal chromosomes).[9] Many non-chromosomal problems have also been associated with miscarriage—these include hormonal abnormalities, physical abnormalities (e.g. an abnormally shaped womb or a weak cervix), platelet problems, environmental exposure to toxins, infections and immunological factors.[10]

Stillbirth

There is still a lot of research that needs to be done to discover the causes of stillbirth. Researchers talk more about 'associations' than 'causes'. In 2011, the top 5 known causes of stillbirths assessed worldwide were:

1. childbirth complications (such as pressure on the umbilical cord, which cuts off the baby's blood supply, or a problem with the placenta such as it tearing away from the uterus wall)
2. maternal infections in pregnancy
3. maternal disorders, especially hypertension (high blood pressure) and diabetes
4. fetal growth restriction (small babies)
5. congenital abnormalities (such as lethal chromosome disorders and malformations in the baby).[11]

In high-income countries, placental problems and infection associated with preterm birth are linked to a substantial proportion of stillbirths.[12] Good antenatal care reduces the risks.

---

9. See appendix III for an explanation of chromosomal changes.

10. S Brown, 'Miscarriage and its associations', *Seminars in Reproductive Medicine*, vol. 26, no. 5, September 2008, pp. 391-400.

11. JE Lawn and M Kinney, *Stillbirths: An Executive Summary for* The Lancet's *Series*, Elsevier, London, 14 April 2011, p. 3 (viewed 13 January 2012): www.download.thelancet.com/flatcontentassets/series/stillbirths.pdf

12. V Flenady, P Middleton, GC Smith, W Duke, JJ Erwich, TY Khong, J Neilson, M Ezzati, L Koopmans, D Ellwood, R Fretts and JF Frøen for the Stillbirths Series steering committee, 'Stillbirths: the way forward in high-income countries', *Lancet*, 14 May 2011, pp. 1703-17.

Is there anything that can be done to reduce the risk of miscarriage or stillbirth?

Stillbirth rates in high-income countries declined dramatically from about 1940, but this decline has stalled in recent years. The present variation in stillbirth rates across, and within, high-income countries indicates that further reduction in stillbirth is possible.[13] Since we don't know what causes many miscarriages and stillbirths, much interest centres on what puts a couple at increased *risk* of pregnancy loss.

Research into risk factors hopes to find ways to reduce the frequency of pregnancy loss. The identification of risk factors is intended to help parents, and not to make anyone feel guilty. Remember that risk factors *can* influence the outcome, but they have not been proven as a definite cause. They are certainly not grounds for blame. Obviously, the risk factors we most want to know about are those we can do something about. Potentially, as many as 40% of stillbirths could be due to the three combined risk factors of maternal age over 35, history of smoking, and being overweight or obese (Body Mass Index [BMI] over 25). These factors also carry an increased risk of miscarriage.[14] It is not unethical to try and reduce risk factors, so long as we are mindful of the need to be wise stewards of our time and our money, and we do not allow it to interfere with relationships.

Advanced age

The majority of early miscarriages are thought to result from chromosomal defects, and the only known risk factor for that is advanced maternal age (greater than 35 years).[15] One study found that while younger women (20-25 years) had chromosomal abnormalities in 17% of their eggs, by 40-45 years this figure had risen to 79%.[16] There is some

---

13.   Flenady et al, loc. cit.

14.   Z Taylor, *Pregnancy Loss*, Harper Collins, Sydney, 2010, p. 62.

15.   L Huang, R Sauve, N Birkett, D Fergusson and C van Walraven, 'Maternal age and risk of stillbirth: a systematic review', *Canadian Medical Association Journal*, vol. 178, no. 2, 15 January 2008, pp. 165-72.

16.   DE Battaglia, P Goodwin, NA Klein and MR Soules, 'Influence of maternal age on meiotic spindle assembly in oocytes from naturally cycling women', *Human Reproduction*, vol. 11, no. 10, October 1996, pp. 2217-22.

evidence that increased paternal age (greater than 40 years) may also contribute.[17]

Smoking

If a mother continues to smoke cigarettes, the risk of the baby dying during pregnancy increases by about 30%.[18] It is important to give up smoking before getting pregnant, even though this may be very difficult. Try to avoid second-hand smoke as well, because even if the smoke comes from someone else's cigarette, it can still cause problems if you breathe it in.

Obesity

Apart from increasing health risks to the mother, obesity also increases the risks of miscarrying a normal baby and recurrent miscarriage. Some studies also show an increase in stillbirths.[19] (There may also be a risk if the mother is underweight before she gets pregnant,[20] so aim for a normal BMI of 20-25.) I know it's not politically correct to say someone should lose weight, but you only need to see the tragedy associated with this reversible problem before you say it anyway.

Illegal drugs

Cocaine use increases the risk of miscarriage in the first trimester, and heroin use increases the risk of the baby dying in pregnancy or soon after.[21]

Previous miscarriage or termination of pregnancy

There does seem to be some association between pregnancy loss and past history of pregnancy loss, but research results are mixed.[22]

---

17. E de la Rochebrochard, K Mcelreavey and P Thonneau, 'Paternal age over 40 years: The "amber light" in the reproductive life of men?', *Journal of Andrology*, vol. 24, no. 4, July/August 2003, pp. 459-65.

18. M Werler, 'Teratogen update: Smoking and reproductive outcomes', *Teratology*, vol. 55, no. 6, 1997, pp. 382-8.

19. H Lashen, K Fear and DW Sturdee, 'Obesity is associated with increased risk of first trimester and recurrent miscarriage: matched case-control study', *Human Reproduction*, vol. 19 no. 7, July 2004, pp. 1644-6.

20. N Maconochie, P Doyle, S Prior and R Simmons, 'Risk factors for first trimester miscarriage—results from a UK-population-based case-control study', *BJOG: An International Journal of Obstetrics and Gynaecology*, vol. 114, no. 2, February 2007, pp. 170-86.

21. Taylor, op. cit., p. 72.

22. M Black, A Shetty, and S Bhattacharya, 'Obstetric outcomes subsequent to intrauterine death in the first pregnancy', *BJOG*, vol. 115, no. 2, January 2008, pp. 269-74.

Caffeine

Some research has indicated a link between miscarriage and the consumption of drinks containing caffeine. A much-publicized study in 2008 suggested that pregnant women who have 2 or more cups of caffeinated drinks a day have twice the risk of having a miscarriage than those who avoid caffeine.[23] By 2 drinks they mean 200mg of caffeine, which is equivalent to 2 mugs of instant coffee, *or* 4 cups of medium-strength tea or hot chocolate, *or* 6 cups (5 cans) of cola per day. If you get your coffee from a café you may be getting more than 200mg of caffeine in one cup, depending on the beans and how it is made. For example, Robusta beans generally contain more caffeine than Arabica beans. (200mg is less than a 'tall' Starbucks coffee.)

The study's authors suggested that women who want to become pregnant should stop drinking coffee for 3 months prior to conception and throughout the pregnancy.

Maternal health

If the mother has health issues such as hormone problems, diabetes or immune disorders, there can be an increase in the incidence of pregnancy loss. However, good control of these conditions before and during pregnancy will reduce the risk.

Regular or high alcohol consumption

This link is not definitely proven, but there is increased risk of stillbirth with heavy drinking, binge drinking (5 or more drinks in a row) and having more than 3 drinks a week in the first trimester.[24] It's safest to avoid alcohol altogether.

Exposure to toxins

High mercury levels can lead to miscarriage. To be safe, pregnant women should avoid sushi, limit their consumption of fish high in mercury levels

---

23. X Weng, R Odouli and DK Li, 'Maternal coffee consumption during pregnancy and the risk of miscarriage: a prospective cohort study', *American Journal of Obstetrics and Gynecology*, vol. 198, no. 3, March 2008, p. 279.

24. K Strandberg-Larsen, NR Nielsen, M Grønbæk, PK Andersen, J Olsen and AN Andersen, 'Binge drinking in pregnancy and risk of fetal death', *Obstetrics and Gynecology*, vol. 111, no. 3, March 2008, pp. 602-9.

(such as tinned tuna), and eat fresh cooked fish no more than 2-3 times per week. It's also good to try to reduce exposure to household pesticides and any toxic chemicals in the workplace.

Experiencing stress

Feeling stressed or anxious—whether from recent emotional trauma, major life events during pregnancy or stressful employment—has been linked to an increased risk of miscarriage, but study results are mixed. Feeling happy and relaxed, or well enough to have sex, may reduce risk[25] (vaginal intercourse can't harm the baby during pregnancy and doesn't cause miscarriages[26]). This is a difficult issue for those couples who have already experienced a pregnancy loss, because it is hard to relax completely when you worry about whether it will happen again.

Antenatal infection

If the mother contracts an infection such as rubella, listeria, chlamydia or toxoplasmosis in early pregnancy, the risk of miscarriage or stillbirth later in pregnancy is increased. Other infections such as cytomegalovirus, parvovirus and Group B streptococcus can also cause problems. Women should check with their doctor or midwife if they are concerned.[27]

Rubella infection (German measles) is best avoided by vaccination against the disease; women of child-bearing age should consult their doctors.[28] Other ways to reduce the risk of rubella infection include staying away from those who are known to be suffering from rubella and those who have been exposed to the disease.

Listeria infections are reduced by not eating contaminated foods. In order to do this, it is best to avoid unwashed vegetables, uncooked meats and fish, unpasteurized milk products (watch out for soft cheeses like brie), cooked delicatessen meats, refrigerated smoked seafood, chilled pâtés and spreads, and ready-prepared meals. Listeria bacteria are destroyed by cooking and pasteurization, but not by refrigeration. Although some foods—such as

25. Maconochie et al., loc. cit.

26. Mayo Clinic staff, *Sex During Pregnancy: What's OK, What's Not*, Mayo Foundation for Medical Education and Research (MFMER), Rochester, 12 June 2010 (viewed 16 January 2011): www.mayoclinic.com/health/sex-during-pregnancy/HOoo140

27. WD Rawlinson, B Hall, CA Jones, HE Jeffery, SM Arbuckle, N Graf, J Howard and JM Morris, 'Viruses and other infections in stillbirth: what is the evidence and what should we be doing?', *Pathology*, vol. 40, no. 2, 2008, pp. 149-60.

28. See chapter 8.

cold cuts of meat and ready-prepared meals—are already cooked, they can become contaminated with listeria when they are chilled.

Chlamydia infection is a sexually transmitted disease. There is a risk of infection from unprotected anal, vaginal or oral sex with someone who is infected. To avoid infection, a condom should always be used during sex; this is especially important if either partner has had multiple partners.

Toxoplasmosis is an increased risk when cleaning the litter box of an outdoor cat, which might have eaten an infected bird or mouse; so too is eating undercooked meat.

Antenatal screening tests

Two tests that are used in normal pregnancy to screen the baby for disease can cause miscarriage. These are amniocentesis (1% risk) and chorionic villus sampling (CVS; 1%-2% risk). Note that these tests do not *need* to be performed.[29] Therefore, this risk can be completely eliminated.

Fetal reduction

This procedure involves the abortion of all but one or two fetuses in a multiple pregnancy so that the remaining ones have a better chance of developing normally. The risk of miscarriage is 5%-10%.[30] Note that this procedure is unethical for those who wish to protect life from its beginning.[31]

Post-term (over 40 weeks) gestation

While most miscarriages occur in the first trimester, there is also an increased risk of pregnancy loss after 40 weeks gestation (this is thought to contribute to about 1% of stillbirths).[32] This has raised the question of whether labour should sometimes be induced rather than waiting for it to happen naturally. It is important to get regular antenatal care so the progress of your pregnancy can be monitored.

---

29. See chapter 8.

30. A Antsaklis, AP Souka, G Daskalakis, N Papantoniou, P Koutra, Y Kavalakis and S Mesogitis, 'Pregnancy outcome after multifetal pregnancy reduction', *Journal of Maternal-Fetal and Neonatal Medicine*, vol. 16, no. 1, 2004, pp. 27-31.

31. See 'Selective/fetal/pregnancy reduction' under '3. What makes a woman choose to have an abortion?' in chapter 7.

32. C Heuser, T Manuck, S Hossain, R Satterfield and M Varner, 'Non-anomalous stillbirth by gestational age: Trends differ based on method of epidemiologic calculation', *American Journal of Obstetrics and Gynecology*, vol. 199, no. 6, supp. A, December 2008, p. S64.

Growth restriction

A significant number of stillbirths are associated with restricted growth in the baby.[33] This is known to be associated with a reduction in fetal movements. The mother's perception of whether she has experienced a decrease in movements for 24 hours is thought to be a reliable guide. The way to find out if fetal kicking is reduced is to count, once a day: in the third trimester, some practitioners will recommend that the mother spends some time each day counting the baby's kicks. There are lots of different ways to do these 'kick counts', so she should ask for specific instructions.

Here's one common approach: choose a time of day when the baby tends to be active (it's preferable to do this around the same time each day). The mother should sit quietly or lie on her side to avoid distractions and then she should time how long it takes to feel ten distinct movements—kicks, punches and whole body movements all count. If she doesn't feel ten movements in two hours, she should stop counting and call the midwife or doctor.[34] It is advisable to avoid comparing notes with other mothers, as every baby has their own routine.

While there is some debate as to the value of fetal movement monitoring (because of the variation in what is 'normal' and the risk of increasing anxiety unnecessarily), a trial which is currently underway in Australia has not only demonstrated that there is an association between a decrease in the mother's perception of fetal movements and stillbirth, but also that 59% of women were not given any specific information regarding fetal movements during their pregnancy.[35]

Diet

A British study found an association between a *reduced* risk of miscarriage and eating fresh fruits and vegetables daily and using vitamin supplementation before and during pregnancy (in particular, folic acid, iron, iodine and multivitamins).[36] Plus—some good news, at last—eating

---

33. J Gardosi, SM Kady, P McGeown, A Francis and A Tonks, 'Classification of stillbirth by relevant condition at death (ReCoDe): population based cohort study', *British Medical Journal*, vol. 331, no. 7525, 12 November 2005, pp. 1113-7.

34. AEP Heazell, M Green, C Wright, VJ Flenady and JF Frøen, 'Midwives' and obstetricians' knowledge and management of women presenting with decreased fetal movements', *Acta Obstetricia et Gynecologica Scandinavica*, vol. 87, no. 3, March 2008, pp. 331-9.

35. A Gordon, C Raynes-Greenow, W Rawlinson, J Morris and H Jeffery, 'Risk factors for stillbirth—The Sydney stillbirth study', *Stillbirth Foundation Australia Research Newsletter*, June 2011, p. 2.

36. Maconochie et al., loc. cit.

chocolate daily was also associated with a reduced risk of miscarriage in the first trimester.

Of all these risk factors, the most important to address in high-income countries are obesity, smoking and advanced maternal age.[37]

Investigations

In most places, one miscarriage in the first trimester does not warrant having any tests because it is so common. If a woman has a miscarriage in the second trimester, or two or three first-trimester miscarriages, her doctor may suggest some tests to try to work out what is causing the miscarriage, in case there is something that can be done to prevent it. All stillbirths should be investigated.

These tests may include:
- blood tests to check for chromosome abnormalities (both parents), hormone or immune problems (mother only)
- tests on the baby's body looking for chromosome abnormalities
- ultrasound or x-ray of the uterus
- endometrial biopsy (suctioning a small piece of the tissue from the uterus lining to check that the hormonal changes are normal).

Genetic screening

Sometimes when a woman has recurrent pregnancy loss, she will be advised to become pregnant using assisted reproductive technology (ART)—in particular, in vitro fertilization (IVF) with preimplantation genetic diagnosis (PGD) screening of the embryos. The idea is that if the miscarriage is due to chromosomal defects, you can check the genetic profile of the embryos created before they are implanted, so that only the normal ones are transferred (one at a time). The rest are discarded. This is not an ethical option for those who value human life from the time of conception.[38]

Living through a loss

There are several things that make the loss of a pregnancy at any stage difficult to cope with. One can be the lack of public acknowledgement, particularly if the loss is early in the pregnancy. Another is that the loss

---

37. Flenady et al., loc. cit.
38. See 'Preimplantation genetic diagnosis (PGD)' under 'Treatment options' in chapter 12.

is rarely expected; one moment the parents are full of dreams about the coming baby, decorating the nursery and welcoming this little one into their lives, and the next moment it's gone. Sandra said, *I thought it was getting pregnant that was difficult. No-one told me that staying pregnant is just as hard.* Ruth said, *I can't get excited about anyone's pregnancy now. I always wonder if something will go wrong.* These losses are so frequent, yet as a society we really aren't very good at dealing with them.

In the delivery room—stillbirth

It may or may not be known beforehand whether the baby has already died or will die soon after delivery. If there is advance warning, plans can be made for the delivery ahead of time so that the parents can make the most of the short time they will have with the baby. Even if the stillbirth is unexpected, many of the suggestions in the box below can be followed.

One thing that parents of a stillborn baby often mention is how quiet the room is when a stillborn baby is delivered. No cry of a newborn baby, no calls of congratulation. Nothing.

They talk about a baby who was born sleeping, and then going home with empty arms. I do not think I can do justice to those parents who have suffered such a loss with my words alone. I recommend reading the texts listed at the end of this book,[39] to hear from those who have experienced the loss of a child in their own words.[40]

Other children in the family

If there are already other children in the family, thought should be given to how they will be told of what has happened or will happen. An open and honest approach is recommended; children can often cope better with loss than their parents. Don't try to pretend it hasn't happened, as it will affect them whether you tell them or not. Thought should also be given to whether they will be given the opportunity to see the baby. Ask them what their questions are, as you might not be aware of what they are thinking.

---

39. See appendix V.

40. Zoe Taylor's book (*Pregnancy Loss*, op. cit.) contains many comments from those who have experienced pregnancy loss. While I do not agree with the ethical perspective taken in the book, this author has experienced pregnancy loss herself and writes about the experience with empathy for fellow-sufferers.

At the funeral for a stillborn sister, a little girl was listening to the sermon. Afterwards she asked her parents why the minister had said there would be no mourning in heaven. Before they could respond, she continued, *If there is no morning in heaven, when will (my sister) wake up?*[41]

For healthcare workers

Research has shown that healthcare workers can influence the intensity of grief by the way they handle the death and interact with the bereaved.[42] *Things that can help the bereaved parents include involving them in medical decisions and decisions relating to the baby's care; skilled, sensitive and caring treatment at the time of the loss; and helping them to create memories.*

Things that make bereavement more difficult include disempowerment; a lack of acknowledgement of their emotional experience; lack of information; and insensitive and unsympathetic care.

Parents appreciate a personal approach rather than a more clinical one, and space to react in their own way in their own time.

The Perinatal Society of Australia and New Zealand has made recommendations to help staff support bereaved parents, which include the following guidelines for those who work in this area:[43]

1. *Treat the deceased baby with the same respect as a live baby.*
2. *Parents need to feel supported and in control; the death should be validated.*
3. *Different approaches to death and other rituals should be respected.*
4. *Allow plenty of time to discuss issues at the most appropriate time,*

41. S Williams, *The Shaming of the Strong*, Kingsway, Eastbourne, 2005, pp. 154-5.

42. H Bryant, 'Maintaining patient dignity and offering support after miscarriage', *Emergency Nurse*, vol. 15, no. 9, February 2008, pp. 26-9; K Stratton and L Lloyd, 'Hospital-based interventions at and following miscarriage: Literature to inform a research-practice initiative', *Australian and New Zealand Journal of Obstetrics and Gynaecology*, vol. 48, no. 1, February 2008, pp. 5-11.

43. V Flenady, J King, A Charles, G Gardener, D Ellwood, K Day, L McCowan, A Kent, D Tudehope, R Richardson, L Conway, A Chan, R Haslam and Y Khong for the Perinatal Society of Australia and New Zealand (PSANZ) Perinatal Mortality Group, *PSANZ Clinical Practice Guideline for Perinatal Mortality*, version 2.2, Perinatal Mortality Group, Canberra, April 2009, pp. 57-66.

being clear, honest and sensitive. Repeat important information. Ensure both parents are present. Provide written information for reference in parent-friendly language. Don't use terms such as 'fetus'. Give parents enough information to make necessary decisions.

5. *Inform parents ahead of time how much time they can spend with the baby, and give them the option of a private room in a surgical, maternity or gynaecology ward. For some parents, it can be distressing to stay in the maternity ward and hear babies crying. Others may find it more upsetting to be moved elsewhere, and interpret this as meaning they are no longer considered to be parents. A discreet sign should be placed outside the door to alert staff of the death.*

6. *Parents should be given time to spend with the baby, with no rush to leave the baby or the hospital. The option to take the baby home should be provided, as well as ongoing access if desired. Other children in the family should be welcome.*

7. *Inform parents that they can hold, undress, and bath the baby. They should not be pressured to do so if they would rather not.[44] Advise them of what equipment is provided by the hospital (blankets, etc.). Advise parents that they can use their own clothing for the baby. Inform them of any anticipated malformations (e.g. deformed head) so that appropriate clothing (a bonnet) can be used for photographs. If parents are unsure how to approach the baby, staff should show them how to hold and bath the child.*

8. *Support the collection of mementos—collect them if the parents are unable, to give to them when they are ready. Staff should at least include hand and footprints, ID bracelet, measuring tape, cot card, digital photographs and a lock of hair (where possible and only after permission of the parents has been given).*

9. *Inform parents that baptism or blessing can be arranged through hospital chaplaincy staff.*

10. *Special care is needed with multiple pregnancies if some infants survive; consider the impact of the previous death(s) on emotional response and coping with current death.*

---

44. KA Cunningham, 'Holding a stillborn baby: does the existing evidence help us provide guidance?', *Medical Journal of Australia*, vol. 196, no. 9, 21 May 2012, pp. 558-60.

11. *Advise mother on milk production after the birth and how to manage it. Give written information regarding support services for parents, children, and bereavement.*
12. *Arrange follow-up and advise parents if other babies will be present.*

Afterwards

Saying goodbye is hard. For Maisie, the most difficult time was leaving the hospital: *I wasn't prepared for it. It just hit me as we were driving out of the parking lot and I cried and cried.* Grief may well up when it is least expected, and that's okay.

Despite the difficulties of coping with a child's death, parents still have to deal with the formalities, such as a funeral. This may be a time when the husband can contribute in a meaningful way while the mother recovers physically. The parents may find it helpful to mark the passing of their baby with some sort of ceremony, even if there is no body. It is a pity that our Western society has lost its traditions around death and that there is no recognized way to mark the passing of a baby through miscarriage or stillbirth. The Japanese have Mizuko kuyō, or 'fetus memorial service', which is a ceremony for those who have had a miscarriage, stillbirth or abortion. Temples usually sell statues for display near the temple, which, in some places, the parents dress up with little clothes. Parents say they have found the ritual comforting.

I think the closest thing we have in the West is a church funeral. *What I felt was so important was the funeral. It enabled us both to plan and be active during that incredibly difficult week after her birth. It also enabled me to recognize her as a real person, who deserved a real goodbye. So it marked a very clear full stop to that terribly sad chapter of my life, and therefore enabled us to move on.* Some hospitals provide memorial services to remember the babies who have died at that hospital. I have attended funerals for stillborn children that, although incredibly sad, were a wonderful testament to the value of every human life.

Parents may choose to make the funeral private or public, and they should be aware that there is no need to rush. Services can help extended family and friends acknowledge their loss too. Once again, it may be difficult. Roxanne and her husband decided to bury their child. She said,

I was okay until they put him into the ground. Then I lost it.

If parents have had to register the birth, they will have given thought to naming their child. Even if the baby was too young for this requirement, it is still helpful to name the child in order to validate the birth and make verbalizing memories easier.

Some parents bury the child's remains in their back yard and mark it with a cross or a tree. Some parents scatter the ashes in a special place. Some families have a formal burial. Close family and friends may have made clothes for the baby, which can be worn by the child at this special time. Jenny and Chris invited their children to put toys in the tiny coffin.

It may take a long time before the parents recover from their grief, and life for them will never be quite the same again.

Many families find ways to remember their baby as life goes on, perhaps with a piece of jewellery, or a memento displayed at home, or maybe each time they see a particular flower. Some families will celebrate the child's birthday each year, or just keep remembering how old their child would have been had they lived. Each family finds its own way to remember the child who isn't there.

Post-mortem examination/autopsy

While it can be distressing to think about having a baby's body examined, it can sometimes provide an explanation as to why the death occurred, and it can contribute to medical understanding of stillbirth in general. It is hard for parents to think this issue through at such a difficult time (immediately after the birth), but only they can make the decision they feel happy with. It is possible to do some tests (such as swabs for infection, x-rays or genetic examination) without a complete autopsy. Results can take up to weeks and months to be completed; parents should discuss the findings with their doctor, as they are usually explained in technical terms, and they will want to know what should be considered for future pregnancies.

Psychological trauma and grief

In many places, there is no routine follow-up for patients who have suffered miscarriage, and so they do not receive the care they need at an emotional level. Miscarriage is known to lead to depression and anxiety, as well as grief. A 2009 survey by the Stillbirth and Neonatal Death Charity (SANDS) in the United Kingdom found that 81% of parents said they suffered depression after the death of their baby; 39% said it affected their physical health; and, 25% said they lost earnings because they had to change jobs or career.[45] The bereavement experienced by these parents may seem protracted and intense compared to other types of grief.

Some researchers have likened it to post-traumatic stress disorder, similar to that suffered by trauma victims.[46] High levels of guilt are common, as well as a sense of having lost part of oneself. There is no standard pattern of grief but talking about it is usually helpful, and although parents won't forget, the grief does ease with time.[47]

One problem is that many people don't realize it is grief they are experiencing. It may be the first time the parents have lost a loved one. They may need to be told that grief is a normal reaction to bereavement. The lack of acknowledgement of the miscarriage or stillbirth may mean that not even the parents consciously register that the death of a real person has occurred. Legitimizing the grief process can help parents move through it.

It is not uncommon for grief to be associated with a sense of physical fatigue. It can be difficult to sleep, concentrate or even communicate with others. Those who are grieving may seem withdrawn and depressed and it may be hard for them to get out of bed some days. It is important that they do not feel they are to blame for what has happened. They should not rush back to work. They should let themselves feel what they feel, because they have had a significant loss.

It is not unusual for mothers and fathers to grieve in different ways.[48] Mothers may have a more intense reaction and be more likely than fathers to cry with others. They are more likely to seek support, desire to talk endlessly about their baby, and be preoccupied by their loss. But this does not mean that fathers care less. It is difficult for grieving men in our society, where displays of male emotion are frowned upon.

---

45.   J Scott and C Bevan, *Saving Babies' Lives: Report 2009*, Stillbirth and Neonatal Death Charity (Sands), London, 2009.

46.   C Lee and P Slade, 'Miscarriage as a traumatic event: a review of the literature and new implications for intervention', *Journal of Psychosomatic Research*, vol. 40, no. 3, March 1996, pp. 235-44.

47.   N Brier, 'Grief following miscarriage: A comprehensive review of the literature', *Journal of Women's Health*, vol. 17, no. 3, April 2008, pp. 451-64.

48.   A Dyregrov and SB Matthiesen, 'Similarities and differences in mothers' and fathers' grief following the death of an infant', *Scandinavian Journal of Psychology*, vol. 28, no. 1, March 1987, pp. 1-15; Flenady et al., *PSANZ Clinical Practice Guideline for Perinatal Mortality*, loc. cit.

However, these fathers often have a preference for solitude, and may be unwilling to discuss the baby in social and work situations. They may feel a responsibility to be 'strong' for their wives and not share their tears, even with them; this can lead to couples feeling even more distant from each other.

Generally, the condolences—if there are any—are directed to the wife. That can leave husbands with very little support. Some may have had to go home from the hospital to an empty house with an empty cot in the nursery, although some will be allowed to stay at the hospital. One of the saddest stories I heard was of a new father cuddling his stillborn daughter with tears in his eyes, saying he just wanted to try and warm her up.[49] Fathers feel protective of their children as well as their wives, and it is a terrible hardship when there is nothing they can do.

A woman is more likely to feel a stronger sense of responsibility for the miscarriage, and guilt that her body has 'let down' both the child and her husband. She may feel she has failed as a woman. Self-blame is increased in those who have missed miscarriages, and in those where no cause for the miscarriage is identified.[50]

Even when they think they have recovered, a wave of sadness may hit these parents when they least expect it. There are 'grief and loss' websites for parents that can be helpful. Sometimes, when everyone around the parents is telling them to count their blessings, it helps for them to connect with other

> ## Helpful online resources for grieving parents
> Search words to use *(any search engine can help you with these descriptors)*: Infant loss; perinatal death; neonatal bereavement; stillbirth; stillborn; miscarriage; pregnancy; multiple; twin; triplet; quadruplet; quintuplet; infertility; multicultural; culture; grieving; grief; mourn; bereaved; child death; self help; parent support; subsequent pregnancy after loss; pregnancy loss.[51]

49. Taylor, op. cit., p. 37.

50. AV Nikcevic, SA Tinkel, AR Kuczmierczyk and KH Nicolaides, 'Investigation of the cause of miscarriage and its influence on women's psychological distress', *BJOG*, vol. 106, no. 8, August 1999, pp. 808-13.

51. Neonatal Intensive Care Unit Bereavement Committee, *Web Sites of Interest To Grieving Parents*, The Hospital For Sick Children's Neonatal Palliative Care and Bereavement Program, March 2005 (viewed 16 January 2012): www.virtualhospice.ca/Assets/websites%20for%20 grieving%20parents%20-toronto_20081127165937.doc

parents who are feeling the same way and not wanting their loved ones to be forgotten. You can count your blessings and still grieve your losses. Parenting after a loss can be complicated by the memory of the one(s) who didn't come home. Counselling may be needed to sort through the confusing thoughts and emotions experienced.

Taboos

Susie turned to me at work and said, *Why don't we ever talk about it? I've been listening to stories about every baby that's born, and I've never heard of one miscarriage.* Miscarriage is still a taboo subject, which makes the grieving harder. Paul said, *I wonder why? Is it because they are worried it might happen to them, or because they've been hurt by it themselves?*[52]

It often helps to talk. It helps make the baby more real and helps people feel better. Words from bereaved parents may help others when it happens to them. So many people don't know how common pregnancy loss still is. Even that term can be unhelpful; it wasn't just a pregnancy that was lost—it was a baby.

Apparently some things have improved over the past few decades; there was a time when the parents would not get to see their baby. I once met an older woman who hadn't been told whether her stillborn child was a boy or a girl. Her husband wasn't even allowed into the delivery room.

It is hard to talk about a child who has died prematurely; we often do not know what to say. But it helps those who are grieving when others resist the desire to avoid the topic altogether. Sarah Williams, who found out that her child would die at birth, was grateful when a pregnant friend reached out to her across the gulf separating them. She remembered a verse of Scripture that instructs us to "rejoice with those who rejoice, weep with those who weep" (Rom 12:15). She writes: *Both grieving and rejoicing are choices we must make actively out of love for one another within the resilience of community.* Her friend chose to mourn with her as she learnt her baby would die. Later, Sarah would choose to rejoice with her friend when her baby was born. *Both choices were costly.*[53]

When should another pregnancy be attempted?

Everyone is different, but it is recommended that parents wait until the woman is physically and emotionally ready, and has had any tests

---

52. A Stanfield-Porter, *A Dad's Story*, Bonnie Babes Foundation, Canterbury, n.d., p. 10.
53. Stanfield-Porter, ibid.; Williams, op. cit., pp. 45-6.

recommended by the doctor, before attempting another pregnancy. Medically, it is safe after one normal menstrual cycle. Most women will have a period 4-6 weeks after a miscarriage. However, it may take much longer for parents to feel ready to try again due to the challenge of coming to terms with the loss.

Talking about the baby

Tammy says, *At our church, on Mother's Day they handed around chocolates to all the mothers. I didn't get one, but I felt like saying, "I had a baby but she died".* Bereaved parents won't want to explain things to everyone, but it may be that sometimes they will want to acknowledge the child that is not sitting beside them. If they think beforehand about how to say what they want to say, it might make it easier. And at church on Mother's Day, give all the women a chocolate. No-one needs a reminder of those they have lost; even if they don't have children, they do all have a mother. Williams notes: *The thing about losing a child is that you do not just lose them once, but you go on experiencing the loss of what they would have been.*[54]

Some parents call their little ones 'angels'. Christians are aware that an angel is another type of being entirely. I think this usage just reflects the difficulties for secular parents attempting to find the vocabulary to talk about these things.

Theology

Where is God in all of this? These are challenging things to comprehend, so thinking about them *before* tragedy strikes can make things easier. However, it does not always work out that way. If your sense of loss is still fresh, it may be better for you to look at the psalms, especially Psalm 23 and Psalm 90. Otherwise, read on.

One of the things I love about the Bible is the way it helps us understand why the world is the way it is. Reading the book of Genesis helps us understand how we should respond to bereavement; sickness, death and grief are now unavoidable realities in our world because of human sin and God's judgement.

We all know the story. God said to Adam, "You may surely eat of every tree of the garden, but of the tree of the knowledge of good and evil you shall not eat, for in the day that you eat of it you shall surely die"

---

54. Williams, op. cit., p. 175.

(Gen 2:16-17). But Adam and Eve, persuaded by the serpent, ate of the prohibited fruit. As a result, God told Adam that he would return to the ground from which he was taken: "for you are dust, and to dust you shall return" (Gen 3:19b). And they were banished from the garden so they could not eat from the tree of life and live forever (Gen 3:22-24).

Death came into the world with the Fall, rendering this life "vanity and a striving after wind" (Eccl 1:14). Death is the last enemy to be destroyed (1 Cor 15:26). It is not what God originally planned for us, and we are right to find it an outrage.

Ecclesiastes is one book of the Bible that clearly talks about the transience of life on earth:

> If a man fathers a hundred children and lives many years, so that
> the days of his years are many, but his soul is not satisfied with life's
> good things, and he also has no burial, I say that a stillborn child is
> better off than he. For it comes in vanity and goes in darkness, and
> in darkness its name is covered. Moreover, it has not seen the sun
> or known anything, yet it finds rest rather than he. Even though he
> should live a thousand years twice over, yet enjoy no good—do not
> all go to the one place? (Eccl 6:3-6)

The life of the stillborn child is compared to that of a rich man. The child has no identity and no opportunity to develop character or personality. It has no experience of life. And yet the Preacher thinks the child is better off for being spared the prolonged misery of the dissatisfied rich man who, like each one of us, will also die.

As Job protests against his suffering and curses the day of his birth, he cries to God:

> "Let the day perish on which I was born,
>> and the night that said,
>> 'A man is conceived'...
>
> because it did not shut the doors of my mother's womb,
>> nor hide trouble from my eyes.
> Why did I not die at birth,
>> come out from the womb and expire?
> Why did the knees receive me?
>> Or why the breasts, that I should nurse?
> For then I would have lain down and been quiet;
>> I would have slept; then I would have been at rest...

Or why was I not as a hidden stillborn child
>   as infants who never see the light?" (Job 3:3-16)

In this passage, Job—out of desperate grief and sorrow—proclaims the life of a stillborn child to be a blessing compared to the intolerable suffering he has just experienced.

Experiencing the harsh realities of our existence, becoming acquainted with grief as the unthinkable happens, and realizing, as we protest helplessly, that sometimes parents must bury their children, we "groan inwardly as we wait eagerly for adoption as sons, the redemption of our bodies" (Rom 8:23). God knows how much we suffer. "Likewise the Spirit helps us in our weakness. For we do not know what to pray for as we ought, but the Spirit himself intercedes for us with groanings too deep for words" (Rom 8:26). And we are not left alone: "for you have been my help, and in the shadow of your wings I will sing for joy. My soul clings to you; your right hand upholds me" (Ps 63:7-8).

There may be times when we doubt the goodness and sovereignty of a God who allows children to die before they are even born. But God knows how many days he has ordained for each baby before one of them comes to be (Ps 139:16). He reserves the right to take human life. Job recognized this when he said "Naked I came from my mother's womb, and naked shall I return. The LORD gave, and the LORD has taken away; blessed be the name of the LORD" (Job 1:21).

It might be difficult to say that God is both good and sovereign, if the death of an unborn child was the only thing we could look at. But it isn't the only thing; we can also look at a dearly loved only Son, who suffered and died for us on a cross while we were still sinners. God is also a parent, whose only begotten Son died before his time. And that tells us how much he loves *all* his children. "Behold, God does all these things, twice, three times, with a man, to bring back his soul from the pit, that he may be lighted with the light of life" (Job 33:29-30). In the words of Don Carson, sometimes God speaks to us in the language of pain.[55]

In Romans 5, we are told that even as death entered the world through one man, Adam, because of sin (v. 12), all men can now have eternal life because the Lord Jesus Christ died for us (vv. 8, 21) if only we will trust in him: "For the wages of sin is death, but the free gift of God is eternal life in Christ Jesus our Lord" (Rom 6:23). We will still

---

55. DA Carson, *How Long, O Lord?* 2nd edn, Baker Academic, Grand Rapids, 2006, p. 149.

mourn, but we know death is not the end.

If life is eternal, where are they now—these children who have died in infancy or in the womb? The Bible does not speak clearly to us on this matter. When King David was told that his son by Bathsheba would die, he fasted for 7 days while pleading with God for mercy. When his servants told him the child had died, they were amazed at his subsequent composure—getting up and washing, going to the tabernacle to worship, and asking the cook for some food. What was David trying to achieve by his praying and fasting? David tells us himself:

> "While the child was still alive, I fasted and wept, for I said, 'Who knows whether the LORD will be gracious to me, that the child may live?' But now he is dead. Why should I fast? Can I bring him back again? I shall go to him, but he will not return to me." (2 Sam 12:22-23)

He knew his God. He knew that his was a God of grace.

We know that David believed in a life after death (see Pss 16:10-11, 17:15). Some commentators have understood his reply, "I shall go to him, but he will not return to me" (2 Sam 12:23) as indicating that children who die young go to heaven. This may be reading too much into the text. It is more likely to reflect the fact that although David did not have the full light of the revelation we have received through Christ, he was aware that there is a life after death, that the child still lived, and that he would join him when he also died.[56] Yet it shows David had the confidence to trust God and leave the child's destiny in his hands.

In the Bible, death does not equal annihilation.[57] Jesus referred to relationships after death while engaging in a debate about the resurrection, in Matthew 22:23-32. He quotes Exodus 3:6 where Yahweh spoke to Moses from the burning bush: "I am the God of Abraham, and the God of Isaac, and the God of Jacob". Jesus reminded the crowd that the use of the present tense in this Exodus passage reflects the unbreakable relationship that God's people have with him beyond the grave, in a living union that continues to honour the covenant he had made with Abraham (Genesis 15). "He is not God of the dead, but of the living" (Matt 22:32).

---

56. Archbishop Dr Peter Jensen, personal communication.
57. This section is derived from DR Davis, 'The unheard of covenant God: The God who commits', address given at Katoomba Easter Convention, Katoomba, 22 April 2011.

Furthermore, God's covenant is upheld even when we can't see how it can possibly prevail. After the miraculous birth of Isaac, Sarah's only child, we struggle to understand why God would ask Abraham to sacrifice his son (Gen 22:1-3). Why does God threaten the child of the promise? We see from the rest of the chapter that God was testing Abraham, and that he reaffirmed his promise after Isaac's last-minute reprieve. Dale Ralph Davis observes that God is very kind in allowing us to see these events in the Bible, showing us that it can be a part of the normal Christian experience to think God is contradicting his own character: after blessing Abraham with a son, God appeared to be sabotaging his own plan. Abraham was praised for obeying God (Gen 22:18) even though he was walking in the darkness, unable to see the light. In Daniel 2:22 we read: "[God] knows what is in the darkness, and the light dwells with him". I do not know what happens to those little ones who die before they are born, but I do know something of the character of our God. In Genesis 18, Abraham asked God for grace and mercy, on behalf of the people of Sodom and Gomorrah. He approached the Lord and said:

> "Will you indeed sweep away the righteous with the wicked? Suppose there are fifty righteous within the city. Will you then sweep away the place and not spare it for the fifty righteous who are in it? Far be it from you to do such a thing, to put the righteous to death with the wicked, so that the righteous fare as the wicked! Far be that from you! Shall not the Judge of all the earth do what is just?" (Gen 18:23-25)

We do not know with certainty what happens to those infants whose passing we mourn. What we do know is this: the Lord and Judge of the universe can be trusted to do what is right. Even though we may be walking through the darkness, God knows what is there and the light dwells with him. He will keep his covenant with us.

Often we live in the here and now, at times forgetting that "the sufferings of this present time are not worth comparing with the glory that is to be revealed to us" (Rom 8:18). We will still weep—knowing that a little one is not going to suffer a lifetime in this fallen world will not make us miss them any less. But in the dark times we must try to look ahead to the resurrection (1 Cor 15:20-26), because "Death is swallowed up in victory... thanks be to God, who gives us the victory through our Lord Jesus Christ" (1 Cor 15:54, 57).

Assisted reproductive technologies

PREVIOUSLY, WE HAVE discussed the role of contraceptives in allowing us to have sex without creating babies. Reproductive technology has further revolutionized child-bearing by allowing us to create babies without having sex. Indeed, childbirth is now possible as an individual project that can be pursued not only without marriage, but also without a partner. The impact this has had on our societal structure is profound, but beyond the scope of this discussion.

ART (pronounced A.R.T.) includes all techniques involving the direct manipulation of human eggs, sperm and embryos outside of the body. The first and still most common form of ART is in vitro fertilization (IVF), but many other related techniques are now available. Modern ART has revolutionized the treatment of infertility, rendering some treatments obsolete because ART is simply more effective and usually cheaper than traditional alternatives. It is now the automatic next step after infertility (the result of a wide range of problems) has been diagnosed; and there is no sign of the trend slowing down.

The number of ways in which human eggs, sperm and embryos can now be manipulated has been increasing at a rapid pace in recent years. This chapter contains a lot of technical detail, highlighting the fact that the very complexity of this technology presents a danger to those attempting to navigate the options. In this area in particular, those who wish to make godly decisions will need to apply themselves to understand what they are being offered. It is very tempting to decide it's too hard, and just accept the judgements of the treating physician who is offering the chance of a baby.

IVF was developed as treatment for the infertility resulting from damage in the fallopian tubes.[1] The original idea was that a blocked tube could stop the sperm and egg from uniting, so by putting them together in a 'test tube' (actually, a flat petri dish is used), an embryo could be formed which would then be transferred to the woman's uterus through the cervix, allowing normal development to take place. This use of medical therapy in the presence of disease is appropriate so long as no scriptural principle is violated.[2] Doctors can restore normal function to the reproductive system if they find a fixable problem.

With the expanding repertoire of ART, however, doctors are now employing procedures that go beyond just fixing what is broken. The demand in our community for biologically related offspring has meant that fertility specialists have kept pushing and pushing to provide an ever-widening range of options, not just for heterosexual couples with medical infertility, but also for those with 'social infertility'—single parents, same-sex couples, and those who could have a child if they wanted to but would prefer someone else to do the hard work. This sometimes requires the donation of sperm, eggs and wombs, and means that our choices go way beyond simple remedial treatment.

The diagnosis of infertility is usually so distressing for a couple that they may not stop to think about the treatment before they begin. They are prepared to go to extraordinary lengths to get the child they desire. This passion for a child is not to be wondered at; in the book of Genesis, we remember Rachel saying to her husband, Jacob, "Give me children, or I shall die!" (Gen 30:1).

It is common for ethical dilemmas to develop in ART, which is not surprising when you think about it; ART is about the creation of human life. To avoid ethical pitfalls, it is vital that couples explore what is involved in ART before making any decisions. Many common ethical dilemmas arising from the use of ART cannot be resolved once action has begun, so thinking carefully before acting is worth it—even worth the frustration caused by delay.

I am sure you see the problem. Who wants to delay having a child when the specialist can tell you everything you need to know? However, the emotional vulnerability of infertile couples means they need particularly careful counselling in the early stages of decision-making,

---

1. For the history of the development of ART, see the beginning of chapter 15.
2. See chapter 16.

once the diagnosis of infertility has been made, so they do not in their enthusiasm agree to things they will afterwards regret. Johann said: *We hadn't ever seriously looked at IVF, but our backgrounds had formed opinions that Christians shouldn't have IVF. So when we heard the news that our only chance at pregnancy was through IVF, we were greatly grieved as we initially thought we couldn't do it as Christians. Also, there was the thought that God had created us this way, so to have IVF was to go against him. These were very challenging issues that we had to work through and we spent a year thinking through the issues, praying, doing research and talking to godly Christians.*

Those who wish to honour God in all areas of their lives will not check him in at the door of the fertility clinic. They will take the time to consider all their options and collect the facts, so that their decisions are godly at all times.

Rocking the boat

Although some fertility clinics go out of their way to accommodate those whose religious beliefs are opposed to some common ART practices, in other places your distinctive requests will be seen as troublemaking. You might as well get ready for it before you start—it is so commonly experienced. I find that if you remain calm and pleasant you are unlikely to offend staff, but you may annoy them by wanting things to be done differently.

Consider the experience of Dennis and Anita. Anita recalls:

Our specialist and scientists' goal was successful pregnancy, with no consideration of the amount of lives created. We were pressured to have maximum embryos created and to only implant embryos that were classified viable for life to give us the highest chance of pregnancy. This was very difficult, as we believed life began when an embryo was formed and this wasn't respected by the IVF system. We chose to have only 6 out of our 11 eggs fertilized, yet despite the fact that we had clearly spoken our wishes to our specialist and put it in detailed writing, when we turned up for egg collection we were pressured to have them all fertilized by the scientist and were told that we were greatly limiting our chances and were made to feel foolish. I was quite emotional that morning already and to have our wishes undermined and not respected made the whole experience so much more stressful. We also had explicitly expressed that we wanted every embryo implanted (at different times) and given a chance at life in the womb. Despite this on day 5 after egg collection, we were told that only 5 eggs became embryos and only 2 were viable for life, so they would implant one that day and freeze one. We again had to state our wishes that the other 3 had started to multiply so we believed life had begun and we wanted to allow them to take their natural course in the womb.

They weren't the only ones. Jill and Frank also had problems:

Infertility was a very hard time for us and we took a year of contemplating IVF before we began, and then, to face a system that didn't respect our views made the process even harder. Although we are very grateful for the gifts given to the specialists and scientist by God to assist with fertility, the process could have been a lot less stressful for us if we had been listened to and respected.

Regulation of ART

This book is an international publication, so it's important to note that the regulation of ART differs widely between countries. In 1991, the Human Fertilisation and Embryology Authority (HFEA)[3] was established in the United Kingdom to regulate in vitro fertilization (IVF), donor insemination (DI) and egg, sperm and embryo storage, and to license and monitor embryo research as well.

ART in Australia was regulated at the state level until 2002, when national legislation was introduced allowing destructive embryo research. Research is now under the supervision of the Licensing Committee of the National Health and Medical Research Council (NHMRC),[4] and clinical accreditation comes under the auspices of the Reproductive Technology Accreditation Committee (RTAC)[5], part of the Fertility Society of Australia (FSA)—which is basically a self-regulating body, though its standards remain high.

In the United States, different aspects of ART are monitored by different authorities in a patchwork approach that does not cover all areas of practice. The United States is among the least regulated of developed

---

3. For more information, visit the HFEA website: www.hfea.gov.uk
4. See NHMRC, *Human Embryos and Cloning*, NHMRC, Canberra, 26 March 2012 (viewed 2 July 2012): www.nhmrc.gov.au/research/embryos
5. See FSA, *RTAC*, FSA, South Melbourne, 2012 (viewed 18 January 2012): www.fertilitysociety.com.au/rtac/

countries.[6] Keep this in mind while we discuss the various treatments available, because not all of them are available everywhere.

Treatment options

The treatments you are offered will vary according to the reason for your infertility.[7] You will remember from chapter 2 that the formation of an embryo requires the joining of a sperm and egg. If embryos represent early human life, what happens to them is morally significant. However, sperm and eggs individually do not represent human life, and their fate does not have the same ethical importance.

We will now run through the armamentarium of ART and evaluate each practice from an ethical perspective. Although several practices may be used together, I think it is easier to understand the ethical issues if we address them separately. Note that not all the options listed will be appropriate choices for those who wish to protect human life from the time of fertilization.

Intrauterine insemination (IUI)

If the man's sperm count is moderately reduced, IUI may be recommended. The first report of a live birth from IUI was published in 1866, when Dr James Marion Sims described performing it in Europe.[8] This treatment increases the number of sperm that get into the uterus. Usually only about 10% of the sperm get there. In this procedure, the man's semen is collected and 'washed' (prepared to select the most motile [mobile] sperm, to concentrate numbers, and to remove the seminal fluid). The prepared sperm is injected into the woman's uterus through the cervix at her most fertile time (ovulation). The woman's cycle is monitored with blood tests and vaginal ultrasound so that insemination timing is exact. The success of IUI is increased if the woman receives ovulation-inducing medication to increase the number of eggs available in the fallopian tubes each cycle.

---

6.   K Riggan, 'Regulation (or lack thereof) of assisted reproductive technologies in the U.S. and abroad', *Dignitas*, vol. 17, nos 1 and 2, Spring/Summer 2010, pp. 8-11. A slightly out-of-date discussion of the regulation of ART can be found in The President's Council on Bioethics, *Reproduction and Responsibility: The Regulation of New Biotechnologies*, Washington DC, March 2004, pp. 46-87; a more enthusiastic account is WY Chang and AH DeCherney, 'History of regulation of assisted reproductive technology (ART) in the USA: A work in progress', *Human Fertility*, vol. 6, no. 2, 2003, pp. 64-70.

7.   See chapter 10.

8.   GN Allahbadia, *Intrauterine Insemination*, Taylor and Francis, London, 2005.

Ethical issues

If the husband and wife use their own egg and sperm, this procedure will be aiming to remedy the problem the couple has in allowing their gametes (sperm and egg) to unite. In principle, it is ethical for Christians to use biotechnology to correct medical problems.[9] However, some couples find it difficult having clinic staff involved in what is intended to be a highly intimate experience, and any form of assisted reproduction is difficult during the period between the procedure and the subsequent pregnancy test, to see if it worked. Carol explained her own experience: *The procedure of IUI was challenging. The first cycle, I was emotionally sensitive already about thinking about having children. But then, everything being new, doctors' appointments, blood tests and everything left me very anxious. It surprises me how uptight I was about just going through the procedures.*

Dana also found it difficult: *Having gone through three IUI cycles has been emotionally draining. It hasn't been overwhelming, but has definitely been a trial, riding the hope rollercoaster all over again. I think it is less of a challenge than it could have been as we started IUI after 8½ years of infertility; we're pretty used to the idea of not being pregnant, but it still hurts when hope is stirred.*

Although the presence of medical staff may be uncomfortable, it is not an ethical barrier.

See below for further discussion regarding the use of IUI with donor sperm.

Sperm collection

The standard technique for semen collection is to ask the man to masturbate in a room at the fertility clinic, with pornographic material for stimulation.

Ethical issues

While I do not personally believe masturbation is necessarily sinful, I realize that some Christian denominations believe ejaculation should never be separated from procreation. If this is your belief, I discuss your options below. Furthermore, in the clinic situation the use of pornographic material could cause lust to be a problem, which is definitely sinful for all Christians if your spouse is not the object (1 Thess 4:3-7).

---

9.   See chapter 16.

There are usually alternatives available for those who ask. Some husbands take their wives with them into the collection room—if they can. *There wasn't even enough room for us both to turn around*, said Ted. Alternatively, the husband could masturbate while filling his mind with images of his wife. Many clinics allow men to collect the semen at home with the assistance of their wife, if they live within an hour of the clinic. Timing is important because the sperm needs to be fresh. If a particular day is difficult, clinics will freeze the specimen to make sure the semen is there when it is needed. Some clinics have developed a system where condoms can be used—either a sterile condom for collection during intercourse (if masturbation is opposed), or a 'holy condom' (a condom with a pinhole in the end) for those couples that oppose contraception. Even if lust is not a problem for you, you may enjoy collecting sperm as a couple considering the goal you have in mind.

In vitro fertilization (IVF)

In basic IVF (natural cycle), the woman's egg is collected in a natural unstimulated menstrual cycle. Usually this would only yield 1-2 eggs, and the success rate reflects the fact that any one embryo has a relatively low implantation rate. This method is used for women who cannot tolerate or do not respond to ovarian stimulation.

The woman is given a human chorionic gonadotropin hormone (hCG) injection when the egg follicle is mature, making it ready to release the egg at ovulation. Usually just one egg is collected from the woman's ovary by inserting a needle through the wall of the vagina under ultrasound guidance. The woman is usually sedated but awake for this procedure, which rarely has serious complications. The egg will be placed in culture media (a fluid—containing water, salts and nutrients for cells—that is formulated to resemble the fluid in the fallopian tubes), where it will be incubated in the laboratory.

Sperm are collected from the male ejaculate and added to the dish. The sperm then work at getting through the wall of the egg. Around 14-18 hours later, if two pronuclei have appeared in the embryo (one from the sperm and one from the egg) this indicates that fertilization has occurred. The embryo will be allowed to grow for 3-5 days in the laboratory then it will be transferred to the woman's uterus, through the cervix. Some clinics transfer the embryo when it has grown to the size of 8 cells at day 3, and some wait until it is a blastocyst (up to 100 cells) at day 5.[10] The woman is given hormones until a pregnancy test is performed 16 days after egg collection.

Ethical issues

If no embryos are destroyed, I can see no ethical problem with basic IVF. All that has happened is that the fallopian tubes have been bypassed, bringing the sperm and egg together artificially to create an embryo because barriers caused by disease won't allow it to happen naturally.

In practice, it is more common for IVF to be combined with ovarian stimulation using gonadotropins, as this increases the number of eggs available for harvest. The success rate for IVF across all procedures and age groups is around 25%. Success rates differ according to age and treatment, and also depend on which clinic you choose. Success rates can also be misleading, as they tend to reflect the number of procedures per live births rather than the number of embryos transferred per live birth. The best results are seen in women who are younger. Most clinics report their success rates on their websites. Try to look at success rates according to age, as a more 'successful' clinic at first glance, may, in fact, just be focusing on treating younger patients. In the end, the safest recommendation is generally word of mouth.

Ovarian stimulation

Medication to promote ovulation can be used alone when the woman has eggs but is not ovulating properly; this may be enough to restore fertility. It is also used with IVF (see below).

The woman's body has 'messenger hormones'—called luteinizing hormone (LH) and follicle-stimulating hormone (FSH)—that are released from the pituitary gland in the brain to tell the woman's body which hormones to produce at different stages of her monthly cycle. These hormones can be measured in the blood along with the oestrogen and progesterone released by the body.[11] Most fertility medications work by interacting with these messenger hormones.

Several types of medication can be used—your doctor will decide which is appropriate.

---

10. For a diagram showing the early stages of embryo development, see diagram 2: Early embryo development in chapter 2.

11. For a detailed description of the female cycle see diagram 3: Normal monthly menstrual cycle in chapter 6.

Clomiphene citrate (*Clomid, Serophene, Milophene*)

These tablets allow low-grade stimulation of the ovaries. They work by blocking feedback to the pituitary gland so that it thinks it needs to secrete extra FSH. The higher FSH level stimulates the ovaries to develop more egg-containing follicles. Often the follicle growth is monitored with blood tests and ultrasound scans. An hCG injection is given as the follicles mature in order to stimulate ovulation at a predictable time (it mimics the natural LH surge that accompanies ovulation).[12] Intercourse—or other interventions, if assisted reproduction is used— is timed to coincide with the release of the eggs. Sometimes another injection (GnRH antagonist) will be given. This is designed to block the body's natural LH surge, which might alter the timing of ovulation and risk the loss of the eggs.

Side effects
Some women feel emotional and irritable while taking Clomiphene. Side effects also include thickening and whitening of cervical mucus, vaginal dryness and hot flushes. Less commonly, there is abdominal bloating, breast discomfort, nausea or dizziness. Sometimes twins result, though this can be avoided if necessary by monitoring how many follicles are developing.

Gonadotropins

These are expensive and powerful medications that act in place of the normal messenger hormones (LH and FSH). There are several alternative preparations, all given by injection. Overall, current evidence indicates that they have similar efficacy, and each doctor has his or her own preference.

Injections of gonadotropins are more effective in stimulating multiple follicles than Clomiphene. A woman on this medication can develop 10-20 eggs (or even more) that reach maturity in a single cycle. This is why it is used in IVF. However, with every extra baby in the womb, risks for both mother and baby increase, so it is best to avoid a multiple pregnancy. Intercourse should be avoided at this time just in case the eggs are released early and you fertilize more than one egg by accident.

---

12.   This hCG is the same as the one measured in a pregnancy test, so if you use a home pregnancy test after receiving the injection, it will be positive. However, this does not mean you are pregnant!

Follicle growth is monitored with ultrasound and blood tests—usually more closely than with Clomiphene—and ovulation is induced with an hCG injection.

In some places, lower doses of gonadotropins are being used, producing fewer eggs, but also causing fewer side effects. Evidence is mounting that this is a preferable approach.[13]

Side effects
With the use of gonadotropins, a multiple pregnancy is a risk, with a 20% chance of twins. Bloating and mood changes are also experienced. *I think I was emotional and teary the whole time*, said Sara. A rare but dangerous complication is *ovarian hyperstimulation syndrome* (OHSS), occurring in a mild form in about 10% of women, with 1% at risk of developing life-threatening blood disorders.[14] The risk of OHSS increases with higher doses of gonadotropins rapidly increasing blood oestrogen levels, and high or repeated doses of hCG given to induce ovulation. Careful monitoring allows early intervention if problems occur. Transfer of the embryo may need to be delayed if this is a problem, just to be on the safe side.

Ethical issues
There are no intrinsic ethical issues in receiving hormones to stimulate ovulation, as it is a therapy designed to restore the body's functioning to normal. But, as discussed above, ovarian stimulation is associated with an increased incidence of multiple gestation pregnancy.[15] While this might initially seem attractive to an infertile couple (instant family!), it is better to avoid it if possible due to increased risks for mother and children. For the babies, there are the risks of premature delivery, low birth weight and health problems because their organs did not have enough time to develop. They are also at increased risk of cerebral palsy and complications such as twin-to-twin transfusion, entangled umbilical cords and possibly stillbirth. The mother is at increased risk of having

---

13.   SJ Muasher and JE Garcia, 'Fewer medications for in vitro fertilization can be better: thinking outside the box', *Fertility and Sterility*, vol. 92, no. 4, October 2009, pp. 1187-9.
14.   A Girolami, R Scandellari, F Tezza, D Paternoster and B Girolami, 'Arterial thrombosis in young women after ovarian stimulation: case report and review of the literature', *Journal of Thrombosis and Thrombolysis*, vol. 24, no. 2, October 2007, pp. 169-74.
15.   For a discussion of how multiple gestation is sometimes 'managed', see 'Selective/fetal/pregnancy reduction' under '3. What makes a woman choose to have an abortion?' in chapter 7.

a caesarean birth, financial costs will be greater, and there is also the problem of coping with more than one baby after the birth. Multiple births result in significant reduction in maternal quality of life, health and functioning, marital satisfaction and quality of life scores. Some mothers regret ever seeking ART after having to manage with twins.[16]

And so in view of the inherent risks of a multiple pregnancy, it is important to adhere strictly to your doctor's instructions, as it would be negligent to expose the mother and children to the risks of a multiple pregnancy unnecessarily. Biblical parenthood involves more than just successful fertilization.[17]

Similarly, doctors have an obligation to be diligent in this area. One of the traditional sayings in medicine is "first, do no harm". The unquestionable risks of multiple pregnancy make the transfer of more than two embryos in an IVF procedure negligent. These risks have led to the introduction of laws in some countries, including Australia and the United Kingdom, which allow only a maximum of two embryos to be transferred at any one time. Research suggests that transferring more embryos does not increase the chances of a successful pregnancy, but simply raises the chances of multiple births.[18] Furthermore, when ART providers in Australia voluntarily moved to single-embryo transfer, the reduction in the multiple-birth rate led to substantial savings in hospital costs.[19] Those who wish to protect their unborn children will refuse to agree to the transfer of more than two embryos at any one time.

Another ethical issue is the fact that research into follicle stimulation has not identified which follicles are the most likely to produce a live birth. It has always been assumed 'the more eggs the better', but if it could be determined that only a small number of fully matured eggs will lead to blastocyst development, there would be no reason for the high doses currently used to produce a large number of eggs, with greater risk to the woman. Current evidence suggests that although eggs that are

---

16. 'IVF multiples "strain marriages"', *BBC News*, 16 October 2003 (viewed 8 March 2012): http://news.bbc.co.uk/2/hi/health/3196850.stm

17. See chapter 4.

18. P Saldeen and P Sundström, 'Would legislation imposing single embryo transfer be a feasible way to reduce the rate of multiple pregnancies after IVF treatment?' *Human Reproduction*, vol. 20, no. 1, January 2005, pp. 4-8.

19. GM Chambers, PJ Illingworth and EA Sullivan, 'Assisted reproductive technology: public funding and the voluntary shift to single embryo transfer in Australia', *Medical Journal of Australia*, vol. 195, no. 10, 21 November 2011, pp. 594-8.

immature at the time of retrieval will usually mature in culture and often fertilize, they lead to relatively poor pregnancy rates.[20] This makes sense, as we know that the number of eggs harvested does not correlate with the number of live births. If it could be established, say, that the leading (largest) follicle was the most likely to give a live birth, it would change routine clinical practice. More work is needed in this area.

While there are no intrinsic ethical problems with the use of hormones to promote ovulation, there are potential ethical problems depending on *how* they are used. Given that more eggs will be produced with stronger stimulation, if they are all fertilized then the issue of freezing excess embryos will arise. This is discussed below.

Egg donation

Ovarian stimulation with gonadotropins is used in women who agree to offer their eggs for donation. Depending on a country's laws, this is either done for free (altruistic) or for money (commercial). Most clinics prefer to accept egg donations from women under 35 years of age who have completed their own families, because a younger woman's eggs will be healthier than an older woman's. Donors are usually screened psychologically and counselled, then treated as an IVF patient. They are given the gonadotropins to promote egg production and to bring their cycle in line with the intended recipient, who is also receiving treatment. The donor's eggs are harvested in the usual way and then incubated with the sperm, and any resulting embryos are transferred in the usual way.

In countries like Australia, where payment for human tissue is prohibited, I have not heard of any abuse of the system. Australian patients are encouraged to find their own donors. However, there is a huge shortage of eggs and clinics report long waiting lists of hundreds of women, with less than a dozen anonymous donors a year coming forward. Karen was unable to ovulate and was told that egg donation was her only chance of having a child of her own. She said, *I didn't like the idea of bearing a stranger's child. Fortunately, my sister volunteered. It was easier with someone I was related to, but it was a big deal for her. I wouldn't*

---

20. LL Veeck, 'Oocyte assessment and biological performance', *Annals of the New York Academy of Sciences*, vol. 541, October 1988, pp. 259-74; Y Lin, S Chang, K Lan, H Huang, C Chang, M Tsai, F Kung and F Huang, 'Human oocyte maturity in vivo determines the outcome of blastocyst development in vitro', *Journal of Assisted Reproduction and Genetics*, vol. 20, no. 12, December 2003, pp. 506-12.

do it again and I wouldn't ask her to do it again. I'm not surprised donor eggs are so scarce.

Because of the scarcity of donors when it requires an altruistic act, in some countries payment is allowed. Not only does this significantly increase the cost of IVF, but there is also growing evidence that in some countries this unregulated procedure has led to significant disease (and even death) from OHSS. Future fertility can also be affected. In some places, companies coerce young women to participate by promising large financial rewards. In the United States, advertisements are placed on college campuses and on the internet promising big payments—usually $5000-$10,000 for a donated egg cycle. Advertisements offering up to $50,000 per cycle have been seen at prestigious universities;[21] extra money is offered for beauty, brains and good family health history. Besides the offer of financial rewards, in the advertisements the girls are asked to "answer prayers", "make dreams come true" and "give hope" with the recipient in mind. Hundreds of women are currently registered in databases for prospective parents to inspect (college transcripts are available on application, for the prospective parents' attorney to peruse).

In the United Kingdom, following a public consultation in 2011, the HFEA announced it would allow an increase in the sum that could be paid to egg donors (from £250 to £750). It also announced the introduction of a £35 per visit compensation for sperm donors.

Some women who offer have generous motives. Katy said, *This was something I could do for someone else that would make this huge difference to their lives.* But most admit it is the money that makes them consider donation. Vicki said, *It's nice to know you're helping someone, but I wouldn't think of doing it except for the money.*

Some centres in the United States have noticed an increase in the number of egg donors following the global financial crisis. One fertility specialist commented: "There's no reason to think that suddenly there's 30% more people who have suddenly had this inner feeling to help out people. And what's changed? It's the economy."[22] The Center for Bioethics and Culture Network in California has sought to identify the extent of

---

21. M Cook, 'Harvard eggs going for US$35,000', *BioEdge*, 2 April 2010 (viewed 8 March 2012): www.bioedge.org/index.php/bioethics/bioethics_article/8939; JA Robertson, 'Is there an ethical problem here?', *Hastings Center Report*, vol. 40, no. 2, March-April 2010, p. 3.
22. Internet Broadcasting, 'More women donating eggs in bad economy', *LifeWhile*, 31 July 2008 (viewed 8 March 2012): www.lifewhile.com/health/17046074/detail.html

this problem. The Center's President, Jennifer Lahl, interviewed a young woman who had gone through the donation process, who warned, *You can possibly die from this, and it's not a joke, or worth $5K or any amount of money. Losing your life would end your chances of making that money, period. I was a victim and will stand and speak about it. They are out preying on ones like me.*[23]

It should be noted that, although there is no correlation between the number of eggs and the number of live babies born, there is a correlation between the number of donor eggs retrieved and how much a clinic gets paid. We should not confuse bad medicine with bad ethics, but they can coincide.

Ethical issues

The ethical problems surrounding commercial egg donation are multiple. If someone is pressured to be involved with a medical procedure that will not improve their health and that they might otherwise not have had, it is called coercion. Their decision is not entirely voluntary, and that means they are unable to give proper informed consent; this makes it unethical, according to the World Medical Association.[24] Offering significant financial rewards is a form of coercion or 'undue influence' that has the potential to exploit vulnerable women.

Currently, it is not known what health implications ovarian stimulation has in the long term, and this is not always explained fully before the procedure, which is another barrier to true consent.[25]

Also, if women give their eggs to strangers in a setting where ART is available to all members of the public without screening, are they avoiding their responsibility as potential parents to ensure the wellbeing of their offspring?

And lastly, I know it's not strictly an ethical problem, but I am troubled by the posters advertising for egg donors that show the 'satisfied

---

23. J Lahl, 'Egg donor interview: Linda* in Los Angeles', *Center for Bioethics and Culture Network*, 30 March 2011 (viewed 8 March 2012): www.cbc-network.org/2011/03/egg-donor-interview-linda-in-los-angeles/. Note that in some countries, problems related to egg donation might be due to medical negligence as well as the dangers of the procedure itself. This is why personal recommendation for a clinic is recommended.

24. JR Williams, *Medical Ethics Manual*, 2nd edn, World Medical Association, Ferney-Voltaire, 2009, p. 42.

25. H Pearson, 'Health effects of egg donation may take decades to emerge', *Nature*, vol. 442, no. 7103, 10 August 2006, pp. 607-8.

customers' (i.e. the donors) *shopping* (spending the payment for their eggs)! Are we really as materialistic as that?

Egg donation from the perspective of the recipient will be discussed below.

For doctors

There has not been extensive research into the long-term side effects of ovarian stimulation. Ethical care of patients involves making sure they are given all relevant information regarding the risks of treatment, as well as the benefits. While there have been concerns about the association between Clomiphene and ovarian cancer, current evidence shows no increased risk. However, results are inconclusive for increased risk for breast cancer and endometrial cancer following exposure to ovarian stimulation medications. More research in this area is needed.[26]

Freezing embryos (embryo cryopreservation)

The desire of fertility doctors to improve their patients' chances of getting pregnant has led to the standard practice of giving hormones to the woman to stimulate the production of multiple eggs in the ovaries (as described above) and to harvest the maximum number of eggs. Clinics generally encourage couples to allow them to create as many embryos as possible by trying to fertilize all the eggs. Egg collection is an invasive and expensive procedure with the potential for serious side effects, so it's better not to do it more often than necessary. And, obviously, it seems logical that the more times you place an embryo in the womb, the greater the chance of a pregnancy developing. Therefore, women are usually advised to collect and fertilize as many eggs as possible to increase the chances of a pregnancy without the extra risk and expense of another egg harvest.

Not all of the eggs will fertilize normally; a fertilization rate of around 80% is considered a good result. This could mean that over a dozen embryos are created, and the expectation is that not all embryos will result in a live birth. The best clinics only transfer one embryo at a time,

---

26. L Lerner-Geva, J Rabinovici and B Lunenfeld, 'Ovarian stimulation: is there a long-term risk for ovarian, breast and endometrial cancer?' *Women's Health* (London, England), vol. 6, no. 6, November 2010, pp. 831-9.

usually the best-looking one (due to the risks of multiple pregnancy as discussed above)—so what happens to the rest of them?

If nothing is done, the leftover embryos will die. Most countries do not allow embryos to continue growing outside the body after 14 days. Despite its popularity in science fiction—from *Brave New World* to *Avatar*—I am not aware of anyone having succeeded in producing an artificial womb. Therefore the usual practice is to freeze (cryopreserve) the embryos and defrost them for use as needed. Some embryos don't survive defrosting (around 50%-90%, depending on the clinic) and others may not develop once in the woman's womb. To increase the chances for success, and to reduce the false hope the parents may have for a pregnancy, many clinics will only freeze the most robust embryos. They judge an embryo's robustness based on its appearance. The problem is that you can't always tell just by looking at them which embryos have the potential to develop. *Embryos to me seem so fickle: good one day, bad the next,* complained Rick. This is definitely an area of concern, and is addressed below (see 'What makes an embryo viable?').

Embryo cryopreservation has been available since 1983, revolutionizing the treatment of infertility.[27] Despite this, there is still no formula to accurately predict how many embryos are needed to produce one live birth; hence, many clinics suggest the more embryos the better, just in case you need them. As previously mentioned, infertile couples tend to be extremely emotionally vulnerable at the beginning of treatment and are understandably amenable to any suggestion that may improve their chances of success. But the implications of freezing embryos needs to be considered.

In 2010, it was reported that a baby boy had been born from an embryo frozen 20 years earlier.[28] There is no deterioration over time for frozen embryos.[29] They can be kept in the cryopreserved state almost indefinitely.

In 2004, the Supreme Court of Australia had to decide whether two

---

27. A Trounson and L Mohr, 'Human pregnancy following cryopreservation, thawing and transfer of an eight-cell embryo', *Nature*, vol. 305, no. 5936, 20 October 1983, pp. 707-9.

28. M Cook, 'Boy born from embryo frozen 20 years ago', *BioEdge*, 15 October 2010 (viewed 8 March 2012): www.bioedge.org/index.php/bioethics/bioethics_article/9240

29. R Riggs, J Mayer, D Dowling-Lacey, T Chi, E Jones and S Oehninger, 'Does storage time influence postthaw survival and pregnancy outcome? An analysis of 11,768 cryopreserved human embryos', *Fertility and Sterility*, vol. 93, no. 1, January 2010, pp. 109-15.

children born from frozen embryos could share in their grandmother's estate. It was decided that they couldn't because they did not fit the definition of 'survive' in its ordinary sense, even though they were in the freezer at the time of her death.[30]

Jody and Tom had great concerns about freezing their embryos:

> As we began to think more about it, we came up with more concerns. The success rate when we looked into it was 30% for fresh embryos and 20% with frozen.[31] That means our children we would create would have a 70%-plus chance of death. Add to that the defrosting process, which can lead to the embryo dying, and we didn't like our children's chances (and still don't, even though the stats have improved). The freezing process doesn't sit well with us. What if I [Jody] died and there were still babies in the freezer? What would you do with them? Also, my husband feels responsible for the care of his family and wonders how do you care for children in a freezer?

There are hundreds of thousands of frozen human embryos in freezers around the world. What does a frozen embryo represent? What should be done with these embryos? How long should they remain frozen and at whose expense? Is it ethical for Christians to freeze them in the first place?

Ethical issues

The freezing (cryopreservation) of embryos is standard treatment in modern ART clinics. But if embryos are human beings, is it morally permissible to freeze them? We don't usually freeze people. A similar comment ("We don't usually do this") is usually made in the early development of any medical technology. We have already covered the reasons for cryopreservation—it saves the trouble, expense and risks of repeated egg collection. Eggs are a limited commodity. These are strong arguments, so why wouldn't we do it?

I find the question of whether we should freeze human embryos one of the most difficult in the whole area of reproduction ethics. To go back to first principles: we discussed in the ethics chapter that the basis of Christian ethics is love—love for our God and love for our neighbour (Matt 22:37-39). If we believe that every embryo is a human being from

---

30. M Pelly, 'Frozen relatives make for frosty wills', *Sydney Morning Herald*, 5 July 2004, p. 3.
31. Success rates vary between clinics, age groups and procedures.

the time of fertilization, then our loving action will be to protect each one from harm. The Christian will therefore need to give every embryo the best possible chance to live. Since this will require transfer to the uterus at the appropriate time, I believe that such transfer should be the goal for each embryo fertilized for treatment. However, this is not the same as saying that every embryo created must survive until it gets to the womb; we know that even in nature the embryonic death rate prior to implantation could be as high as 75%. It would be unreasonable to expect that all embryos would survive; but if they don't, it should not be because we did not try to protect them. This will be the case regardless of judgements about the 'quality' of the embryo.

Peter noted: *After our first son was born, and experiencing the amazing realization that he had been formed from tiny cells that they wanted to discard, I became overwhelmingly concerned about our two embryos left in frozen storage.*

There is quite a range of protocols for dealing with human embryos, depending on where you are. In Italy, under the Medically Assisted Reproduction Law of 2004, human embryos must always be treated in a way that preserves life, which means they must all be implanted. An IVF mother can't change her mind—once she has procreated through IVF, the embryos must be transferred to her womb. In the rare instance when this is not possible, embryo donation is required.[32] In fact, this law favours the adoption of embryos already in existence over the creation of new embryos.

In Germany, the strict protection of embryos is grounded in its constitution—which protects the dignity and life of all human beings—the Federal Constitutional Court having interpreted this as applying to unborn human beings as well as human beings already born. Unlike the United States Constitution—which protects citizens only against state interference with their fundamental rights—the German constitution also has a positive aspect, where the state has a duty to prevent citizens from harming one another, thus giving the state the responsibility to protect the unborn from harm. Germany's Embryo Protection Act of 1990 allows up to three embryos to be transferred to a woman's uterus, but the number of eggs that may be fertilized must be equivalent to the number it is planned to transfer. Then they must all be transferred in one go, regardless of quality, because embryo selection and storage by freezing is forbidden.

---

32. For further discussion of embryo donation, see chapter 14.

While I am aware there is much pressure in these countries to relax their laws, it goes to show that there are places where embryos are more highly regarded than in most of the English-speaking world.

There are several arguments against freezing that I am aware of:

- It is unnatural, unnatural being equated with immoral (natural law). As I have previously mentioned, I have reservations about natural law, where right and wrong are determined by human reason. This is because the Bible teaches that the Fall has affected the original creation, which includes man's ability to reason properly. Natural law also reduces the importance of Scripture, if man can understand revelation without it.

- It introduces a 'slippery slope' or 'thin edge of the wedge' aspect to the treatment of embryos. This argument suggests that by allowing the freezing of embryos now, we are 'normalizing' embryo abuse. I think this argument is now out-of-date; with the legalization of human cloning and animal/human hybrids, we are probably near the bottom of the slope by now.

- Freezing embryos allows time to pass between when a couple decides to have children (enter the ART program) and when they thaw the embryo. During this period many things might change— for example, the couple may divorce. If the embryo was created for them both and one now wants to transfer an embryo (with a new partner), and the other opposes it, who should have the final word? At the moment the courts seem to be favouring the one who doesn't want the embryo (although it was encouraging to see a 2011 judicial ruling in Argentina, which allowed that a woman can use frozen embryos fertilized with her ex-husband's sperm to get pregnant again).[33] If an embryo was created as the first step of creating a family, should either parent be able to stop the process mid-stream? Or take another scenario: what happens to orphan embryos? A real-life dilemma was created when the wealthy parents of two frozen embryos died in a plane crash. In the absence of any other contenders, were the embryos heirs to the estate? What should the doctors do with them? Despite many offers to gestate the embryos (so long as the inherited fortune came too), in the

---

33. AP Foreign, 'Argentine court: Divorcee can use ex's embryos', *Guardian*, 24 September 2011.

end they were treated as property and destroyed.[34] This is a strong argument against freezing, because we freeze in anticipation of *good* consequences but we cannot foresee what will happen in the future.

Another problem associated with the freezing of embryos is that it creates the potential for leftover frozen embryos even if there are no relationship problems. The dread of remaining childless at the beginning of treatment can mean that the thought of having too many children doesn't even cross the prospective parents' minds.

When a couple has the number of children they want, or they stop treatment for another reason, they may find they have surplus embryos. What are they to do? On the one hand, they see the embryos as their own precious children. On the other hand, many couples feel there is a limit to how many children they can manage. 'Cheaper by the dozen' can be an overwhelming concept. Sadly, many Christians don't think about this issue until they have embryos sitting there in the freezer and a 'complete' family.[35]

In fact, the most common fate of excess frozen embryos in Australia is that over time the persons responsible for them cannot be contacted and the clinic is no longer paid the fee to cover the cost of the freezing.[36] After the legal storage period has expired, the embryos are taken out of the freezer and left to thaw on the bench. This problem could be surmounted if just one or two embryos were created each time they were needed. I look forward to the day when eggs and sperm are routinely stored separately until an embryo is needed, so that no excess embryos can result.

An interesting development—to assist those with ethical and religious reservations about freezing embryos—is the practice of freezing eggs in the two-pronuclear (2PN) stage. This is done in Germany, Italy and Switzerland as a way of getting around the embryo storage ban, and it is also available in many other countries for those with moral objections to freezing embryos. The argument is that the embryo does not become a human being until the DNA of the egg and sperm combine (syngamy)—when the two pronuclei combine—so that when you freeze at the 2PN stage, you are only freezing the 'pre-syngamy egg': not an embryo. Mark said: *At the time it seemed reasonable. It solved our problem. Looking back,*

---

34. C Grobstein, M Flower and J Mendeloff, 'Frozen embryos: policy issues', *New England Journal of Medicine*, vol. 312, no. 24, 13 June 1985, pp. 1584-8.
35. The issue of what can be done is addressed in chapter 14.
36. Prof. Peter Illingworth, personal communication.

I realize I had no idea what we were doing. Part of me didn't want to know.

Opponents of the storage ban have argued that this practice is unsound as it means that embryo selection (for transfer purposes) has to be done at an early stage of development before you know which ones are of the highest quality.[37] I have argued in chapter 2 that human life begins when fertilization begins. In fact, it is the appearance of the 2PN that is used as an indication that fertilization has occurred. I would consider this practice to be no different ethically from freezing embryos at any other stage of development.

A different kind of argument against freezing is that it is unsafe for the embryos. The percentage of embryos that do not survive defrosting varies enormously between clinics. But, as mentioned earlier, embryos don't deteriorate over time in the freezer like leftover chicken does. Any increased survival rate of embryos frozen more recently is more likely due to an improvement in culture media than to deterioration during the length of time an embryo is frozen.

But what if it wasn't the actual freezing itself that damaged the embryos? What if it was just that only the embryos with development potential were able to survive freezing? In fact, there is (unpublished) evidence that all that happens during the freezing process is that the embryos which were never going to make it are weeded out—in which case, the process of freezing itself has not increased the risk to the embryo; it has just allowed self-selection to take place. (See below for a possible explanation of this mechanism.)

If it turns out that freezing of embryos does not decrease the overall risk of survival, and all embryos are transferred to the womb, then it is an ethical practice for Christians. See below for discussion regarding viability of embryos.

So the take home message is this: if you do decide to freeze embryos, create no more embryos than the number of children you are prepared to have. If you don't want more than 6 children, don't create more than 6 embryos. Make sure they are all transferred to the womb at some stage, if they do not pass away during development in the laboratory. It's only when there are no excess embryos that the problem of embryo destruction is avoided.

---

37. R Chian and P Quinn (eds), *Fertility Cryopreservation*, Cambridge University Press, Cambridge, 2010, p. 78.

What makes an embryo 'viable'?

We have already discussed how Christians can use ART ethically when they respect all human life from the time it is created. And the challenge of protecting their embryos will become apparent to Christian couples right from the beginning of treatment. When eggs are fertilized in the laboratory and the embryos start to grow, decisions are made about which ones to transfer, which ones to freeze and which ones to discard.

These decisions are based on what the embryos *look* like (their 'morphology') at around day 2 or 3 in most clinics. As mentioned above, the problem is that it's not possible to tell, just by looking at them, which embryos will survive transfer and then develop in a womb.[38] While there is a widespread belief that there is some correlation between the external appearance of an embryo and its likelihood of implantation and successful development, research has previously shown that appearances can be misleading.

Embryos can be sorted into three grades, and the 'best' of the bunch will be transferred. This means that a grade-3 (the lowest grade) embryo *may* be transferred, but only if it's the best of a bad bunch (which is usually the case in older women). The only ones that would never be transferred are the ones that are already dead. But, in the current system, if there is a 'good' bunch then some of the 'bad' embryos won't make the grade.

Systems for grading embryos vary from place to place, but they are all based on features including cell number, symmetry and shape, the extent of fragmentation in the cytoplasm, and the rate of cleavage (cell division). The ideal 3-day embryo has 6-8 cells of equal size and no fragmentation. Fewer cells, unequal size and more fragmentation reflect 'poorer quality', according to these systems. However, evidence suggests "that the best quality embryos on day 3 become the best quality blastocysts on day 5 in only 50%-60% cycles".[39] Some unhealthy-looking embryos implant and develop successfully while some healthy-looking embryos fail to implant or have developmental problems.[40]

I am not aware of any method of embryo morphology assessment that

---

38. MC Magli, L Gianaroli and AP Ferraretti, 'Chromosomal abnormalities in embryos', *Molecular and Cellular Endocrinology*, vol. 183, supp. 1, 22 October 2001, pp. S29-34.

39. MA Fritz and L Speroff, *Clinical Gynecologic Endocrinology and Infertility*, 7th edn, Lippincott Williams and Wilkins, Philadelphia, 2005, p. 1239.

40. RT Scott Jr, GE Hofmann, LL Veeck, HW Jones Jr and SJ Muasher, 'Embryo quality and pregnancy rates in patients attempting pregnancy through in vitro fertilization', *Fertility and Sterility*, vol. 55, no. 2, February 1991, p. 426.

has been proven effective or valid in terms of predicting the viability of IVF embryos. Unless definitive morphological criteria has been developed and verified, such selection criteria would be arbitrary. If there are any viable cells present, some clinicians would consider going ahead with uterine transfer despite unfavourable morphology, considering this the only way to determine true viability: if they grow, you know they were viable. It is my opinion that, in the absence of new information about the prediction of embryo viability, the viable/non-viable distinction based on morphology is invalid.

Consider Hal and Maddy's story: *The results of our IVF treatment were we lost the first 2 embryos that were classified 'viable for life' and we have 2 beautiful boys from our 3rd and 5th 'non viable for life embryos' (we lost the 4th embryo). We praise God that he convicted us about where we stood in regards to our treatment as, if we had given in to the pressures (to discard the 'non viable' embryos), we wouldn't have met our 2 beautiful boys.*

Extended (blastocyst) culture
Having said that, we do have a slightly better way of deciding which embryos are viable. It is called 'extended culture'.

Although the first human birth from IVF (Louise Brown) resulted from the transfer of a blastocyst (an embryo 5 days after fertilization),[41] most transfers since then have involved younger cleavage stage embryos (day 2 or 3). The main reason for this is the lack of culture media that is able to reliably sustain embryos up to the blastocyst stage. Further research has led to the development of 'sequential' media, which is varied according to the stage of embryo development and is made to simulate conditions in the fallopian tubes or uterus—wherever the embryo would normally be at that stage.[42] Extended culture is not available at all clinics.

For years now, IVF specialists have justified the number of embryos that die during IVF treatment as a reflection of the large amount of wastage observed in normal reproduction. This is a reasonable theory,

---

41. PC Steptoe and RG Edwards, 'Birth after the reimplantation of a human embryo', *Lancet*, vol. 312, no. 8085, 12 August 1978, p. 366.

42. DK Gardner, M Lane, I Calderon and J Leeton, 'Environment of the preimplantation human embryo in vivo: metabolite analysis of oviduct and uterine fluids and metabolism of cumulus cells', *Fertility and Sterility*, vol. 65, no. 2, February 1996, pp. 349-53; DK Gardner, 'Changes in requirements and utilization of nutrients during mammalian preimplantation embryo development and their significance in embryo culture', *Theriogenology*, vol. 49, no. 1, 1 January 1998, pp. 83-102.

but there has not been any evidence to support it until fairly recently.

It is thought that by growing embryos to blastocyst stage (day 5), the true viability of the embryo is tested.[43] By this time, the DNA is functioning and so chromosomal problems may be identified. This is also the stage at which the embryo normally implants and so it is better suited to surviving in the new environment. Blastocysts implant at higher rates than younger embryos, but only about 50% of embryos make it to blastocyst stage.

It may be that those embryos that cannot get to blastocyst stage in the laboratory would not reach blastocyst stage in the woman's body either. Therefore, growing embryos to blastocyst stage would avoid the problems inherent in choosing 'viable' embryos based on what they look like (because the 'bad' ones simply would not survive), and would possibly reduce the number of embryos transferred. It would also allow the effects of hyperstimulation in the woman to settle down before implantation.

Those who don't support blastocyst transfer worry that if all the embryos are of poorer quality, there may be no embryos to transfer (because none survive to blastocyst stage at day 5), and perhaps they would have implanted successfully if they were transferred at day 3. It is true that you would not be able to proceed with transfer if all the embryos died in culture, but would they have continued developing even if they were transferred? Overall, it seems that blastocyst transfer improves outcomes, and this is probably because it allows for better 'natural' selection of embryos. Difference in morphology becomes more obvious on days 5 and 6 because there is more to look at in embryos of greater age. It would therefore be reasonable to use blastocyst morphology to decide which embryo to transfer first.

There is a higher rate of pregnancies per blastocyst transfer, leading to live births in shorter periods of treatment time. The definitive research has not been done, and it will probably never be done due to the costs involved and a lack of political will. But all current evidence points to the likelihood that by growing embryos to blastocyst stage, we are not 'wasting' embryos but merely distinguishing which ones were never going to survive.

Risks associated with blastocyst transfer include a possible higher rate of multiple gestation, as there is an increased incidence of monozygotic twins (4.25 times higher risk).[44] It is therefore even more important that

---

43. Up to the 8-cell stage (day 3), the survival of the embryo is associated more with the quality of the egg.

44. S Vitthala, TA Gelbaya, DR Brison CT Fitzgerald and LG Nardo, 'The risk of monozygotic twins after assisted reproductive technology: a systematic review and meta-analysis', *Human Reproduction Update*, vol. 15, no. 1, January-February 2009, pp. 45-55.

only one embryo is transferred if it is done at blastocyst stage. Reports that blastocyst transfer has not reduced the incidence of multiple pregnancy is primarily due to how few clinics are willing to transfer only a single blastocyst in jurisdictions where transfer of more than one is allowed.[45]

Ethically, any embryos that reach blastocyst stage should be transferred to a womb.

Ethical issues

The decision about which embryos to keep and which to discard will need to be made relatively quickly, as in most clinics there will be a 3-day window (at the most) in which the embryos can be transferred successfully. In order to avoid being under pressure in their decision-making, couples should think about this issue ahead of time.[46] They may also need to mention it to their doctor, as some doctors would assume that couples are happy to discard those embryos labelled 'non-viable', so would not even ask them about it.

At such an early stage of treatment, when parents are extremely vulnerable and expecting treatment to be successful, I am very concerned about whether it is possible for them to be completely sure they will have no further use for the embryos. Doubtless they will expect that one of the viable embryos will implant. If none of the 'viable' embryos do implant, will they still think the 'non-viable' embryos are unnecessary? What if the parents' choice ends up being between transferring a 'non-viable' embryo and none at all? This is a complex decision to make in only a day or so.

If there is any chance at all that those responsible for the embryos would ever not consider the 'non-viable' embryos to be excess—in the event that the 'viable' embryos failed to implant—it will be difficult to ensure that you have proper consent before the commencement of treatment.

For those who wish to protect human life from fertilization, if there is any possibility that the embryos in question may be viable, they should be transferred. The only distinction that is important is whether the embryo is alive or dead.

---

45. M Henman, JW Catt, T Wood, MC Bowman, KA de Boer and RPS Jansen, 'Elective transfer of single fresh blastocysts and later transfer of cryostored blastocysts reduces the twin pregnancy rate and can improve the in vitro fertilization live birth rate in younger women', *Fertility and Sterility*, vol. 84, no. 6, December 2005, pp. 1620-7.

46. If consent to agree to discard embryos were to be given immediately, it would be difficult to be sure there was no coercion involved, given the time pressure on decision-making. This would invalidate the informed consent procedure, but it would also make the decision much more difficult for the parents.

For doctors

The NHRMC Embryo Research Licensing Committee states that "an embryo is considered to be a living embryo unless:

- when maintained in suitable culture conditions, the embryo has not undergone cell division between successive observations not less than 24 hours apart, or
- the embryo has been allowed to succumb by standing at room temperature for a period of not less than 24 hours.

Once an embryo has more than 12 cells it is not possible to determine whether any individual cell has divided within a 24-hour period. Therefore, such embryos can be considered to have succumbed only after a 24-hour period at room temperature."[47]

According to national guidelines in Australia, "unsuitable for implantation, in relation to a human embryo, means a human embryo that … is determined by a qualified embryologist to be unsuitable for implantation according to the objective [morphological] criteria below:

Day 1:   No 2PN from the first mitotic division

Day 2:   ≥50% fragmentation/degeneration/vacuoles

Day 3:   < 4 cells or with ≥50% fragmentation/degeneration/vacuoles

Day 4:   < 8 cells or with ≥50% fragmentation/degeneration/vacuoles

Day 5-7:   Blastocyst with ≥80% reduction in size of inner cell mass, ≥50% fragmentation/degeneration/vacuoles, no compaction

In addition: Any embryo with ≥50% multinucleated blastomeres."[48]

I realize that morphology is the only generally applicable, non-invasive guide we have for assessing embryos, but that does not mean it is reliable. I would hope the fact that 'discarded' fresh embryos are eligible for research purposes in some countries does not influence this debate.

---

47. NHMRC, *NHMRC Embryo Research Licensing Committee Information Kit*, NHMRC, Canberra, 2008, p. 9 (viewed 8 March 2012): www.nhmrc.gov.au/publications/synopses/hc56.htm

48. NHMRC, *Objective Criteria for embryos unsuitable for implantation*, NHMRC, Canberra, 6 December 2007 (viewed 8 March 2012): www.nhmrc.gov.au/research/embryos/information/index.htm#c1

Blastocyst transfer is ethically acceptable for Christians so long as other aspects of the treatment are morally correct.

Oocyte cryopreservation (freezing eggs)

One way to avoid the ethical problems of freezing embryos is to freeze the excess eggs collected from a woman and then defrost them as needed. As previously mentioned, eggs by themselves are not human beings and so their treatment does not require the same care as human embryos. Sperm is routinely frozen without a problem, and it is relatively easy to collect; but it is the difficulty, risk and expense of egg collection that has led to embryo freezing.

Egg freezing has been slow to develop because of technical difficulties and early concerns that it was associated with genetic (chromosomal) abnormalities.[49] The egg is the largest cell in the body, with a large surface area and high water content. In the past, freezing eggs was associated with damage to the spindles (part of the egg structure). The traditional method has had a low success rate, but a newer method—egg vitrification (see below)—is looking much more promising.

The first children to be born from frozen eggs were twins in Adelaide, Australia, in 1986.[50] Since then, egg-freezing technology has been made available as a method of fertility preservation for women with cancer (approximately one third of young women exposed to chemotherapy develop ovarian failure).[51]

More recently, single women—whose biological clocks are ticking—have been the marketing target of 'insurance' against the risk of either

---

49.   J Boldt, D Cline and D McLaughlin, 'Human oocyte cryopreservation as an adjunct to IVF-embryo transfer cycles', *Human Reproduction*, vol. 18, no. 6, June 2003, p. 1250.

50.   JFHM Van Uem, ER Siebzehnrübl, B Schuh, R Koch, S Trotnow and N Lang, 'Birth after cryopreservation of unfertilised oocytes', *Lancet*, vol. 329, no. 8535, 28 March 1987, pp. 752-3.

51.   Research involving the use of the gonadotropin-releasing hormone analogue triptorelin during chemotherapy may make egg freezing unnecessary. A study using triptorelin to cause temporary ovarian suppression in premenopausal patients with early-stage breast cancer reduced the occurrence of chemotherapy-induced early menopause (8.9% in the triptorelin group compared to 25.9%). This technique is superior to egg freezing in that it is simple, less invasive and less expensive, and it does not require time that might otherwise delay chemotherapy. See L Del Mastro, L Boni, A Michelotti, T Gamucci, N Olmeo, S Gori, M Giordano, O Garrone, P Pronzato, C Bighin, A Levaggi, S Giraudi, N Cresti, E Magnolfi, T Scotto, C Vecchio and M Venturini, 'Effect of the gonadotropin-releasing hormone analogue triptorelin on the occurrence of chemotherapy-induced early menopause in premenopausal women with breast cancer: a randomized trail', *Journal of the American Medical Association*, vol. 306, no. 3, 20 July 2011, pp. 269-76.

not finding a partner or not being ready to have a child before the alarm on the biological clock starts ringing and fertility plunges. Commercial fertility services have sprung up in several countries with executive women aged 30 and older as their object. While some doctors are concerned that provision of this service may raise false hope in women, others think that by freezing their eggs while they are young, these women improve their chances of becoming pregnant in the future.

Egg-freezing technology is also used by those who desire to avoid embryo freezing due to ethical or religious convictions that it is wrong, and in situations where it has not been possible to collect sperm at the time of egg collection. Interest has also been consistent in those countries where legislation has prevented the freezing of embryos—particularly Italy and Germany.

There are two methods used to freeze eggs.

1. **Traditional (slow) egg freezing:** The egg is cooled slowly as the temperature drops gradually to below freezing. During this process, ice crystals form inside the egg and damage cell membranes. Damage to the structure of the egg is common. Only about half of the eggs survive the thawing process, and they are usually of poor quality.

2. **Snap freezing (egg vitrification):** The egg is cooled rapidly which allows the water inside the egg to become solid instantly without the formation of ice crystals. Most of the eggs survive the thawing process, with a much better success rate than with slow freezing. This is the technique that has propelled egg cryopreservation into mainstream ART.

Cryopreserved eggs are difficult to fertilize due to hardening of the zona pellucida (outer membrane of the egg), which is accommodated by using intracytoplasmic sperm injection (see below) to fertilize the eggs.[52]

Frozen eggs have a potential similar to fresh eggs for embryo development.[53] Research has shown that the pregnancy rate per uterine

---

52. K Riggan, 'Egg cryopreservation: an update on an emerging reproductive technology', *Dignitas*, vol. 16, no. 2, Fall 2009, p. 1.

53. A Cobo, Y Kuwayama, S Pérez, A Ruiz, A Pellicer and J Remohí, 'Comparison of concomitant outcome achieved with fresh and cryopreserved donor oocytes vitrified by the Cryotop method', *Fertility and Sterility*, vol. 89, no. 6, June 2008, pp. 1657-64.

transfer with egg vitrification is 63.2%.[54] So far, research indicates there is no increased risk to mother or child and no increase in congenital abnormalities compared to naturally conceived children, although obviously no long-term study has yet been done.[55] The bad news is that this technique is very expensive—usually over $10,000 per cycle. In some jurisdictions, deductions apply if it is used for medical reasons (e.g. related to cancer treatment).

Ethical issues

The development of the technology to freeze eggs is welcome as an alternative to freezing embryos, and it is hoped that it will continue to become more common. Freezing eggs is an ethical alternative for those who wish to protect embryonic human life, so long as associated concerns are addressed. Concerns about informed consent when ovarian stimulation is used are discussed above. Concerns about the possible donation of eggs to a third party are discussed in the gamete donation section below.

Ovarian tissue cryopreservation

Some research units have experimented with storing strips of a woman's ovary in the hope that the eggs could be stimulated to develop and later used to create an embryo. This offers the possibility of restoring reproductive function in women after they have received treatment for cancer (it could also help women who need to have their ovaries removed for any reason). Although egg-freezing techniques are now more advanced, once cancer is diagnosed, there usually isn't time to organize an IVF cycle before beginning cancer treatment. Also, with the improvement of cancer treatment for children, a growing number of pre-pubertal females will be interested in preserving fertility.

The technique has been successful in animal research, and while it is currently considered experimental in humans, in some cases it

---

54. A Cobo, J Domingo, S Pérez, J Crespo, J Remohí, A Pellicer, 'Vitrification: an effective new approach to oocyte banking and preserving fertility in cancer patients', *Journal of Clinical and Translational Oncology*, vol. 10, no. 5, May 2008, pp. 268-73.

55. N Noyes, E Porcu and A Borini, 'Over 900 oocyte cryopreservation babies born with no apparent increase in congenital anomalies', *Reproductive BioMedicine Online*, vol. 18, no. 6, 2009, pp. 769-76; R Chian, JYJ Huang, SL Tan, E Lucena, A Saa, A Rojas, LAR Castellón, MIG Amador and JEM Sarmiento, 'Obstetric and perinatal outcome in 200 infants conceived from vitrified oocytes', *Reproductive BioMedicine Online*, vol. 16, no. 5, 2008, pp. 608-10.

remains the only hope for some women to preserve fertility. At least 11 pregnancies have been reported worldwide from this procedure.

The main aim of this strategy is to re-implant ovarian tissue into the pelvic cavity, the forearm or abdominal wall once cancer treatment is completed and the patient is disease-free.[56]

Ethical issues

The development of ovarian tissue cryopreservation is also welcome as an alternative to freezing embryos. As an experimental treatment, it needs to be considered carefully. While it is an experimental technique, if it is proven to be safe in animals and it is the only way a woman can hope to maintain her fertility, it is an appropriate medical intervention. Fully informed consent would be required from the patient—in the case of a minor this becomes more complex—but if the risks and benefits are understood and the patient wants to proceed, it is ethically appropriate.

For possible alternatives to freezing ovarian tissue for women undergoing chemotherapy, see 'egg freezing' above.

Sperm cryopreservation

Sperm freezing has been available since 1953. Sperm are often frozen before use in ART to remove the risk of infection. They may also be frozen if the husband has a low sperm count (so multiple samples can be used at the one time) or if he will be away at the time of the wife's egg collection. Sperm may also be frozen to protect the fertility of cancer patients, which can be affected by cancer treatment. In 2010, a baby was born having been conceived with sperm that had been frozen 22 years earlier.[57]

Children conceived from previously frozen sperm have no increased risk of birth defects. Although a significant number of sperm die in the process of being frozen and thawed, sperm usually come in large numbers (see above) and only one per egg is needed. Usually several sperm samples from a particular patient are frozen at any one time.

Ethical issues

As mentioned above, while there are no intrinsic ethical issues in the

56. J Donnez and M Dolmans, 'Cryopreservation and transplantation of ovarian tissue', *Clinical Obstetrics and Gynecology*, vol. 53, no. 4, December 2010, pp. 787-96.
57. Cook, 'Boy born from embryo frozen 20 years ago', *BioEdge*, loc. cit.

treatment of sperm—as gametes are not human beings in an early stage of development—care should be taken with collection. Cryopreservation of sperm is an ethical practice.

Gamete intra-fallopian tube transfer (GIFT)

Fertilization of the egg by the sperm normally occurs in the woman's fallopian tubes (on the side where the egg was released from the ovary). It is known that 'signalling' occurs between the developing embryo and the wall of the uterus prior to implantation, and this knowledge led some researchers to develop a technique using the woman's fallopian tubes to assist in establishing a pregnancy. (Note that this depends on the woman having normal fallopian tubes.)

In GIFT, ovary stimulation and egg retrieval proceed as in normal IVF. After this, the woman undergoes surgery (a laparoscopy) where eggs and sperm are transferred to her fallopian tubes. They are left there to work things out themselves. GIFT is not often used now that IVF has a much better success rate and usually does not involve the risk of surgery.

GIFT has a higher rate of ectopic pregnancy (tubal pregnancy) than IVF and a similar multiple pregnancy rate, unless only one egg is transferred.

Ethical issues

GIFT is an ethical choice for Christians as it involves manipulation of eggs and sperm, not embryos. Eggs and sperm, not being equivalent to a human being, are not morally significant. The extra medical risks and possibly the expense may be morally significant depending on the situation of the couple concerned.

Zygote intra-fallopian tube transfer (ZIFT)

ZIFT is a technique similar to GIFT. Ovarian stimulation and egg retrieval proceed as in normal IVF, as does the creation of embryos in the laboratory. Zygotes (one-cell embryos) are then transferred to the woman's fallopian tubes the following day.

Risks are similar to GIFT, except that limiting the embryo transfer to one can minimize multiple births.

Ethical Issues

Ethical issues for ZIFT will be the same as for IVF. The only difference is that the embryo is transferred to the fallopian tubes instead of the uterus.

Intracytoplasmic sperm injection (ICSI)

This practice has been used with IVF since 1991 to aid fertilization. Tens of thousands of ICSI babies have been born since then. The need to use ICSI can result from a low sperm count, low sperm motility, previous failure to fertilize with IVF, or the presence of sperm antibodies.

In this process, a single sperm can be selected and directly injected into the egg. The sperm will be selected on the basis of its normal appearance and energetic swimming style. Sperm can be collected from the ejaculate, or it can be obtained by using a needle to withdraw it from the man's testes (sometimes the sperm are unable to get into the semen due to a blockage in the testicular 'plumbing'). Two methods of sperm retrieval are available: microsurgical epididymal sperm aspiration (MESA) or testicular sperm aspiration (TESA). A minimum number of sperm are necessary.

Although this technique was not thoroughly investigated before clinical use, it is now felt that a decade of experience has proven its overall safety. However, research indicates that offspring conceived using ICSI may be at increased risk of imprinting disorders (genetic problems), and male offspring may have fertility problems similar to their father. It is not clear whether this is due to ICSI itself or to the disease that makes ICSI necessary. Certainly having the doctor select the sperm instead of the sperm 'selecting' itself (by being the first to penetrate the egg) must make a difference. Using ICSI, therefore, will increase the number of infertility genes in the community gene pool, as men who previously were unable to procreate can now do so and can also pass on their genes. This shows how some of the side effects of ART take a long time to manifest themselves.

Ethical issues

As previously discussed, sperm do not have the ethical significance of embryos and so their manipulation is not morally troublesome in itself.[58]

Assisted hatching

'Hatching' describes what happens when the embryo breaks out of its 'shell' (the zona pellucida—the thick outside layer of the embryo) in order to implant into the wall of the uterus. The way this occurs in natural conception differs from IVF. In the laboratory, assisted hatching

---

58. For a discussion regarding manipulation of the community gene pool, see appendix III.

is recommended when embryos resulting from IVF or ICSI may have a reduced ability to hatch. This procedure is typically performed:

- for women who are 38 years and older
- for women who have embryos with abnormally thickened shells
- sometimes after freezing, which can harden the zona pellucida
- for those who have had difficulty becoming pregnant for other reasons.

Assisted hatching may be done in a number of ways. It is a microscopic surgical technique performed by an embryologist. While viewing the embryo through a microscope, a small hole is gently made in the embryo shell, or the shell wall is artificially thinned, so that the embryo can hatch several days after it is transferred to the woman's uterus.

Assisted hatching may cause embryo damage and increases the risk of twins.

Ethical issues

If you are undergoing ART and your doctor believes that assisted hatching will increase the chances of a successful transfer, it is an ethical and responsible choice. Your doctor will weigh up benefits and risks when assessing whether the technique is appropriate.

Donor gametes (eggs and sperm)

Sometimes, for a number of reasons, the husband's sperm or the wife's eggs cannot be used. In this situation, donor sperm or donor eggs are often recommended. Those who support donor gametes consider the benefits of having at least one parent genetically linked to the child(ren), and the fact that it means your infertility usually remains a private matter.

Egg donation

When IVF was first introduced, women who did not have their own eggs were considered to be sterile. In 1983, the first successful egg donation was reported. Several techniques have been used, but nowadays the (usually younger) donor and the recipient both are given medication for ovarian stimulation and synchronizing cycles, and the eggs harvested from the donor are combined with the sperm of the recipient's husband through the usual IVF process. The resulting embryo(s) are transferred to the uterus of the recipient. It can also be done through variations of GIFT and ZIFT.

Depending on the country, donors may be difficult to find. While there are many willing donors available on the internet (for a fee), in some countries (such as Australia) it is illegal to pay for human tissue and couples have to find someone themselves. If no friend or family member is able to help, couples usually place an advertisement in the newspaper. Kay and Steve had a lot of trouble finding a donor. Kay remembers: *We did find one woman who was willing at first, but when she met me, she had a problem with my weight. I'm not all that heavy, but she pulled out because she said she didn't want a 'fat' child. She didn't seem to realize that it wasn't going to be her child.*

Recipients should be evaluated (screened and counselled) before donation because of the problems encountered by many couples using donor gametes. In addition, guidelines have been developed by ART regulating bodies such as the Fertility Society of Australia (FSA),[59] the American Society for Reproductive Medicine (ASRM)[60] and the Human Fertilisation and Embryology Authority (HFEA).[61] The kinds of things that are checked are the age of the donor (preferably under 35 so that eggs are still healthy) and the donor's health. Standard pregnancy screening,[62] the donor's own established family and psychological evaluation are also advised.

Once the donor has handed over the eggs, she has no legal parenting rights over the child who is born. Nadia remembers her experience of looking for a donor: *I asked one of my sisters and she said 'no'. In hindsight, it was wise as she has not had children and is now in the same predicament as her two older sisters, so there could have been resentment if I had children from her eggs. The counselling we received at the Fertility Centre was for a woman under 35 who had finished having her own children. I didn't want to ask anyone for fear they would say 'no'. So we prayed that God would provide the right woman. We waited—that was very hard.*

Sperm donation: Donor insemination (DI)

Artificial insemination with sperm may have been done in humans for the first time in 1909 when Professor Pancoast of Philadelphia treated the wife of an infertile merchant. The donor was one of his medical

---

59. Reproductive Technology Accreditation Committee, *Code of Practice for Assisted Reproductive Technology Units*, FSA, South Melbourne, 2008.

60. Practice Committee of the American Society for Reproductive Medicine and Practice Committee of the Society for Assisted Reproductive Technology, *2008 Guidelines for Gamete and Embryo Donation: A Practice Committee Report*, ASRM, Birmingham AL, 2008 (viewed 8 March 2012): www.asrm.org/publications/detail.aspx?id=3963

61. HFEA, *Code of Practice*, 8th edn, HFEA, London, 2009.

62. See chapter 8.

students. Apparently the doctor didn't tell the husband until afterwards and they both agreed never to tell the wife.[63]

DI is the most widely used technique in assisted reproduction worldwide. It is sometimes used if the husband is sterile or if he carries a genetic disease he could pass on and he doesn't want to use preimplantation genetic diagnosis (see below). Nowadays, sperm samples for donation are collected after masturbation in the clinic. Usually there is a payment (usually less than $100), but nothing like the money given for eggs as the effort and risk involved is quite different. Sperm donors are screened for health and fertility, and can be located on the internet or through advertisements in a similar way to egg donors.

The donor insemination procedure is done the same way as IUI, except for the different source of the sperm. The semen samples are usually frozen before use to reduce infection risk. This can reduce motility, which is why the sperm are injected into the uterus and not just the vagina.

When I was a medical student, they would mix the donor sperm with the husband's sperm so no-one ever really knew for sure...

Legal issues for gamete donation

Due to the difficulty of finding egg donors, anonymity of egg donors has never been as common as it has been for sperm donors. Sperm donation remained an anonymous activity for a long time after its commencement. But at the time of writing, anonymous gamete donation has been banned in Austria, the Netherlands, New Zealand, Norway, Sweden, Switzerland, the United Kingdom and some states of Australia as a result of lobbying by ART offspring regarding their right to know their biological heritage. In the United States, anonymous gamete donation is permitted,[64] but in 2011 the state of Washington made it possible for children conceived with donated gametes to gain access to the donor's name and medical history, if the donor agrees (the ASRM opposed the law).[65] In the province of

---

63. A Hard, 'Artificial impregnation', letter to the editor, *Medical World*, vol. 27, April 1909, pp. 163-4.

64. The anonymity is not absolute. The California Supreme Court ruled that an anonymous sperm donor had to testify in court in 2008, saying that donors do not have an unlimited right to privacy. See D Kravets, 'Court limits sperm donors' rights', *Associated Press*, 24 August 2008.

65. B Rochman, 'Where do (some) babies come from? In Washington, a new law bans anonymous sperm and egg donors', *TIME: Healthland*, 22 July 2011 (viewed 18 January 2012): www.healthland.time.com/2011/07/22/where-do-some-babies-come-from-in-washington-a-new-law-bans-anonymous-sperm-and-egg-donors/

British Columbia in Canada, there was a legal ruling in 2011 that banned donor anonymity (the government has appealed the ruling).

However, although there is progress on donor identification in these places, the child who is not told they were born from donated gametes will still not know to enquire. Furthermore, without a current register, contact details become out-of-date and it can be impossible to locate the donor.

Where anonymous donation is no longer allowed, the gamete donor will usually be asked to undergo counselling so that they understand the implications of donating one's gametes and the arrangements in place to allow the offspring to make contact in the future. Unlike the birth mother and her husband, donors will not be the legal parents and will not be responsible for the offspring after birth. In countries like Australia where counselling is required by law, it is done by qualified practitioners who are very careful to make sure that all parties involved understand the arrangements fully before proceeding; this reduces the likelihood of complicated transactions after the birth. In Australia, guidelines stipulate that counsellors will also discuss the needs of the offspring.

Laws have been introduced in some places to limit the number of offspring, or families of offspring, from any one donor.

Psychological issues for gamete donation

As donor offspring have grown to adulthood, we have become aware of the deep disturbance and confusion about identity that can result from the knowledge that they were conceived from donor gametes. It was once assumed that adopted children did not need to know about their birth parents, and that perhaps it was better if they did not even know about the adoption. We now know this is not true and that, in fact, it is normal for adopted children to want to know about their genetic heritage— whether it be from curiosity about their parents' physical attributes or a need to know details like family medical history. We now also know that donor gamete offspring feel the same way.[66]

It is important to them to know their origins, and so even in places where it is not a legal requirement, donor offspring have tried to persuade donors to give details of their identity anyway. Here is Lila's way of

---

66. V Jadva, T Freeman, W Kramer and S Golombok, 'Experiences of offspring searching for and contacting their donor siblings and donor', *Reproductive BioMedicine Online*, vol. 20, no. 4, April 2010, pp. 523-32.

describing how she felt: *half of my ancestors are ghosts.* She and others like her have received a lot of support from donor conception support groups.[67] Yet governments are slow to develop the networks needed for donor offspring to be able to trace their roots.

This is the case in Australia. In a recent Senate enquiry investigating the need for a national register, one woman said:

> *I cannot begin to describe how dehumaniz[ed] and powerless I am to know that the name and details about my biological father and my entire paternal family sit somewhere in a filing cabinet… with no means to access it. Information about my own family, my roots, my identity, I am told I have no right to know.*[68]

The Australian state of NSW introduced a central register in 2010, not only banning anonymity in the future, but also addressing past anonymity by making it possible for previous donors to add their identifying details to the register voluntarily.[69]

Some donor offspring feel so strongly the pain of 'genetic bewilderment' that they even feel angry they were ever born.[70] It is not clear that this is the majority view, but it is definitely a sincere concern of a section of the donor offspring population.

There is also a concern that where donor anonymity has been banned in those countries where only altruistic donation is permitted, donations have dropped off. As a result, IVF clinics have suggested the ban be overturned. However, the UN Convention on the Rights of a Child declares that children have the right to know their parents and that the state has a responsibility to preserve their identity:

> *Article 7*
>
> 1. The child shall be registered immediately after birth and shall have the right from birth to a name, the right to acquire a nationality and, as far as possible, the right to know and be cared for by his or her parents…

---

67. For example, the Donor Conception Support Group of Australia: www.dcsg.org.au
68. A Shanahan, 'Murky business of donor conception is having a brutal effect on the offspring', *Australian*, 19 February 2011.
69. NSW Ministry of Health, *Assisted Reproductive Technology*, NSW Ministry of Health, North Sydney, 2012 (viewed 8 March 2012): www.health.nsw.gov.au/art/
70. A McWhinnie, *Who am I?*, Idreos Education Trust, Leamington Spa, 2006.

Article 8

1. States Parties undertake to respect the right of the child to preserve his or her identity, including nationality, name and family relations as recognized by law without unlawful interference.

2. Where a child is illegally deprived of some or all of the elements of his or her identity, States Parties shall provide appropriate assistance and protection, with a view to re-establishing speedily his or her identity.[71]

Even though we know from research that donor offspring cope best when they are told about their origins early on—with better outcomes for depression, delinquency and substance abuse[72]—at most, only about a third of children are told by their parents that they were conceived using donor gametes.[73] The authors of one study, which found that offspring of lesbian parents learned of their DI origins at earlier ages than offspring of heterosexual parents, suggest that their findings could reflect men's discomfort with their own infertility.[74] (Note that this study did not use a random sample.)

Whatever the underlying problem is, this situation has led to donor offspring requesting that their birth certificates contain some reference to their genetic parentage (so they can find out if donor gametes were involved)—but so far, without success. In fact, in Australia, where only two parents may be listed on a birth certificate as legal parents, things seem to be moving in the opposite direction.[75] Where previously sperm donors have been listed as 'father' on the birth certificates when no other male was involved, a 2008 law has given retrospective parenting rights to lesbian partners of women using ART. One man's name was removed

---

71. *Convention on the Rights of the Child* as adopted by the General Assembly of the United Nations on 20 November 1989 in New York, and entered into force on 2 September 1990. See United Nations, *Treaty Series*, vol. 1577, United Nations, New York, 1999, p. 47.
72. E Marquardt, ND Glenn and K Clark, *My Daddy's Name is Donor*, Institute for American Values, New York, 2010.
73. V Jadva, T Freeman, W Kramer and S Golombok, 'The experiences of adolescents and adults conceived by sperm donation: comparisons by age of disclosure and family type', *Human Reproduction*, vol. 24, no. 8, August 2009, pp. 1909-19.
74. DR Beeson, PK Jennings and W Kramer, 'Offspring searching for their sperm donors: how family type shapes the process', *Human Reproduction*, vol. 26, no. 9, September 2011, pp. 2415-24.
75. N Wallace, 'Sperm donor could lose his status', *Sydney Morning Herald*, 3 August 2011.

from his 10-year-old daughter's birth certificate in 2011 and replaced with the name of the mother's former lesbian partner.[76]

Ethical issues for gamete donation

Ethical issues raised by the practice of gamete donation are complex, and in many cases yet to be resolved.

Donor identification

The call to ban anonymous donation has intensified since the marriage in the United Kingdom of twins who had been separated at birth (annulled in 2007) sparked discussion about the 'irresistible attraction' often felt by reunited siblings and the concern that unwitting incest between half-siblings may occur.[77] The news that a British sperm donor had fathered 17 families despite the government limit of 10, and that an American sperm donor had fathered more than 150 children, has not allayed these fears.[78]

Mixing gametes

Mixing gametes of different parental origin, so as to confuse the biological parentage of the child, is never morally justified.

Anticipated consent

The ethical doctrine of anticipated consent requires that when a person seriously affected by a decision cannot give his or her consent to that decision, we must ask ourselves whether we can reasonably anticipate that, if they were present, they would consent. If not, it is unethical to proceed.[79] The feeling on donor offspring websites is that not only have they been relinquished by a parent at birth, but also the whole ART system has ignored their interests. Kim says: *Donor conception has and always*

---

76. 'Sperm donor loses birth certificate fight', *ABC News*, 18 August 2011 (viewed 8 March 2012): www.abc.net.au/news/2011-08-17/father-loses-birth-certificate-fight/2843288

77. 'Unknowing twins married, lawmaker says', *CNN.com/europe*, 11 January 2008 (viewed 18 January 2012): www.edition.cnn.com/2008/WORLD/europe/01/11/twins.married

78. D Macpherson, 'British sperm donor fathers seventeen families', *Mail Online*, 18 September 2011 (viewed 18 January 2012): www.dailymail.co.uk/news/article-2038701/Incest-fears-British-sperm-donor-fathers-17-families-breach-10-family-limit.html; J Mroz, 'One sperm donor, 150 offspring', *New York Times*, 5 September 2011.

79. M Somerville, 'Should we create a market for making children?', *MercatorNet*, 10 August 2007 (viewed 18 January 2012): www.mercatornet.com/articles/view/should_we_create_a_market_for_making_children/

will serve the rights of the parents, while the child remains voiceless.[80]

The biblical perspective

Biblical examples of 'third parties' contributing to reproduction can be found in the Old Testament. But while polygamy is often mentioned in this context, it is not a parallel to gamete donation as any children were still offspring of a husband and wife. Perhaps a closer example was when Sarah gave her maid, Hagar, to her husband, Abraham, after years of waiting for the offspring promised by God. Without appealing to God, she decided to get 'her' offspring through her maid (Gen 16:1-3). Likewise, Jacob's wives, Rachel and Leah, competed by using their maids to produce children (Gen 29:31-30:24). However, even if the 'donors' were not actually married to the father, both parents had a role in raising the child, which is not the case with donor gametes in the modern sense.

Another example cited to justify donor gametes is that of levirate marriage:

> "If brothers dwell together, and one of them dies and has no son, the wife of the dead man shall not be married outside the family to a stranger. Her husband's brother shall go in to her and take her as his wife and perform the duty of a husband's brother to her. And the first son whom she bears shall succeed to the name of his dead brother, that his name may not be blotted out of Israel."
> (Deut 25:5-6)

On the surface, this looks very similar to the previous example: the brother of the dead man (possibly already married) impregnates the widow, and the first son becomes the dead man's heir. But once again, both parents are involved with the raising of the child, for the widow becomes the wife of the brother and her subsequent children are his.

The first son was needed to protect the family inheritance of the dead man. In the case of Ruth and Boaz, there was no brother, so a close relative performed the task; but again, Ruth married Boaz and they raised their son, Obed, together (Ruth 3-4). Therefore, the biblical expectation that parents take responsibility for a child after birth is met.

Theological problems arise with gamete donation, from both the

---

80. Quoted in '"Donating" sperm (or egg) is NOT similar to being a blood or organ donor', *Donor Conceived: Perspectives from the Offspring* blog, 16 April 2010 (viewed 18 January 2012): www.donorconceived.blogspot.com.au/2010/04/donating-sperm-or-egg-is-not-similar-to.html

receiving and the giving end. With regard to receiving donor gametes, while I would not say this is a form of adultery, Islamic doctors in Dubai (for example) would—that's why governments control IVF clinics there. It *does* bring a third person into the 'one flesh' relationship, though, and I would suggest that it is contrary to Scripture. On a practical level, gamete donation can cause an imbalance in the marriage relationship; some men have reported feelings of sexual jealousy when they have seen their wife pregnant by another man, even though no actual sexual relationship has existed.

In terms of giving, the gamete donor is involved in child-bearing without the intention of fulfilling their parental responsibilities to nurture the child. Even when donation is no longer anonymous, opportunity for a relationship is often not possible until the child is 18 years old, although there have been court cases where donor parents have gained access to their children despite not having discussed prior to the birth any involvement in the child's life. The involvement of both parents is closer to the biblical model.

Furthermore, once the gametes are donated, the donor has no say in what happens to the child that results from their use. What if the recipients decided to abort the child after finding an abnormality on the ultrasound, or even for no reason at all? What if the mother kept smoking and harmed the baby during the pregnancy? Allen recalled, *My brother asked me if I would give him and his wife some sperm so they could have a baby. At first, it seemed like a reasonable thing to do. Then I thought about how they aren't Christian and wouldn't take the kid to Sunday school. I feel pretty uncomfortable about it now.* Since the Bible teaches that the role of the parent continues after birth, these are all issues of concern.

I know there are Christians who disagree with me on this point and who report that DI has been used for years with few problems. They point to the numerous ways in which biblical couples overcame infertility, and they therefore see a place for modern creative thinking. However, in the end I believe that the biblical teaching of the marriage relationship as 'one flesh' and the ongoing responsibility of parenting indicate that gamete donation is not in the spirit of Scripture.

If you do decide to go ahead and use donor gametes, I would advise the following:

1. Both husband and wife should have counselling before deciding to use donor gametes so that you are fully aware of all the implications. In particular, make sure there is discussion about informing (or

not informing) the child about their genetic origins.

2. Don't go ahead if either of you have doubts, as this will add extra stress to your marriage.

3. Adopt a policy of honesty from the start regarding your child's genealogy. If possible, make sure your child can contact the gamete donor once they turn 18. Consider only using a donor who is prepared to be contacted. (Note: there are internet groups that help donor offspring find their donors.)

Surrogacy

A surrogate mother is a woman who agrees to carry a child through pregnancy and deliver it on behalf of another. Surrogate mothers may also be called gestational carriers. The commissioning/intended/ contracting parents arrange for a surrogate to carry a pregnancy on their behalf, on the understanding that after birth she will relinquish the child and transfer custody of the baby. The commissioning parents will then be able to raise the child as its legal/social parents. They may or may not also be its genetic parents. Therefore, a number of different situations are possible:

- **Traditional/genetic/full surrogacy:** The surrogate is the child's genetic mother.
- **Gestational/partial surrogacy:** An embryo is transferred to the uterus of the surrogate and she carries a child with whom she has no genetic relationship.
- **Altruistic surrogacy:** The surrogate does not get paid for carrying the pregnancy and there may be no enforceable contract, although medical and other reasonable expenses may be covered.
- **Commercial surrogacy:** The surrogate receives compensation for carrying the child, as well as reimbursement for medical and other expenses.

In Australia and the United Kingdom, surrogacy for commercial gain is against the law, and in many European countries both commercial and altruistic surrogacy are also banned. Although altruistic surrogacy is claimed to be not-for-profit, in reality it is difficult to distinguish from commercial surrogacy as the line between what is a 'reasonable expense' (which can be covered by the commissioning parents in altruistic surrogacy) and what is only 'compensation' is difficult to define, and there is no bar to gift giving. It would not be unusual for an altruistic surrogate in the United Kingdom to receive around £10,000 for expenses.

In many countries, all forms of surrogacy are legal, although that does not always mean that contracts can be enforced. Rates of surrogacy vary.

Why do people consider using a surrogate?

Surrogacy would usually be considered after the failure of IVF as a way for a couple to have a genetically related or partially genetically related child. It is also considered when the woman is unable personally to carry a pregnancy, perhaps because she has no uterus (from birth, or as a result of surgery), or is unable to bring a pregnancy to term for other reasons. Increasingly, surrogates are also being used by homosexual male couples to enable them to have a child who is genetically linked to themselves.

Why do women choose to be surrogates?

Research has been patchy in this area. Certainly, there are examples of women who selflessly carry a child for complete strangers out of the kindness of their hearts, wanting to give others the gift of a child—something they find so fulfilling in their own lives. This happens even in commercial settings. Most have reported that they find personal fulfilment in surrogacy, and that it adds something to their lives (such as increased self-esteem). Few surrogate mothers report doing it just for the money.[81]

Surrogacy in society

Community acceptance of surrogacy has been slow, and is associated with a growing recognition of the changing nature of the family in society. Some have compared it to adoption, emphasizing improved outcomes for surrogate offspring because they are with their parents from the start. I do not think this is a valid comparison. First, adoption is an act of charity for a child already born—quite different from the conscious decision involved with a surrogate birth. Second, there are insufficient surrogate offspring in the teenage years to really know yet what their identity issues will be, if indeed they develop any.

One issue of concern to authorities is that the socioeconomic status of intended parents has been shown to be significantly different from that of surrogates. Commissioning mothers tend to be older and better educated than surrogates, raising concerns that surrogate mothers may

---

81. OBA van den Akker, 'Psychosocial aspects of surrogate motherhood', *Human Reproduction Update*, vol. 13, no. 1, January/February 2007, pp. 53-62.

be at risk of exploitation. Although there is little evidence that this occurs in Western countries, the long-term effects of surrogacy have not been examined. Some surrogates have reported feeling betrayed if they were told they would be permitted to keep in touch with the baby and this promise was later rescinded.[82]

Commercial surrogacy—cause for concern

A more worrying trend is the 'rent-a-womb' businesses appearing in the developing world. In India, a recent investigation by the London *Sunday Telegraph* reported that according to a senior Indian government official, up to 1000 IVF clinics are currently operating across the country. Reproductive tourism is expected to earn $2.3 billion in 2012.[83] The primary appeal of India is that it is cheap, legal but barely regulated, and relatively safe. Surrogacy can cost $50,000-$100,000 in the United States, while many Indian clinics charge $22,000 or less. Local women find the work tempting for financial reasons, though they earn only a fraction of the fee collected by the clinic. A woman can expect to earn at least 300,000 rupees (US$6,000/£4,000), with a bonus if there are twins. If a surrogate miscarries during the first term, she will get a third of the cash. One pregnancy can be enough to get her out of the slums, while two may educate her children to university level.[84] It's easy to see the temptation for these women, even though death is occasionally the result. (Life insurance is now available.)

In order to increase efficiency for their customers, PlanetHospital provides an 'India Bundle' that includes 4 embryo transfers into 4 separate surrogate mothers at the same time. If the customers end up with more pregnancies than required, some commissioning parents find the extra money while others just abort the 'spares'.[85]

Thailand is also becoming known for its surrogacy industry. The

---

82. ibid.

83. S Bhatia, 'Revealed: how more and more Britons are paying Indian women to become surrogate mothers', *Telegraph*, 26 May 2012 (viewed 2 July 2012): www.telegraph.co.uk/health/healthnews/9292343/Revealed-how-more-and-more-Britons-are-paying-Indian-women-to-become-surrogate-mothers.html

84. J Burke, 'India's surrogate mothers face new rules to restrict "pot of gold"', *Guardian*, 30 July 2010 (viewed 18 January 2012): www.guardian.co.uk/world/2010/jul/30/india-surrogate-mothers-law

85. T Audi and A Chang, 'Assembling the global baby', *Wall Street Journal*, 11-12 December 2010, pp. C1-2.

Babe-101 website announces that they are based on eugenics: "We could create the finest procreation condition for your baby, mainly through the efficient embryo refining" (they also mention the importance of fertility in the Chinese culture).[86] They list the benefits of hiring a surrogate mother, including:

3. [You] can continue to work without worrying about losing job or business intermission. It is quite suitable for the women who desire to have kids but no time for pregnancy.

4. Unnecessary to fear the pain of birth pangs.

5. Unnecessary to worry about out of shape on your stature, neither to fear the intimacy fading...

7. ...However the baby is 100% blood relationship with you.[87]

It doesn't mention how you will manage to have time for a baby when you didn't have time to be pregnant.

The use of commercial surrogacy arrangements in any country is banned in parts of Australia.[88] In 2011, France refused to give citizenship to twins of French parents, born through a surrogate in the United States, because of their own national ban.[89] Germany decided that not only would they not issue a passport to a child born by a surrogate mother in India, but also that the legal parents are the surrogate and her husband.[90]

Further complicating the potential abuse of commercial surrogacy is the news that a California attorney who championed surrogacy was found guilty of selling babies. Apparently, Theresa Erickson and her partners recruited women to act as surrogates, and arranged implantation with donated gametes in the Ukraine (thereby bypassing the usual formalities). When the second trimester was reached, Erikson advertised the babies

86. Babe-101 Eugenic surrogate, *Understanding Us*, Centre of Surrogate Maternity < Baby 101 > Ltd, Cambodia, 2012 (viewed 18 January 2012): www.baby-1001.com/eng/about.htm

87. Babe-101 Eugenic surrogate, *Advantage to Hire Surrogate Mother*, op. cit. (viewed 18 January 2012) www.baby-1001.com/eng/faq.htm

88. 'Overseas surrogacy ban comes into force', *ABC News*, 1 March 2011 (viewed 18 January 2012): www.abc.net.au/news/stories/2011/03/01/3151534.htm

89. Associated Press, 'France bars surrogate twins' citizenship', *Boston.com*, 7 April 2011 (viewed 18 January 2012): http://articles.boston.com/2011-04-07/news/29393551_1_surrogate-mother-twin-girls-legal-limbo

90. DPA/The Local/djw, 'Surrogate children have no right to German passport, court rules', *Local*, 28 April 2011 (viewed 18 January 2012): www.thelocal.de/society/20110428-34681.html

for sale, fabricating false records that suggested the children were the result of a cancelled legal surrogacy arrangement. Couples were charged $100,000-$150,000 per baby.[91]

The techniques used for surrogacy are the same as standard ART (with or without donated gametes), but the legal, ethical and psychosocial issues can become complex.

Legal issues

In those places where the birth parents are recorded on the birth certificate, the social parents may not get custody of the child for months or years. This means, for example, that they are not legally able to consent to surgery in an emergency. The problem is reduced when the surrogate and the intended parents have an ongoing relationship, as is required in some jurisdictions. If the child is born in a different country, as noted before, citizenship in the parents' country cannot be taken for granted. Some countries with an established surrogacy industry are requiring intending parents to prove the child can be repatriated, before the surrogacy is finalized.

International surrogacy isn't the only source of problems. An English couple, having already lost custody of a child to a surrogate mother (the biological mother) who changed her mind, was ordered to pay £568 (A$900) per month in child maintenance because the husband is the biological father. He plans to appeal.[92]

If surrogacy is intended, it is important that all parties receive counselling and legal advice at the outset, so that they know where they stand.

Ethical issues

Surrogacy has often had a bad name due to high-profile media cases where, for example, the surrogate refused to give up her child (1987),[93]

---

91. A Newcomb, 'Baby-selling enterprise busted, three plead guilty', *ABC News*, 10 August 2011 (viewed 18 January 2012): www.abcnews.go.com/US/attorney-pleads-guilty-baby-selling-ring/story?id=14274193

92. L Eccles, 'Couple are ordered to pay surrogate mother £568 a month for the baby they will never see', *Mail Online*, 12 April 2011 (viewed 18 January 2012): www.dailymail.co.uk/news/article-1375861/Child-custody-Couple-ordered-pay-surrogate-mother-monthly-baby-wont-meet.html

93. M Fleeman, 'Surrogate mom trial to begin Monday', *AP News Archive*, 4 January 1987 (viewed 27 July 2012): www.apnewsarchive.com/1987/Surrogate-Mom-Trial-To-Begin-Monday/id-6bf966cda95cb7eab61bedfa60953975

or the commissioning parents sued a surrogate for bringing twins to birth when they only wanted one child (they had wanted an abortion for one of the twins; 2001).[94] However, the fact that it does work sometimes means that not all problems are insurmountable.

Supporters of surrogacy argue that life through surrogacy is better than no life at all; that it respects marriage by rejecting adultery or divorce as a way to get a child; and that it is not harmful. In response to these supporters, I would say that arguing about whether life through a surrogate is better than never being born is really an invalid thought experiment, since life is the basic good on which we measure other goods. I agree that it is better to avoid adultery and divorce as ways to get a child. Yet surrogacy is not the only alternative. Is surrogacy really not harmful at all?[95]

There are many factors that can potentially create problems in a surrogacy transaction.

One potential problem—and an argument against surrogacy—is its effect on the child born. The concern is that it is a transaction that starts to treat the child involved as a commodity to be bought and sold.

Of course there will always be exceptions, but the testimony from children born through assisted conception is clear: their biological identity is important to them and every time an extra parent is added to the mix, it increases confusion and reduces their sense of belonging. When you consider that children born through surrogacy may have to contend with, potentially, up to five parents (egg donor, sperm donor, surrogate and two social parents), what will these children say when they are old enough to speak for themselves? They have had no opportunity to consent to these experiments. It is possible they will have similar concerns to children born with donor gametes (see above), as it seems that most parents do not plan to tell their children about the surrogacy,[96] and in most jurisdictions the birth certificate denotes legal parentage, not genetic parentage. And if donor gamete children feel they were

---

94. 'Surrogate mother sues California couple', *CNN.com*, 13 August 2001 (viewed 27 July 2010): http://articles.cnn.com/2001-08-13/justice/surrogate.dispute_1_surrogacy-california-couple-adoptive-parents

95. For a comment on the 'need' to have a biologically related child, see footnote 18 in chapter 10.

96. O van den Akker, 'The acceptable face of parenthood: The relative status of biological and cultural interpretations of offspring in infertility treatment', *Sexualities, Evolution and Gender*, vol. 3, no. 2, 2001, pp. 137-53.

relinquished at birth, how are surrogate children going to feel?

Feminists, on the other hand, are very concerned about the effects of surrogacy on the surrogates themselves. They believe surrogacy debases women by reducing them to their reproductive functions. They argue that it demeans the meaning of motherhood to use these women to 'manufacture' a 'product'. It turns children into commodities of exchange, which is degrading for them. Pregnancy becomes a service rather than a relationship.[97] They also argue that it is not acceptable to solve one woman's pain by creating it for another.

I certainly agree that commercial surrogacy is wrong, particularly as it is practiced in developing countries where women can be exploited through financial incentives. An Indian friend suggested that I was trying to take away a lucrative source of income for those poor women, and that they were free to make their own choices. I agree the choice is theirs, but can it be completely voluntary when the money is such a coercive factor?

Surrogacy, whether commercial or altruistic, also introduces a third party into the marriage relationship, which is not consistent with the 'one flesh' teaching of the Bible. This risks the surrogacy arrangement having a negative impact on the marriage. Some women report feeling like an outsider when they are 'bypassed' by the surrogacy. Vera said, *We thought about it, but I didn't think I could handle seeing another woman pregnant with my husband's child.* Some couples see it in a more practical way: *We want a biological child. I have eggs, he has sperm. Why not use a surrogate so we can get what we want?*

Even though I am hesitant to recommend legal surrogacy, I believe that if no donor gametes are used, altruistic surrogacy is not necessarily inherently immoral. This is not to say, however, that it is a wise choice. By definition, surrogacy requires a woman to break the relationship she has formed with the child she has been carrying for 9 months. I do not believe it is ever right to suppress the bonds of love between parents and children. Grief resulting from giving up a child for adoption, even when it is voluntary, is well known.[98] It is natural for a mother to bond to her unborn child, and surrogacy goes against the biblical idea that parenting a child involves responsibility beyond the birth. It is also reported that

---

97.   JC Ciccarelli and LJ Beckman, 'Navigating rough waters: An overview of psychological aspects of surrogacy', *Journal of Social Issues*, vol. 61, no. 1, March 2005, pp. 21-43.

98.   G Parker, 'Relinquishing mothers', *Medical Journal of Australia*, vol. 144, no. 3, 3 February 1986, p. 113.

the natural children of the surrogate mother experience a sense of loss of a sibling and abandonment anxiety (that their mother has given away one child and they may be next).[99] No long-term research has, as yet, studied what effect their mother's surrogate birth has on them.

The scenario is further complicated by the ethical problems that could develop for both commissioning and surrogate parents. What if one party demands an abortion against the wishes of the other? What if the child is disabled and none of the parents want it? What if the surrogate disagrees with how the social parents choose to bring up the child, particularly if her egg was involved? These are not just hypothetical questions.

There is no law that ensures the commissioning parents will adopt the commissioned baby. Just as a surrogate can keep the baby, so a commissioning couple can refuse to raise a child born as a result of their arrangements. In 2010, a surrogate pregnancy in Canada resulted in a baby with Down syndrome. The commissioning parents requested an abortion. The surrogate mother refused. The commissioning parents insisted and eventually the child was aborted:

> The case led to lively discussion in the Canadian media. "Should the rules of commerce apply to the creation of children? No, because children get hurt", Juliet Guichon of the University of Calgary, said in the National Post. "It's kind of like stopping the production line: 'Oh, oh, there's a flaw'. It makes sense in a production scenario, but in reproduction it's a lot more problematic."
>
> On the other hand, a surrogacy broker, Sally Rhoads of Surrogacy In Canada Online, said that the parents needed to be protected. "The baby that's being carried is their baby. It's usually their genetic offspring", she said. "Why should the intended parents be forced to raise a child they didn't want? It's not fair."[100]

Clearly they didn't want just *any* baby—only a perfect baby.

The issue of the surrogate mother's consent is troubling. Giving up a child is not as easy as one might initially think. The experience

---

99. M Harrison, 'Psychological ramifications of "surrogate" motherhood', in NL Stotland (ed.), *Psychiatric Aspects of Reproductive Technology*, American Psychiatric Press, Washington DC, 1990, pp. 97-112.

100. M Cook, 'Surrogate agrees to abort "defective" child', *BioEdge*, 15 October 2010 (viewed 8 March 2012): www.bioedge.org/index.php/bioethics/bioethics_article/9245

of gestation and the hormonal changes in the surrogate mother can dramatically change her perspective of what is involved. If her motivation for volunteering to be a surrogate was the need for self-affirmation, are we happy for it to be achieved this way? It would be tragic if such a situation led to the vulnerable woman being open to coercion. Even more difficult may be the situation for a closely related woman who is pressured by her family to be the surrogate, against her will, for an infertile relative. If she decides she wants to keep the baby, most courts would decide in her favour. Intuitively, this feels right to me.

I can think of only one scenario where surrogacy may be the best choice ethically. This would be if a couple who had frozen embryos in storage suddenly found themselves unable to transfer their embryos because, for example, the wife developed an illness preventing a safe pregnancy, or needed to have her uterus removed. If a woman close to the family was happy to act as a surrogate in order to avoid the destruction of the frozen embryos, this would be preferable to either destroying the embryos or giving them away. Because of her relationship with the family involved, the surrogate could have an ongoing relationship with the child and thereby continue a parenting role of sorts. Meanwhile, the genetic parents would be able to raise their own child. This is not to say the scenario is free from problems, but it could help solve the dilemma for a couple who, through no fault of their own, found themselves with frozen embryos but no means to carry a pregnancy to term.

Two beautiful daughters were born to Julie and her husband before Julie was diagnosed with cancer. The surgery for cancer included removing her uterus; so they knew she could never have their last embryo transferred. *We thought of the embryo as one of our children and just couldn't let it die, but we weren't happy with adopting it out and have someone else bring up our child. We were always planning to use all the embryos. It was such a blessing when my sister, who has a family of her own, offered to be our surrogate to give our embryo a chance at life.*

If surrogacy is contemplated, it should be a last resort. It is important that all parties receive independent counselling regarding the physical, emotional and legal implications of the process. Fully informed consent on the part of the surrogate would require her to be at least 18 years old and the mother of at least one living child. Even so, she should be warned that it is hard to predict in advance how she will feel about giving away her child after a 9-month relationship.

Children need to be told about their origins "early and often".[101] While a toddler may not understand the intricacies of sperm and egg, they will understand that there were two people who really, really wanted a baby, with perhaps a 'tummy mummy' thrown in there too.

Embryo adoption (donor embryos)

With the surplus of frozen embryos accumulating as a result of the policies discussed above, one of the options open to parents who find they have excess frozen embryos at the end of their treatment is to donate them to other couples for reproduction. This option is discussed from the point of view of donating in chapter 14. Here we consider the decision to accept a donated embryo.

Embryos intended for donation will generally stay frozen in the treatment clinic until a couple is identified as recipients. If the clinic does not offer embryo adoption, it may be necessary to store them in a clinic that does. At this stage, the donor parents pay the cryostorage fees. Once the embryos are transferred to the care of the recipients, the recipients take over payment for storage; they do not pay for the creation of the embryos, so this tends to be cheaper than IVF. The embryos are then thawed and transferred in the usual way.

Transfer of donated embryos is a relatively new phenomenon. The success rate depends on many factors, but one report assessed the success rate for frozen donor embryos at 27.3% live births per transfer, compared to 23.4% per transfer for frozen non-donor embryos.[102]

Benefits of pursuing embryo adoption include some advantages claimed for ART over adoption generally. The baby can be cared for from the beginnings of the pregnancy (unlike adoption, where the biological mother's behaviour is beyond the control of the adoptive parents); and the couple can experience pregnancy, birth and breastfeeding.

Ethical issues

I believe embryo donation is ethical for Christians. This may surprise you. Why, when I am unenthusiastic about gamete donation and

---

101. ME Dallas, 'Donor-assisted conception sparks disclosure dilemmas', *U.S. News and World Report*, 3 June 2010 (viewed 16 July 2012): http://health.usnews.com/health-news/family-health/womens-health/articles/2010/06/03/donor-assisted-conception-sparks-disclosure-dilemmas

102. SL Glahn and WR Cutrer, *The Infertility Companion,* Zondervan, Grand Rapids, 2004, p. 206 (citing 2001 figures).

surrogacy, do I approve of embryo adoption? For two simple reasons: first, the 'one flesh' principle is not challenged unequally within the marriage, as both husband and wife are accepting another's gametes instead of their own, so the jealousy factor is unlikely to be a problem. Second, they are making it possible for the embryos to have a chance at life they otherwise would not have had. A third reason is that it is good stewardship of resources such as time, money and energy, as the donor embryos have already been formed.

Cytoplasmic and germinal vesicle transfer

The main problem for older women trying to have a baby is that their fertility is reduced because their eggs are less healthy. Initially, it was thought that the eggs might become healthier and embryo development be improved if the mitochondrial function (energy production) in the cell was better. This led to the practice of cytoplasmic transfer, where some of the cytoplasm (the contents of the cell apart from the nucleus, consisting of fluid and everything it contains) is taken from a younger woman's eggs and injected into the older woman's eggs. Alternatively, the germinal vesicle (the nucleus in an immature egg) can be transplanted into a younger woman's egg after the nucleus is removed.

Since 1998, more than 30 children have been born after the direct injection of cytoplasm from fresh, mature or immature, or cryopreserved and thawed, donor eggs into recipient eggs through a modified ICSI technique. It is not completely clear what benefit it gives, and there is no evidence that it improves the development or implantation of the embryos subsequently created. Nonetheless, it is astonishing how quickly cytoplasmic transfer in humans has been applied, especially given the lack of extensive research to evaluate the efficacy and the possible risks of the method.

Both of these techniques aim to combine the nucleus from the older woman's egg (containing the DNA) with the cytoplasm of a younger woman's egg (containing the mitochondria [energy]), to enable the older woman to have genetic offspring. An alternative use of the technology allows a woman with hereditary diseases of the mitochondria (mitochondrial myopathies) to have genetic offspring without passing on the genetic defects to her children. This is still an experimental technique, which has yet to prove its efficacy and safety. Therefore, researchers maintain that the indications for applying this technology in human clinical practice need to be clearly defined. Although there may be theoretical benefits, research into the potential side effects of these techniques must not be neglected. At present, in the absence of validation by proper cell culture experiments or detailed animal research, the application of such therapies in humans is difficult to justify.[103]

Ethical issues

Apart from the issues of using a technique that is not proven to be safe, this technique is troublesome because of the genetics involved. Although the main part of our genetic inheritance comes from the DNA in the nucleus, there is also DNA in the mitochondria. This means the offspring in this situation will have three genetic parents—one father (sperm nuclear DNA), and two mothers (egg nuclear DNA and egg mitochondrial DNA—mtDNA). Humans do not inherit mtDNA from the father, so this means that the ancestry of the offspring will be confused. While perhaps not an absolute reason for prohibition, evidence from ART offspring suggests that this may present a problem for the child. In my personal experience, the community in general is also uncomfortable with the thought of a child with three genetic parents.

An interesting sidetrack

Unlike nuclear DNA, which is inherited from both parents and in which genes are rearranged in the process of recombination, there is usually no change in mtDNA from mother to offspring. Because of this, mtDNA is a powerful tool for tracking ancestry through females and has been used in this role to track the ancestry of many species going back hundreds of generations. Human mtDNA can also be used to help identify individuals. Forensic laboratories occasionally use mtDNA comparison to identify human remains, and especially to identify older unidentified skeletal remains. Although, unlike nuclear DNA, mtDNA is not specific to one individual, it can be used in combination with other evidence to establish identification. For example, mtDNA was used along with nuclear DNA to identify bodies after the terrorist attacks in the United States on 11 September 2001.[104]

---

103. R Levy, K Elder and Y Ménézo, 'Cytoplasmic transfer in oocytes: biochemical aspects', *Human Reproduction Update*, vol. 10, no. 3, May/June 2004, pp. 241-50.
104. JM Butler, *Forensic DNA Typing*, Elsevier, Burlington MA, 2005, p. 551.

Preimplantation genetic diagnosis (PGD)

Our understanding of human genetics has grown enormously in recent years,[105] and this has been associated with the identification of the genetic basis of many diseases. PGD has been available since 1990 to genetically screen embryos created through IVF, before transfer to the woman's uterus.

Typically, the technique involves taking one or two cells from an 8-cell embryo, examining them under a microscope, and determining the genetic characteristics. While PGD of the egg alone has been performed (preconception genetic diagnosis), it is technically more difficult and less definitive than PGD of an embryo's makeup and thus less common.

There is concern that PGD may cause damage to the embryo, though this has not been proven. It is not clear whether the removal of up to 25% of the embryo's mass affects its development. Microarray comparative genomic hybridization (CGH) is a recent development that allows blastocysts to be genetically analysed. This causes less damage, but leaves little time for genetic analysis before the embryo must be transferred. This is not a problem in fertility centres that have the technology to facilitate rapid genetic screening (such as 24sure methodology, known as Advanced Embryo Selection), which allows the selection of chromosomally healthy embryos that are more likely to implant. In the past, biopsied embryos were more likely to be damaged by freezing and thawing, but with modern freezing techniques there is less concern.

Technically, each of the cells removed from the embryo for analysis has the potential to become an embryo, since the cells are still totipotent at the 6-8 cell stage (meaning that they still retain the ability to develop into a human individual). This is an argument against PGD itself—regardless of whether the initial embryo is damaged—which is used in countries such as Germany to prohibit the practice.

Currently, we can test for a lot more disorders than we can cure, so the only 'treatment' available if a disorder is detected is to discard the abnormal embryos and transfer the ones that are thought to be 'normal'.

Supporters of PGD see it as an opportunity to remove abnormal genes from the community by screening the embryos of couples that carry serious genetic disorders. This allows them to have a healthy child without the 'practical and ethical problems' of experiencing the abortion

---

105. See appendix III.

of an affected child after traditional prenatal diagnosis (chorionic villus sampling and amniocentesis).[106]

After undergoing PGD, Sennia became pregnant after 13 years of trying. *I was afraid to even think I could have a baby, and now I'm having twins!* And they are beautiful boys. It can seem so cruel to criticize this technology. Robert Winston, the British doctor who first performed PGD, is not concerned that this technology will change humans significantly. Education, economics and the care of families makes people what they are, he said—the most important being human love. An orthodox Jew, Professor Winston does not believe embryos are truly human, but he does believe that the use of PGD by parents with a family history of genetic disease is simply "a matter for the individuals concerned".[107]

PGD was first used to screen for serious life-threatening diseases; then it was used to screen for diseases that were treatable, or had their onset in adulthood, or were associated with *risk* of disease rather than a definite diagnosis. Now PGD is used in many places to choose the sex of the child, with completely normal embryos discarded because they were not the gender preferred by the parents. Chromosome abnormalities are found in over 50% of embryos examined. Some commentators have suggested that all ART pregnancies should be screened with PGD—at least for Down syndrome and cystic fibrosis—whether the parents have a history of genetic disease or not, in order to reduce the incidence of genetic abnormalities in the community.[108]

Ethical issues

It's important to note that for PGD proponents, abortion is seen as an ethical problem while discarding embryos is not. I have seen PGD specifically recommended by fertility clinics as a way for Christians to avoid abortions. In fact, I have been accused of not caring about women having abortions when I have opposed PGD!

But this approach assumes that the human embryo is not a human person who deserves protection. Discarding an embryonic human because they do not have certain characteristics is discriminatory and not consistent with treating each human as one who is made in

---

106. See chapter 8.
107. D Smith, 'Babies born and not made, says this lord of the genes', *Sydney Morning Herald*, 14 May 2001.
108. For further discussion of this trend, see chapter 9.

the image of God. Discarding abnormal embryos also risks increasing prejudice against the disabled in our community. Discarding embryos that are not completely normal but are expected to survive is different from discarding embryos that will definitely not develop (because they are dead). The latter is ethically appropriate and avoids unnecessary medical procedures for the woman.

As discussed earlier, consent is another ethical issue. Would the parents feel differently about the discarded (abnormal) embryos if no others were available? One would want to be convinced that the parents—at such an early stage of treatment when they will be extremely vulnerable and expecting treatment to be successful—were completely sure they had no further use for the abnormal embryos. Doubtless they will expect that one of the non-affected embryos will implant. Are the genetically affected embryos still considered 'excess' if the parents' choice is between a genetically imperfect child and no child, rather than between an affected and a non-affected one?

Although some parents say they would like to screen so they can be prepared for whatever problems the baby may have, they should consider whether the risk to the embryo is worth satisfying their curiosity. I suspect it is not. One also needs to consider whether their resolve to have the child might be weakened if an abnormality were revealed. Or would they be pressured to change their minds?

Some limits must be put on what conditions can justify discarding embryonic humans. While clinical specialists such as Professor Winston say the decision is just a matter for the individuals concerned, we already have the recommendation for PGD to become routine in order to abolish the existence of a certain kind of human in our midst. What started as an expression of free choice could become an obligation if intolerance of imperfection becomes widespread.[109]

As the human genome project delivers more information, allowing the number of conditions we can test for to increase exponentially, we must decide as a community which humans we will continue to exclude from the human race on grounds of faulty genetics.

If embryos are screened for multiple conditions, we may find at times that all embryos created in one cycle have a fault of some sort. Will parents then need to choose which of several diseases they want to

---

109. These questions are discussed in chapter 8.

inflict on their offspring? ("Would you rather they have breast cancer or Parkinson's disease?") Will they be encouraged to go through another cycle of IVF and try again? How many times can they try again? How will their offspring feel about it?

The use of PGD for the purpose of discarding certain embryos is unethical for those who wish to protect human life from its beginning.

Sperm sorting

Sperm sorting is a technique used to select specific sperm for use in fertilization. It can sort out which sperm are the healthiest, and it can determine more specific traits, such as which sperm are X- (female) and Y- (male) chromosome bearing. The resultant 'sex-sorted' sperm can then be used in conjunction with other ART methods, such as IUI, IVF and ICSI, to produce a child of the desired gender. It is not 100% accurate. It remains in the 'experimental' category and has limited availability.[110]

Ethical issues

Since sperm is not equivalent to an embryo in moral significance, there is no problem with using sperm sorting to identify healthy sperm. With regard to gender selection, it is preferable to PGD in that the choice is made prior to conception, so no embryos are discarded. One concern with any technology that aims to produce specific characteristics in the offspring is that there may be psychological implications for both the parents and the child if the procedure does not produce a child of the desired gender. Furthermore, problems may also arise if the gender-related expectations of the parents are not subsequently fulfilled by the child. (What if the rugby-playing boy you were hoping for decides to take up ballet?) The Bible expects parental love to be unconditional, and unmet expectations will make this harder. This concern is not a reason to avoid using sperm sorting, so much as a reason to consider carefully the motivation for its use.

Issues of access: who should use ART?

In most jurisdictions there is no limit on who has access to ART—not even infertility is a prerequisite—and the desire for a genetically linked child continues to drive an increasingly wide range of treatments.

---

110. For more information, visit the MicroSort website: www.microsort.com

So I am concerned about the reduction in efforts to take the welfare of ART offspring into account where decisions about access are concerned. First, the issue of child safety: does the adult have a history of child abuse or psychotic disease? Should this at least be checked at the outset? Opponents point out that normal parents aren't screened, so why should we screen ART parents? I would say that if we are using public funds to subsidize ART then we have an obligation to make sure basic standards are met. And I am not interested in the idea that the government should have no say in reproduction; it has always had a say in issues of reproduction, prohibiting incest, rape in marriage and paedophilia, for instance.

At one time, many legislatures included the child's need to have a father in regulations for ART, but this is gradually being removed as single women and lesbian couples access these services. However, in the biblical model of family, a child ideally has one parent of each gender.

Further discussion on the topic of access to ART in general is beyond the scope of this book.

Older parents

In 1994, Italian fertility researcher Severino Antinori helped a 63-year-old woman get pregnant through IVF. Newspaper commentary was vigorous. But that was before two 70-year-old women delivered children following treatment in 2008. When asked whether this was prudent, considering they had one foot in the grave (I didn't ask the question!), one of the fathers said cheerfully, "Oh, that won't be any trouble. We have a large family and there will be plenty of helpers".[111]

Commercial companies are popping up all over the place to take advantage of older couples wanting a family. They are in it for profit. Christy Jones, an entrepreneur who was setting up her egg-freezing network Extend Fertility in 2004, was asked at the time what would happen if a woman wanted to have children at the age of, say, 82. She said, "My aim is to be the enabler and not the one guiding the ethics". Her market is primarily those women who are not ready to have children in their twenties or early thirties. "I am part of a generation of women who have been told we can have it all. The only thing that is holding us back is our biological clock. Egg freezing is the missing link. Many have

---

111. R Shears, 'Pictured: The Indian mother who had an IVF baby at the age of 70', *Mail Online*, 9 December 2008.

described it as the most revolutionary and empowering science since the birth-control pill." She was confident of success: "Really, it just gives women the opportunity to have a child. It's hard to argue with."

I think she's right there. While it is likely that Ms Jones had professional women more in mind than geriatrics, it is interesting to consider whether it is ethically appropriate for an older Christian couple to use ART, using their own cryopreserved gametes.

The most common objections to older parents that I hear centre on the notion of what is in the best interests of the child involved. What are the risks involved in having a parent who is older than the norm? Obviously, the possibility of the parent dying while the child is growing up is increased. Yet the likelihood of this event occurring would be so difficult to predict, on average, that it seems a risky basis for judgement. Would we extend the same restriction to a younger parent with a strong family history of heart disease? It would also be difficult to establish that the loss of a parent is such a disaster that the life of the child is unjustifiable.

What about energy levels? Four-hourly night feeds are a struggle for many young parents and a parent taking up backyard cricket in their mid-sixties may flounder in the outfield. Yet we do not screen younger parents for their athletic capabilities. And older fathers, often the parent more interested in outdoor sports, have been the norm in many cultures for centuries. It soon becomes apparent that in fact opposition is not to older parents, so much as to older mothers.

Are there any advantages to being an older parent? In terms of the last criticism, one should remember that the older parent is more likely to be financially secure than their younger counterpart. If the 4-hourly feeds are too much, they could hire a nurse, and employing similar strategies as the child grows would mean they could save their energy for more sedentary occupations. In fact, the older parent is more likely to have 'quality' *and* 'quantity' time with their child, as they would be less likely to be obliged to spend long hours at work establishing their career.

I have heard it said that it is selfish for a couple to have a child later in life—but why do any of us have children? Would you say that carrying on the family name, or having someone around to care for you, or fulfilling an overwhelming biological urge, were less selfish reasons?

If what is at stake is access to the artificial reproductive therapies that make postmenopausal child-bearing possible, the arguments above would make it difficult to justify exclusion on grounds of justice, when similar grounds for exclusion are not applied to younger mothers with similar impediments. However, the misgivings can remain.

Could it be that we are ambivalent about this issue because in our hearts we know the value of family relationships and the joy they can bring, and we hesitate to deny them to others? Yet when we think of a woman in her sixties or seventies, we imagine not a new mother, but a grandmother. In this instance, ART is not treating a disease but a normal stage of female life—menopause. Our increasing technological control over natural life processes has allowed us as a society to blur the lines between the once-inevitable 'seasons of life'. Our objection to the older mother is not that allowing access to ART would be wrong so much as that it might not be wise. Traditionally, the seasons of life have matched our physical capabilities with our life changes. Now we have the technology to overrule these seasons. I would like to see an open community discussion about whether we want to do this.

Post-mortem gamete collection

A 34-year old man is brought into emergency after a traffic accident where he sustained a fatal head injury. He dies soon after arrival at the hospital. When police contact his wife to notify her of the death, she requests that sperm be extracted from her husband as they had been trying to have a baby.[112]

Dianne Blood conceived her two sons using sperm taken from her husband, Stephen, shortly before he died from meningitis. She battled the British government, first to use the sperm, and then to have Stephen's name recorded on the boys' birth certificates as their father.[113]

In 2011, an Israeli court allowed parents to harvest eggs from their dead 17-year-old daughter. They then wanted the eggs to be fertilized with sperm from a dead donor. The second request was denied, but had it proceeded, any child born would have had parents who were dead before the child was conceived.[114]

---

112. Hypothetical case.

113. E Fitzmaurice, 'Dead dad wins father's rights', *Sun-Herald*, 2 March 2003.

114. D Even, 'Israel court allows egg extraction from deceased woman in unprecedented ruling', *Haaretz.com*, 7 August 2011 (viewed 18 January 2012): www.haaretz.com/news/national/israel-court-allows-egg-extraction-from-deceased-woman-in-unprecedented-ruling-1.377482

Legal issues

Laws concerning the collection of gametes (sperm or eggs) after, or around, death will differ between jurisdictions, but generally they cover the issues of consent to collection and regulation of use. Usually the donor will have had to give clear consent to the use of their gametes after death. Written consent is preferable in order to remove ambiguity about the deceased's wishes and to help a child deal with the circumstances under which they were born.[115]

In May 2012, the United States Supreme Court ruled that children conceived through IVF after the death of a parent were not automatically eligible for Social Security survivor benefits.[116]

Ethical issues

The biblical model for family is that a child has a male and a female parent. While children do grow up with only one parent because tragedy takes the other away, this is not the same as deliberately creating a child who can never know one of their parents. Apart from issues regarding consent, this is another situation that may not be wise, although it can't be described as definitely morally wrong.

If, on the other hand, there were frozen embryos *in storage*, following that person's death it would be ethical to transfer these embryos. This is because the fact that the embryos have been formed proves beyond doubt that the parent intended to have the children, so there are no doubts about consent. Also, it is ethically correct to protect the lives that have already been created.

Safety for ART offspring

Although the majority of ART children are normal, there are concerns about the increased risk of adverse pregnancy outcomes. More than 30% of ART pregnancies are twins, triplets or greater gestation, which means they will be at greater risk of prematurity, with all the consequent complications. We have already discussed the role of single-embryo

---

115.   SL Middleton and MD Buist, 'Sperm removal and dead or dying patients: a dilemma for emergency departments and intensive care units', *Medical Journal of Australia*, vol. 190, no. 5, 2 March 2009, pp. 244-6.

116.   J Vicini, 'U.S. top court decides in vitro fertilization benefits', *Reuters*, 21 May 2012 (viewed 16 July 2012): www.reuters.com/article/2012/05/21/us-usa-socialsecurity-benefits-idUSBRE84K0SD20120521

transfers in reducing this statistic. But even single ART pregnancies demonstrate increased rates of perinatal complications—small for gestational age infants, prematurity and stillbirth, as well as maternal complications such as preeclampsia, gestational diabetes, placenta praevia, placental abruption and caesarean delivery—when compared to non-assisted pregnancies.[117]

Research also shows that children born following ART treatment are at increased risk of birth defects compared to spontaneously conceived infants.[118]

For doctors

Major structural birth defects that are more common with ART include cardiac defects, orofacial clefts, oesophageal and anorectal atresia and hypospadias.[119]

In addition, problems particularly associated with ICSI include urogenital malformations such as hypospadias (where the opening of the urethra is on the underside, rather than at the end, of the penis), genetic (imprinting) disorders—although these disorders remain extremely rare—and male infertility.[120]

It is not clear whether these abnormalities result from ART procedures

---

117.   UM Reddy, RJ Wapner, RW Rebar and RJ Tasca, 'Infertility, assisted reproductive technology, and adverse pregnancy outcomes: Executive summary of a National Institute of Child Health and Human Development workshop', *Obstetrics and Gynecology*, vol. 109, no. 4, April 2007, pp. 967-77.

118.   M Hansen, C Bower, E Milne, N de Klerk and JJ Kurinczuk, 'Assisted reproductive technologies and the risk of birth defects—a systematic review', *Human Reproduction*, vol. 20, no. 2, February 2005, pp. 328-38.

119.   J Reefhuis, MA Honein, LA Schieve, A Correa, CA Hobbs, SA Rasmussen and the National Birth Defects Prevention Study, 'Assisted reproductive technology and major structural birth defects in the United States', *Human Reproduction*, vol. 24, no. 2, February 2009, pp. 360-6.

120.   F Belva, S Henriet, E Van den Abbeel, M Camus, P Devroey, J Van der Elst, I Liebaers, P Haentjens and M Bonduelle, 'Neonatal outcome of 937 children born after transfer of cryopreserved embryos obtained by ICSI and IVF and comparison with outcome data of fresh ICSI and IVF cycles', *Human Reproduction*, vol. 23, no. 10, October 2008, pp. 2227-38; C Feng, L Wang, M Dong and H Huang, 'Assisted reproductive technology may increase clinical mutation detection in male offspring', *Fertility and Sterility*, vol. 90, no. 1, July 2008, pp. 92-6.

themselves or if they are associated with the underlying infertility for which ART is sought. Whatever the cause, those considering ART should be aware of the risks.

Further risks

We have looked at an enormous amount of information in this chapter as we have considered the rights and wrongs of various procedures. However, even when ART is ethically permissible, it may not be right for every Christian couple that considers it. While thinking about whether it is the right choice for a marriage, the following should be considered:

1. ART involves physical risks, especially for the woman. The risk of side effects from the drugs used to stimulate ovulation is not fully understood. Also, invasive procedures have inherent risks, and increased risks are associated with any ART pregnancy.

2. ART is emotionally traumatic for all couples. A cycle develops where the transfer of an embryo is followed by a period of intense anxiety as they wait to see if the embryo will 'take'. Every time menstruation recurs, it takes those involved down an emotional rollercoaster of disappointment before they build themselves up to try again. Bess remembers: *The uncertainty of IVF is awful. You desperately want to have a baby, you see the embryo under a microscope before it is transferred and you pray that it will 'stick'. When you get the phone call to tell you that you're not pregnant, no matter how much you have tried to not have high hopes, you are devastated. It is hard to hold it together. Your family is disappointed for you as well. Fortunately my husband was strong for us and helped me hold it together. We were third time lucky getting our first daughter—we knew she was a miracle. With only two embryos left we didn't expect to have another child, but God was amazingly generous and blessed us on our lucky last embryo with our second daughter. Even now, I feel quite emotional reminiscing on the experience more than four years ago.*

3. ART is time-consuming and distracting. The investigations, the visits to the clinic and the distraction of putting life on hold while trying to grow a family are unavoidable. Those in a Christian marriage need to consider if it is God's will for them. Geordie and Pam recall, *From the start, we were very aware of how all-consuming trying to conceive could be. So early on, we prayed and tried to prioritize contentment in God rather than being consumed*

with getting children at all costs. Initially IVF was off the cards for that reason—I didn't think I could hold it together—being content whether God gave us children or no children, at the same time as making children.

4. ART is expensive. Financial costs quickly run into thousands of dollars and not all therapies are covered by insurance: *Financially IVF was out of the question for us for a long time, as we were students. Even now, we'd struggle if we wanted to,* said Billie. *Paying for IUI hasn't been a huge stress—I just take a deep breath, hand over my card and then try and forget that another $1800 is spent this month!* According to the American Society of Reproductive Medicine, the average cost for an IVF cycle in the United States is about $12,400. It's also possible to calculate how much it costs to get a baby: in Australia, the cost of an IVF baby to a woman aged 30-33 years is $27,000. The cost to women aged 42-45 years is $131,000.[121] I am now hearing stories of couples finding themselves with excess embryos because they can't afford to have them transferred.

The clinical aspect of ART can be a source of tension—it is a dehumanizing experience for many people, in what should be an intimate and pleasurable process. Think of the collection of sperm into plastic cups and repeated hormone injections.

The difficulties of negotiating the ART process are obviously stressful for any marriage, and not all marriages survive. Knowing where to get support can be difficult. Counsellors suggest it is unlikely that couples will be able to adequately support each other, given that they are both trying to cope. It is prudent to think about sources of support before starting.

And in your deliberations you should also consider that you might want to avoid some morally troubling options. Will your doctor help you do this?

What questions should a Christian couple ask before starting ART?

Here are some important questions a Christian couple should think through before beginning a course of ART:

1. What is involved? (Get the facts.)
2. Will the specialist respect your theological views?

---

121. RJ Norman, 'The power of one and its cost', *Medical Journal of Australia*, vol. 195, no. 10, 21 November 2011, pp. 564-5.

3. Will the number of embryos created be limited (his number should not be higher than the number of children you are willing to have), and can they all be transferred regardless of appearance?
4. What is the cost and can you afford it?
5. How important is it to you to have a biological child?

Cowboys

Some initiatives by specialists in the ART arena have not been acceptable, even to their ART colleagues—for example, the French brother and sister who had a child together by a surrogate in California;[122] the British IVF specialist who faked embryo transfers;[123] and the American physician who transferred 12 embryos at once, an action that resulted in the birth of octuplets.[124] Then there are the accidental transfers of the wrong embryos to the wrong women. Fertility clinic accidents are often in the news, but overall such events are uncommon. They should not make you disregard ART so much as use your judgement in choosing a clinic.

However, as a society, the fact that these events occur at all should make us pause and consider whether we need to start placing limits on these technologies. Perhaps the most bizarre story I have read came from a paper published in 2006.[125] A 55-year-old Russian woman used IVF surrogacy to have a baby using her dead son's sperm with donated eggs. In the absence of any identified live parent the courts declared that the child did not exist, and refused to issue a birth certificate.[126]

Moving on

Sometimes, through all the technology, God allows a child to be born. This is absolutely wonderful when it happens. But be aware that the success rate of ART is variable. Not everyone gets to take a baby home.

Sometimes, even when every morally permissible technique is tried

122. J Tizzard, 'Salomone case is not the tip of the iceberg', *BioNews*, 25 June 2001 (viewed 27 July 2012): www.bionews.org.uk/page_37581.asp
123. 'Medic "faked embryo implants"', *BBC News*, 25 November 2002 (viewed 27 July 2012): http://news.bbc.co.uk/2/hi/uk_news/england/2511959.stm
124. Associated Press, 'Octuplets' mom implanted with 12 embryos', *Sydney Morning Herald*, 19 October 2010.
125. M Leidig, 'Russian woman may lose grandson conceived from dead son's frozen sperm', *British Medical Journal*, vol. 332, no. 7542, 18 March 2006, p. 627.
126. For further discussion on limiting ART, see chapter 13.

over and over again, no pregnancy develops. Deciding to stop treatment is a very difficult issue.

It can be helpful to have a frank talk with your doctor about what has been happening in the ART process. If the feedback is that you have very little chance of becoming pregnant, it may be time to stop. As a woman, you may be checked for your blood anti-Müllerian hormone (AMH) levels, which can give some indication of how much ovarian reserve is left. Take into consideration your chances of conceiving, given how many attempts you have made. These days, most women under 37 years should become pregnant within 3 cycles, though many doctors would suggest that trying 6 times is reasonable. Also consider how you are going: how is your mental, physical, emotional and spiritual health, and how is the state of your marriage? What is the cost? Is it worth continuing?[127]

You may have been meticulous about obeying God's word every step of the way, and in the end he may still withhold the gift of a child. It can be heartbreaking. Hilda said, *In the end we planted a tree, to remember all the children we never had. It was so sad. But it helped me move on.*

---

127.   See chapter 10 for further discussion about coming to terms with infertility.

Saying 'no' to assisted reproductive technology

I REMEMBER THE FIRST TIME I publicly suggested that there was no ethical obligation for infertile couples to use assisted reproductive technology (ART) to have children. After my talk there was a line of women waiting to thank me.

ART is held up as a benevolent technology that compassionately allows couples their final opportunity to obtain their deeply desired biological child. It is still publicly considered to be the source of eternal fertility for women, many of whom keep ignoring their 'biological clocks' despite the warnings from IVF doctors themselves that the treatments become less successful as age increases. Many people continue to access treatment despite the obvious hardships involved.

As I have discussed in chapter 6, the creation mandate to "be fruitful and multiply" is not a command for each couple to have the maximum number of children possible. There is no moral obligation or imperative to use every possible means to have as many children as one can.

However, because the desire for children is so strong for so many couples, ART becomes an obvious next step. Some women talk about the 'merry-go-round' they can't get off, ART being the inevitable step following tests for infertility, without any question of whether it is right or wrong for them and their husbands. Rachel commented, *There are lots of groups to help you get started with ART, but who helps you say 'no'?*

Some couples do say no, for a range of reasons. In this chapter I want to cover some of these reasons, if for no other reason than the fact that for most couples on the 'merry-go-round', the reasons *not* to pursue ART will rarely be mentioned or discussed.

1. Poor success rates

The first and perhaps most obvious reason to think twice about ART is its failure rate. We often hear of the successes, but IVF failure is relatively invisible in public representations. I look at the advertisements for IVF clinics on my desk: gorgeous babies, happy (young) women with gloriously pregnant tummies, lots of pastel artwork. The truth, however, is that it fails more often than it succeeds. While ART has helped many couples, there are many more in its history that have not benefited from treatment and have suffered physically, emotionally and financially without taking the longed-for baby home. Even now, over 30 years since the first 'test tube' baby was born, the overall success rate per cycle is under 25%,[1] with cumulative live birth rate around 50%.[2] Cumulative live birth rate reflects the delivery of ≥ 1 live infants in ≤ 6 cycles. It does not count those who have dropped out. So the overall chance of success is actually less than 50%.

2. Costs of treatment

Despite its social acceptability, not everyone is comfortable with the process of ART. Among the couples I have spoken to, concerns about treatment included the lack of adequate counselling before treatment started and after it failed; stress on the marriage relationship, which peaked every time an embryo was transferred and the pregnancy test awaited; and feelings of personal guilt when treatment failed. Joe and Vanessa were given the consent forms to sign while in the waiting room, before they even saw the doctor. They proceeded despite their ignorance of what lay ahead. They admit now: *We would have done anything to get a child at that point.* Their lack of information caused them ethical trouble further down the track.

ART is very costly in terms of time, money, resources and energy. Many Christian couples have decided it is not the best use of the resources they have received to invest in years of ART treatment.

---

1.   SK Sunkara, V Rittenberg, N Raine-Fenning, S Bhattacharya, J Zamora and A Coomarasamy, 'Association between the number of eggs and live birth in IVF treatment: an analysis of 400,135 treatment cycles', *Human Reproduction*, vol. 26, no. 7, July 2011, pp. 1768-74.
2.   VA Moragianni and AS Penzias, 'Cumulative live-birth rates after assisted reproductive technology', *Current Opinion in Obstetrics and Gynecology*, vol. 22, no. 3, June 2010, pp. 189-92.

3. Theological objections

Theological opposition to ART has been expressed most publicly by the Roman Catholic Church. As previously explained, the Catholic position has been argued from the perspective of natural law.[3] According to their teaching, in keeping with how God designed us, all sexual relations in marriage should aim towards procreation as well as union (oneness in marriage). Both the procreative and unitive aspects of marital intercourse should be present in every conjugal act. Nothing is allowed that interferes with the natural process that results in conception of a child by the husband and wife.

The Catholic Church also teaches that technology should be used in keeping with the moral principles of natural law. The human embryo must be protected from the time of fertilization, and any process that results in its destruction is wrong. As husband and wife are to conceive children only with each other, the use of a third party (by gamete donation or surrogacy) is also prohibited. Anything that assists conception without replacing the conjugal act is allowed (such as fertility drugs to boost ovulation), but those things that do replace it (such as fertilization outside the woman's body, or sperm collected by masturbation) are not allowed. Frozen eggs are excluded. No official position on embryo adoption has been issued, and theologians are divided on this subject.

In summary, according to Roman Catholic teaching, sex without procreation, and procreation without sex, are forbidden. These teachings were laid out in three Vatican documents: *Humanae Vitae* (1968), *Donum Vitae* (1987), and *Dignitas Personae* (2008).[4]

As already discussed, not all of the Catholic Church's objections to ART are valid, particularly those that stem from a natural law approach to ethics.[5] However, Protestant theology would certainly agree that the human embryo should be protected from the time of fertilization.

4. Effect on population

Some commentators question the wisdom of 'creating' new babies in an overpopulated world. When there are so many orphans around the world

---

3.   See chapter 6.
4.   The original documents are available online and easy to read. A critique of the natural law position is made in SB Rae and DJ Riley, *Outside the Womb*, Moody, Chicago, 2011, pp. 55-75.
5.   See chapter 6.

needing adoption, why go to such lengths to create more children? They suggest that adoption rates will fall if reproductive technology is used instead.[6]

However, others are concerned that ART will actually reduce birth rates, at least in the West, because it leads many women to delay childbearing, assuming (mistakenly) that ART can overcome fading fertility at any age.

5. Social prejudice

Liberal feminists argue that any woman should be able to use ART if she wants to, since it harms no-one else.[7] This is part of the pro-choice stance that wants a guarantee of 'reproductive rights' for all women. It is claimed that the right to choose if and when to have a child is as important for the infertile woman as it is for the woman with an unwanted pregnancy.[8]

Infertility can certainly be personally devastating, with an enormous impact on our sense of self. But there is conjecture over whether this is due to individual judgement or to a social construct. Susan Sherwin thinks that the emphasis on ART as a solution to infertility has weakened the case for other options. It is part of the trend in our society towards offering a technological fix for problems that are actually interpersonal and social.[9]

It is also worth asking what it is about an ART child that makes it 'a child of your own'. Brent Waters suggests that it can't be a genetic connection, if donated sperm and eggs are used. It isn't connected to actually carrying a child, if surrogates are used. Is it more about being in control and being able to produce offspring that meets your specifications? Waters defines a parent as "one asserting the will to obtain a child".[10] This is far from the biblical idea of children as gifts from God.

Other writers also have concerns that there is a stigma in society

---

6.   G Meilaender, 'A child of one's own: at what price?' in JF Kilner, PC Cunningham and WD Hager (eds), *The Reproduction Revolution*, Eerdmans, Grand Rapids, 2000, pp. 36-45.

7.   MA McClure, 'Infertility', in R Chadwick (ed.), *Encyclopedia of Applied Ethics*, vol. 2, Academic Press, San Diego, 1998, pp. 673-8.

8.   K Sharp and S Earle, 'Feminism, abortion and disability: irreconcilable differences?', *Disability and Society*, vol. 17, no. 2, 2002, pp. 137-45.

9.   S Sherwin, *No Longer Patient*, Temple University Press, Philadelphia, 1992, cited in McClure, op. cit., p. 677.

10.   B Waters, *Reproductive Technology*, Darton, Longman and Todd, London, 2001, p. 54.

against childless people, and contempt for infertile women. Renate Klein comments:

> As long as 'childless' is seen by society at large as 'deficient' and 'abnormal', reproductive medicine and science will profit—in fact live off—the steady stream of women who have been made to believe that they must put themselves through the treadmill of baby-making, the roller coaster of exciting hopes and shattered illusions.[11]

Karen Throsby explains her concern that ART is seen in our culture as a "seductive image of benign, rational, efficient science giving imperfect nature a helping hand".[12] Consider the advertisements of doctors in white coats, of gleaming laboratories, of smiling parents holding their 'miracle' baby in the background. She notes that these pictures of trustworthy professionals make us stop worrying about "meddling with nature", and make ART seem normal, mainstream and unproblematic. This leads to a process of "technological creep", where any concerns we might have about, say, IVF are made to seem unimportant by comparison with more radical and troubling technology—such as preimplantation genetic diagnosis (PGD), designer babies, stem cells and therapeutic cloning.

The normalization of IVF makes it seem as if we are obliged to use it, implying that those who do not have treatment are unnatural and abnormal. This normalization of IVF also makes it harder to have public conversations about the potential risks for women in relation to treatment. It also tends to minimize the significant social, financial and emotional costs of treatment, particularly when it is unsuccessful.[13]

A similar point has been made by Israeli feminists who are concerned at the development of widespread surrogacy programs:

> It is our belief that perceiving pregnancy and childbirth for another couple or individual solely as a financial business transaction is inappropriate and unthinkable. The fact that surrogacy is a complex relationship which might be fertile ground for harm and exploitation must be recognized, especially when private organizations with financial interests are allowed to become involved. We believe, that surrogacy in Israel should be prohibited.

---

11.   R Klein, *The Exploitation of a Desire*, Women's Studies Summer Institute, Geelong, 1989, p. 47.

12.   K Throsby, *When IVF Fails*, Palgrave MacMillan, Basingstoke, 2004, p. 2.

13.   ibid, p. 189.

In the least, surrogacy must not be allowed to becomes [sic] an accepted, routine procedure, and should provide a solution only in rare, very extreme cases...

Surrogacy is an experimental procedure with great potential for harm, especially if it will become prevalent and accepted. The distance between heroically presenting a unique human gift to a childless couple and time spent on a 'fertility farm', which uses human machines, is not large, and the ability to preserve this distance will diminish as surrogacy becomes more widespread and routine.[14]

Perhaps there is a new category of childlessness now, which is more acceptable—so long as you are willing to confess that you tried, and failed, ART.

6. Risks of treatment

Some risks of ART are well known. For example, it is established that multiple pregnancy is more common in ART pregnancies, pregnancy loss is more common, and children born following ART are at increased risk of birth defects compared with spontaneous conceptions.[15]

However, there are other risks that are suspected but currently unclear. For example, the long-term side effects of ovulatory stimulation drugs are unknown.[16] Risks of a different sort exist when experimental treatments are introduced to clinical practice too quickly. ICSI (intracytoplasmic sperm injection) was introduced without proper validation and now, years later, we are finding that there is an increased genetic abnormality rate in offspring.[17]

7. Embryo destruction

Some commentators are concerned about the morality of ART as an industry. They suggest that there is a problem of complicity (cooperation

---

14.   N Lipkin and E Samana, *Surrogacy in Israel*, Isha L'Isha, Haifa, 2010, pp. 3, 16 (viewed 12 March 2012): www.isha.org.il/upload/file/surrogacy_Eng00%5B1%5D.pdf

15.   M Hansen, C Bower, E Milne, N de Klerk and JJ Kurinczuk, 'Assisted reproductive technologies and the risk of birth defects—a systematic review', *Human Reproduction*, vol. 20, no. 2, February 2005, pp. 328-38.

16.   H Pearson, 'Health effects of egg donation may take decades to emerge', *Nature*, vol. 442, no. 7103, 10 August 2006, pp. 607-8.

17.   See 'Intracytoplasmic sperm injection (ICSI)' under 'Treatment options' in chapter 12.

with evil) if we make use of ART, even if we do so without the destruction of our own embryos. This is because the destruction of embryos will always be implicit in the process itself, and by engaging with ART, we are implying that we accept the underlying assumption—namely, that destruction of human embryos is acceptable in the pursuit of a child of one's own.

Let's go back to the beginning: IVF was developed in England by scientist Robert Edwards, who started work in the 1950s. Gynaecologist Dr Patrick Steptoe later assisted him.[18] Edwards performed IVF on 1200 women before any studies were reported on primates.[19] (It is traditional in medicine to do the animal studies first to reduce the use of human subjects.) Edwards wrote:

> …[eggs] and embryos were grown during early… investigations without the intention of replacing them in the uterus…

> This preliminary period is by no means completed, even in hospitals and clinics where many pregnancies have already been established by IVF. Improved methods are needed to assess the normality of growth of the embryos, and to sustain or monitor their development without impairing the development of those which are to be replaced in the mother.[20]

Edwards is saying here that non-clinical embryo research is necessarily part of the process. Those working in the field have always wanted to improve outcomes for their infertile patients, so they have continued to search for improvements in treatment, thus requiring more embryos on which to test new techniques and develop new procedures. The motive is good; the question is whether the end can justify the means, when the means is experimentation upon and destruction of large numbers of human embryos.

Bioethicist Wesley Smith has reflected insightfully on the development of the ART industry in the United States:

> Supporters of unregulated IVF promised us that the technology would be limited to married couples who could not otherwise have

---

18. For the history of the development of ART, see the beginning of chapter 15.
19. M Cook, 'Nobel committee brushes ethics aside', *Australasian Science*, December 2010.
20. RG Edwards and JM Purdy (eds), *Human Conception In Vitro*, Academic Press, London, 1982, p. 372.

children. Those who raised concerns about the consequences and potential societal costs of removing reproduction from intimacy and placing it literally into the hands of laboratory technicians were castigated as alarmists—people whose fears were disproportionate to the very limited changes in reproduction that IVF would bring. The syndicated columnist Ellen Goodman put it this way in a column called 'Making Babies', published in the *Austin American Statesman* on January 17, 1980:

> A fear of many protesting the opening of this [the first IVF] clinic is that doctors there will fertilize myriad eggs and discard the 'extras' and the abnormal, as if they were no more meaningful than a dish of caviar. But this fear seems largely unwarranted... We have put researchers on notice that we no longer accept every breakthrough and every advance as an unqualified good. Now we have to watch the development of this technology—willing to see it grow in the right direction and ready to say no.

It has been 31 years since Goodman wrote those words and we haven't said no yet.[21]

Earlier in his article, Smith says:

> The baby manufacturing industry also has an aggressive political lobbying arm, ever on the ready to castigate those who question the wisdom of the current *laissez faire* system as being cruelly insensitive to the pain of barren families. No wonder cowardly American politicians have yet to muster the true grit to enact even modest regulations.

The argument is this: the practice of ART necessarily requires an ongoing supply of embryos to facilitate further technological development, such as improvement of culture media, training of ART staff, and quality control in laboratories. If we really believe we should protect human life from the time of fertilization, should we cooperate with an industry that normalizes embryo destruction?

Many Christian writers approve ART so long as embryo wastage in minimized.

---

21. WJ Smith, 'IVF: Enough will never be enough', *Center for Bioethics and Culture Network*, 16 March 2011 (viewed 12 March 2012): www.cbc-network.org/2011/03/ivf-enough-will-never-be-enough

8. ART errors

The ever-growing incidence of treatment errors within ART clinics is considered by some to be a reason for avoiding it entirely. As mentioned in the previous chapter, we might view this as a reason for more careful selection of a provider, as is the case for any medical intervention, rather than a reason to avoid ART entirely. Everyone makes mistakes, and even ART has its share of negligent providers. However, most errors do not have a happy ending, and the embryo may not be the only one to suffer. Consider just a few examples:

- A Northern Ireland family sued their IVF service for using the wrong sperm, which resulted in their children being born with darker skin than expected. They had requested a white sperm donor, and the technician who retrieved the sperm had misunderstood the label 'Caucasian (Cape Coloured)'. 'Cape Coloured' refers to South Africans of mixed race.[22]
- A Singaporean Chinese woman and a Caucasian man discovered that their IVF baby had a different blood type from either of them. On genetic testing, they found that the baby shared the mother's DNA, but not the father's.[23]
- An Australian couple sued their IVF clinic for their son's medical expenses (for life) and compensation for their emotional pain, after finding that their child carried an inherited gene for cancer. They had used preimplantation genetic diagnosis to screen out a cancer gene carried by the mother, and insisted that they would have adopted a child if they had not been promised a disease-free child by the clinic.[24]
- Then there is the couple that returned to their IVF clinic to have further treatment only to find their embryos gone, probably because they had been implanted in someone else.[25]

---

22.   B Luscombe, 'Lawsuit over children born the wrong color after IVF', *TIME: Healthland*, 14 October 2010 (viewed 12 March 2012): www.healthland.time.com/2010/10/14/lawsuit-over-children-born-the-wrong-color-after-ivf

23.   M Cook, 'IVF blunder in Singapore', *BioEdge*, 6 November 2010 (viewed 12 March 2012): www.bioedge.org/index.php/bioethics/bioethics_article/9281

24.   K Benson, 'Embryos at risk of disease can pass clinic tests, parents warned', *Sydney Morning Herald*, 22 January 2008.

25.   SD James, 'California couple sue fertility doctor over "lost" embryos', *ABC News*, 23 August 2011 (viewed 12 March 2012): www.abcnews.go.com/Health/california-couple-sue-fertility-doctor-lost-embryos/story?id=14355815

Often when a couple finds out they have been implanted with the 'wrong' embryo, they have an abortion. Not all do, however. A Christian couple in the United States who were accidentally impregnated with the wrong embryo decided against abortion, and generously gave the child to its biological parents with no strings attached.[26]

Whether you should make use of ART is a decision you and your spouse will need to make together, but do not feel there is an obligation at any level to do so if you have any doubts. This is not 'just a medical decision'. This is a moral decision, and God claims all of our lives for his service (Deut 10:12).

It's not just the embryos destroyed in IVF research or IVF accidents that concern Christians—what about all the ones still left in the freezer? Dealing with the leftovers is an ongoing dilemma discussed in the next chapter.

---

26.   They have written a book about it: C Savage and S Savage, *Inconceivable*, HarperCollins, New York, 2010.

What to do with leftover embryos

MOST COUPLES, WHEN THEY are undergoing ART treatment, do not think about making decisions about leftover embryos. Once treatment is complete, the realization that there are frozen embryos excess to their needs often comes as an unwelcome surprise and an unforeseen ethical dilemma. It is the most common problem I find raised in counselling sessions with Christians.

A 2009 study from the University of California in San Francisco found that 72% of couples were undecided about the fate of their stored embryos. In 2008, it was reported to the House of Lords that 1.2 million human embryos had been destroyed in the United Kingdom over the previous 14 years, 82,955 of which were used in destructive research.[1]

Sally, pregnant with twins, said, *I never thought there would be leftovers. I was only thinking about having a baby.* Jodie said, *I think someone may have mentioned it at the beginning, but my thoughts were completely consumed by the children I wanted. There wasn't room to think of anything else.*

Anne Drapkin Lyerly, a professor of obstetrics and gynaecology at Duke University Medical Center, agrees: 'When you're pouring your money, your heart, and your soul into creating an embryo and creating a life, the last thing you want to think about is how you're going to dispose of it'.[2]

---

1.   '1 million embryos destroyed in UK in 14 years', *BioEdge*, 10 January 2008 (viewed 12 March 2012): www.bioedge.org/index.php/bioethics/bioethics_article/1_million_embryos_destroyed_in_uk_in_14_years/
2.   L Beil, 'What happens to extra embryos after IVF?', *CNN.com/health*, 1 September 2009 (viewed 12 March 2012): www.edition.cnn.com/2009/HEALTH/09/01/extra.ivf.embryos

A couple may arrive at this point for several reasons. Their treatment may have been successful and they have as many children as they want. They may be finding treatment so stressful that they feel they cannot undergo any more cycles. Don said, *We were planning to use all our embryos, but after having a scary emergency delivery and a baby in intensive care, we decided we'd been through enough.* Sometimes the couple would like more children but cannot transfer the embryos for medical reasons. Sadly, couples may divorce during treatment. Whatever the reason, the embryos are there in the freezer, and their destiny is in the hands of their parents. Several studies testify to the difficulty of this decision.[3]

Research aimed at understanding how clinic patients manage this situation is in its early stages, and there is still much ambiguity in the results. But by looking at what has been done, we can start to get an idea of the extent of this problem and the challenges it holds for those involved.

One problem identified is that parents often have difficulty talking about their frozen embryos because they have no language to describe them. They have no words available to express their experience of having their potential child outside of the body and in cryostorage (frozen).[4] (I don't think the parents are the only ones who struggle with this.)

Research suggests that many patients not only know very little about the technical side of freezing embryos but also do not demonstrate a need to know, their confidence in the medical team being enough. However, it has also been noted that patients tended to make comparisons between frozen embryos and food storage, possibly because we use the same words—'fresh' and 'frozen'—for both. The idea that an embryo can reach its expiry date (as can frozen food) may reinforce the idea for some patients that the embryos are just 'ingredients' for their fertility treatment. This can be reflected at times in less concern for the embryo's destiny (see below). Some patients did not realize they had any say in whether embryos would be frozen, but secretly felt that those embryos would be of poorer quality. At times they would create new embryos

---

3.   See, for example, S de Lacey, 'Decisions for the fate of frozen embryos: Fresh insights into patients' thinking and their rationales for donating or discarding embryos', *Human Reproduction*, vol. 22, no. 6, June 2007, pp. 1751-8; SC Klock, S Sheinin and RR Kazer, 'The disposition of unused frozen embryos', *New England Journal of Medicine*, vol. 345, no. 1, 5 July 2001, pp. 69-70.

4.   S de Lacey, 'Parent identity and "virtual" children: why patients discard rather than donate unused embryos', *Human Reproduction*, vol. 20, no. 6, June 2005, pp. 1661-9.

even though frozen ones remained. This indicates a need for further discussion at the outset of treatment about frozen embryos and their fate.[5] In fact, storage time has no effect on the success of a pregnancy.[6]

Most parents report that something happens to make them begin to start thinking about the leftover embryos—for example, the time limit for storage approaches, or the bill arrives for the clinic storage fees. Anne and David didn't know what to think, so they paid the bill. The next year when the bill arrived, they paid it again. Adele asked, *What do people do? Keep on paying, like me?* A 2008 study in the United States of 1000 patients found that 20% of couples who wanted no more children said they planned to keep their embryos frozen indefinitely.[7]

According to a 2010 journal article, while there is no single statistic on the number of 'surplus' embryos in storage worldwide, it is estimated that there are roughly 400,000 frozen embryos in the United States, approximately 12% of which will not be used by the couples that are storing them.[8] Australia has up to 120,000 frozen embryos, up from 70,000 a decade ago[9]—although according to the clinics, some of these embryos may still be transferred. The United Kingdom has about 52,000. The number of such embryos is thought to be increasing due to the significant improvement in the technology of cryopreservation (freezing), and the increasing regulation that restricts the number of embryos that may be transferred during a single treatment cycle. At present there is no mechanism in place to minimize the number of embryos made for each couple. In Australia, the ethical guidelines for use in ART recommend that "Clinics must limit the number of embryos created to those that are likely to be needed to achieve a pregnancy",[10] but as long as there is

5.   V Provoost, G Pennings, P De Sutter, J Gerris, A Van de Velde and M Dhont, 'Patients' conceptualization of cryopreserved embryos used in their fertility treatment', *Human Reproduction*, vol. 25, no. 3, March 2010, pp. 705-13.

6.   R Riggs, J Mayer, D Dowling-Lacey, T Chi, E Jones and S Oehninger, 'Does storage time influence postthaw survival and pregnancy outcome? An analysis of 11,768 cryopreserved human embryos', *Fertility and Sterility*, vol. 93, no. 1, 1 January 2010, pp. 109-15.

7.   Beil, loc. cit. Note that this is not possible in all jurisdictions.

8.   MS Paul, R Berger, E Blyth and L Frith, 'Relinquishing frozen embryos for conception by infertile couples', *Families, Systems and Health*, vol. 28, no. 3, September 2010, pp. 258-73.

9.   R Browne, 'Giving birth to a costly quandary', *Sun-Herald,* 6 March 2011, p. 22.

10.   National Health and Medical Research Council (NHMRC), *Ethical Guidelines on the Use of Assisted Reproductive Technology in Clinical Practice and Research*, NHMRC, Canberra, 2007, p. 51 (viewed 12 March 2012): www.nhmrc.gov.au/_files_nhmrc/publications/attachments/e78.pdf

no correlation between the number of embryos created and the number of live births, it will be impossible to enforce such a recommendation. The maximum number will continue to be encouraged by the clinics (which won't hurt success statistics, either). One hopes that there is no correlation between the increase in the number of embryos made and the number of embryos used for research.

Some countries, such as Italy and Germany, do not allow cryopreservation of embryos. Others, such as Australia, have statutory limits on the duration of storage; these vary from state to state. The United States also has state-based guidelines, but embryos may be stored indefinitely. In the United Kingdom, embryos may be stored for up to 10 years, with possible extension to 55 years. In Belgium, patients have to decide what they are going to do with possible leftover embryos (embryo disposition decision—EDD) before their first treatment.[11] The cost of storage varies between clinics, averaging between $300-$600 per year.

Professor Jenni Millbank, an Australian health law specialist, is aware of how difficult it is: "It's a very, very painful decision and it's one that many couples never consider they'll have to make when they start down the IVF path".[12] She notes that at the time of this decision, parents are no longer involved directly with the clinic for support and are not usually offered counselling. She agrees that it might help for clinics to forewarn patients at the outset of treatment about the possibility of surplus embryos. Certainly, I would suggest it is far better to think ahead and try to avoid this situation altogether by limiting the number of embryos created.

Some parents become conscious of the potential problem during their treatment. It can get complicated. Sandy found the prospect of having excess embryos one of the most challenging aspects of ART:

> [Becoming concerned about the fate of excess embryos] was difficult, as I became consumed with the ethical dilemma of thinking what to do if something happened to me. What would happen to our children that had been created? And also what if my husband died—would I still have the embryos implanted? We thought through issues like me being pregnant

---

11. V Provoost, G Pennings, P De Sutter, J Gerris, A Van de Velde, E De Lissnyder and M Dhont, 'Infertility patients' beliefs about their embryos and their disposition preferences', *Human Reproduction*, vol. 24, no. 4, April 2009, pp. 896-905.

12. Browne, loc. cit.

with no husband; or having my sister carrying our children if I were to die; or adopting our embryos to another Christian couple if we both died. These were issues we hadn't thought through before we began treatment, and if we had, we might not have frozen the embryos. We felt such an urgency to have our other embryos implanted after our first son was born. I remember feeling such relief after our last embryo was implanted that God in his goodness had allowed our embryos to have a chance in the womb.

Basically, there are 6 alternative disposition options for excess frozen embryos following completion of ART treatment:

1. Avoid the decision (thus discarding the embryo by allowing it to 'expire')
2. Continue storage
3. Thaw and discard
4. Use the embryos
5. Relinquish the embryos to another couple for reproduction
6. Donate to research

Not all of these options are always available, but we will look at each one in turn.

1. Avoid the decision

A substantial number of parents find it all just too hard, and walk away from their embryos. When the storage term is up for the embryos, if the parents are lost to follow-up and there is no-one to pay the storage costs, the embryos are usually removed from the freezer and allowed to thaw out and perish. Sometimes the parents will pay the storage costs but delay making a decision so that the embryos 'expire' legally and can no longer be used for further treatment, research or donation to others. But no decision is itself a decision when such arrangements are in place.

This phenomenon has not been closely studied, but may be associated with the idea some patients have that cryopreserved embryos are a bit like frozen food, which deteriorates over time. It may also be based on the idea of letting "'nature' take its course", and thus seeking to avoid responsibility for the decision.[13] Similarly, a non-decision accompanied

---

13. Provoost et al., 'Patients' conceptualization of cryopreserved embryos used in their fertility treatment', loc. cit.

by prayer to allow God's sovereign will to prevail is essentially a decision to abandon the embryo.

Whatever the motivation behind this decision, it is not consistent with the biblical responsibilities parents have for their offspring. The parent's obligation goes beyond procreation, and continues during the child's upbringing.[14]

2. Continue storage

This is basically the same decision as (1), except that the storage fees are paid and the decision is put off indefinitely. This is obviously not possible in those jurisdictions where storage time limits are enforced. This is one of the reasons time limits were introduced—because of the number of orphan embryos that were accumulating in clinic freezers.

In 2009, the United Kingdom's Human Fertilisation and Embryology Authority debated whether frozen embryos could be stored to serve as spare parts; a body repair kit, as it were. The idea was that you would store the embryo(s) until a problem occurred, then thaw it and develop it into stem cells. This was said to be "an attractive commercial possibility".[15] Pro-life campaigner Josephine Quintavalle commented, "It is sadly almost inevitable that bespoke embryonic stem cells created from frozen surplus will become the latest must-have healthcare accessory".[16] This would not be an ethical option for Christians.

One problem with postponing the decision is that if you wait too long, you just shift the decision to someone else—whether to a clinic staff member after you have moved without telling them, or to a family member after you die. A famous case in Australia involved the question of whether frozen embryos could inherit from the estate after their wealthy parents were both killed in a plane crash.[17] (Apparently they can't.) Some decisions are enforced when marriages end. There have been several cases where divorced couples have fought legal battles over the custody of frozen embryos, where one partner wants them transferred and the other doesn't. It would be wonderful if courts tended to err on the side of

---

14. See chapter 4.
15. 'UK studying whether embryos can be stored for spare parts', *BioEdge*, 3 May 2009 (viewed 12 March 2012): www.bioedge.org/index.php/bioethics/bioethics_article/8571
16. ibid.
17. C Grobstein, M Flower and J Mendeloff, 'Frozen embryos: policy issues', *New England Journal of Medicine*, vol. 312, no. 24, 13 June 1985, pp. 1584-8.

life, but more often they seem to be reluctant.

Once again, a non-decision represents an abandonment of the embryo that is not consistent with biblical directives for parents to provide ongoing care for their children (Eph 6:4; 1 Tim 5:8).

3. Thaw and discard

This option involves taking the embryos out of the freezer and leaving them on the laboratory bench. Without a supportive culture medium (nutrient fluid), the embryos expire as they thaw.

It has been reported that "about 90% of IVF couples choose to discard surplus frozen embryos rather than give them to infertile couples, or donate them for scientific research".[18] IVF Clinic director Gab Kovacs describes this as "a shameful waste", saying that clinics need to provide patients with better information about their options: "It breaks my heart to discard embryos. They're such a valuable asset. People go to so much trouble and expense to produce them."[19]

While some would see this option as an abandoning of the embryo, often it is done as a sign of respect. Some Christians distinguish between 'letting die' and 'killing by destructive research', and would consider the first option to retain the embryo's dignity and be morally permissible. I must say that I have struggled with this area. The literature supports my own findings that some parents who think of their embryos as children would rather have these 'children' discarded than give them a chance at life (through transfer to a uterus).[20] I find this irrational. But I have never been in this position myself.

My own view is that if these embryos were created with the goal of transferring them to a uterus, they should at least be given that chance at life.

Some religious denominations rule out the option of embryo donation, based on the belief that the generative capacity of a woman belongs to the marital union, and so may not be given outside the marriage. In this

---

18.   Browne, loc. cit.; GT Kovacs, SA Breheny and MJ Dear, 'Embryo donation at an Australian university in-vitro fertilisation clinic: issues and outcomes', *Medical Journal of Australia*, vol. 178, no. 3, 3 February 2003, pp. 127-9.

19.   Browne, loc. cit.

20.   C Laurelle and Y Englert, 'Psychological study of in vitro fertilization-embryo transfer participants' attitudes toward the destiny of their supernumerary embryos', *Fertility and Sterility*, vol. 63, no. 5, May 1995, pp. 1047-50.

argument, embryo donation is seen as equivalent to adultery. Once an embryo is created from the parents' own gametes, it is argued that it is sinful to place it in the reproductive tract of a third party. Similarly, it would be sinful to receive a donated embryo, as the wife becomes 'with child' from outside the marital relationship. On this view, withdrawing the embryo from storage and placing it in a more natural environment to allow it to complete its short life is the most respectful way to treat it.[21] Some parents perform a ceremony to mark the demise of the embryo with reverence.

Some doctors provide the service of 'compassionate transfer'. This procedure involves transferring the embryo(s) into the woman's uterus at a time in her cycle when embryo implantation is unlikely/impossible. I have heard people describe this as a way to ease their consciences about letting the embryos die, because they can pretend they tried to give them a chance at life. While the action of uterine transfer is ethical, the intention to do so at a time when pregnancy is nigh impossible is definitely not. (Remember, you need good *intentions* as well as good actions.) Therefore this would not be a morally acceptable option for Christians.

4. Use the embryos

Some parents find they just can't make the decision to let their embryos go. *I don't think anybody knows what their opinion is until they're in this situation,* said Betty. She had one embryo left after giving birth to her sons, 8 and 6 years old at the time. After two more years of deliberating about their options, she and her husband finally decided to have a third child. *One excess embryo changed my whole life,* she says. She is thankful for her daughter, but also thankful that she had only one excess embryo.

Katie and her husband, on the other hand, had 5 embryos plus twins aged 6 years. *Every time a bill came in the mail I thought about it, but I couldn't let them go.* Now, at 48 years of age, she has decided to have more children, through a surrogate if necessary, until all the embryos have been transferred. She is very emotional, but also very determined.

Judy and her husband had 6 frozen embryos, plus 3 children, two of whom were born through IVF. *I can't have nine children,* Judy said. But neither could she bring herself to consider any other option. Finally she

---

21. N Tonti-Filippini, 'Cryopreservation, embryo rescue and heterologous embryo transfer', unpublished.

and her husband decided to have one embryo transferred. Now they have 5 frozen embryos, but they only have to decide about one at a time.

The option of using excess embryos yourselves may not be available to all couples, as sometimes a complication of pregnancy or another illness may make a further pregnancy highly dangerous or impossible. This is one of the few cases where I think it would be ethical to consider a surrogate if you wanted more children, or else consider another of the ethical options listed here.[22]

Embryos created by assisted reproductive technology are intended for uterine transfer. Giving them a chance at life in this way is entirely consistent with biblical value for all human life made in the image of God (Gen 1:27, 9:6).

5. Relinquish the embryos to another couple for reproduction

Once they have their own families, it is not uncommon for parents to consider helping other infertile couples. Having known the pain of infertility themselves, they immediately think of others in the same position. A 2009 study examined the way parents make a decision about whether to donate their embryos to another couple. Initially, most would consider donating to another couple, and it was found that the way the parents thought about their embryos was important in whether they decided to go ahead. Parents who thought about their embryos in terms of a "genetic link" or a "symbol of the [marriage] relationship" were less likely to go ahead with relinquishing the embryo to another couple than those who thought of the embryo more as something useful.[23] The "genetic link" and "symbolic meaning" views both involved seeing the embryo as a union of the two parents, the 'one flesh' idea, "something of the two of us".[24] This was associated with positive feelings towards the embryos, but a reluctance to relinquish them to other couples because it would be too difficult to know that their child was 'out there' and be unable to protect them. *I'd always be thinking whether that child in the street looked like my other children*, said Jane. Sandra said: *Now suppose that you did that and when that child is 18 years old, in it walks and it*

---

22. For further discussion on surrogacy, see chapter 12.
23. Provoost et al., 'Infertility patients' beliefs about their embryos and their disposition preferences', loc. cit.
24. ibid.

has had a very bad childhood. Then that would be painful. This in part helps me understand the conundrum of parents who prefer that their 'children' perish rather than be transferred to another family.

By contrast, those who saw the embryos as 'something that is useful' saw them more as objects that were valuable because of the effort involved in their creation—and thus their value to the potential beneficiaries of their donation. This was associated with a conscious effort to create emotional distance between themselves and the embryos (to protect themselves), and the parents' reluctance to destroy the embryos because it would be a waste of their value. However, the main motive in donating to others was to help them.

While interest in relinquishing to another couple has been reported for 5%-39% of participants in research, it appears to be more often contemplated than actually performed.[25] Indeed, the transferring of frozen embryos to another couple raises so many complex psycho-social dilemmas that some countries have prohibited the practice. At the time of writing, relinquishing embryos for transfer by others was not allowed under law in Austria, Denmark, Germany, Israel, Italy, Latvia, Norway, Slovenia, Sweden, Switzerland, Taiwan, Tunisia and Turkey.[26] Check with your clinic—sometimes it is possible in your country but not at your clinic, in which case you may need to have your embryos moved to a clinic that does offer the service. Countries that permit relinquishment of embryos to others for reproduction have procedures in place to regulate the practice. This may include making decisions about who will receive the embryos, intended contact between the genetic parents and the recipients, and arrangements for the child to learn the identity of their genetic parents. Sometimes clinics impose their own rules, such as how many embryos you need to have before they will arrange the relinquishment. This is an area that needs further development. Current legislation is inadequate. Most problematic for legislators is whether you treat the transaction as an adoption (with full screening of the prospective parents) or as a donation (which tends towards anonymity). Lessons have been learnt about the damage done in the past by anonymous adoption of babies, and laws are now in place encouraging contact between birth

---

25. Paul et al., op. cit., p. 259; A Lyerly, E Brelsford, B Bankowski, R Faden and E Wallach, 'A qualitative study of individuals' attitudes regarding their cryopreserved embryos', *International Congress Series*, vol. 1271, September 2004, pp. 353-6.
26. Paul et al., loc. cit.

mothers and children. These issues remain unaddressed with embryos in many jurisdictions.[27]

In 1997, the Nightlight Christian Adoptions organization in the United States began the Snowflakes Frozen Embryo Adoption Program, which helps frozen embryos realize their ultimate purpose—life—while helping infertile couples. They named the program 'Snowflakes' because every embryo, like every snowflake, is frozen and unique.[28] The first snowflake baby was born in 1998, and the term 'Snowflake babies' has continued to be used to describe babies born in this manner. Last I heard, over 200 babies had been born through this program, which uses the language of adoption even though the actual legal process is different.[29] An Australian study reported many more couples willing to adopt than there were embryos available.[30]

It is interesting to note the response of one United States specialist in reproductive law to the sudden popularity of embryo adoption: "The problem with this label [adoption] is it elevates embryos to the status of a child in many people's minds, and then you end up on a slippery slope. If you can adopt embryos, how can you do stem-cell research on them or discard them?"[31] How indeed?

One study reported on a small sample of mainly Christian parents who had to make EDDs[32] and who decided to relinquish their surplus embryos to infertile couples (this sample reflecting the population of those most likely to do so). The study found that the reasons for their decision included a sense of responsibility toward their unused embryos, and the thought that it would be wrong not to donate them:

- *NOT donating the unused embryos to another couple would have weighed on my conscience…*

---

27. For more information about embryo adoption, visit the Embryo Adoption Awareness Centre website: www.embryoadoption.org

28. Apparently every snowflake is a different shape. For more information on the Snowflakes embryo adoption program, visit the Nightlight Christian Adoptions website: www.nightlight.org/snowflake-embryo-adoption

29. This in itself is an interesting debate—whether those responsible for human embryos should be seen as guardians of children, or owners—in which case we are treating the children as property. Does this concur with the general community view that the human embryo is more than just tissue?

30. Kovacs et al., loc. cit.

31. S Smalley, 'A New Baby Debate', *Newsweek*, vol. 141, no. 12, 24 March 2003, p. 53.

32. Embryo disposition decisions.

- *...we wanted them to go to something or someone who would do something life sustaining with them...*
- *...we had created these lives and were responsible for finding them good homes if we could not be that home.*[33]

These thoughts were often based on Christian beliefs. All the same, not everyone found it an easy choice:

- *...it was the lesser of all evils* [compared to destroying the embryos].[34]
- *The initial decision was difficult because I felt like I was giving away my children.*[35]

In the end, the child's best interests were what swayed all people in the study.

Once the decision had been made, all participants found the process of relinquishment easier: *The biggest feeling was relief. We had given them [the embryos] a shot at life and the rest was in the hands of God.*[36] There was a varying amount of contact desired with the adopting families. Some expressed satisfaction in having ongoing contact as 'aunts' and 'uncles', while others decided to keep their distance. Feelings often changed once a child was born.

The shipment date for the embryos going to another clinic was significant for many, bringing with it a sense of loss:

- *There was just a sense of finality about knowing that they were leaving "home" and starting their journey to become someone else's children.*
- *I knew one hundred percent that we didn't want any more children but it was bittersweet.*[37]

It can be difficult to know that you no longer have a say in what happens to your embryos. You may feel responsible if the transfer fails, and it could be distressing if there is prenatal screening and the adopting couple decides to abort. You can avoid some problems by careful choice of who will adopt the embryos (e.g. choice of a Christian family), but there are no guarantees. Wes and Gina chose a family they knew and were in regular contact with, but in the end it left them feeling they could have raised

---

33. Paul et al., op. cit., p. 263.
34. ibid.
35. ibid., p. 264.
36. ibid., p. 266.
37. ibid.

the little boy better. *I think we now regret our choice. We realize what we missed*, said Wes. One mother found it challenging when she heard the adopted baby was a girl, having had only boys herself. Many continued to feel that 'their' child was living with another family, but for some this was a positive thing—to know, having been infertile themselves, that they had been able to give the joys (and trials!) of parenting to another couple. Many couples saw relinquishment as a lifelong process. It would be good to see the development of appropriate support services for those involved.

While I am aware there are some Christians who oppose embryo adoption because they believe that procreation should always be the result of normal sexual relations using the gametes of husband and wife, I consider that relinquishment of excess frozen embryos to another couple for the purpose of reproduction is an ethical option for Christians. It rescues embryos that would otherwise be destined for destruction. It gives the embryos a chance at life, which was why they were created. And it is consistent with being as responsible a parent as possible in the situation where one cannot nurture the embryos personally.

'Snowflake babies' are the most powerful visual illustration we have of the continuity of life from embryo to live birth.

6. Donate to research

While embryo research has always been associated with the development of IVF, legislation around the world allowing destructive research on human embryos was closely connected to interest in embryonic stem cells (ES cells). This was certainly the case in Australia, where destructive research has been legal since 2002. Soon after taking office in 2008, President Obama lifted a ban on federal funding of ES cell research that had been in place in the United States for 8 years.

I liked the idea of donating to scientific research because without research we would never have been able to have our babies through IVF, said Rhoda. *We thought about donating to another couple*, said Joe, *but I couldn't live with the idea of my child growing up without me.* He and his wife decided to donate to science *because without science we wouldn't be parents.* Mary decided to donate to science to give life to other people: *I know it's not life for our embryos, but we're still giving life.*

One study found that the decision of whether or not to donate to science depended more on the parents' perception of science and scientists, rather than their perception of the embryo.[38] They found that feelings of not having control over what would happen to their embryos, and vivid fears that scientists would allow their embryos to develop into children, were the main arguments against donation to research. One participant thought that "letting an embryo grow" was the only thing you could do with an embryo, obviously ignorant of the destructive nature of most research.[39] This also reflected a poor understanding of the 14-day rule for keeping embryos alive, as well as ignorance of research methods in general and embryonic stem-cell research in particular. A few participants thought research was inappropriate for an embryo: *It is really like 'do some tests on it' and then into the rubbish bin with it. That's science all right.*[40] But most doubts were directed at the science itself: *It may be a strange thought but they might very well transfer it into an animal, you know… Of course, this is a stupid example, but you never know, right?*[41]

In terms of medical ethics, there is general consensus that parents must give informed consent before embryos can be donated for destructive research—that is, they must be given adequate information that is comprehended by a mentally competent person in a voluntary manner. However, there is no agreement on what 'adequate information' entails. It will vary with the parents concerned.

Donation of excess embryos for use in destructive research will be an unethical choice for Christians. This is because all human beings are made in the image of God and should be treated with respect (Gen 1:27, 9:6). It is wrong to kill innocent people (Exod 20:13). In view of the confusion surrounding stem-cell research, we will look at it more closely in the next chapter to discover the unique ethical challenges it involves.

Conclusion

One thing the research shows is that when there are leftover frozen embryos, parents need to be told about all their options, and these options need to be fully explored before a decision is made. In the end we

---

38. V Provoost, G Pennings, P De Sutter, J Gerris, A Van de Velde and M Dhont, 'Reflections by patients who undergo IVF on the use of their supernumerary embryos for science', *Reproductive BioMedicine Online*, vol. 20, no. 7, 2010, pp. 880-91.

39. ibid., p. 888.

40. ibid., p. 885.

41. ibid., p. 886.

account for all our own decisions to God and, we need to be at peace with that. This includes taking responsibility for having allowed the embryos to be created in the first place. In some places, the decision as to whether your embryos really are 'surplus' to your needs is made separately from the decision regarding what you will do with them. I think this can be a helpful distinction.

Finally, knowing that there may be options for leftover embryos should not make you more cavalier regarding how many embryos you request at the beginning of treatment. It is because of the accumulation of frozen embryos in the first place that these options are necessary. Apart from using all your own embryos, I see even the 'ethical' options as a compromise in a fallen world.[42]

> Open your mouth for the mute,
> > for the rights of all who are destitute.
> Open your mouth, judge righteously,
> > defend the rights of the poor and needy. (Prov 31:8-9)

---

42. See chapter 5 for discussion of a 'retrieval' ethic. Michael Hill explains this 'retrieval ethic' in M Hill, *The How and Why of Love*, Matthias Media, Sydney, 2002, pp. 132-4. Also consider Mark 10:5, where Jesus explains that Moses permitted divorce because of hard hearts, even though God hates divorce (Mal 2:16).

Human embryo research, stem cells and cloning

ONE OF THE OPTIONS that may be available to parents who find themselves with excess frozen human embryos at the end of ART treatment is to donate the embryos for use in research.

This may sound like a reasonable thing to do. Many people think that although the destruction of human embryos in research is regrettable, at least some good may come as a result—for example, possible medical cures that the research may produce. The widely-reported potential of human embryonic stem cells (ES cells) has been influential in building community support for human embryo research. It is seen as a compassionate response to those disabled people who might benefit from such research. But is it consistent with a Christian world view? Must Christians 'heartlessly' oppose scientific progress—or is there an ethically acceptable way to support new medical technologies like stem cells?

The global discussions concerning human embryo research have been as passionate as they have been misinformed. In this chapter, I will explain how we arrived at the current situation regarding stem-cell and destructive-embryo research, present a summary of the arguments that are commonly used in community debates on this issue, and also reflect on the biblical view.

I do this in the hope that as social discussion of this matter becomes more sophisticated, ethical choices will be better informed. I recognize that there are a range of opinions on this topic, even amongst Christians, so I will give you my views and explain my reasoning.

We have discussed the humanity of the embryo in previous chapters. This chapter will not revisit those issues but instead will consider whether, given that the embryos are indeed human, it is right to use them in destructive scientific research.

Human embryos in the laboratory

Human embryos were first created and grown in the laboratory as part of the research that led to the development of assisted reproductive technologies (ART).

The British scientist Robert Edwards, who was controversially awarded the Nobel Prize for Medicine in 2010, began his basic research on the biology of fertilization in the 1950s. He proposed that fertilization outside the body could represent a possible treatment for infertility. Other scientists had shown that egg cells from rabbits could be fertilized in 'test tubes' (usually petri dishes) when sperm was added, giving rise to offspring. Edwards decided to investigate whether similar methods could be used to fertilize human egg cells.

It turned out that human eggs have an entirely different life cycle to those of rabbits. But Edward's team discovered how human eggs mature, how different hormones regulate their maturation, and at which point the eggs could be fertilized. In 1969, his efforts met with success when a human egg was fertilized in a test tube for the first time.

However, that first embryo did not develop. Edwards suspected he would have more success by working with eggs that had matured in the ovaries before they were removed for *in vitro* ('in glass') fertilization (IVF). He started looking for possible ways to obtain such eggs in a safe way.

Edwards contacted the gynaecologist Patrick Steptoe. Steptoe became the clinician who, together with Edwards, developed IVF from the experimental stage to applied medicine. Steptoe was a pioneer in laparoscopy, a technique that allows the doctor to see the inside of the abdomen and pelvis. Steptoe used the laparoscope to see the ovaries and remove eggs. Edwards put the eggs in culture medium (a fluid containing water, salts and nutrients in which cells can be grown) and added sperm. This time the embryos grew to the 8-cell stage. (Interestingly, this first zygote was formed by Edwards collecting his own semen one night in the lab and adding it to a ripe human egg in a dish. The next morning he observed the embryo's typical cell division).[1]

---

1.   GE Pence, *Classic Cases in Medical Ethics*, 2nd edn, McGraw-Hill, New York, 1995, p. 96.

Despite these scientifically 'promising' early studies, the Medical Research Council decided not to fund an extension of the project. However, a private donation allowed the work to continue.

It has been suggested that Edwards performed this research in an "ethical desert", carrying out IVF on 1200 women before any studies were reported on primates.[2] There may be some truth in this, although Edwards himself initiated some ethical debate in a paper published in 1971. It is interesting that he saw ethics as involving issues of safety for patients and children but not issues based on "vague religious or political reasons".[3] He claimed it was up to scientists to set ethical standards, not politicians or religious leaders.[4] While Professor Christer Höög, a Nobel official, felt that the ethical controversies in IVF had been resolved at the time of the award, Edwards himself always saw it as morally divisive. In 2003, he said that "It was a fantastic achievement, but it was about more than infertility. It was also about issues like stem cells and the ethics of human conception. I wanted to find out exactly who was in charge, whether it was God himself or whether it was scientists in the laboratory."[5] And he discovered that "it was us". Note that this whole argument depends on the assumption that a human embryo is *not* a child under his care.

Edwards and Steptoe established the Bourn Hall Clinic in Cambridge in 1974—the world's first centre for IVF therapy. In 1978, Lesley and John Brown came to the clinic after 9 years of failed attempts to have a child (Mrs Brown's fallopian tubes had been damaged by ectopic pregnancies some years earlier). IVF treatment was carried out, and when the fertilized egg had developed into an embryo with 8 cells, it was returned to Mrs Brown's uterus. These first 'experiments' at IVF and embryo transfer had been repeated 101 times on other patients before the first successful delivery was achieved. A healthy baby, Louise Joy Brown, was born through caesarean section after a full-term pregnancy on 25 July 1978—the world's first IVF baby. She weighed 5 pounds, 12 ounces, and

2. M Cook, 'Nobel committee brushes ethics aside', *Australasian Science*, December 2010.

3. RG Edwards, 'The bumpy road to human *in vitro* fertilization', *Nature Medicine*, vol. 7, no. 10, October 2001, pp. 1091-4.

4. RG Edwards and J Sharpe, 'Social values and research in human embryology', *Nature*, vol. 231, no. 5298, 14 May 1971, pp. 87-91.

5. Cook, loc. cit.

was completely normal.[6]

Gynaecologists and cell biologists from all around the world trained at Bourn Hall, where the methods of IVF were continuously refined, inevitably causing the destruction of more unwanted human embryos. IVF is now an international practice, and has led to the birth of 5 million babies since then.[7]

It is worth observing that destructive human embryo research (of the kind required for IVF therapy to be successfully developed) marked the first time pure science researchers had come up against the ethical restrictions on human experimentation that had been in place since the end of World War II. It was at the Nuremberg Trials following the end of World War II that the medical atrocities of the Nazis came to light, and statutes were created to protect human subjects of medical research so that such abuse would never happen again.[8]

The Nuremberg Code (1947) was one significant articulation of research ethics principles for human experimentation, and many similar declarations have followed. These principles include the need to ensure that human experiments will only ever be performed on subjects who have given voluntary consent, and that subjects should never be exposed to research that is expected to cause death or disabling injury. A version of *The Nuremberg Code* developed by the World Medical Association, the *Declaration of Helsinki* (1964), is widely regarded as the cornerstone document of human research ethics, and has influenced national human research guidelines in many countries. It must be followed by doctors who wish to publish medical research in peer-reviewed journals.

Medical researchers have grown up with these guidelines and have until recently seen them as a challenge to lateral thinking rather than

6.   RG Edwards and PC Steptoe, *A Matter of Life*, Hutchinson, London, 1980.
7.   European Society of Human Reproduction and Embryology (ESHRE), *The World's Number of IVF and ICSI Babies Has Now Reached a Calculated Total of 5 Million*, press release, ESHRE, Beigem, 2 July 2012 (viewed 20 July 2012): www.eshre.eu/ESHRE/English/Press-Room/Press-Releases/Press-releases-2012/ESHRE-2012/5-million-babies/page.aspx/1606
8.   For discussion of some of the appalling experiments undertaken by Dr Josef Mengele, see N Brozan, 'Out of death, a zest for life', *New York Times*, 15 November 1982. Interestingly, after escaping to Brazil following the war, Mengele told his son Rolf that he did not consider he had done wrong, reasoning that it was not his fault the prisoners were being killed in the concentration camps, and since they were going to die anyway, why not use them first to advance medical knowledge? See Pence, op. cit., pp. 226-9.

as a barrier to progress. Medical advances have continued despite the existence of what some regard as 'limitations of freedom'. We have not allowed people to be experimented on if they do not freely consent. We have not allowed researchers to bribe research subjects to participate in dangerous trials.

However, pure science researchers such as Edwards had never previously wanted to conduct human experiments that were dangerous for the subject—traditionally, they have used animal experimentation. When it was first proposed that experiments on human embryos should not be permitted on moral grounds, they were taken aback. The mantra of science has been, 'If you *can* do it, you *should* do it'. Like Edwards, many researchers think the scientists should be in charge of the research agenda, not the 'establishment' (whether that means politicians or religious figures).

Yet an ethical approach needs to consider the *rightness* of the proposed research, not merely whether or not it is technically possible. If we think we *can* do it, we need to consider whether we *should* do it, without an automatic assumption that all technological progress is good for us. In particular, we need to consider whether it has been good for the hundreds of thousands (possibly millions) of embryos that have been destroyed in the course of IVF being developed and then practised around the world.

It is clear that IVF was originally intended as a medical treatment for couples that were unable to conceive naturally. However, for many years, Edwards noted that "implantation rates remained stubbornly low", as if embryo quality had been decided long before transfer.[9] Those running IVF clinics obviously wanted to do everything they could to help infertile patients, and several practices developed in order to improve success rates.

For example, clinics began to encourage couples to give them permission to create as many embryos as possible after egg collection from the woman's body. Egg collection is an invasive and expensive procedure with the potential for serious side effects. You don't want to do it more often than you have to. And obviously, the more times you place an embryo in the womb, the better the chance of a pregnancy developing. There is no formula to predict accurately how many embryos are needed

---

9.   Edwards, 'The bumpy road to human *in vitro* fertilization', loc. cit.

to produce one live birth—hence many clinics today continue to suggest 'the more embryos the better'.

Infertile couples tend to be extremely vulnerable emotionally at the beginning of treatment, and are understandably amenable to any suggestion that may improve their chances of success. This can mean that the number of embryos created is much greater than the number of children the couple would ever want—perhaps more than 20 embryos for one couple. But the expectation is that not all embryos will end up as live births. Any embryos left over from the first treatment will be frozen for future use (although if there are a large number, often only the 'best' ones will be frozen). Some embryos won't survive defrosting, and others may not develop once in the woman's womb.

This ethical dilemma is too difficult for some parents to resolve, and so they walk away from their embryos rather than making a decision regarding their fate. As a result, there are now hundreds of thousands (it is thought) of frozen excess human embryos around the world.[10]

So consider the situation that was developing: scientists could see that the number of surplus embryos was adding up. At the same time, many questions concerning early human development remained unanswered. Why not, they thought, utilize these surplus embyros to advance our knowledge?

Following a long consultation in the United Kingdom, the destruction of excess frozen human embryos in research was approved by parliament in 1990. I was living in London at the time and remember it well. It was a difficult question in a secular, pluralist society. Some believed that all tampering with the human embryo from the time of fertilization onwards was wrong, but doubted that it should be subject of criminal sanctions. Others wanted such tampering to be treated by the law as murder. Still others were happy for the research to go ahead unchecked, and ended up embroiling their opponents in arguments over time limits, which were reluctantly accepted as the lesser of two evils.

In the end, a 14-day rule was instituted, whereby research resulting in the destruction of human embryos was permitted up until the time the embryo reached 14 days old. Until the 14-day rule, there had been no law at all, and researchers had been legally able to undertake any research

10. Discussed in the first part of chapter 14.

they wished. At least the 14-day rule brought some regulatory constraints to embryo research. It is fair to say that most people at the time seemed to think that some legal regulation was necessary. An editorial in *The Times* responded to the Warnock committee's case for the 14-day limit on research[11] by saying that it was "as convincing a statement of where sanity should rest as can be hoped for", but also, more ominously, "It would be idle to pretend that such a limit is for all time, but for now the public would appear to accept it".[12]

Initially, much of the resulting experimentation was aimed at improving ART techniques and training technicians, and this type of research continues to this day. Then, in 1998, human embryonic stem cells were isolated and cultured for the first time.

Two independent teams of researchers in the United States were involved in this scientific milestone. One team, from the University of Wisconsin-Madison and led by Dr James Thomson, derived stem cells from surplus embryos donated to fertility clinics, and established the first embryonic stem cell lines.[13] At approximately the same time scientists from Johns Hopkins University, led by Dr John Gearhart, derived germ cells from cells in fetal gonadal tissue, using aborted fetal tissue as their source.[14] Pluripotent (i.e. capable of differentiating in various ways) stem cell lines were developed from both sources.

Stem cells

There are two things that make stem cells special. Firstly, they have not yet committed to any particular cell type, and can turn into any one of the body's several hundred tissue types (e.g. bone, muscle, nerve or skin). Secondly, unlike other cells in the body, they can keep replicating indefinitely.

Scientists are excited about the potential use of stem cells in

---

11. Discussed under 'Personhood' in chapter 3.

12. Editorial, 'A question of tolerance', *Times*, 24 April 1990.

13. JA Thomson, J Itskovitz-Eldor, SS Shapiro, MA Waknitz, JJ Swiergiel, VS Marshall and JM Jones, 'Embryonic stem cell lines derived from human blastocysts', *Science*, vol. 282, no. 5391, 6 November 1998, pp. 1145-7.

14. MJ Shamblott, J Axelman, S Wang, EM Bugg, JW Littlefield, PJ Donovan, PD Blumenthal, GR Huggins and JD Gearhart, 'Derivation of pluripotent stem cells from cultured human primordial germ cells', *Proceedings of the National Academy of Sciences USA*, vol. 95, no. 23, 10 November 1998, pp. 13726-31.

combating diseases for which we currently have no cure, diseases that involve the death of tissue the body cannot regrow—diseases like spinal cord problems, heart attacks, different types of blood disorders, brain disorders like Parkinson's Disease, diabetes, and many others. This is a very promising area of medical research, often called 'regenerative medicine', to which no sensible person objects.

Now, many people are confused about stem cells because they don't realize there are several types, classified according to where you collect them from. Firstly, there are *embryonic stem (ES) cells*, collected from the inner cell mass of a 6-day-old blastocyst[15]—a process that kills the embryo. Secondly, there are *adult stem cells*, which is a slightly confusing term as they are collected not just from adults but also from children, the placenta and the umbilical cord blood—in fact, from any source other than embryos.[16] The harvest of these stem cells does not cause any lasting damage to the person from whom they were collected. (I will discuss other types of stem cells below.)

Those who value human life from the time of fertilization immediately recognize an ethical difference between these two types of stem cells, as one involves death of the developing human from which it is harvested, while the other causes no lasting damage.

The idea for using stem cells (of both main types) in therapy goes like this: once the cells are grown in the laboratory, if they could be turned into the type of cell needed for a particular patient, the cells could be injected at the site of tissue damage, and thus repair the patient's problem—heart cells for a damaged heart after a heart attack, nerve cells for a damaged spinal cord after a neck injury, insulin-producing (islet) cells for a diabetic, and so on. So far, research has been very encouraging for adult stem cells in many areas, with progress being made in the treatment of more than 70 diseases.[17] You may have heard of a bone marrow transplant for someone with diseases of the blood or cancer. This is an example of adult stem-cell treatment that has been standard treatment for years. Currently more than 200 trials are under

---

15.   For a reminder of the early stages of embryo development, see the beginning of chapter 2.

16.   Many new parents are targeted in marketing for the collection of stem cells from umbilical cord blood. These are classified as adult stem cells, not embryonic stem cells. They are described in appendix IV.

17.   For a listing of conditions where adult stem-cell research is progressing, visit the Do No Harm website: www.stemcellresearch.org

way around the world using adult stem cells that have been extracted from bone marrow.[18]

There are difficulties with embryonic stem cells, as they can turn into cancers (teratomas)[19] when injected into animals for experiments. Obviously this is a major concern, and human research has been slow in winning approval. Despite this cancer problem, some scientists want to persist with the research because ES cells are easier to harvest than adult stem cells and may be more flexible—in fact, they were once thought to be the only pluripotent cells available for treatments. There have been emotional debates in many countries over the past decade regarding whether this research should be permitted. Early on in these discussions, the public was promised that research on ES cells would mean quadriplegics would be able to walk within the decade, cancers would be cured, and Alzheimer's disease would be conquered. These cures have not eventuated.

It is now more than 10 years since

Slow progress

To date, the United States Food and Drug Administration (FDA) has approved only 3 clinical trials, and has delayed registration because of safety concerns. The first was Geron Corporation's Phase 1 study of GRNOPC1 (oligodendrocyte progenitor cells) in paralysed patients.[20] The plan was that 10 spinal cord injury patients would be injected with stem cells within 7 to 14 days of injury and monitored for adverse events. While the study was to report on negative outcomes occurring within one year of treatment, the prospective patients had to agree to a 15-year follow-up due to the largely unknown possibility of tumour formation. In view of the safety issues involved, it is unclear why this trial was approved when there are alternative treatments available for this condition in the form of adult stem cells, which have already shown efficacy during clinical ➥

---

18.   A list of studies that involve the study of mesenchymal (adult) stem cells can be found at ClinicalTrials.gov, a website courtesy of the U.S. National Institutes of Health, Bethesda MA (viewed 14 February 2012): www.clinicaltrials.gov/ct2/results?term=mesenchymal+stem+cells

19.   A teratoma is a type of cancer made up of several different types of tissue.

20.   ClinicalTrials.gov, *Safety Study of GRNOPC1 in Spinal Cord Injury*, U.S. National Institutes of Health, Bethesda MA, 3 January 2012 (viewed 15 February 2012): www.clinicaltrials.gov/ct2/show/study/NCT01217008

trials.[21] However, Geron Corporation officially abandoned the trial when it closed down its embryonic stem-cell work in November 2011 for financial reasons. At the time of writing it was continuing to monitor the 4 enrolled trial patients, but looking for another company to take them over. While no side effects have been reported yet, neither have any signs of improvement.[22]

Another United States-based company, Advanced Cell Technology, which has already had its United States-based protocol approved, has received permission to start Europe's first clinical trial involving human ES cells. The United Kingdom Medicines and Healthcare Products Regulatory Agency (MHRA) has given authorization to begin a trial that will treat 12 patients with Stargardt's macular dystrophy, a rare disease that causes blindness in juveniles (for which there is currently no treatment). Scientists will inject retinal pigment →

the first human embryonic stem cells were isolated, and the promise of miraculous cures remains hollow. ES cell research has provided no therapies to date, and continues to drain limited medical research dollars away from other more promising areas of science.

Those opposed to ES cell research have no ethical objection to regenerative medicine that uses adult stem cells. The main reason they object to ES cell research is that it involves the destruction of embryonic humans. But there is another ethical problem involved in ES cell therapy: cloning.

Stem cells and cloning

Obviously, the aim of research on ES cells is a worthy one: the development of therapies to help sick patients. We can understand the motivation. However, imagine this scenario: suppose I sustain an injury to my spinal cord so that I can no longer walk. In the future, doctors may decide to treat me with ES cell therapy if such a therapy has been developed. However, if

21.   LF Geffner, P Santacruz, M Izurieta, L Flor, B Maldonado, AH Auad, X Montenegro, R Gonzalez and F Silva, 'Administration of autologous bone marrow stem cells into spinal cord injury patients via multiple routes is safe and improves their quality of life: Comprehensive case studies', *Cell Transplantation*, vol. 17, no. 12, pp. 1277-93; AF Cristante, TEP Barros-Filho, N Tatsui, A Mendrone, JG Caldas, A Camargo, A Alexandre, WGJ Teixeira, RP Oliveira and RM Marcon, 'Stem cells in the treatment of chronic spinal cord injury: evaluation of somatosensitive evoked potentials in 39 patients', *Spinal Cord*, vol. 47, no. 10, October 2009, pp. 733-8.

22.   P Shanks, 'Geron quits the embryonic stem cell industry', *Biopolitical Times*, 16 November 2011 (viewed 15 March 2012): www.biopoliticaltimes.org/article.php?id=5943

they took a frozen embryo from an IVF laboratory, grew it up into a blastocyst, harvested the ES cells (killing the blastocyst in the process), turned them into nerve cells, and injected them into my neck, my body would reject them. This is because my body would recognize that those cells have different DNA (genetic material) from my cells.

To overcome this rejection problem it has been suggested that instead of using a frozen excess embryo, we make an embryo clone of me. (A clone is another human with the same DNA.) It is expected that this would be done with a procedure

epithelial cells derived from human ES cells into patients' eyes. The cells have been able to stave off or even reverse disease progression in animal models. The phase 1/2 trial will primarily examine the treatment's safety.[23]

Advanced Cell Technology also received approval for a third trial, to use a similar protocol to treat a more common form of blindness in adults—dry age-related macular degeneration. Once again, it is a phase 1 trial to test treatment safety.[24]

called somatic cell nuclear transfer (SCNT), where the genetic material from one of the patient's cells replaces that in a donated human egg, which is then stimulated to grow.[25] We then grow *that* embryo into a blastocyst, harvest the stem cells, turn them into nerve cells and inject them. In this case my body would accept the cells, because they have the same DNA as my other cells. This type of cloning is usually called 'therapeutic cloning', as it is hoped that therapies will be developed from it. It is also called 'cloning for research'. (Note that this procedure is not yet possible—and it is certainly not 'therapeutic' for the embryo involved.) Therapeutic cloning was always, therefore, implicit in the development of ES cell therapies.

---

23. G Vogel, 'U.K. approves Europe's first embryonic stem cell clinical trial', *Science Insider*, 22 September 2011 (viewed 15 March 2012): http://news.sciencemag.org/scienceinsider/2011/09/uk-approves-europes-first-embryonic.html

24. M Wadman, 'FDA approves third human stem cell trial', *Nature News Blog*, 4 January 2011 (15 March 2012): http://blogs.nature.com/news/2011/01/fda_approves_third_human_stem.html

25. This is not the only technique for cloning, but it is the one that scientists have been most interested in until now. The cell is stimulated using an electric current or chemical stimulus.

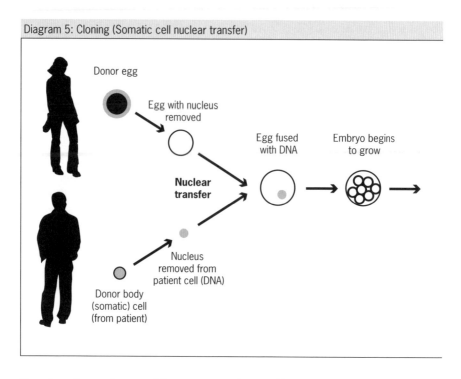

Diagram 5: Cloning (Somatic cell nuclear transfer)

Donor egg

Egg with nucleus removed

Egg fused with DNA

Embryo begins to grow

Nuclear transfer

Nucleus removed from patient cell (DNA)

Donor body (somatic) cell (from patient)

But there's another problem. Remember Dolly the cloned sheep?[26] Dolly was cloned using 'reproductive cloning', which is cloning to create a live birth rather than an embryo to be used in research. But the technology used to create her is exactly the same as that used in therapeutic cloning. If doctors decided not to use the cloned blastocyst of me to get ES cells, but instead transferred it (or 'her' or 'me') to a woman's womb, it could technically come to birth as my clone. The initial technique is the same; it is just pursued with different goals. (Note that cloning is not necessary for therapies involving adult stem cells, since we can harvest the stem cells from the patient being treated, meaning that the DNA matches and there is no immune rejection problem.)

Philosophical objections to reproductive cloning are widespread in our community. There is concern about issues of confused identity, difficult family relationships and unrealistic expectations (e.g. to become

26. The idea of human cloning first came to public attention in 1997 when Sir Ian Wilmut, a Scottish scientist, cloned Dolly from a 6-year-old ewe. See I Wilmut, AE Schnieke, J McWhir, AJ Kind and KHS Campbell, 'Viable offspring derived from fetal and adult mammalian cells', *Nature*, vol. 385, no. 6619, 27 February 1997, pp. 810-13.

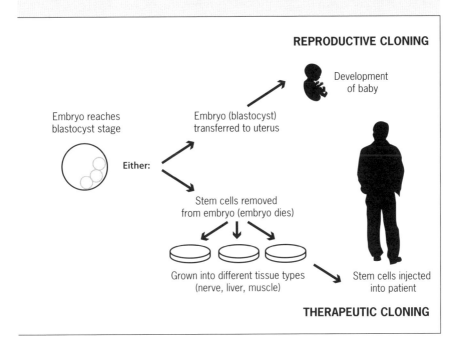

REPRODUCTIVE CLONING

Development of baby

Embryo reaches blastocyst stage

Embryo (blastocyst) transferred to uterus

Either:

Stem cells removed from embryo (embryo dies)

Grown into different tissue types (nerve, liver, muscle)

Stem cells injected into patient

THERAPEUTIC CLONING

like the one cloned).[27]

Some countries have responded to this problem by legislating a partial ban on cloning—where therapeutic cloning is permitted but reproductive cloning is prohibited. They think these rules will keep scientists from using the technology to bring a human clone to birth. But the technology is the same for each, and it will be impossible to prevent scientists from progressing to reproductive cloning once the technology is better understood. Given that a fertilized embryo and a cloned embryo look the same under a microscope, it would be impossible to police a partial ban, because the permitted activity (fertilized embryo transfer in a clinic) and the prohibited activity (cloned embryo transfer in a clinic) look identical. The law would be unenforceable.

We know there are doctors who claim to have already attempted reproductive cloning, such as those in Clonaid, a group associated with

27. Even when cloning technology is restricted to *therapeutic* purposes, it remains ethically troubling for many people. The problem is that the process involves creating human life expressly for the purpose of killing it. In some ways, this can be seen as more morally abhorrent than reproductive cloning, where at least the clone is given a chance of life by transfer to a womb.

the Raelian sect. Raelians believe the human race was started by aliens who cloned the first human. They believe that reproductive cloning is the pathway to eternal life, and claim to have achieved cloning (in Canada and Australia, where it is illegal). Raelian reports of successful clone births have yet to be substantiated.[28]

Perhaps the most prominent supporters of reproductive cloning have been Panos Zavos, a reproductive physiologist from Kentucky who claims to have implanted clones that did not develop,[29] and his colleague, Italian fertility doctor Severino Antinori. These two doctors are responding to a large group of people who see cloning as a way to replace a lost loved one (Severino claimed that more than 1,500 couples had volunteered as candidates for his research program).[30] It has also been suggested that cloning is one way a single or homosexual person could have genetically-related offspring.

Up to this point, these doctors have not obeyed the law prohibiting reproductive cloning. So it is hard to imagine what will cause them to obey it once the technology is better developed.

Human embryos were multiplied for the first time in 1993, when Dr Jerry Hall and Dr Robert Stillman successfully split one human embryo in two.[31] However, they could not prove that the genetic profiles were identical, in which case they were not technically clones.

In 2001, scientists at Advanced Cell Technology in Massachusetts claimed to have cloned human embryos by the process of SCNT, but as only one embryo got to the 6-cell stage, it was not regarded as a true clone.

The idea of using clones for spare parts was the basic plot of the movies *The Island* (2005) and *Never Let Me Go* (2010). It seems inconceivable that any government would allow the killing of live infants for such a purpose. However, the ideal gestation of a fetus for tissue transplant has already been investigated in animal models in serious academic

---

28. Bell Media, 'Raelian group claims birth of first human clone', *CTV News*, 27 December 2002; N Todd, 'Clone baby "born in Australia"', *The Advertiser*, 11 February 2004.

29. 'Human cloning attempt has failed', *BBC News*, 4 February 2004 (viewed 15 March 2012): http://news.bbc.co.uk/2/hi/health/3459009.stm

30. 'Profile: Dr Severino Antinori', *BBC News*, 7 August 2001 (viewed 15 March 2012): http://news.bbc.co.uk/2/hi/science/nature/1477698.stm

31. G Kolata, 'Scientist clones human embryos, and creates an ethical challenge', *New York Times*, 24 October 1993.

investigation.[32] And we already allow the selection and gestation of saviour sibling embryos to provide regenerative tissue transplants.

In recent times, the most notable event in human embryonic stem-cell research was the exposure of fraud on the part of South Korea's Woo Suk Hwang and the retraction of his papers from the journal *Science*.[33] This brings the total of successful, non-fraudulent reports of cloning of human beings to zero. While early human embryos have been created by SCNT, human ES cells have not been derived from them (which is considered the test of a successful experiment by leaders of the field). Therefore despite over two decades of effort, this research has still not succeeded.

Ethical issues for reproductive cloning

Debates about human cloning have fascinated Hollywood for years. Here I will list just a few prominent arguments. Further detail can be derived from the references. It is worth noting that while I am addressing the common view of cloning (i.e. that a human clone will be identical to the one who was cloned), the reality is less straightforward. How our genes are expressed depends on their environment, so a clone would probably resemble the original person less than twins would resemble each other, who are conceived and nurtured in the same environment.

a) Arguments against reproductive cloning

Philosopher Leon Kass is concerned about the pervading belief that all children should be *wanted* children.[34] He recognizes that the logical result of such thinking will be that in the end, only those children who fulfil our wants will be fully acceptable.

Kass is also concerned that modern bioethics seems to believe all evils can be avoided by compassion, regulation and a respect for autonomy. While these developments have done some good to protect personal

---

32. S Kim, S Gwak, J Han, HJ Park, MH Park, KW Song, SW Cho, YH Rhee, HM Chung and B Kim, 'Kidney tissue reconstruction by fetal kidney cell transplantation: Effect of gestation stage of fetal kidney cells', *Stem Cells*, vol. 25, no. 6, June 2007, pp. 1393-1401.

33. D Kennedy, 'Responding to Fraud', *Science*, vol. 314, no. 5804, 1 December 2006, p. 1353.

34. The following is highly recommended reading: LR Kass, 'The Repugnance of Wisdom', in LR Kass and JQ Wilson, *The Ethics of Human Cloning*, AEI Press, Washington DC, 1998, pp. 3-59 (first published in *The New Republic*, vol. 216, no. 22, 2 June 1997, pp. 17-26, and freely available on a number of internet sites).

freedoms, sadly they have also devalued the big questions of human existence. He questions the problem of confused family relationships— for example, if a woman gave birth to a clone, genetically it is not her child but her twin (identical twins are naturally-occurring clones). It is also possible that a clone may have to live with unrealistic expectations that they would be identical to the person who was copied—after all, why would you want to clone someone unless you wanted to replace them exactly? This could make it harder for cloned children to believe they are loved unconditionally. In each scenario, cloning represents reproduction for the benefit of the parents, rather than embracing the child as a gift from God. It also raises difficult issues of identity and individuality for the clone.

But Kass is concerned most of all about the instinctive 'repugnance' we feel when we think about cloning human beings. He believes this repugnance reflects an intuitive recognition that the procedures involved are dehumanizing, even if we cannot articulate exactly how we know this. He believes this should not be ignored.

The United Nations condemned all human cloning as being incompatible with human dignity and the protection of human life, passing a declaration to that effect in 2005.[35]

b) Arguments for reproductive cloning

Philosopher John Harris is not impressed by the appeal to human dignity. He points to identical twins as an example of clones we regard as non-problematic.[36] If they are acceptable, he reasons, then why not clones—particularly since the phenotype (genetic expression) is expected to be different? He also points to situations where human embryos are destroyed or endangered by widely accepted ART practices, and suggests that we need a strong moral objection to prevent a woman from having a child this way. He disregards the argument that clones would have only one social parent, because that happens in real life all the time. Furthermore, he denies that it makes the clone a commodity, suggesting that if you create an individual capable of autonomy, then their existence (i.e. being created) is in their best interests, and motives

---

35. UN General Assembly, *United Nations Declaration on Human Cloning*, 8 March 2005. The non-binding declaration called for a ban on all forms of human cloning.
36. J Harris, '"Goodbye Dolly?" The ethics of human cloning', *Journal of Medical Ethics*, vol. 23, no. 6, December 1997, pp. 353-60.

for their creation are either morally irrelevant or subordinate to other considerations.

Harris's arguments depend on giving the human embryo no moral significance, and believing that doing some good is better than doing no good. He therefore goes so far as to say it would be violating human dignity to prohibit reproductive cloning, since we would be limiting the so-called 'right to reproductive freedom'. Harris's argument is very similar to the one advanced by Joshua Lederberg 30 years earlier.[37]

Egg donation

Introduction of therapeutic cloning would demand a large supply of human eggs. At current rates, it would not be unusual to use 100 eggs to achieve one cloned embryo.

Up until now, United Kingdom law has prohibited the payment of egg donors for IVF, but it allows them to be compensated for expenses and for the inconvenience of donation (to £250 maximum). It also allows payment for eggs donated to research (also to £250 maximum). At the time of writing, the Human Fertilisation and Embryology Authority in the United Kingdom is reviewing the guidelines for compensation for donation of eggs and sperm for reproduction, and it is anticipated that compensation will be increased. Private organizations in the United States pay thousands of dollars for donated eggs to use in IVF. Many advertisements on the internet promise $8,000-$10,000 per cycle, and there are reports of Ivy League college students receiving as much as $50,000 per cycle.[38] In April 2011, thousands of women across the United States joined a class-action suit demanding better compensation for egg donors.[39] The selling of human tissue is prohibited in Australia.

A rare side effect of the drugs given to allow the harvesting of more than one egg is ovarian hyperstimulation syndrome (OHSS). There are now reports of significant illness and even death in egg donors from OHSS, due to complications such as twisting or rupturing of the ovaries and kidney problems. There have also been reports of cancers in women

---

37. J Lederberg, 'Experimental genetics and human evolution', *The American Naturalist*, vol. 100, no. 915, September-October 1966, pp. 519-31.

38. See 'Egg donation' under 'Treatment options' in chapter 12.

39. 'Finkelstein Thompson LLP and Cafferty Faucher LLP announce human egg donor files class action lawsuit challenging anticompetitive agreement among reproductive clinics and agencies', *Reuters*, 13 April 2011 (viewed 15 March 2012): www.reuters.com/article/2011/04/13/idUS240110+13-Apr-2011+BW20110413

who have donated eggs, possibly associated with the drugs injected into them. The long-term effects of undergoing egg donation are not fully known.[40]

To protect the vulnerable and financially needy women who might be susceptible to financial exploitation, I would suggest we need to pressure our governments to limit the use of human eggs to the creation of an embryo only for the purpose of achieving pregnancy, and that payment for eggs should be banned. Even though many of the advertisements for donors focus on the benevolent aspects of donating eggs so that those donating can "answer prayers", "make dreams come true" or give "new hope, new life", many women have testified to the fact that it is the money that tempts them to become egg donors.[41] Women considering the donation of their eggs need to be fully informed of the risks involved. The United Nations' cloning resolution refers explicitly to the need to prevent the exploitation of women.

We should note in conclusion that human eggs themselves are not ethically significant (in the way that a human embryo is). It is the coercion of the donor women that causes an ethical problem here.

Safety aspects

Reproductive cloning in animals is still extremely inefficient—it took over 275 attempts before Dolly the sheep was born—and of the 5% of cloned animals who survive, a disproportionate number suffer from deformities, early death, heart, kidney and liver disorders, and other health problems.[42] All cloned animals appear to have genetic abnormalities.[43]

In February 2011, a New Zealand state research organization, AgResearch, abandoned trials of cloned animals due to unacceptable death rates of laboratory animals:

---

40. H Pearson, 'Health effects of egg donation may take decades to emerge', *Nature*, vol. 442, no. 7103, 10 August 2006, pp. 607-8; see also *Eggsploitation* (The Centre for Bioethics and Culture, Pleasant Hill CA, 2010, directed by Justin Baird and Jennifer Lahl), a documentary film that examines the human egg donation industry.

41. *Eggsploitation*, ibid.

42. National Research Council and Institute of Medicine of the National Academies, *Safety of Genetically Engineered Foods*, National Academies Press, Washington DC, 2004, pp. 219ff.

43. i.e. shortened telomere length. See DH Betts, SD Perrault, J Petrik, L Lin, LA Favetta, CL Keefer and WA King, 'Telomere length analysis in goat clones and their offspring', *Molecular Reproduction and Development*, vol. 72, no. 4, December 2005, pp. 461-70.

Applied biotechnologies general manager Jimmy Suttie said that after 13 years of studying how to prevent abnormalities forming in cloned animals, AgResearch had ended its cloning research. "The decision was made, enough is enough."

Only about 10% of cloned animals survived through the trials, with the main problems being spontaneous abortions [miscarriage] and hydrops—where a cow's uterus filled up with water, leading to the mother being euthanised as well.[44]

In addition, scientists do not know how cloning affects mental development. While factors such as intellect and mood may not be so important for a cow, they are crucial for the development of healthy humans. With so many unknowns concerning reproductive cloning, it is generally accepted that applying this technology to humans would be negligent on the part of those involved. Even the creator of Dolly, Sir Ian Wilmut, says it would be "utterly irresponsible" to clone humans.[45] These problems would no doubt be resolved if we 'practised' enough, but how many lives would be lost in the meantime?

Ethical alternatives

Opposition to embryo destruction in research prompted some creative thinking that has led to the discovery of ethical alternatives. The Yamanaka Lab in Kyoto, Japan, found that ES cells were not the only source of pluripotent cells. They discovered that 4 transcription factors in ES cells could induce pluripotency in skin (read somatic) cells. The reprogrammed skin cells were called 'induced pluripotent stem cells' (iPS cells). They were isolated first in mice (in 2006)[46] then in humans (in 2007).[47] These iPS cells look the same as ES cells, proliferate like ES

44. K Chug, 'Animal death toll ends cloning trials', *Dominion Post*, 21 February 2011.

45. R Highfield, 'You're looking swell, Dolly, but no human copies, please', *Sydney Morning Herald*, 21 August 2010.

46. K Takahashi and S Yamanaka, 'Induction of pluripotent stem cells from mouse embryonic and adult fibroblast cultures by defined factors', *Cell,* vol. 126, no. 4, 25 August 2006, pp. 663-76.

47. J Yu, MA Vodyanik, K Smuga-Otto, J Antosiewicz-Bourget, JL Frane, S Tian, J Nie, GA Jonsdottir, V Ruotti, R Stewart, II Slukvin and JA Thomson, 'Induced pluripotent stem cell lines derived from human somatic cells', *Science*, vol. 318, no. 5858, 21 December 2007, pp. 1917-20; M Nakagawa, M Koyanagi, K Tanabe, K Takahashi, T Ichisaka, T Aoi, K Okita, Y Mochiduki, N Takizawa and S Yamanaka, 'Generation of induced pluripotent stem cells without Myc from mouse and human fibroblasts', *Nature Biotechnology*, vol. 26, no. 1, January 2008, pp. 101-6.

cells, and even have the same ability as ES cells to produce teratomas. While iPS cells are not problem free, they are ethically preferable to ES cells because they do not require the destruction of human embryos or the use of human eggs. They have the added advantage that the somatic (body) cell involved can be harvested from the patient needing treatment, thus eliminating the problem of immune rejection.

In early 2010, scientists at Stanford University succeeded in transforming mouse skin cells directly into functional nerve cells with just 3 added genes, bypassing the step of becoming a pluripotent stem cell completely.[48] This method was an improvement over iPS cells, with increased speed and efficiency of transformation. Then in October 2011, scientists at Harvard Medical School developed a way of producing ES cell alternatives without requiring genetic modification at all, making the reprogramming process easier and safer. Synthetic modified RNA molecules encode the proteins without integrating into the cell's DNA. Dr Derrick Rossi and his team were able to turn RNA-induced pluripotent stem cells (RiPSCs) into muscle cells.[49] These cells function like ES cells without the problems of ES cells.

Worldwide, many scientists previously investigating ES cells have turned to reprogramming of somatic cells as a more reliable and less controversial option. Meanwhile, adult stem-cell research has continued quietly. No laws had to be changed to allow it to progress because it does not involve the ethical problems of ES cells. References to papers showing advances in adult stem-cell research are too numerous to list. Therapies are being developed in clinical trials for many medical conditions including diabetes mellitus, multiple sclerosis, many malignancies, and cardiac problems.[50]

---

48. T Vierbuchen, A Ostermeier, ZP Pang, Y Kokubu, TC Südhof and M Wernig, 'Direct conversion of fibroblasts to functional neurons by defined factors', *Nature*, vol. 463, no. 7284, 25 February 2010, pp. 1035-41.

49. L Warren, PD Manos, T Ahfeldt, Y Loh, H Li, F Lau, W Ebina, PK Mandal, ZD Smith, A Meissner, GQ Daley, AS Brack, JJ Collins, C Cowan, TM Schlaeger and DJ Rossi, 'Highly efficient reprogramming to pluripotency and directed differentiation of human cells with synthetic modified mRNA', *Cell Stem Cell*, vol. 7, no. 5, 5 November 2010, pp. 618-30.

50. Some researchers claim an advantage for adult stem cells over more pluripotent types in that they alone exhibit the asymmetric cell kinetics required for ongoing renewal in adult human tissues. ES cells do not have this quality and thus it is unlikely they could achieve the cures envisaged even if the practical problems are overcome. See JL Sherley, 'Human embryonic stem cell research: No way around a scientific bottleneck', *Journal of Biomedicine and Biotechnology*, vol. 2004, no. 2, 2004, p. 71-2.

According to the opponents of destructive embryo research, none of it is necessary. It is possible to develop stem-cell therapies with no ethical problems by using adult stem cells, or perhaps iPS cells, or cells reprogrammed in one of the newer ways. Neither adult stem cells nor the other more recent alternatives require cloning or egg donation, because you can harvest the cells required from the patient being treated, with no DNA incompatibility. No embryos need be destroyed. The original grounds given to justify embryonic stem-cell research—that it offered cures available by no other method—are no longer valid.

Quite frankly, I think therapeutic cloning was never going to take off as a standard treatment. Eminent stem-cell scientists were ruling out the possibility of using therapeutic cloning in clinical scenarios as early as 2001. At that time Australia's Dr Alan Trounson commented, "They're never going to have enough women's eggs to do it", while Dr Alan Colman, then research director of the company that helped clone Dolly the sheep, explained, "It's too laborious and costly to employ as a routine therapeutic procedure".[51]

All the same, the first person to clone a human being is going to be famous, and many people are still trying.

The debate

Having outlined some of the facts and the history that has unfolded, we are in a position to assess the progress of the public debate on human embryo research.

So far, more than 30 countries have introduced laws prohibiting human cloning, including therapeutic cloning. Given that those with comprehensive bans include Canada, Germany and Switzerland, it does not seem to be a reaction of conservative morality that is driving these laws, but a concern for human dignity and safety.

The arguments

Opponents of human ES cell research reason that if a human being exists from the time of fertilization, and the harvesting of the stem cells destroys that human being, then the research is unethical.

In making this argument, opponents of destructive research on human

---

51. A Pollack, 'The stem cell debate: Use of cloning to tailor treatment has big hurdles, including cost', *New York Times*, 18 December 2001.

embryos do not think they are risking the loss of any medical therapies. They regard the success of adult stem-cell research, and the discovery of other ethically sound alternatives, as evidence that regenerative medicine can develop without using ES cells. Generally, they suggest that excess embryos in IVF clinics be adopted by infertile couples or allowed to die undisturbed. Opponents of ES cell research would also like to see a tightening of safeguards to prevent further accumulation of excess human embryos. Use of 'spare' embryos has resulted in the development of a market for human embryos, which in turn has led to legislation allowing the creation of more embryos for destructive research.

As previously argued, supporters of destructive embryo research have suggested that legal protection is due only to human *persons*, and that personhood is not achieved merely on biological grounds but also requires the development of characteristics that are not found in a human embryo in the first two weeks.

Supporters of ES cell research point to other social policies that imply the same notion (that the nascent human does not deserve protection), such as access to elective abortion, the use of post-conception contraceptives, and the research already occurring in IVF clinics. The high rate of natural embryo implantation failure is also used in support of this position.

It is also argued that since the surplus frozen embryos are going to die anyway, we might as well gain some benefit from them before that happens. This position relies on the philosophical theory of consequentialism—that it is only the *consequences* of our actions, not the actions themselves, that determine right from wrong. By suggesting that the moral interests of the surplus embryos are trumped by the needs of the sick who would benefit from the possible therapies developed, some have even argued that it is unethical *not* to use the embryos for research.

In fact, destructive embryo research was first championed using a variation of this argument—namely, that ES cell research is ethical so long as only surplus embryos are used, and so long as informed consent is obtained from those for whom the embryos were created. While the loss of the embryos is seen as regrettable, the benefits of the research justify their use.

Note that there are several unspoken assumptions in this argument. The first is that the ends can justify the means, especially if the ends are great health benefits. The second is that there are no ethical problems in destroying embryos *on purpose* rather than just letting them die. And there is even a suggestion that those who raise ethical questions lack compassion in denying potential cures to many people who are suffering debilitating or life-threatening illnesses.

Of course, all these arguments in support of human embryo research depend on the assumption that the human embryo is not a human person deserving of protection.

Before I finish this section, I would also like to point out that those in the community who support destructive embryo research are not necessarily heartless monsters. Most proponents of embryo destruction that I have met are driven by the desire to find new treatments for disabling disease. They honestly do not believe that a human being exists at this stage of development. And the reason they think that is because it is what they were taught at university.[52]

The way the debate has been conducted

As in many of our public bioethical debates, community discussion regarding the benefits or dangers of ES cell research has been superficial and inaccurate. Exaggerated claims from scientists and the media regarding the state of ES cell research have led to unrealistic expectations on the part of many citizens. While this is a perennial problem in medicine, where any breakthrough in a lab becomes a headline for a cure, even some stem-cell scientists have admitted that in their enthusiasm they might have overestimated what could be done. Liberal bioethicist Arthur Caplan has complained:

> Embryonic stem-cell research was completely overhyped, in terms of its promise. And people knew it at the time. I tried to say so myself at different times myself, even though I support embryonic stem-cell research. But this notion that people would be out of their wheelchairs within a year if we could just get embryonic stem-cell research funded was just ludicrous…
>
> Here's an assertion that you hear all the time: "Stem-cell research will help Alzheimer's". But stem-cell research has no *possibility* of helping Alzheimer's. Alzheimer's is a gunk-up-the-brain disease,

---

52. For a description of the definitional alteration for pregnancy in 1972, see 'Marketing strategies' under '3. Understanding different contraceptives' in chapter 6.

where every cell is affected. You can't fix it by any sort of stem-cell research. Model it? Maybe. Cure it? Never.[53]

'Dumbing down' of the debate by newspapers, so that it was presented as a simple choice between benefits for the disabled versus unwanted embryos, meant that the distinction between adult and embryonic stem cells was completely lost for many citizens. Take a look at the newspapers; if it is a report about advances in stem-cell treatments it is labeled simply 'stem cells' (although it involves adult stem cells). If it's about the way conservatives are slowing down progress due to their anti-science dogma, it's labeled 'embryonic stem cells'. Ask your friends—you will find that most people think that there is only one type of 'stem cell': the kind that requires human embryos.

In Australia, at least, there was also the persistent reminder that if we did not let our top scientists do what they wanted, they would go overseas and we would be worse off medically, academically and financially. Financial incentives for allowing ES cell research is a regular feature of the debate.

At best, the quest for ES cell treatments has been misguided. At worst, it has been manipulative hype. Given that we now know embryonic stem-cell research is never likely to yield therapies, bioethicist Anthony Fisher has questioned the real agenda:

> In the first place, I think it is an example of the so-called salami technique. People are unwilling to concede all of A to Z, but if you slice thinly enough, A, then B, then C, one at a time, eventually you will have the whole salami. Sell people on using just a few *excess* embryos from IVF programmes that would be disposed of anyway, while promising them miracle cures for high-profile individuals. Then it will be much easier down the track to sell them on allowing you to manufacture new, better *designer* embryos to use for cells, tissues and other things you want. Take cloning off the agenda for a while, then introduce it under the title of 'therapeutic cloning' while pretending to be appalled by any suggestion that cloned children would be allowed. Then find a sad case of someone whose only chance of

---

53. S Girgis, 'Stem cells: The scientists knew they were lying?' *Public Discourse: Ethics, Law and the Common Good*, 13 April 2011 (viewed 15 March 2012): www.thepublicdiscourse. com/2011/04/2490. This is an interesting discussion of the need for ethical guidance in science.

having a genetically related healthy child is by embryo cloning and before you know it, cloning will be fine too. Next introduce animal-human hybrids, again promising responsible limits and endless cures. All along there is really nothing you presently want to do that is excluded or unfunded, but you can make it look as if you are reluctantly submitting to severe constraints… and so it goes.

The really big markets for embryos may well be not in therapies but in gaining research grants, kudos and rewards for embryologists and their associates. Large stocks of embryos may also have been used for technician training, drug testing, toxicology and research on new contragestives and abortifacients. This was expected to yield sufficient new markets for the near future. But the general public remained queasy, and so was repeatedly fed scientifically implausible promises of cures for Ronald Reagan, Christopher Reeve, Michael J Fox or their successors.[54]

In public debates, it is always a challenge for us to get to the facts and the truth, especially when we are dependent on the media for information. It is a challenge for our churches to find knowledgeable Christians who can help us understand the issues, to the point where we can make informed choices that reflect our values.

The Christian approach

For all ethical dilemmas, Christians have a moral compass derived from the Bible.[55]

In summary, the Bible recognizes that all human beings bear the image of God, and therefore have unique value and deserve to be treated with respect. At the very least, the concept of being made in God's image has profound implications for the value to be placed on human life, the protection and care it deserves, and the gravity of interfering with it. This might do nothing to convince those who don't believe in God, but it should help them to understand where Christians are coming from in this debate.

The Bible also teaches that the end does not justify the means. It refutes the notion that we should do evil that good may result (Rom 3:8).

---

54. Anthony Fisher, *Catholic Bioethics for a New Millennium,* Cambridge University Press, Cambridge, 2012, pp. 137-8.
55. An outline of Bible-driven Christian ethics is provided in chapter 5.

Community consensus?

Destructive human embryo research will, I expect, continue. It will be opposed by most Christians. I would like to see, at the very least, stipulations that the proposed research must always demonstrate proof of concept in an animal model before embryonic humans are destroyed. But given that there will be support for it to continue, as well as opposition, how do we find consensus as a community?

I would suggest it is not possible. In the end, the moral status of the embryo is not a fact, but a value. Whether or not we choose to value and protect the embryo will depend largely on our world view and our ethical framework. Those who would pursue destructive embryo research are considering consequences only—the possible benefits. Those opposed to it are concerned with the act itself—there are some things you should just never do. The two parties are passing like ships in the night. They will never meet because they are talking about different things.

These are important moral issues. In a pluralistic society like ours, we cannot just ignore the people we disagree with; we need to consider all the different views in our community when we are making decisions. Where there is no consensus, in democratic countries we take a vote. And those whose views have not prevailed need to obey the law. Personally I am happy with this, on two conditions—that those who vote are informed regarding all the facts, not just some of them, and that tolerance and respect remain for those whose moral convictions leave them deeply disturbed.

Modern healthcare: are we playing God?

So far we have discussed the morality of different types of medical treatments, but we have not paused to consider whether it is ethically acceptable to use modern medical technology *at all* to manipulate our child-bearing. Are we playing God when we try to control when and how we have children?

There has always been a wide range of opinion and practice among Christians on this matter. Soon after his conversion, my physician husband was taken aback when a woman in his congregation explained she was not going to visit a doctor to treat a thigh abscess, but was instead going to pray according to the instructions of James:

> Is anyone among you suffering? Let him pray. Is anyone cheerful?
> Let him sing praise. Is anyone among you sick? Let him call for the
> elders of the church, and let them pray over him, anointing him
> with oil in the name of the Lord. And the prayer of faith will save
> the one who is sick, and the Lord will raise him up. And if he has
> committed sins, he will be forgiven. (Jas 5:13-15)

She was waiting for God to heal her. Likewise, a friend of mine was devastated when a well-intentioned group of parishioners visited her to pray for her chronic back pain, and then accused her of having inadequate faith when she did not immediately improve.

There has always been a level of suspicion or unease among some Christians about medical technology. And it is not getting any easier. Healthcare is changing rapidly. The escalation in the number of ways we can manipulate the unborn human is regularly creating ethical dilemmas that we have never had to confront before. The developing scientific environment will demand a constant shift of focus and approach to the moral challenges, and new situations will require us to keep re-examining the subject. Rote answers won't be enough.

What are Christians to do as we try to determine God's will for us in this area of our lives? Is it legitimate for Christians to use medical treatments at all, or should we always depend on prayer? Are we trying to usurp God's sovereignty when we visit a doctor, or does he work through the treatment? What is the relationship between divine healing and the practice of medicine? Is it okay to restore health so long as we don't try to improve on nature? How should we respond to suffering as followers of a suffering God?

In order to address these challenging questions, I want to start by thinking more broadly about *technology*, for that is what medicine is—a particular form of human technology.

God and biotechnology

Good afternoon, ladies and gentlemen. This is your pilot speaking. We are flying at an altitude of 35,000 feet and a speed of 700 miles an hour. I have two pieces of news to report, one good and one bad. The bad news is that we are lost. The good news is that we are making very good time.

This anonymous quote is often used to introduce discussions of bioethics, expressing the common feeling that we humans often seem better at devising technology than knowing how to use it.

The word 'technology' is derived from the Greek *techne*, meaning art and craft, and *logos*, meaning discursive reason or rational discussion. Technology is the making or crafting of things using our reason. While the term itself was not used by the Greeks, the idea of technology was recognized by Aristotle when he described a productive state (as opposed to an action) involving true reason.[1]

The appropriate use of technology is an aspect of our stewardship of the earth, in obedience to God's cultural mandate in Genesis 1:28, to "fill the earth and subdue it" (cf. Ps 8:4-8; Heb 2:5-8). Hebrews 2:8 clarifies the scope of our stewardship: "…in putting everything in subjection to [man], he left nothing outside his control". We understand this to mean

---

1.   Aristotle, *Nicomachean Ethics* 6.4.1140a, trans. and ed. R Crisp, Cambridge University Press, Cambridge, 2000, pp. 106-7.

that the creation is subject to mankind's benevolent rule under God.

The Bible gives us many examples of the high value given to man's technological skill. Early technologists in the Bible are introduced in Genesis 4, with Jubal developing musical instruments (v. 21) and Tubal-Cain forging tools out of iron and bronze (v. 22). Taking the specifications God had given him, Noah built an impressive three-decker ark to ride out the flood (Gen 6:13-22). In the construction of the tabernacle, God chose Bezalel and "filled him with the Spirit of God, with ability and intelligence, with knowledge and all craftsmanship, to devise artistic designs, to work in gold, silver, and bronze, in cutting stones for setting, and in carving wood, to work in every craft" (Exod 31:3-5). The exquisite detail of Solomon's temple displays the intricate beauty wrought with skill by the craftsman Hiram, thus making the temple fit for the Lord of hosts (1 Kgs 7:13-51). Christ himself was a carpenter's son and presumably continued the family trade (Matt 13:55), and the apostle Paul made tents (Acts 18:3).

But from the earliest times, it was not only the godly who were given these gifts from God. After all, Cain (who murdered his brother, Abel) built the first city (Gen 4:17). And it is disappointing, if not surprising, that the description of Tubal-Cain's ability to forge iron tools is immediately followed by his father Lamech boasting of killing a young man (vv. 23-24). Did the 'tools' quickly become weapons?

At a basic level, then, the skill and ability to use the materials of the created order to make things is one of God's good gifts to us—whether the ability to make a chair, or to make music on the guitar, or to make a house that is beautiful and functional in its design. We do not somehow cease to trust God when we work or use our skills in this way—as if God's provision for us can only operate when we are doing nothing! We work for our food, and at the same time we give thanks to God and pray for him to bless our labours. Medical technology is just another example of the skill, knowledge and ability that mankind has been able to develop because of how God has made us.

However, the Bible contains many warnings of what can go wrong when our God-given technological creativity is abused. The builders of the tower of Babel in Genesis 11 were skillful but fundamentally opposed to God. The technology the Israelites used to decorate the tabernacle was the same technology they had used to make the golden calf centuries before. Technology can be utilized for good or evil.

The same is true today. The technology we use to identify the genetic code for the purpose of curing disease is also being used to screen unborn children so they can be aborted. We should not be naïve about the risks that technology holds.

Since the Renaissance, technology and science have steadily assumed a more and more important place in Western society. Francis Bacon (1561-1626) mapped out a specifically Christian vision of using science for the welfare of human kind. In his *New Atlantis* (1627), he describes a society governed by the use of modern science and technology that could conquer nature for human benefit. Robert Boyle (1627-1692) and Isaac Newton (1642-1727) also saw the possibility of bringing glory to God through discovering the nature of his creation.

But it is not always a simple matter of man using technology. Technology also shapes and changes us. The Industrial Revolution (1750-1850) saw a drastic change in the profile of society—from a rural economy with families involved in cottage industries, to an urban economy built on manufacturing and commerce, in which women stayed home with the children while men went out to work. This changed social and family life enormously. The transformations of the past 50 years—many of them driven by technology—have brought yet more changes. With the rise of the service economy and the knowledge economy, there are now many more clean and safe jobs that women want. With the simultaneous development of reliable birth control, women now have an unprecedented level of biological and economic independence.[2] This has had a massive impact on the institution of the family, and not always in a way that nurtures the children involved.

The dangers inherent in technological progress have been voiced by Christians (e.g. CS Lewis) and non-Christians (e.g. Aldous Huxley). Huxley's *Brave New World* (1932), a satirical portrayal of a scientific utopia, has been influential in the debate over the morality of technology in modern society. The novel warns of the power of technology to dehumanize mankind; it portrays a world where suffering has been eliminated, but at the expense of our real humanity and individuality. Lewis, on the other hand, in his *The Abolition of Man* (1943), acutely sees technology not so much as "Man's power over Nature" but as "a power exercised by some men over other men with Nature as its instrument".[3]

---

2.   S Buckle, 'The seconded sex', *Australian's Review of Books*, 16-17 April 2001.
3.   CS Lewis, *The Abolition of Man*, Collins, Glasgow, 1986, p. 35.

Theologian Oliver O'Donovan suggests that what makes ours in particular a technological culture is not so much what we can do, but how we think about it. He insightfully suggests that our culture is not technological because of the sophistication of our "instruments of making" so much as because we think of everything we do as a *form* of instrumental making: "Politics... is talked of as 'making a better world'; love is 'building a successful relationship'. There is no place for simply *doing*."[4] O'Donovan continues:

> The fate of a society which sees, wherever it looks, nothing but the products of the human will, is that it fails, when it does see some aspect of human activity which is not a matter of construction, to recognize the significance of what it sees and to think about it appropriately. This blindness in the realm of thought is the heart of what it is to be a technological culture.[5]

The result is that we then fail to recognize the inappropriateness of applying technology in certain situations: "When every activity is understood as making, then every situation into which we act is seen as a raw material, waiting to have something made out of it."[6] It is not difficult to see how this 'mechanization' of human life can influence our attitude to pregnancy and child-bearing and the unfettered use of interventions such as ART.

Jean Bethke Elshtain points out that the human body is increasingly being thought of as the exclusive property of an individual, to do with exactly as he or she sees fit.[7] Encouraged by the biotech industry, we think of our bodies as malleable, as putty in our hands to be altered and re-shaped in pursuit of our needs and desires. She ponders the difficulty for Christians of arguing against the rush towards genetic and biological engineering when these things are offered to us in the name of progress, freedom and choice.

We can't hide from the fact that technology does make many aspects of life easier, more comfortable, more pleasant. It makes us healthier,

---

4.   O O'Donovan, *Begotten or Made?*, OUP, Oxford, 1984, p. 3.
5.   ibid.
6.   ibid.
7.   JB Elshtain, 'Biotech and human community', plenary session at the Remaking Humanity? Conference, Center for Bioethics and Human Dignity, Deerfield, 17-19 July 2003. Some of the themes addressed here are discussed in JB Elshtain, *Who are We?*, Eerdmans, Grand Rapids, 2000.

safer and richer. These are good things that all of us enjoy, and it is not wrong to desire them. Many lives have been saved as a result of medical technology. We can use radio to preach the gospel to nations whose borders are closed. Personally, I would hesitate to give up my washing machine. How can Christians challenge technology? Do we even want to?

For those of us living in this fast-paced, youth-oriented culture, the ongoing quest of biotechnology to perfect the human body can be difficult to assess, because it comes to us in the dominant language of our culture—the language of freedom, and of avoiding pain and suffering. We all feel the pull of these things. They promise an escape from the uncertainties of the human condition into a realm of near-mastery. With God supposedly removed as a brake on human self-sovereignty, we see no limit to what human power may accomplish. And if someone objects that it is sinful pride to take the place of God, this is taken as a piece of antiquated superstition. Anyone voicing concerns about the rush towards genetic and biological engineering is seen as either anti-science or callous towards those who may benefit.

Elshtain sees the ever more radical manipulations of the human body as a cultural "flight from finitude". It undermines recognition of the complexities and limitations and joys of embodiment—the givens of what it means to be human, to be a creature. As creatures we are dependent upon our creator. And it follows that we are not absolutely free, but free only within the limits set by our sovereign God. There is a difference between those projects where we pursue God-likeness for ourselves, and those where we act as co-creators respectful of the limits of our creatureliness. Christians grasp this distinction, and therein lies our real freedom.[8] In Romans 12:2, the apostle Paul encourages us: "Do not be conformed to this world, but be transformed by the renewal of your mind, that by testing you may discern what is the will of God, what is good and acceptable and perfect".

George Grant questions whether technology really makes society as 'free' as we think it does. While the basic knowledge (the science) that underlies technology is itself morally neutral, each technology is inevitably accompanied by an ethic of how it should be used, because each technology is designed for a specific task. We may think it is up to

---

8.   ibid.

us to decide how to use a computer, but we can only do so within the boundaries of its design. So technology is not neutral, and the 'freedom' it gives us is limited to selecting between the options available, rather than expressing our full creativity in search of alternatives. In the example of procreation, for instance, what was once an exercise in receiving and caring for the gift of a child becomes a reproductive project of obtaining a child of one's own, choosing the best route through existing treatment pathways. "And in doing so, it is difficult to see how such a child cannot be regarded as something other than a commodity."[9]

Paradoxically, this presumed 'freedom without limits' is achieved for the individual through a loss of freedom for others. Parents achieve freedom from caring for a disabled child through prenatal screening, which gives them the information needed to make sure all pregnancies brought to term are normal. As a result, pressure is already being brought to bear on parents who hesitate to screen or refuse to abort: "How could you *choose* to burden society in this way?" Is this freedom? Elshtain worries not only about the elimination of a whole category of persons, but also about the prospects for those who are born damaged from any cause. There are already moves to screen every pregnancy for Down syndrome. And so, in the name of expanding individual choice, we are narrowing our definition of what it means to be human.[10]

Technology is now harnessed not just for the restoration of normal human function but also to provide options that our ancestors never dreamed of. ART has expanded its market to provide services not only for infertile heterosexual couples but also for single parents, homosexual parents, menopausal parents and now even fetal parents.[11] Some people hope to live forever.[12] What is now possible has created a perceived need that did not previously exist. Who would ever have thought that 60-year-old women would seek children of their own? Supply now drives demand, not vice versa, because we are using medicine not only to overcome disease, but also to overcome and supersede normal human

---

9.   B Waters, *Reproductive Technology*, Darton, Longman and Todd, London, 2001, discussing G Grant, *Technology and Justice*, University of Notre Dame Press, Indiana, 1986.

10. Elshtain, loc. cit.

11. Ovarian tissue from aborted female fetuses has been used to produce eggs for use in ART.

12. Tranhumanists, for example. To read about transhumanism, visit the Humanity+ website: www.humanityplus.org

functioning. And the financial rewards are enormous.

In recent years, new medical technologies are increasingly used to create wealth for small groups of individuals, rather than primarily as tools for the improvement of human health. While most scientists aim to better the human experience, the use of patents and confidentiality agreements are slowly dissolving the community of mutual cooperation that previously existed between international scientists. Previously scientists would work together and share results to enable progress to be made more rapidly, but now results are often kept secret until a lucrative application can be patented.

The power of commercial interests in scientific research has also meant that ethical boundaries have been challenged by the push for profits. Laws have been overturned to clear the way for destructive research on human embryos, as well as the creation of human embryos with three genetic parents.[13] Human cloning is now legal in several countries. These are worrying developments. When the focus of research moves from healing to profit-making, ethical considerations are unlikely to receive much consideration.

So there is a profit motive but also a technological imperative, which is the idea that progress is always good and that what *can* be done *should* be done. But as Christians we do not endorse progress at any cost. We may be willing to forego some treatments, despite the material benefits, because we deem them unethical. This is not only because some biblical prohibitions are absolute, but also because of the biblical understanding that there can be meaning in suffering. We can learn from suffering; it can have a purpose.

Suffering

The Christian world view has a distinctive view of suffering. We do not see suffering as illusory or unreal (as a Buddhist would), nor as the ultimately meaningless result of different sets of evolved molecules interacting with each other (as a consistent atheist would). For the Christian, suffering lies within the sphere of God's sovereign rule as the creator and governor of our world. Indeed, the presence of sickness, decay and death is the

---

13.   Three genetic parents will exist for any embryo that develops from an egg that has undergone cytoplasmic transfer—the DNA of the mitochondria from the donor's cytoplasm will mix with the DNA of the mother.

result of his judgement on our rebellious world.

In other words, although (like nearly everyone) Christians do not wish to suffer and do not enjoy suffering, we know that we experience suffering under the sovereign rule of God.

Thus, suffering can function as God's loving discipline designed to correct our ways (Heb 12:5-11). Suffering can test us, prove us and purify us (Ps 66:10; Jas 1:3; 1 Pet 1:7; Rom 5:3-5). Christians will also suffer because of persecution (Mark 10:29-30; 2 Cor 12:10; 2 Thess 1:4-5).

Sometimes suffering is a direct consequence of our sin. Consider the Corinthians who participated in the Lord's Supper "in an unworthy manner" (1 Cor 11:27-30). We can see other examples in 2 Kings 5:20-27, Psalm 32, John 5:14 and Acts 5:1-10 and 12:19-23. Sometimes suffering is unrelated to our sin. Consider the blind man in John 9, as well as the example of Christ, who suffered though being without sin (2 Cor 5:21; Heb 4:15; 1 Pet 2:22; 1 John 3:5). In the same way, we see around us some people becoming sick as a direct result of their actions (smokers come to mind), while other people who have taken great care of themselves appear to have been randomly struck down with disease.

Yet these 'random' events may still have meaning. In John 9, Jesus said the man was born blind in order that God's work could be displayed in his life (v. 3). We are told that suffering can be for our good even when we don't understand it (Rom 8:28ff.). Job never understood the reason for his suffering, and doggedly refused his friends' 'rational' explanations. After an overwhelming experience of God himself, he was able to triumph nonetheless.

In other words, although we naturally and rightly want to minimize suffering where we can, we do so under the rule of God. We accept the ethical boundaries he has put in place, and acknowledge that if suffering is to be our experience then good will also emerge from it within the plans of God. We also know that suffering will be temporary and, from an eternal perspective, brief. As Paul says:

> Though our outer self is wasting away, our inner self is being
> renewed day by day. For this light momentary affliction is preparing
> for us an eternal weight of glory beyond all comparison, as we look
> not to the things that are seen but to the things that are unseen. For
> the things that are seen are transient, but the things that are unseen
> are eternal. (2 Cor 4:16-18)

But the individualistic, secular public isn't interested in the spiritual benefits of suffering, or in considering whether there might be a higher good than simply avoiding suffering at all costs. I remember hearing a parent at my child's school talking about prenatal genetic screening: "Of course, it's normal to want the best for our children; why would we ever hesitate to take full advantage of such opportunities to rule out the possibility of disease?" But in pursuing 'the best' for some children, we are prepared to terminate the lives of other children who might experience disease.

In our world of instant gratification, the public would rather just get results. This attitude is not new. Especially since the 17th and 18th centuries, suffering has been considered pointless, and man has sought to eliminate it by the instrumental control of nature. With suffering being thought to hold no meaning, the willingness to endure it has, understandably, been reduced. We find ourselves, then, at an impasse. Christians accept that some degree of illness and disability is inevitable in a fallen world, while the secular community is determined to conquer illness and disability at any cost.

We live in difficult times. The kingdom of God has come in Christ but will not be fully revealed until Jesus returns. We may not be able to control the technological pretensions of those who seek to build their biotechnological towers up to heaven, but the people of God can still bring glory to God as we practise wise stewardship of all the good things he has made. In our personal choices, we can still make practical decisions to ensure our own use of biotechnology reflects the values of God's kingdom, because in the end we know that our physical bodies, complete with genome, will pass away. In our public and social interactions, we can argue and lobby for healthcare policies that protect and nourish life.

Christians have an advantage in considering these issues because we are under no illusions regarding this fallen world. Even if our community acknowledges there is a risk of misuse with any technology, the usual response is that regulations and prohibitions will control use of new techniques. As Christians, we know better, because we know that all people everywhere are predisposed to sin (Rom 3:23). Regulations don't work. People break them. This understanding will prompt Christians to lobby against the development of technologies such as cloning. At times, all we may be able to do is encourage the enforcement of prohibitions that already exist. We do this for the sake of those who will be harmed by biotechnology's excesses.

However, we also need to remember that we are dealing with real people's problems. We need to extend compassion even when we are morally opposed to what other people want. When I am arguing against the abortion of disabled children, I am very conscious of the burden a mother takes on when she brings a disabled child to term. Of course all babies are beautiful, but we should not underestimate the toll of caring for one of these little ones. I am conscious that I also need to argue for better community support for these families, and I need to encourage fellow Christians to do likewise. Christian ethics are not just about saying 'No' to particular technologies, but about practical love and care for our neighbour (Jas 2:14-17).

My final comment is that, regardless of its problems, we as Christians should not turn our backs on technology. I applaud the efforts of bioethicist Nigel Cameron, who promotes the role of Christians in hosting debates on the challenges of technology:

> The key need is to mainstream this discussion, and get it out of
> the hands of transhumanists on the one hand and Luddites, if
> there really are any, on the other. Our embrace of the technologies
> of the 21st century depends vitally on our understanding of
> their implications and our ability to take responsibility for their
> development.[14]

> Those of us who are pro-tech and pro-human need to shape the
> future…[15]

Out of love, we need to keep engaging with our society on these issues, giving specific attention to the urgent need for moral leadership as we encounter the difficult challenges posed by biotechnology.[16]

---

14.   N Cameron, 'On enhancement', *Bioethics.com*, 10 March 2008 (viewed 20 July 2012): www.bioethics.com/?p=4299. For further exploration of Dr Cameron's work, see the Center for Policy on Emerging Technologies website: www.c-pet.org

15.   N Cameron, '(Trans)humanist thoughts', *Bioethics.com*, 17 March 2008 (viewed 20 July 2012): www.bioethics.com/?p=4360

16.   For further commentary on emerging technologies, visit the website of BioCentre, a British think tank on emerging technologies and their ethical, social and political implications: www.bioethics.ac.uk. Also recommended: The President's Council on Bioethics, *Beyond Therapy: Biotechnology and the Pursuit of Happiness*, Washington DC, October 2003.

Healing

Where does healing fit in? If sickness and death are the results of God's judgement on human sin, are our medical problems done away with by the victory over sin that Christ has won? And if so, does this render medical treatment and technology a problem for Christians?

This has been a controversial issue among Christians, and it's not within our scope here to conduct a full investigation of the subject. However, the outlines of an answer would be as follows.

The Old Testament word that comes closest to 'health' is *shalom*. It is usually translated as 'peace', but its meaning is much richer. *Shalom* represents salvation, wholeness, integrity, community, righteousness, justice and wellbeing.[17] This helps us to see health as God sees it. It is a holistic experience that extends beyond the physical and is grounded in our relationships.[18]

There are many Old Testament examples of God as healer. Following the exodus from Egypt, God reassures Israel that he is not only the judge who can afflict them with disease, but also the healer who restores them: "If you will diligently listen to the voice of the LORD your God, and do that which is right in his eyes, and give ear to his commandments and keep all his statutes, I will put none of the diseases on you that I put on the Egyptians, for I am the LORD, your healer" (Exod 15:26). His healing is manifested in physical wellbeing, such as when he used Elisha to restore the Shunammite's son to life (2 Kgs 4:32-35), or when he restored Job's fortunes following his time of trial (Job 42:10-17); but it is also connected with spiritual wellbeing and forgiveness (2 Chr 30:18-22).

Sometimes 'healing' takes place quite apart from any normal activity or agency, such as when Moses' hand suddenly becomes leprous and is just as suddenly healed (Exod 4:6-7). Sometimes symbolic actions are undertaken that precede the healing—such as when Elisha instructed the rather sceptical Naaman to wash 7 times in the Jordan River as a cure for his leprosy (2 Kgs 5:1-14). At other times the Lord uses medical means, such as when God heals Hezekiah by getting Isaiah to prescribe him a fig poultice (2 Kgs 20:4-7).

---

17. DW Brown, 'Peace', in DJ Atkinson and DH Field (eds), *New Dictionary of Christian Ethics and Pastoral Theology*, IVP, Leicester, 1995, p. 655.
18. For a discussion of the holistic nature of persons, see The Jubilee Centre, *Biblical Perspectives on Health and Health Care Relationships*, Jubilee Centre, Cambridge, 1998, pp. 8-34.

In the New Testament, holistic healing is an integral part of Jesus' ministry as he announces the coming of the kingdom of God: "And he went throughout all Galilee, teaching in their synagogues and proclaiming the gospel of the kingdom and healing every disease and every affliction among the people" (Matt 4:23). The Greek verbs used to describe Jesus' healings include *therapeuo* (to care for the sick, treat, cure, heal), *iaomai* (physical treatment, to make whole, spiritual healing), *sozo* (to save, make whole, save from the effects of disease), and *diasozo* (to save thoroughly).[19] Jesus didn't just apply a bandaid; he completely restored his patients to full flourishing, whether they suffered from blindness (Mark 8:22-25, 10:46-52; John 9:1-11), deafness and dumbness (Matt 9:32-33; Mark 7:32-37, 9:17-27), or paralysis (Mark 2:3-12). He healed those suffering from demon possession (Mark 1:23-26, 34; 5:2-13; Luke 4:40-41), and could even overcome death (Luke 7:11-15; 8:41-42, 49-55; John 11:1-44). Indeed, healing of the sick was to be the sign that the Messiah had come (Isa 35:5-6; cf. Luke 7:18-23). Jesus also sent out his disciples to heal the sick as a demonstration of the coming of the kingdom (Matt 10:5-8; cf. Luke 10:9). We also know that when the kingdom comes in all its fullness, in the new creation there will be no more evil and death and crying and pain (Rev 21:4).

All this has led some Christians to the view that it is God's will for all sickness to be cured here and now through miraculous means. This is an understandable desire, and it is certainly true that God can and does heal people now in his kindness and grace—often through medical means, but also in ways that we cannot explain.

However, the idea that God will heal *all* our diseases now—if we have faith—has two serious flaws. The first is a problem of timing. One of the benefits of Christ's victory and kingdom is that all death and disease will be done away with—but not until the new creation. In this present age, the whole creation is still groaning, Paul says, and waiting for that day (Rom 8:18-25). Suffering is still a reality, including sickness and death. In fact, it is quite clear from the New Testament that Christians should still expect to sicken and die (if Jesus doesn't come first). Nearly all human death is a result of what we would call 'sickness'. No-one dies of 'old age'. They die because of some medical problem that we can't cure. In God's

---

19. WE Vine, *Vine's Expository Dictionary of Old and New Testament Words*, World Bible Publishers, Iowa Falls, 1981, p. 203.

timing and plans, sickness is still an unavoidable reality of our fallen world, and he will not 'cure' it until the Last Day.

However, the second flaw in the 'everything healed now' view is that it restricts 'healing' to the physical. God is interested not just in our physical wellbeing but also in our spiritual, emotional and psychological wellbeing. No illness is beyond his ability to heal, but his intentions towards us are holistic. He wants to see all areas of our lives flourishing. We need to keep this in mind when we pray for resolution of the physical problems that afflict us. It could be that, as for the apostle Paul, God will choose not to relieve our physical suffering for non-physical reasons— for example, to keep us from becoming conceited, or to demonstrate his power in our weakness (2 Cor 12:7-10). 'No' is just as much an answer to prayer as 'Yes'. We pray requests, not answers.

If God does choose to heal one of our physical ailments, he can do so directly and without any human intervention. However, he very often uses some kind of intermediary, such as a doctor—and this makes it no less an example of his kindness and grace. In the example I mentioned at the beginning of this chapter, my husband's urging led the woman to get medical help and to have her problem subsequently resolved.

Medicine, world views and ethics

Let's tie these thoughts together. When we go to a doctor or utilize some form of biotechnology, we should not check God in at the door. There is no such thing as a purely 'medical' decision that lies outside the context of a world view. We all have a world view that shapes our thinking, our values and our ethics—even your doctor has one!

Secular or scientific neutrality is a myth. When a difficult decision arises in medicine there will often be an ethical aspect that is not recognized for what it is. It may be cast as a completely 'medical' decision when in fact it involves issues of morality. For example, should we undergo genetic testing or screening? Should we try an expensive experimental treatment if there is little chance of it working? Should we utilize medical treatments that were discovered and developed by morally questionable means? If we wish to honour God in all areas of our lives, we will bring all these questions before him.

Very often, medical decisions are made on utilitarian grounds—that is, within a world view that sees the ends as justifying the means. Doctors are taught to use the most cost-effective treatment, or the therapy with the best success rate, but they may not stop to think: is this treatment morally permissible? Doctors will often not raise these ethical questions; we will need to do that ourselves. We will then need to use a biblical approach to decision-making,[20] taking into consideration the advice given.

Each decision we make during treatment needs to be approached with prayerful requests for wisdom, and held up to God's word to make sure it does not breach biblical ethics. But beware—this may make you unpopular in some treatment centres! You may be viewed as difficult and unreasonable by those who do not value human life as you do. You may be considered disruptive if you ask for more time to consider your preferences and get more advice. But in the end we will all have to account for our own decisions before God. The Bible teaches us that we must take responsibility for our actions (2 Cor 5:10), and it is not enough to say, "The doctor made me do it".

It will certainly help if you can think things through *before* you go for treatment, so that you can anticipate some of the issues that may arise. You may benefit from asking around and finding a doctor sympathetic to Christian values. God has given us a Christian community for support in difficult times of our lives, and this may be a good time to call on it.

Given all that we have said so far, it is ethical to use medical treatments that respect human life and respect biblical models of marriage and family. It is consistent with biblical teaching to restore malfunctioning body systems to the way they were intended to be, and to facilitate the act of procreation as it is normally performed. Note that I am not saying here that childlessness is a disease that needs a medical remedy. I am pointing to the underlying pathology that may prevent normal marital intercourse from resulting in pregnancy.

From God's perspective, our health includes our spiritual, emotional and psychological wellbeing, so it is also appropriate to seek help for treatment if any of these are damaged. Accordingly, it would be appropriate to ask for counselling to help cope with the psychological and emotional challenges of infertility if you find it difficult to work through the issues on your own. You might decide to speak to your minister, or you may go to a professional counsellor. Good professional counsellors don't tell you what to do so much as help you understand your own thoughts and feelings. Some Christians find it easier with a

---

20. Discussed in chapter 5.

Christian counsellor, although (as with doctors) many counsellors are happy to take your belief system into account even if they don't share it themselves.

It would also be appropriate for a married couple with medical infertility to seek assistance in treating medical and surgical problems that are a barrier to normal procreation. This might include hormonal supplements to correct deficiencies, surgery to unblock a fallopian tube, or treatment for endometriosis. If these sorts of problems cannot be overcome, bringing the sperm and egg of a husband and wife together to make an embryo by IVF is, I believe, permissible if no unethical practices (such as embryo destruction) are involved. These treatments or interventions all work to facilitate normal conception. However, it would not be consistent with biblical ethics for a single woman to use assisted reproduction to have a baby, since the Bible teaches that procreation is *intended* to occur within a marriage between a man and a woman, and a family is *intended* to consist of two parents of the opposite gender. Sometimes, of course, this intention isn't fulfilled in our fallen world. Single women have children; marriages split up. But these sad realities aren't justification for arranging it that way intentionally.

What about the next step, where a couple cannot conceive and tests reveal that the husband has no sperm? The standard medical treatment would be to substitute donor sperm to make the embryo, usually by donor insemination. Here the medical intervention is going beyond 'restoring what is broken', in that it is not the man's ability to make sperm that will be mended. Instead, another man's sperm will be substituted. In this instance, there will be three people involved in making the embryo, thus moving outside the biblical model of two parents per family. Again, I am talking about what we are *aiming* for. I realize that some families may lose a parent, or gain a step-parent, but God's intention in creation was for children to be raised by two married biological parents.[21]

In the same way, deciding whether babies may live or die according to their genetic makeup or physical wholeness is outside biblical norms. The Bible teaches that all human beings have value, regardless of their individual characteristics, because we are all made in the image of God (Gen 1:27) and should not be killed (Gen 9:6).

---

21. For further discussion, see chapters 4 and 12.

Use of controversial treatments for alternative purposes

What about employing unethical or controversial treatments for purposes other than their original design? For example, if you decide that using the oral contraceptive pill for prevention of pregnancy is wrong, is it also wrong to take an oral contraceptive pill for an unrelated purpose? The hormones in oral contraceptives work on several different mechanisms in the body and may be prescribed to treat problems as diverse as severe acne or abnormal hair growth. I would suggest that such use is permissible for that person. As we have already noted in chapter 5, it is not only the action itself that we need to consider, but also our motives. In this instance, so long as: (a) our intention is to treat the alternative problem, not contraception, even if the action of the pill is contraceptive at the same time; and (b) you do not achieve the treatment effect through preventing a pregnancy; then you have not contravened your ethical opposition to using oral contraception. Even the leaders of the Catholic Church, who traditionally have opposed the use of hormonal contraceptives, allow them for such purposes.[22] This pattern of reasoning is technically called the 'principle of double effect'.

Having said all of this, there is no instruction in the Bible that makes taking advantage of modern healthcare a moral requirement in itself. Life itself is not the ultimate good. We are not obliged to seek life and health at all costs. In fact, to do so would be to make it an idol.

---

22. Encyclical of Paul VI, *Humanae Vitae*, Australian edn, St Pauls Publications, Homebush, 1990, p. 23.

Epilogue

I BEGAN THE RESEARCH that led to this book mainly to assist many friends and acquaintances who had asked me questions about the appropriate use of modern reproductive technology. I had no idea what I would find.

What I found left me deeply unsettled as I realized the extent to which our society has decided to accommodate selfish adults at the expense of the children involved. We want 'perfect' children through genetic screening, freedom from inconvenient pregnancies, and the ability to override normal human biology when it suits us—all at the cost of embryonic and fetal human life. Personally, I consider it a travesty that medicine is being used for these ends. This is not what I signed up for when I became a doctor.

Consider, for example, the decreasing tolerance for imperfections in our community. When did we decide that any of us were perfect specimens? We are all of us damaged; it is just more noticeable in some than in others. And why is physical brokenness tolerated so poorly while moral brokenness is not just tolerated but chronicled, accepted and even celebrated in magazines and newspapers?

At the heart of the problem is the persistent human desire to be in control of our own lives, and to determine for ourselves what we should do and be (the Bible has a word for this). We plan our families carefully to fit in with our dreams, and then feel put out when things don't go according to schedule. We expect to be comfortable. We expect to be safe and prosperous. We do not want needy children who will change our lifestyle for the worse. In a society that has lost touch with any higher purpose in life which might give significance to suffering, we are left with no other purpose than the avoidance of suffering and the maximizing of pleasure and comfort.

As Christians, we know that far from dispensing with the vulnerable, God carries the weak and the helpless close to his heart. And he wants us to do the same: "Religion that is pure and undefiled before God, the Father, is this: to visit orphans and widows in their affliction, and to keep oneself unstained from the world" (Jas 1:27). How can Christians express this care for the weak and defenceless?

One thing we can do is speak up. There is a conspiracy of silence and euphemism surrounding many of the unethical practices I have described in this book. Political correctness has prevailed and we have not named these interventions for what they are. Most people don't realize what is going on, for example, when doctors say that they can prevent the birth of children with Down syndrome. It sounds like a new cure. It isn't. It just means that they can now tell (at least most of the time) when a developing fetus has Down syndrome, and can kill the fetus before he or she is born. We need to educate and inform, so that people can make wise and ethical choices with the information in front of them.

We also need to learn and communicate our history. I have ended up including more history in this book than I had originally planned because it seems to me that our society, including the Christian community, has the lowest opinion of developing human life than of any other time in Western history. At a time when we have more understanding than ever of the intricacies and wonders of intrauterine life, we see it wantonly destroyed in the name of freedom and choice and autonomy.

Christians can also offer genuine and practical support to couples that struggle with the brokenness of life. We can help men and women talk about their dilemmas and share their deepest needs and concerns. We can get alongside those who are faced with hard decisions and help them with the day-to-day consequences of their choices.

Christians also need to model a richer understanding of what it means to be human—including an understanding of responsibility for the little ones who depend on us to protect them. We can slow down and accept the relationships we are given, and find joy and contentment in service and obedience even though we know it will often be costly.

In choosing to love and serve at the cost of our comfort, we are imitating the God who loved us and gave himself up for us (Eph 5:2). Dorothy Sayers puts it strikingly:

For whatever reason God chose to make man as he is—limited and suffering and subject to sorrow and death—he (God) had the honesty and the courage to take his own medicine. Whatever game he is playing with his creation, he has kept his own rules and played fair. He can exact nothing from man that he has not exacted from himself. He has himself gone through the whole of human experience, from the trivial irritations of family life and the cramping restrictions of hard work and lack of money to the worst horrors of pain and humiliation, defeat, despair, and death. When he was a man, he played the man. He was born in poverty and died in disgrace and thought it well worthwhile.[1]

I hope that as we make decisions about pregnancy and childbirth, we will also think it worthwhile to live in faithfulness and love. And I hope and pray that this book has provided the necessary information, as well as the biblical ethical framework, for you to do just that.

I can vividly remember the nights each of my two daughters was born— lying in bed in a quiet room, just the two of us, with the yellow light of a lamp allowing me to savour every detail of the perfect little person before me. Dark eyelashes on the cheek, tiny little nails that already needed cutting, soft little breaths that caressed my bare arm. I could barely contain the sense of amazement and love I felt at each occasion. Is there anything more wonderful that holding your own baby for the first time?

It is so good and normal to long for a child. I thank God that I have had this blessing of being a mother. I look forward to the day when all children are as welcome as ours were.

---

1.   DL Sayers, *Christian Letters to a Post-Christian World*, Eerdmans, Grand Rapids, 1969, p. 14.

Appendix I

Does the oral contraceptive pill cause abortions?

T HERE HAS BEEN MUCH discussion in Christian circles about whether the oral contraceptive pill (OCP) causes early abortions. The debate began in 1997 when Randy Alcorn, an American pastor, published a book called *Does the Birth Control Pill Cause Abortions?* The debate is significant because the OCP is widely used and regarded as an easy and effective method of birth control. There is concern that this controversy will mean many Christian families will be unable to reliably control their fertility. As a result, this has caused much anxiety on the part of believers who wish to protect human life from its earliest stages.

It is worth recognizing at the outset that there are people on both sides of the debate who are sincerely pro-life and have much in common. All are concerned about the protection of unborn human beings from the time of fertilization, given that they are all made in the image of the God who imbues them with dignity and worth. All recognize that since we have been able to work out how fertilization occurs through application of human reason, we now have the responsibility to use that knowledge to ensure that the process of embryonic development is not interrupted.

To understand the debate, you need to know how the OCP works. The OCP is known to work as a true contraceptive, by:
1. inhibiting ovulation, so there are no eggs available to be fertilized
2. thickening cervical mucus, making it difficult for the sperm to get through the cervix, so they are not available to do the fertilizing.

People on both sides of the debate agree on these points. But it also has a third effect:
3. it makes the lining of the womb thinner and hostile to the embryo.

This third effect is where the contention lies.

The argument goes this way: *If* a woman taking the pill experiences failure of the first mechanism, and she ovulates so that an egg is produced; and *if* the second mechanism fails and sperm gets through the cervix; and *if* an embryo is then formed; and *if* the third mechanism prevails; *then* it means that the endometrium may be unable to support the embryo that is formed, and an early abortion may occur. The study quoted to support this hypothesis claims to demonstrate that women who had ovulated while taking the pill had atrophic (thinned) endometrium.[1]

The problem lies in the methodology: the investigators' criterion to 'establish' that the women had ovulated was to have a blood progesterone level over 4ng/ml. So far so good. But most medical experts would say that you need a progesterone level over 9ng/ml to be sure that ovulation had occurred,[2] so it is possible that women in the study with progesterone levels over 4ng/ml but under 9ng/ml may not have ovulated. The results therefore do not help prove the theory. If the women did not ovulate then the condition of the endometrium doesn't matter, because if there is no egg then there is no embryo to implant.

Furthermore, the argument that opposes the abortifacient theory claims that ovulation and endometrial thickening go hand in hand. It rejects the notion that the first two mechanisms could fail and the third mechanism could still prevail. Instead, it suggests that if you had failure of ovulation inhibition, and an egg was produced (this is known as *escape ovulation*), and if you had failure of cervical mucus thickening and the sperm got through, the hormone surge that normally accompanies ovulation would be released and it would stimulate the endometrium to grow and prepare the uterus for implantation of an embryo, as it is designed to do, over the 7 days it takes for the embryo to reach the womb. In this case, if the egg were fertilized, you would not have an early abortion but an unplanned pregnancy. Supporters of this argument note that the endometrium isn't ready for an embryo in the two weeks

1.   V Chowdhury, UM Joshi, K Gopalkrishna, S Betrabet, S Mehta and BN Saxena, '"Escape" ovulation in women due to the missing of low dose combination oral contraceptive pills', *Contraception*, vol. 22, no. 3, September 1980, pp. 241-7.

2.   MG Hull, PE Savage, DR Bromham, AA Ismail and AF Morris, 'The value of a single serum progesterone measurement in the midluteal phase as a criterion of a potentially fertile cycle ("ovulation") derived from treated and untreated conception cycles', *Fertility and Sterility*, vol. 37, no. 3, March 1982, pp. 355-60.

before ovulation in a fertile woman even if she doesn't take the pill. The endometrium always needs the hormone surge to prepare for an embryo, and it is this thickened endometrial lining that is shed each month in menstruation (the woman's 'period' bleed) when no embryo arrives. It builds up again following ovulation the next month, and so the cycle continues. These doctors see no reason biologically why the pill would stop this automatic response to ovulation.

Nobody disputes that with normal OCP usage, the pill-user has a thin endometrial lining. What is important is to find out what happens when ovulation occurs while taking the pill. Just because the pill *can* cause endometrial thinning does not mean it relies on that thinning for its effectiveness. Suppression of ovulation is the most important aspect of its function.

Ectopic pregnancy risk

A further line of argument used to support the abortifacient position is related to ectopic (tubal) pregnancy rate for hormonal contraceptives. This argument is a bit more complicated. It is postulated by OCP opponents that if the OCP has no effect after fertilization (i.e. it does not interfere with the embryo once it is formed), then reductions in the rate of intrauterine (normal) pregnancy in pill-users would be the same as reductions in the rate of pregnancy outside the uterus (ectopic pregnancy). They argue that if the action of the OCP is occurring before implantation then it has a general reduction effect on all pregnancies regardless of where they would have ended up *if* they had been fertilized. Those supporting this position suggest that as there is a lesser reduction in the incidence of ectopic pregnancy (that is, there are more of them) with hormonal contraceptive use compared to non-pill users, the most likely explanation is that the OCP does something to prevent the embryo from implanting in the right place (once again, the hostile endometrium hypothesis) and therefore forces the newly conceived child to implant in the wrong place. They quote papers that they say demonstrate an increased extrauterine/intrauterine pregnancy ratio in women taking the pill.[3]

---

3.   J Thorburn, C Berntsson, M Philipson and B Lindblom, 'Background factors of ectopic pregnancy I: Frequency distribution in a case-control study', *European Journal of Obstetrics and Gynecology and Reproductive Biology,* vol. 23, no. 5-6, December 1986, pp. 321-31; J Coste, N Job-Spira, H Fernandez, E Papiermik and A Spira, 'Risk factors for ectopic pregnancy: A case-control study in France, with special focus on infectious factors', *American Journal of Epidemiology,* vol. 133, no. 9, 1 May 1991, pp. 839-49.

Those opposing this argument acknowledge that there is an increased tubal pregnancy rate with some contraceptives, but point out that the studies cited put other hormonal contraceptives (which work differently) in the same category as the OCP. They suggest that if you look at the research for the hormonal contraceptives individually, in fact the increase (per pregnancy) in ectopic pregnancy occurs only with the progestin-only pill and Norplant, not with injectables or the OCP.[4] This increased risk of ectopic pregnancy may be the result of progestin acting on the fallopian tube to delay egg transport to the uterus, so the embryo is still in the tube when it is time to implant—but it is not fully understood.[5] There is no evidence to support that it is due to a hostile endometrium. Opponents of the abortifacient theory suggest once again that if escape ovulation occurs, the hormonal surge will prepare the endometrium in time for implantation. They suggest that an incorrect conclusion has been drawn from this research. They postulate that the fact that an embryo *can* implant in the fallopian tubes or other places in the abdomen suggests that an ideal endometrium is not actually necessary for successful implantation and thus further supports use of the OCP.

This is a simplification of the debate—there have been further lines of argument offered and refuted. Please review the given references if you would like to pursue this question further.[6] And as I said in chapter 6, do not use the pill if your conscience forbids it (Rom 14:23b).

---

4. HJ Tatum and FH Schmidt, 'Contraceptive and sterilization practices and extrauterine pregnancy: A realistic perspective', *Fertility and Sterility*, vol. 28, no. 4, April 1977, pp. 407-21.

5. MF McCann and LS Potter, 'Progestin-only oral contraception: A comprehensive review', *Contraception*, vol. 50, no. 6, supplement, 1994, pp. S1-195.

6. For material that addresses both sides of the debate, see LK Bevington and R DiSilvestro (eds), *The Pill*, Center for Bioethics and Human Dignity, Deerfield; for material that explains the argument for hormone contraceptives as abortifacient, see R Alcorn, *Does the Birth Control Pill Cause Abortions?*, 10th edn, Eternal Perspective Ministries, Sandy OR, 2011; for the contrary view, see SA Crockett, JL DeCook, D Harrison and C Hersh, 'Hormone contraceptives: controversies and clarifications', ProLife Obstetricians, Fennville MI, 1999, in Bevington and DiSilvestro (eds), op. cit., pp. 71-96.

Appendix II

Commercial markets created by abortion

A RE FINANCIAL REWARDS driving an increasing level of activity in the growth and harvesting of babies? Who benefits financially from abortion?

In the first instance, the abortionist will obviously benefit financially. Regardless of his motivation for entering the field, the doctor who performs an abortion will receive significant financial reward. While each routine first-term abortion may not individually have a big return, the sheer number that can be done in one session allows considerable profits. Unlike many other types of operation, abortions (in many countries) are subsidized through government programs, thus increasing payment reliability.

The cost of an abortion depends on the location, the facility used, the stage of pregnancy, and the type of procedure. Costs therefore vary widely, but the following provides a guide to typical costs in a few locations:

- **United Kingdom:** The National Health Service provides a free abortion service. If you choose to use the private system, medical abortions cost £440-£470 during the first trimester, and up to £1225 at 23 weeks gestation; surgical abortions cost from £350-£550 during the first trimester, and up to £1700 at 23 weeks.
- **United States:** There are large variations, but medical abortions tend to cost $300-$650 during the first trimester, and as much as $3000 for a later abortion; surgical abortions can cost $200-$1000 during the first trimester, as much as $5000 (but more commonly $700-$2000) during the second trimester, and up to $10,000 for a third-trimester abortion. Reductions may be possible with private insurance or Medicaid.

- **Australia:** First-trimester abortions cost $300-$800, and second-trimester abortions cost $640-$1800. Reductions may be possible with private insurance or Medicare.

The largest abortion provider in the United States is Planned Parenthood Federation of America, which posted a net profit of $85 million in 2008 on gross revenue of $1.038 billion, some of which was used to fund political strategies to protect the right to abortion.[1]

When Abby Johnson first went to work for Planned Parenthood, she believed that the organization aimed to reduce the abortion rate by increasing the availability of contraceptives. But when she became a clinic director, she was told to increase the number of abortions being performed, because that was the way to increase revenue. This directive was reflected in the overall rise in abortions over the previous years: in 2005 there were 264,943 abortions performed through Planned Parenthood Federation of America, rising gradually to 324,008 in 2008.[3]

In May 2011, Planned Parenthood Minnesota, North Dakota and South Dakota sued the state of South Dakota, challenging a new law that required women to undergo counselling before seeking abortion. The law also imposed a 72-hour delay following a woman's initial consultation with her doctor before the abortion could be performed, and required doctors to obtain proof in writing that the counselling was completed.[2]

The fetal tissue industry

An unintended consequence of the widespread right to abortion has been the creation of a vast and lucrative market in fetal tissue, fetal organs and fetal parts.

The fate of aborted fetuses is not often discussed. If they are disposed of by the clinic, incineration is the usual method. But where it is legal, there are financial incentives to look at alternative means of disposal.

---

1.   V Evans, *Commercial Markets Created by Abortion*, dissertation for the Licentiate (Master's) Degree in Bioethics, Athenaeum Pontificium Regina Apostolorum, Rome, 18 November 2009. This paper has informed discussion of commercial markets created by abortion, and is an interesting read regarding the interplay of politics and the abortion industry.

2.   A Gallegos, 'Planned Parenthood sues states over abortion restrictions', *American Medical News*, 20 June 2011.

3.   A Johnson and C Lambert, *Unplanned*, Tyndale, Carol Stream, 2010.

Research

Fetal tissue—that is, any part of the fetus's body—can be used for research, transplantation and product development in the medical and pharmaceutical industries. Fetal tissue is attractive to researchers because it retains the potential to grow and change into different types of cells, similar to embryonic stem cells. It has been used in research since the 1930s and in transplants since the 1960s. The transplants were initially aimed at curing illnesses like Parkinson's disease and diabetes. Some jurisdictions have introduced legislation to make sure pressure is not put on women to abort in order for tissue to be obtained (the industry being worth potentially thousands of dollars per month for a clinic).

Fetus farming

Fetus farming is a way of obtaining whole organs that can be used in transplants. Experiments in mice have shown that fetal kidneys grow extremely quickly when transplanted into adult animals. It is easier to take a liver from an 8-month gestation fetus than to grow the liver from embryonic stem cells. While the industry as visualized in movies like *The Island* (2005) is still in the realm of science fiction, some jurisdictions have been worried enough to introduce legislation to prevent it (United States Congress prohibited it in 2006).[4] In 2009, Oxford University Professor and advisor to Britain's Human Fertilisation and Embryology Authority Sir Richard Gardner called for studies into the feasibility of transplanting fetal organs. He said he was surprised the possibility had not been considered, and that "It is probably a more realistic technique in dealing with the shortage of kidney donors than others".[5] Note that to harvest an organ for transplant, one would have to abort the fetus in the second or third trimester with arrangements in place for careful transfer of the tissue to the transplant facility so that it remained fresh. But in a society that allows abortion on demand, why wouldn't this be attractive to the parents of a dying child who was desperately in need of an organ transplant?

---

4. The Fetus Farming Prohibition Act of 2006.
5. F Macrae, 'Use aborted foetus organs in transplants, urges scientist', *Mail Online*, 11 March 2009 (viewed 4 October 2011): www.dailymail.co.uk/sciencetech/article-1161085/Use-aborted-foetus-organs-transplants-urges-scientist.html

The pharmaceutical industry

The pharmaceutical industry has consistently ranked highly in the Fortune 500 since the 1980s.[6] It has historically manufactured vaccines using cell lines derived from aborted fetuses.[7]

Cell lines (continually renewed cultures of specific cells in a laboratory) are used to grow the viruses used in the production of vaccines. Viruses require the presence of cells in order to replicate, and some human-specific viruses will only grow on cell lines originally derived from a sample of human tissue. They are incubated until enough virus has grown for harvest.

In the 1960s, certain cell lines (WI-38 and MRC-5) were developed from fetal tissue that came from elective abortions indicated for medical reasons. WI-38 came from lung cells of a female fetus of 3 months gestation, and MRC-5 came from lung cells of a male fetus of 14 weeks gestation. (The abortions were not conducted for the purpose of collecting cells for cell lines.) The cells currently in use have been growing independently for more than 40 years, and so were never part of the original aborted fetus's body.

These cell lines (which are different from embryonic stem cells) have been used to manufacture vaccines for rubella (German measles), MMR (measles, mumps and rubella), hepatitis A and B, varicella (chickenpox and shingles), polio, smallpox and rabies. Further research is ongoing to develop new vaccines. The question is not whether these are useful vaccines—of course they are. The question is: can we make the same vaccines in an ethical manner? Is it necessary to use fetal cells in this process?

Is it necessary?

The PER.C6 technology is based on the PER.C6 fetal cell line, which was developed from embryonic retinal cultures taken from a 1985 elective abortion. This is an example of newer technology, developed to industry standards and marketed by the company Crucell as a "safe and cost-effective manufacturing system for high-yield, large-scale production of

---

6. The Fortune 500 is an annual list compiled by *Fortune* magazine that ranks the top 500 US corporations by their gross revenue.

7. Human diploid fibroblast cell strains (HDCS), which are groups of human diploid cell strains that maintain normal human chromosomal numbers and characteristics, while dividing throughout their limited lifetime in a laboratory setting.

vaccines, recombinant proteins including monoclonal antibodies, and gene therapy products".[8]

It is not necessary to use aborted fetal tissue for these processes. It would be possible to make vaccines and monoclonal therapies with recombinant DNA technology, or using human tissue from another source.

It would be possible to develop future vaccines without culture of human diploid cells for the attenuation of the virus and its growth. Vaccine could be prepared from the genome of the virus and its antigens. This would be a scientifically valid and ethical alternative. However, it will be difficult to change a practice that is already in place and upon which a whole industry is built—not only due to cost but also the challenge of having manufacturers agree that an alternative is necessary.

If alternatives are not available and you are concerned about using vaccines that were developed using tissue from aborted fetuses, what should you do?

The ethics of vaccine use

The ethical concern for Christians is that by using these vaccines we are somehow complicit in the abortions that led to the death of the fetuses used to harvest the original cells for culture. To be complicit means to be a partner in an evil act.

Moral complicity can be judged by asking several questions:

1. **Have you had any role in causing the wrong act?** Did we intend the original abortion? In this case, obviously not. Whatever the 'medical indications' for the abortion were, we were not involved in the original decision.

2. **Are you facilitating the wrong act directly?** Does our action (using the vaccine) promote the performance of the morally wrong act (the abortion)? Again, the answer is no—the collection of the fetal cells has long since passed.

3. **Does your action perpetuate the moral wrong?** No. By using the vaccine now, we do not promote further abortions for this particular purpose. However, we still can let manufacturers know we object to the use of fetal cells for ongoing development of vaccines.

In other words, we did not cooperate in the performing of the abortion

---

8.   Crucell, *Technology*, Crucell, Leiden, 2009 (viewed 4 October 2011): www.crucell.com/Technology

that led to the death of the fetus whose tissue was used in developing the cell lines used in producing virus vaccines. Therefore, using the vaccines is morally justified, since we are not morally complicit in the original abortions.

Furthermore, we have an important moral reason *for* using the vaccines: the protection against potentially life-threatening infectious diseases. Not only do we help those we vaccinate directly (for example, children), but we also make these diseases less common, thus benefitting the general community—including pregnant women, whose unborn children could be adversely affected by infections such as rubella. Immunization has been demonstrated to be one of the most effective medical interventions available to prevent disease, estimated to save 3 million lives per year throughout the world.[9] This argument for allowing the use of vaccines produced using fetal cell lines is supported by the Vatican.[10]

Parents with specific concerns regarding immunization should discuss the issue with their local doctor before deciding against such an important medical intervention.[11]

The cosmetics industry

The new technology of stem cells has found its way to the beauty department. Biotechnology companies have started developing anti-ageing cosmetics using fetal stem cells, marketed as 'cosmeceuticals'—a topical application with active ingredients that apparently have medical-type benefits.

Enormous financial investments have been made in embryonic stem-cell technologies worldwide, with little return so far. At the 2008 World Stem Cell Summit held in Madison, Wisconsin, the mood was pessimistic:

> Commercialization is "excruciatingly slow", said Michael Haider,
> CEO of BioE Inc., a St Paul company that extracts stem cells from
> blood in human umbilical cords. "I'm not aware of a successful

9. Department of Health and Ageing, *Immunisation Myths and Realities*, 4th edn, Commonwealth of Australia, Canberra, 2008, p. 5.

10. Pontifical Academy for Life, 'Moral reflections on vaccines prepared from cells derived from aborted fetuses', *National Catholic Bioethics Quarterly*, vol. 6, no. 3, Autumn 2006, pp. 541-50.

11. These ethical arguments apply to treatments developed from long-established cell lines. For the ethics of ongoing developments, see chapter 15.

stem-cell company. If you thought gene therapy was difficult, then [stem cells] are astronomically difficult."[12]

Some people hope that cosmetic applications will be one way to get some money back. Like all cosmetics these products need to be safe, but unlike pharmaceuticals, they don't have to prove that they actually do what they say they do (much to the manufacturer's relief, as this process of documenting efficacy is long and costly—though it would be interesting to see how many face creams passed the test!).

This use of stem cells on skin arose from the successful application of fetal tissue to treat burn victims. Skin cells taken from an aborted male fetus of 14 weeks gestation were used to grow sheets of skin that healed children's burn wounds without scarring, in research at the University Hospital of Lausanne, Switzerland.[13] The team went on to use the fetal cells to develop a cell bank, to be the ongoing supply for a cream designed to reduce the signs of ageing, improve skin texture and reduce wrinkles. The active ingredient (Processed Skin Cell Proteins, or PSP) has been trademarked by Neocutis, a company founded as a spin-off from the Lausanne University Hospital, with the research team becoming the founding entrepreneurs.

A new market has been created by the arrival of the baby-boomer generation at a stage when work needs to be done if they are to avoid looking their age. This group includes many individuals with the determination and resources to stay 'young' at any cost. According to one report, "The global anti-aging market for the boomer generation was worth $162.2 billion in 2008. This should reach $274.5 billion in 2013…"[14]

What cosmetics are available for those with the will and wallet to proceed? At the budget end you can buy 'miracle' serums developed from fetal cell technologies (all unproven as to efficacy, remember), such as Voss Laboratories' *Amatokin*, 25 ml for $69.99; Neocutis's *Journee Bio-Restorative Day Cream with PSP*, 1 oz for $120; or ReVive Skincare's *Peau Magnifique*, 4 x 1 ml bottles for $US1,500, £930 or $AU2,500, depending on where you shop. The products are expensive because they have a

12.   T Lee, 'Stem cells: Time to make good on promises', *Star Tribune*, 28 September 2008.

13.   J Hohlfeld, A de Buys Roessingh, N Hirt-Burri, P Chaubert, S Gerber, C Scaletta, P Hohlfeld, and LA Applegate, 'Tissue engineered fetal skin constructs for paediatric burns', *Lancet*, vol. 366 no. 9488, 3 September 2005, pp. 840-2.

14.   S Sugla, *Anti-aging Products and Services*, report highlights, BCC Research, Wellesley MA, May 2009 (viewed 4 October 2011): www.bccresearch.com/report/HLC060A.html

limited shelf life and are not mass-produced.

At the more exclusive end of the line, you can go to a clinic at an international tourist destination and receive an injection of fetal stem cells for a 'mere' $US25,000/£15,000 per session. Cited benefits include improvements in appearance, sleep, libido and general quality of life. The clinics, operating without regulation or external supervision, apparently exist (or have existed) in Barbados, Ecuador, Russia and the Ukraine.[15] These centres do not just give beauty treatments, but also stem-cell remedies for a wide variety of problems.[16] The director of King's College London stem-cell biology laboratory, Dr Stephen Minger, commented that the therapies were "not based on scientific evidence".[17]

Alarming though the use of fetal stem cells for this type of unsubstantiated treatment may be, their source is even more disturbing.

Fetal trafficking

The Institute for Regenerative Medicine (IRM) in Barbados was closed down in 2007 after business slowed following a critical BBC television report. It named the Institute as one of the clinics using stem cells from aborted fetuses and dismembered babies that were imported from the Ukraine. The Institute's Scientific Director, Professor Yuliy Baltaytis, had another stem-cell treatment centre closed down in Hungary in July 2009 for illegal practices, which once again cost the equivalent of $US25,000 each. Shipments from the Ukraine were also received at the Budapest clinic.[18]

In 1995, the trafficking of babies from the Ukraine was already well known, with arrests on record for doctors in Lvov who had sold newborn babies to foreigners. Even then it was said it have been going on for a decade.[19]

In 2006, BBC reporter Matthew Hill published an exposé on the possible kidnapping and murder of babies in Ukrainian hospitals to furnish the international stem-cell trade with lucrative biological

---

15. S Bloomfield, 'Britons fly abroad for stem-cell makeovers', *Independent*, 16 October 2005.

16. S Barrett, 'The shady side of embryonic stem cell therapy', *Quackwatch*, 9 September 2010.

17. Bloomfield, loc. cit.

18. R Laeuchli, 'Illegal stem cell operation', *Budapest Times*, 5 August 2009.

19. 'Ukraine arrests 2 in baby-selling case', *New York Times*, 3 March 1995.

material.[20] Reporters interviewing many women in the Ukraine at the time found an atmosphere of fear, with many claiming that their babies had been stolen; that they had been told they had died but then were not allowed to see them.

In 2003, the authorities had agreed to exhume around 30 bodies of infants (pre- and full-term) from a cemetery used by maternity hospital number six in the city of Kharkiv. One campaigner was allowed into the autopsy to gather video evidence. She gave that footage to the BBC and the Council of Europe. The pictures apparently show tiny dismembered bodies stripped of organs (which is not standard post-mortem practice). Some injuries could be the result of harvesting stem cells from the bone marrow. Hospital authorities denied the allegations.

In August 2005, Ms Ruth-Gaby Vermot-Mangold was sent by the Council of Europe to investigate the maternity clinic in Kharkiv at the centre of the allegations. She expressed "extreme concern about the disappearance of new-born babies in the country and allegations of trafficking of babies for adoption and of fetuses for scientific purposes".[21]

In response, the Council of Europe recommended in 2008 that the authorities of the countries concerned reopen investigations into the disappearance of newborn babies.[22]

The Institute of Cryobiology in Kharkiv, which supplied the IRM with stem cells, refused to be interviewed for the BBC documentary. The scandal affected many clinics around the world that had their use of fetal and umbilical stem cells called into question, and a number of clinics remain tainted by association. Some clinics have subsequently chosen to use only autologous adult stem cells (harvested from the patients themselves) in order to avoid the legal, ethical and political consequences of using either embryonic stem cells or umbilical cord blood from undisclosed sources.

Concerns have also been expressed over the lack of evidence that any

---

20. M Hill, 'Ukraine babies in stem cell probe', *BBC News,* 12 December 2006 (viewed 4 October 2011): http://news.bbc.co.uk/2/hi/europe/6171083.stm

21. Parliamentary Assembly Council of Europe (PACE), 'Disappearance of new-born babies in Ukraine: PACE rapporteur calls for an immediate re-opening of judicial investigations', press release, PACE, Strasbourg, 5 September 2005 (viewed 4 October 2011): www.assembly. coe.int/ASP/Press/StopPressView.asp?ID=1673

22. PACE, *Recommendation 1828: Disappearance of Newborn Babies for Illegal Adoption in Europe,* PACE, Strasbourg, 24 January 2008 (viewed 4 October 2011): www.assembly.coe. int/Mainf.asp?link=/Documents/AdoptedText/ta08/EREC1828.htm

of the treatments work, not to mention the direct-selling methods used to entice vulnerable patients into having often exorbitantly priced treatments with no guarantee of success. A 2011 edition of *Nature* highlighted the problem, and the United States Food and Drug Administration (FDA) is responding by clamping down on the proliferation of unapproved stem-cell treatments being offered to Americans.[23] Currently the FDA is involved in a court case demanding that Regenerative Sciences of Broomfield, Colorado, which has a clinic treating patients with their own adult stem cells for $7000-$9000 per treatment, stop selling its adult stem-cell product Regenexx, on grounds of concerns about safety and efficacy. The International Society for Stem Cell Research (ISSCR) has established a service that, on request, will judge whether a treatment or clinic provides a safe and effective treatment,[24] although practitioners in the field complain that their real intention is to outlaw these centres completely.[25]

As long as there are financial rewards, human fetuses will be viewed through the lens of profit. Enterprises such as these will continue until there is significant public outcry at the harm being caused. Those involved in the business may initially feel repugnance, but we know from experience that they will quickly become desensitized to the horror of their actions.

But this is not just the result of callous entrepreneurs looking at an unused 'resource' (the growing number of aborted fetuses as a result of abortion on demand) and trying to make a quick buck. There are other problems here—such as the cultural worship of the young and healthy, and the persistent underlying belief that the unborn are not fully human and not deserving of respect. If the use of fetal tissue continues by mavericks, how long will it be before scientists want to push past the current 14-day limit for experimentation on human embryos?

Legislation can be educative. Just as *Roe v. Wade* made abortion seem more acceptable, so could prohibition of fetal stem-cell therapy make it less palatable. Insufficient action in the developed world can lead to the development of substantial unethical industries that affect large numbers of people in the developing world.

---

23. D Cyranoski, 'Texas prepares to fight for stem cells', *Nature*, vol. 477, no. 7365, 22 September 2011, pp. 377-8.
24. 'Order from chaos', *Nature*, vol. 466, no. 7302, 1 July 2010, pp. 7-8.
25. D Cyranoski, 'FDA challenges stem-cell clinic', *Nature*, vol. 466, no. 7309, 19 August 2010, p. 909.

Appendix III

Human genetics

T HE STUDY OF HUMAN genetics is developing rapidly, bringing with it a paradigm shift in our understanding of the molecular basis of disease. Genetics will have an important role in shaping society in the future because it increases our understanding of how disease occurs and how treatments work differently between individuals. It promises new ways to improve the health of the population. But perhaps even more significantly, genetics will shape society in the future because it is now allowing an insidious form of eugenics to develop within the reproduction industry.

The genetic revolution is mind-blowing in its benefits when we consider that 100 years ago, physicians didn't even have antibiotics to offer their patients. But once again, we are faced with the double-edged dilemma of technology: it promises great benefits on the one hand, but great dangers on the other. If you have already read earlier chapters in this book, you will realize that widespread genetic screening of the unborn is occurring in our community without an informed public debate about whether it is necessary or acceptable.

This appendix provides a basic introduction to genetics, covering basic terms that have appeared through the book and then conducting a closer examination of the potential benefits and problems of a genetic future. It aims to give you some background regarding the ethical challenges of human genetic technology, rather than dealing with the ethical dimensions of personal decision-making for Christians (this is covered in the relevant chapters of the book). Some of the options that are available to the public and mentioned in this appendix will not be ethical for Christians.

DNA and genes

The chemical nature of inheritance was discovered in 1953 by James Watson and Francis Crick at Cambridge University, when they determined the structure of the DNA (deoxyribonucleic acid) molecule. They discovered that DNA is in the form of a double helix—a twisted ladder—and that its information-carrying capacity is determined by the series of chemical compounds that comprise the rungs of the ladder. There are only 4 different chemical bases in DNA—adenine, thymine, cytosine and guanine—but they can be arranged and rearranged in countless ways. The order in which the bases occur determines the messages to be sent, much as different letters of the alphabet combine to form words and sentences. In DNA, God has designed an astoundingly elegant and efficient system, and the information it contains is known as our genetic code. There are small differences between every individual's genetic code. The chance of two unrelated people having identical DNA is at least 1 in 6 million. (But you already knew that from watching CSI, didn't you?)

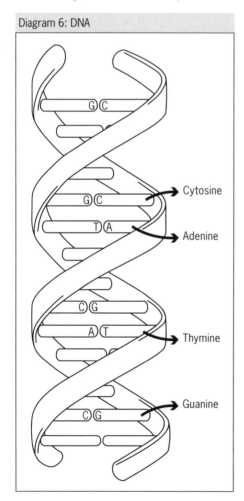

Diagram 6: DNA

The structure of DNA[1]

In the nucleus ('control centre') of each of your body cells, there are long strands of DNA that are coiled up into packages called chromosomes. If we untwisted a chromosome it would look like a string of beads, and each of the beads is called a gene. A gene is a particular section of a strand of DNA. Thousands of genes

---

1.   This section is informed by K Barlow-Stewart and G Parasivam (eds), *The Australasian Genetics Resource Book*, 8th edn, The Centre for Genetics Education, St Leonards, 2007. Fact sheets can be downloaded for those who would like more information: www.genetics.edu.au

make up each chromosome, and altogether we have around 20,000 genes making up our entire genetic code (or 'genome').

Each cell in your body contains 23 pairs of chromosomes, one side of the pair from your mother and the other from your father. (Another way of saying this is that humans have 46 chromosomes: 23 from your mother and 23 from your father.) The 23 pairs are numbered 1-22 (called autosomes), with the final pair being two sex chromosomes (X and Y).

Since the chromosomes come in pairs, the genes also come in pairs. The exceptions to this rule are the genes carried on the sex chromosomes. Since men (XY) have only one copy of the X chromosome, they have only one copy of the all the genes carried on that chromosome, and they have a Y chromosome that women (XX) don't have, which is responsible mainly for the development of male characteristics.

Just as we read the words on a page to understand what the author is telling us, the body reads the genetic code like a recipe book so that it can make proteins, which are the building blocks for our bodies. The genetic code in the DNA is very similar across all living organisms. The way our bodies metabolize iron, for example, is determined by part of the genetic code that is shared by all humans and by many other living organisms. You have probably heard that you have around 98% of your genes in common with a chimpanzee. Did you realize you also have about 60% in common with a banana?

Although the genetic code is highly similar in different humans, it is not identical. And what makes each of us different or unique is carried within this very small percentage of our genes that varies from one person to the next. This is what accounts for differences in such things as hair colour, facial appearance, height and so on. I have genes inherited from my parents that resulted in my blue eyes and brown hair.

Now all the different types of cells in your body contain the same genetic code, but we have many different types of cells—such as those in skin, muscle, liver and brain. What happens is that different genes are active in different cell types, producing the necessary specific proteins for different tissues and organs to function correctly; some genes are 'switched off' and others are 'switched on'. For example, the genes that are active in a liver cell are different from the genes that are active in a brain cell. That is because these cells have different functions and therefore use different parts of the genetic code.

Just as we may read a book under different circumstances or bring different backgrounds to it, so our genetic code is 'read' by our cells on a background of our personal internal and external conditions. Internally this includes our diet, the chemicals we are exposed to, and the other genes in the cells. Externally our environment plays a major role in how we develop and how our bodies work.

It was previously thought that some diseases are caused entirely by the environment and others by our genes, but we now realize our diseases are caused by a combination of the two. Even 'pure' genetic diseases (such as problems with metabolism) can be controlled by environmental factors such as diet, and 'pure' environmental diseases (such as HIV/AIDS) can be influenced by a protective gene variant (CCR5del132).

Many researchers have made the decision to start studying disease almost entirely from the perspective of genetics instead of environment because it is technically easier.

Faulty genes

We are all born with several faulty genes. Our genetic code may also change during our lifetime for a variety of reasons, including exposure to radiation or certain chemicals. The most common cause of faulty genes is ageing: as our bodies age, our cells need to be continually replaced, and the cells (and their genetic code) are copied over and over again as time goes by. Sometimes mistakes occur in this copying process, and changes in the genetic code build up in our cells. This explains why the egg and sperm of older parents are more likely to have chromosomal abnormalities.

The types of changes that occur can include:
- a variation in the sequence of 'letters' in the message
- a deletion or insertion of either individual 'letters' or whole 'words'
- the deletion of a whole 'sentence'.

A permanent change in the genetic code that may make it faulty is called a *mutation*. Some mutations may not cause any problems. As genes occur in pairs there will be a 'back-up' copy of the gene that can keep working, and this usually protects us from any problems.

But sometimes when the genetic code is changed, a different message is given to the cells of the body. Sometimes this might mean we have an increased susceptibility to disease. But if the gene becomes so faulty that the message is not read correctly, it can interfere with our development and functioning.

When cells have the wrong number of chromosomes, this is called *aneuploidy*. A well-known example is Down syndrome (where there are 3 copies of chromosome 21). Chromosomal abnormalities lead to miscarriage 70% of the time, and stillbirth 3% of the time, and they will usually be due to aneuploidy. Aneuploidy occurs either as a mutation during replication in the developing baby, or it is passed on from one (or both) of the parents. The risk of miscarriage depends on which chromosomes are altered.

The Human Genome Project

The most significant event leading to rapid changes in genetics in recent years was the mapping of the human genome.

The Human Genome Project was an international collaboration established in 1990 with the goal of producing biological maps of human chromosomes and determining the complete chemical sequence of human DNA. The announcement that the human genome had been mapped came (two years early and under budget!) in April 2003. This achievement generated an enormous amount of genetic information, but the discovery of the structure of the human genome didn't give scientists as much information about its function as they had hoped. Determining the function of the 20,000 or so genes is a task that continues today.

As we understand more about human genetics, we will gain a greater understanding of the extent to which our individual genetic codes matter in determining particular traits and behavior. It will also help us better understand and modify human disease. We have always known the value of genetic history in medicine (that's why doctors ask you about the diseases affecting people in your family). But instead of thinking of genetics as the study of relatively rare genetic conditions (as was the case not very long ago), we now realize it will need to be incorporated into our understanding of possibly all diseases in some way. It is therefore of increasing importance in the delivery of healthcare.

As Christians, we will not underestimate man's tendency to sin (Rom 3:23). As in any new industry, the problem of commercial and utilitarian values driving developments will always need to be watched. But the beneficial potential is enormous.

Current issues in genetics

Direct gene testing

Direct gene testing is an examination of human tissue to look at the sequence of letters in the gene to determine whether a known gene mutation is present. You might have seen it on television, when someone collects a sample of blood, saliva or hair from a child or adult. As mentioned in previous chapters, in unborn babies cells are taken from the placenta, the fluid around the baby (amniotic fluid), or from the developing embryo to examine the genes. Newer tests use the mother's blood.

The tissue DNA is examined under the microscope and the genetic sequence is read. This can give us information about the health of the baby now, as well as an indication of illnesses it may develop in the future. (This is slightly different from the tests done in forensic laboratories that aim to match tissue samples and establish identity.) The number changes often, but at the time of writing there are more than 1200 genetic tests available to physicians to aid in the diagnosis and therapy for more than 1000 different diseases.[2]

While in some cases genetic tests provide reliable and accurate information, in other cases it is not possible to obtain a definitive result. Our genetic understanding is not yet complete. We are not always sure when the body will be able to cope with a mutation or when it will be expressed as an abnormality. Some genes only indicate that you have an increased *risk* for a particular problem, with no guarantee that it will ever develop (think weather forecast). This may be because more than one gene is involved with the disease, and we don't yet know which one/s. Many results are therefore expressed as probabilities. A friend of mine has an 80% chance of developing breast cancer. That statistic is based on populations, not individuals. What does that mean for her personally? Either she'll get it or she won't, and she doesn't know which, because she doesn't know if she's in the 20% group or the 80% group. So these probabilities are not as useful as you might think. Most people, including doctors, find probabilities difficult to understand, and need help to work through what the statistics mean for a particular person.

The degree of complexity involved in genetics is such that it is recommended genetic testing (and in fact all areas of genetic treatment) be done in the context of genetic counselling so that the advantages and disadvantages of testing are considered before the test is done. Some possible implications are mentioned below. Remember, once you know, you can never go back.

---

2. American Medical Association (AMA), *Genetic Testing*, AMA, Chicago, 2012 (viewed 17 January 2012): www.ama-assn.org/ama/pub/physician-resources/medical-science/genetics-molecular-medicine/related-policy-topics/genetic-testing.page?

Genetic testing on the internet

The many genetic tests available on the internet represent a real problem, since counselling is not available and participants may not be aware of the implications of the information they receive. They may also find it difficult to interpret the results if it is a probability score. Reliability of testing can also be questionable. Some tests have not been properly validated before being sold (if companies are in a rush to get a return on their investment), and not all internet companies are screened for standards. A United States government undercover investigation found that 4 genetic testing companies delivered contradictory predictions based on the same person's DNA, and that test results often contradicted patients' actual medical histories. This has led to consideration of regulations by the United States Food and Drug Administration.[3]

Online paternity testing is of particular concern. Testing can be done by examining the DNA of hairs pulled out by the roots, or from a swab taken from the mouth (or a child's dummy/pacifier). It is therefore possible to test without the mother, the child or even the father knowing.

Who should have to consent before the test is done? If we say that the parents should give consent, what happens if one parent wants it and the other doesn't? Considering the implications for custody of the child, financial support and family bonding, should the rules be tightened to include consent and counselling?

Who owns genetic information?

Because genetic information is inherited, genetic disorders are family health problems, not just an issue for an individual. A diagnosis in one member has implications for other family members. For example, consider Huntington Disease (HD).

We know that HD is inherited

Huntington Disease

Huntington Disease is a neurological degenerative condition with onset at around 30-60 years of age. There are currently no preventative measures or cures available. It is slowly progressive over around 10 years, and involves deterioration of movement, reasoning and general functioning, leading to death. It is autosomal dominant inheritance, meaning that a child of an affected person has a 50% chance of getting the gene. Worldwide, only about 20% of those at risk have taken up the option of testing.

---

3. 'DNA tests give bogus results, U.S. probe finds', *Msnbc.com*, 22 July 2010 (viewed 17 January 2012): www.msnbc.msn.com/id/38363300/ns/health/

from one's parent, so if the child has the faulty copy of the HD gene (located on chromosome 4), we know the parent must have it. If you have the HD gene you are almost 100% sure to get this terrible disease.[4]

But who has the right to own or share this information? Say, for example, that a mother (let's call her Rita) wants to test for the HD gene because of her husband's family history, and the father (let's call him Joe) doesn't want to know if the baby has the HD gene because he doesn't want to know if he has the HD gene himself (because it would make him anxious). Here we have a conflict between the right of the mother to know if her child is at risk, and the right of the father not to know his own genetic status. (Of course, if the baby doesn't have the gene, Joe still doesn't know if he has the HD gene, but at least there is still a chance he doesn't.)

Now, HD is a disease with no preventative measures available. But for diseases where there *is* preventative treatment available, it is good to know if you have a risk of developing a disease so you can take measures to stop it from appearing[5]—hence the recommendation for counselling.

Genetic discrimination

Do employers have the right to demand genetic history information from an employee?

The risk of discrimination against those at risk for diseases that may either affect their work performance or cost the employer money in sick benefits has led to the passing of legislation in some countries to outlaw discrimination in the workplace on the basis of genetic makeup. Once again there is a tension: the rights of the individual to privacy versus the rights of the employer, and at times the public, if their safety is threatened. For example, using the analogy above, if Joe's daughter was found to have the HD gene, meaning that he also has it, is he obliged to tell his employer? What if he is an air traffic controller? The early symptoms of HD can be impairment of reasoning and judgement, of which the sufferer may be unaware.[6]

---

4.   PS Harper, C Lim and D Craufurd, 'Ten years of presymptomatic testing for Huntington's disease: the experience of the UK Huntington's Disease Prediction Consortium', *Journal of Medical Genetics*, vol. 37, no. 8, August 2000, pp. 567-71.

5.   W Burke, 'Genetic testing', *New England Journal of Medicine*, vol. 347, no. 23, 5 December 2002, pp. 1867-75.

6.   This example is taken from NSW Ministry of Health, *Ethical Code Governing the Provision of Genetics Services*, state health publication no. (SWS) 980068, NSW Genetics Service Advisory Committee, North Sydney, 1998, p. 6.

Insurance

In many countries the current policy is that the insurer and applicant should have equal access to known information, but that no-one can be forced to have genetic testing. However, could the testing of one family member have an impact on the insurance application of another? In the example above, if Joe knows the result of his child's HD test was positive, does he have a responsibility to tell his insurer? There is concern that some people may avoid genetic testing for this reason and miss out on the opportunity to take preventative measures.

With regard to prenatal testing, you are testing another individual (that is, the fetus) without his or her knowledge or consent. The results will be known before the child is born. Should there be a restriction on genetic testing for adult-onset disease until a child is 18 years old so they can decide for themselves whether they want to know their genetic destiny?

Prenatal genetic screening

There are several standard methods used to check the genome of an unborn child,[7] although there is no test that gives a 100% guarantee of a healthy baby. The tests give some information about the baby's health,

The Genetic Information Non-discrimination Act of 2008 was passed by the United States Congress to prohibit the improper use of genetic information in health insurance and employment. It should be noted that the legislation excludes life insurance, disability insurance and long-term care insurance, and so is not all-encompassing.

The use of genetic information in insurance is not such an issue in Australia at present, as health insurance is community rated— that is, everyone pays the same premiums regardless of their personal or family health history or genetic test results (a situation similar to the United Kingdom and Canada). On the other hand, genetic information can be taken into account in applications for life insurance products like cover for death or income protection, because these types of insurance are risk rated. In Australia, the insurance industry has agreed that it will not require people to have DNA tests before taking out life insurance. But if individuals have had DNA tests, they must report the results as part of their life insurance application.

In the United Kingdom, there ➥

---

7.   These are explained in chapters 8 and 12.

is a voluntary moratorium between the government and the insurance industry on the use of genetic test results until 2014. Exceptions include testing for Huntington Disease in patients requesting life insurance above £500,000 or health cover above £300,000. By comparison, France and Spain strictly outlaw all use of genetic test results by all insurers.

With regard to employment, the United Kingdom's Disability Discrimination Act 1995 and Equality Act 2010 contain anti-discrimination provisions for all grounds, including disability. Together, these acts could mean that an employer refusing employment because of a genetic predisposition will be acting in breach of the legislation.

Similarly, the Australian Disability Discrimination Act 1992 was amended in 2009 so that the definition of 'disability' makes it clear that it covers a genetic predisposition. Discrimination includes denying access to employment.

but they do not find all potential health problems. We do not yet know which genes are involved in some illnesses, and so we can't check for all of them.

The number of conditions we can test for is increasing all the time, and we already have far fewer treatments than tests. The expectation behind prenatal screening is that if your embryo or fetus is found to be abnormal it will be discarded. Either the embryos without the preferred characteristics will not be transferred to the womb (in assisted reproduction) or the fetus will be aborted (in pregnancy). The unspoken inference is that only normal babies should be born—or at least only babies where prenatal screening has not thrown up any red flags.

What kind of diseases should be screened for?

We can describe the different genes being tested with regard to the type of disease they indicate, and how strong the link is between having the gene and having the disease. When genetic testing was first introduced, it was only used for very serious conditions that were very likely to cause illness or death early in life. In their 2005 review, the Human Fertilisation and Embryology Authority (HFEA) in the United Kingdom reviewed which conditions could be screened for in preimplantation genetic diagnosis (PGD), focusing on some types of cancer.[8] These are the qualities they considered:

---

8. Human Fertilisation and Embryology Authority (HFEA), *Choices and Boundaries,* HFEA, London, 2005.

1. **Penetrance:** This is the probability that the presence of a gene will lead to disease. For example, some cancer genes can be present in an individual who never gets cancer. Perhaps more than one gene is required for cancer to be expressed. Perhaps it depends on an environmental trigger to be expressed. The HFEA report suggested that a 30%-80% risk of developing a condition is significant enough to justify PGD. Some people would go even lower.

2. **Treatability:** Originally only untreatable illness was screened for. Now it seems that you can screen for treatable diseases if the treatments are unpleasant or unreliable (like chemotherapy). The HFEA report suggested that a disease requiring "regular invasive treatment" (such as the regular blood transfusions required by some diseases) would be serious enough to warrant PGD.[9]

3. **Age of onset:** In the past, screening was done for diseases that would be present when the child was born. Now it seems you can screen for diseases that do not affect an individual until adulthood—like some cancers.

Screening characteristics in

It is also possible to check embryos and fetuses for a genetic feature you *do* want. Once again, you simply allow only the preferred embryos to develop. There is much debate about which conditions should be screened for. While we have all heard about genes for serious diseases like cancer being checked so that the baby will be born without a risk of contracting those diseases, few are aware of the parental requests to identify genes carrying a disorder so that it can be screened *in*. PGD has now been used in several countries by deaf parents who want to screen their embryos for genetic evidence of the 'deafness' gene—that is, to make sure that their child is deaf. According to one British news report:

> [One] couple have become icons in a deaf movement which sees this impairment not as a disability but as the key to a rich culture which has its own language, history and traditions: a world deaf parents would naturally want to share with any offspring. Moreover, they argue that to prefer a hearing embryo over a deaf one is tantamount to discrimination.[10]

---

9.   ibid., p. 11.
10.   C Murphy, 'Is it wrong to select a deaf embryo?' *BBC News*, 10 March 2008 (viewed 17 January 2012): http://news.bbc.co.uk/2/hi/health/7287508.stm

A 2006 survey by the Genetics and Public Policy Center in Washington DC on how PGD is being used in the United States found that 3% of fertility clinics had used the technology this way.[11] I think one of the worrying things about these technologies is that there has been so little public discussion about whether the community supports these trends. If society identifies deafness as a disability, are we happy for parents to choose this for their child? Is this a form of child abuse? How will the child feel once he knows that he was denied a chance of being able to hear? Or is it simply a case of 'parents know best'? The parents quoted did think what they were doing was in the child's best interests.

Saviour siblings

Since 2008, the HFEA has allowed preimplantation tissue typing (PTT) on a case-by-case basis and as a 'treatment of last resort'.[12] If you have a child with a life-threatening blood disease (such as Fanconi's Anaemia), one of the best treatments available is a transfusion of stem cells from cord blood provided by a related donor who has the same tissue type. By using PTT, parents have a chance of conceiving a child who is a tissue match for the older sibling. The child born through this process—the 'saviour sibling'—may be expected to donate further tissue after birth to support the sick child.[13] It may take several cycles of IVF and the discarding of many embryos before the saviour embryo is identified, and sometimes even then none is found.

In the United Kingdom, the Hashmi family, who applied to the law courts to be allowed to have a tissue-matched IVF child to save their son Zain (suffering from Beta Thalassaemia), had 6 IVF cycles and discarded numerous embryos and still found no match. In the United States, the Nash family was successful in the birth of Adam, a tissue match for his sister Molly, who had Fanconi's Anaemia. It took the creation of 30 embryos and 4 pregnancies to achieve this. In this process each discarded embryo may have appeared normal, but it was still discarded if it was not a tissue match for the sick child.

When the suffering of these families is plainly in the public eye, and

---

11. S Baruch, D Kaufman and KL Hudson, 'Genetic testing of embryos: practices and perspectives of US in vitro fertilization clinics', *Fertility and Sterility*, vol. 89, no. 5, May 2008, pp. 1053-8.

12. HFEA, *Code of Practice*, 8th edn, HFEA, London, 2009.

13. A fictional book, *My Sister's Keeper* by Jodi Picoult, portrays this scenario.

the embryos remain unseen, it is difficult to deny hope to the sufferers. But if the solution to disease remains the pursuit of the 'perfect' embryo, it allows parents to engage in a kind of "embryonic creation and destruction relentlessness" with no foreseeable end.[14] However, this is not a strong argument for those who do not value embryonic life. "Parents have the right to choose technology to help them overcome their extraordinarily painful circumstances", said ART doctor Simon Fishel when this practice was allowed in the United Kingdom. "I have no doubt that this is the right decision [i.e. to allow PTT]. In the real world these families are often faced with trying to conceive a tissue-matched child through natural conception and this can result in numerous heart breaking terminations of pregnancy, the birth of children not tissue matched or further children with a life-threatening disease." A spokeswoman for the British Medical Association agreed: "If the technology to help a dying or seriously ill child exists, without involving major risks for others, then it can only be right that it is used for this purpose."[15]

Ethical arguments against the use of PTT include the concern that the donor child is treated as a commodity and that his or her welfare may be subjugated to that of the sick child. Exploitation of the child could lead to potentially damaging psychological effects on children born not for themselves but to save another. And what happens if the sick child is not saved? Those in favour of the practice describe it as ethical and humane, and argue that many of these problems could be avoided with careful counselling. They argue that a child may in fact feel proud to have contributed to the wellbeing of a sibling. It is the kind of thing family members do for each other, they say.[16] John Harris, professor of bioethics at the University of Manchester commented, "There could be no better reason for having a child than to save the life of another child… so this is genuinely a 'pro-life' decision by the parents and the HFEA and they are to be congratulated".[17] Besides, as one little girl said of her soon-to-

---

14. Scottish Council on Human Bioethics, *Choices and Boundaries*, consultation response to the Human Fertilisation and Embryology Authority, Scottish Council on Human Bioethics, Edinburgh, 2006.

15. '"Designer baby" rules are relaxed', *BBC News*, 23 July 2004 (viewed 17 January 2012): http://news.bbc.co.uk/2/hi/health/3913053.stm

16. K Sermon, A Steirteghem and I Liebaers, 'Preimplantation genetic diagnosis', *Lancet*, vol. 363, no. 9421, 15 May 2004, pp. 1633-41.

17. A Coghlan, '"Saviour sibling" babies get green light', *New Scientist*, 22 July 2004 (viewed 17 January 2012): www.newscientist.com/article/dn6195-saviour-sibling-babies-get-green-light.html

be-born saviour sibling, *We're going to love our new baby*. And who can argue with that? It seems that the discarded embryos have faded into insignificance even before the saviour sibling arrives.

Sex selection

The HFEA has been criticized for their "conservative approach" in not allowing PGD for sex-selection purposes.[18] The main argument for sex selection is respect for procreative autonomy—that is, the right for couples to decide for themselves how to procreate and what children to have. The main reason given for requesting sex selection in developed countries is 'family balancing' (so you can have pink *and* blue towels in the bathroom).

However, the United Nations opposes sex selection for non-medical reasons. (Some places allow it when a particular serious disease is linked to one of the sex chromosomes.) This is because the preference for boys in China, India and other Asian countries has led to widespread aborting of female fetuses. China's one-child policy is thought to have made matters worse. Across human populations, the normal sex ratio at birth—the number of boys born to every 100 girls—is about 105. However, with the advent of ultrasounds that enable sex selection, the sex ratio at birth in some cities in South Korea climbed to 125 (males to 100 females) by 1992, and it is over 130 in several Chinese provinces from Henan in the north to Hainan in the south. The problem in India is thought to be related to the cultural requirement for a dowry to be given by the bride's family to the groom's family at the time of a daughter's marriage. This can be financially ruinous for a family. In agricultural areas, boys are preferred as they inherit the land. In India, the 2011 census revealed 7.1 million fewer girls than boys aged under 7 years—up from 6 million in 2001 and 4.2 million in 1991. The sex ratio in this age group is now 915 girls to 1,000 boys, the lowest since record-keeping began in 1961.[19] The societal implications mean that a significant percentage of the male population will not be able to marry or have children because of a scarcity of women. In China, 94% of unmarried people aged 28 to

---

18. J Savulescu, 'The HFEA has restricted liberty without good cause', *Guardian*, 7 February 2011.

19. P Jha, MA Kesler, R Kumar, F Ram, U Ram, L Aleksandrowicz, DG Bassani, S Chandra and JK Banthia, 'Trends in selective abortions of girls in India: analysis of nationally representative birth histories from 1990 to 2005 and census data from 1991 to 2011', *Lancet*, vol. 377, no. 9781, 4 June 2011, pp. 1921-8.

49 are male, 97% of whom have not completed high school.[20] There are fears that the inability to marry will result in psychological issues and possibly increased violence and crime.[21] Supporters of sex selection have suggested that these arguments do not apply in non-Asian contexts. Sex selection is not allowed in Australia at the time of writing, but fertility clinics are lobbying hard to change the ruling.

Prenatal genetic testing raises a minefield of difficult ethical issues. Who should decide which conditions may be tested for before birth? Which conditions make the life of the embryo not worth salvaging? What about conditions where there is a risk of disease, but not a guarantee of it? What about diseases that are not fatal? Should parents be allowed to screen unborn children for a condition that may not develop until adulthood? Is it fair to abort a child who may have 50 healthy years before getting sick (by which time a cure may have been found)?

What of saviour siblings? Are they disadvantaged by being created to save another? They may never have been born otherwise. Would your attitude to saviour siblings change if a doctor told you that this was the only way to save your own sick child?

What about sex selection for the purpose of family balancing? Are we just accommodating the selfish desires of the parents rather than aiming at the best interests of the child? Does the whole idea of genetic screening for the unborn make it harder for parents to unconditionally love their children?

Sandra Dill, executive director of IVF support organization ACCESS, has agreed that discarding human embryos raises ethical questions, but she says "it's an ethical question for the couple involved. We argue that the people who create the embryos are the ones who value life and value

---

20.   It is encouraging to read that the Chinese government plans to ban non-medical use of ultrasound tests and abortion of fetuses based on gender, though no specifics have been released. See 'China vows to crackdown on sex-selective abortions in bid to close yawning gender gap', *Washington Post*, 8 August 2011.

21.   T Hesketh, L Lu and ZW Xing, 'The consequences of son preference and sex-selective abortion in China and other Asian countries', *Canadian Medical Association Journal*, vol. 183, no. 12, 6 September 2011, pp. 1374-7.

children. Regardless of whether they are infertile or not, their wishes should be respected, because they are the ones who value the embryos the most."[22] I have discussed with Ms Dill my difficulty in reconciling 'valuing the embryos the most' with deciding to destroy them, but she remains firm.

Genetic screening before birth and the subsequent discarding of embryos and fetuses that do not have the preferred characteristics, whatever they are, is not consistent with the Bible's teaching that all human beings are made in the image of God and deserve to be treated with respect.

Genetic engineering

Genetic engineering is the general term for manipulation of the genetic code. It includes *gene therapy*, where the human genetic code is altered as a form of medical treatment to correct a mutation—for example, inserting a working copy of a gene to repair a faulty copy. Progress has been slow in this complex area of research. In theory, it would also include manipulation of the human genetic code to enhance physical or mental characteristics, making them 'better' than normal. This would be a form of 'selecting in' preferred characteristics, but instead of eliminating disease the goal would be improving the appearance and capabilities of the child. Now we are in the science-fiction territory of the 'designer baby'.

Genetic engineering could potentially be used to select genetic advantages for one's offspring, such as increased height, intelligence, beauty, athletic ability or similar. In a way, we already do this when we choose our spouse. Creation of designer children may never eventuate— it could be that the genetics are so complex that it will never be possible. But lots of people are interested in trying. One fictional portrayal of the consequences can be seen in the movie *Gattaca* (1997).

Enhancement

But really, what is science fiction? When Aldous Huxley wrote *Brave New World*, IVF was science fiction. Now much of it is routine practice in fertility clinics. I saw a movie set in the 1960s where they got excited because a computer could fit into a single room! But whether or not

---

22. M Bradley and A Smith, 'Church warns of designer children', *Sydney Morning Herald*, 9 March 2004.

something is possible does not determine its morality.

Where is the line between healing and enhancing? On the 50th anniversary of his discovery of DNA, Nobel prize winner James Watson proposed that low intelligence is an inherited disorder and that molecular biologists have a duty to devise gene therapies or screening tests to tackle stupidity:

> If you really are stupid, I would call that a disease. The lower 10% who really have difficulty, even in elementary school, what's the cause of it? A lot of people would like to say, "Well, poverty, things like that". It probably isn't. So I'd like to get rid of that, to help the lower 10%...
>
> It seems unfair that some people don't get the same opportunity. Once you have a way in which you can improve our children, no-one can stop it. It would be stupid not to use it because someone else will. Those parents who enhance their children, then their children are going to be the ones who dominate the world.[23]

Genes that influence beauty could also be engineered, Watson suggested. While Watson is known for his provocative remarks, he is not alone in his views. I have asked many parents what they think about creating designer children. Generally it seems to be seen as a benevolent extension of the nurturing process. "Of course, I would want to give my child every advantage", responded Daniel enthusiastically as we waited in line at a school function. He was convinced it would be widely accepted: "It's perfectly natural to always want the best for our children". But will it be rewarding to win a race when your advantage is due not to your own talent and hard work, so much as the skill of a technician? Don't we normally call this cheating?[24] And if some children in the class were enhanced, wouldn't that put pressure on the other parents to enhance their children too?

Author Kenan Malik, has commented:

> Medicine, and hence biotechnology, is only necessary because evolution has left us with shoddily built bodies that constantly break down, leaving us with headaches and backaches, cancers and

---

23. Quoted in M Henderson, 'Let's cure stupidity, says DNA pioneer', *Times*, 28 February 2003.
24. For further discussion of enhancement, see M Best, 'Designer Humans: Is any room left for God?', lecture given for The Smith Lecture, Sydney, 2004.

coronaries, schizophrenia and depression. So why shouldn't we try to improve our genome?[25]

He doesn't see why there is so much fuss over technology that is so unlikely to be possible in the foreseeable future, and suggests we focus instead on what can be done now with current technology. He has a point. We don't want to discourage the good outcomes from the study of genetics, and if we already use reading glasses and hearing aids, aren't we already 'enhancing' those people who have the money and the opportunity? Why stop there?

One difference between inserting a pacemaker and genetically enhancing a child is that the pacemaker dies with the patient (in a manner of speaking), whereas the genetic manipulation may be passed on to the patient's offspring. The cells from the parents that pass to the child are the egg and sperm—these are called germ cells. The rest of the cells in the body are classed as somatic cells. If you change a germ cell, the changes are passed on. If you change a somatic cell, they probably aren't. There is a strong consensus view among scientists at present that the risks of manipulating the germ cells far outweigh the benefits. This is partly due to inadequate knowledge of the intricacy of human genetics and the technical challenges of gene therapy itself. This will change with time.

Addressing the needs of future generations is complex, even apart from the consent issues. As the world changes, how can we be sure which genetic characteristics are going to be an advantage in the future? Who, for example, would have predicted a generation or two ago how important typing skills would become?

The late Marc Lappé was in touch with the politics of expediency when he wrote:

> Were the technique of somatic cell therapy plus indirect germ line alteration to prove successful to both the parent *and* his offspring, it would provide appreciable impetus to do more such experimental manipulations irrespective of the ethical nuances raised by non-consenting experimentation and embryo research. (This is exactly what happened with *in vitro* experimentation.)[26]

---

25. K Malik, 'Realism in biotechnology—or how to stop worrying and learn to love playing God', *Sydney Morning Herald*, 11 July 2003.

26. M Lappé, 'Ethical issues in manipulating the human germ line', *Journal of Medicine and Philosophy*, vol. 16, no. 6, December 1991, pp. 621-39.

In other words, if ever it is found to be beneficial to alter the germ line, the ethics will be thrown out as fast as you can say 'genetic improvement'. Anyway, as Lappe goes on to say, there's no need to make a big deal out of it, because it's easier just to abort any affected individuals and get rid of so-called 'deleterious' genes that way.

Will a 'deleterious' gene of today still be considered a 'deleterious' gene tomorrow? Ethical concerns around gene therapy include the need to protect human genetic diversity. We know that the gene for sickle cell anaemia is protective against malaria. Removing some so-called 'faulty' genes from the human gene pool may make us more susceptible to other conditions. Bill McKibben, a scholar who warns against genetic engineering on these grounds, says that as a species we are good enough, and not in need of a drastic redesign: "A species smart enough to discover the double helix should be wise enough to leave it more or less alone".[27] Who will be the lifesaver in the gene pool?

I may have asked more questions in this chapter than I have answered. In many ways, this reflects the number of problems concerning genetic technology that have not been adequately debated in the public forum. If this is the public consensus in a democratic society, so be it. But I don't think we know at the moment what the consensus is. There is confusion rather than clarity. Scarce funds for medical research are being spent on developing therapies to repair faulty genes, and at the same time on developing tests that allow us to abort the children who would have been able to use the gene therapies had they lived.

Materialism and genetic determinism

A final point for Christians to remember is that scientific research is often conducted within a materialist framework—that is, the idea that what you see is what you get; that physical matter is the only thing that exists. Following on from this thinking, there is an implication in much of the genetic revolution that our genes determine who and what we are. When the Human Genome Project was completed, there were headlines around the world proclaiming that we now had 'the book of life' in our hands. Have we?

We have already discussed the legitimate genetic basis for disease, but the media has promoted the idea that we simply have 'a gene for this and

---

27. B McKibben, 'Only human, and that's good enough', *Sydney Morning Herald*, 21 April 2003; see also B McKibben, *Enough*, Henry Holt, New York, 2003.

a gene for that'—as if to deny the existence of environmental factors and human agency. We now have a book about a 'God' gene—the absence of which, it is suggested, may explain why some people don't go to church.[28] There has also been research suggesting the possibility of an 'infidelity' gene.[29]

On the basis of this line of thinking, it would be easy to draw the conclusion that anything bad you do is the result of your genes. You're just a victim of your DNA. It's not your fault. But this is not a biblical view. From the Bible we know that we are not just physical but also spiritual beings. Human beings are responsible for our choices and we are warned: "Do not be deceived: God is not mocked, for whatever one sows, that will he also reap" (Gal 6:7). Genetic determinism is not consistent with scientific observation either—identical twins are genetically similar and yet individual. This attitude assumes a view of the human person that is too superficial. The author of Hebrews reminds us:

> "What is man, that you are mindful of him,
>> or the son of man, that you care for him?
> You made him for a little while lower than the angels;
>> you have crowned him with glory and honour,
>> putting everything in subjection under his feet." (Heb 2:6-8)

We are so much more than our DNA.

Public accountability

It is encouraging to see that governments have responded to concerns about genetic discrimination in the workforce and in the insurance industry, at least for now. It shows what can be achieved when people speak up and the political will exists.

What can be done about the steady march towards eugenics for the unborn? Certainly more transparency is needed so that the public knows exactly what is being done, especially with regard to genetic screening of the unborn. For example, we need centralized records of exactly which conditions are being screened out, and how many embryos and fetuses

---

28. DH Hamer, *The God Gene*, Doubleday, New York, 2004.

29. H Walum, L Westberg, S Henningsson, JM Neiderhiser, D Reiss, W Igl, JM Ganiban, EL Spotts, NL Pedersen, E Eriksson and P Lichtenstein, 'Genetic variation in the vasopressin receptor 1a gene (AVPR1A) associates with pair-bonding behavior in humans', *Proceedings of the National Academy of Sciences*, vol. 105, no. 37, 16 September 2008, pp. 14153-6.

are discarded for each disorder. The general public may be consulted the next time government institutions want to relax the guidelines—but how can we sensibly respond to discussions about where we want to head with these procedures when we don't know what is happening now?

You may be thinking that all this is very complex and that you need not be concerned with such issues. But apart from the need for Christians to be more involved with public debate about the future of technology,[30] genomics is growing in importance by the week. It may be a friend having to decide whether to have a genetic test to see if she is at risk of cancer. It may be a suggestion that you genetically screen your pregnancy. It may be your own physician wanting to check your genetic profile to let you know what interventions could improve your health over the next 20 years. Full of promise, full of challenges—we will all be involved in the genetic revolution before we know it.

---

30. See chapter 16.

Appendix IV

Umbilical cord
blood collection

P REGNANT COUPLES are often the target of advertisements recommending umbilical cord blood (UCB) collection at the time of their child's birth: *Support your child's future—the best decision you'll ever make.*

What does UCB involve, and is it ethical for Christians?

Umbilical cord blood

During pregnancy, the umbilical cord connects the baby to the mother's placenta in the uterus. It contains blood vessels. UCB refers to the human blood that remains in the placenta and the umbilical cord following the birth. Umbilical cords have traditionally been discarded following the birth. However, they have been found to be a rich source of multipotent hematopoietic stem cells (HSCs), which can be used in transplants to treat more than 70 different diseases, including diseases of the blood, the heart and the immune system. This branch of therapy is called regenerative medicine.

Stem cells are special cells that are capable of developing into many of the different types of tissue in the human body (so blood stem cells can be turned into nerve cells, for instance). The stem cells in UCB are classified as adult stem cells, even though they come from a baby. These are different from embryonic stem cells (which are taken from a 5-day-old embryo), and their use is ethically acceptable for those who wish to respect embryonic human life.[1]

---

1.   For an explanation of the different types of stem cells, see chapter 15.

How is UCB collected?

After the delivery (vaginal or caesarean), the cord is clamped and cut in the normal manner (often by the proud father). This separates the baby from the mother and the placenta, and it doesn't hurt because there are no nerves in the cord. The part of the cord still attached to the placenta is cleaned, and a needle is used to drain the blood into a storage bag. This can be done before or after the placenta is delivered. The blood is then taken away for processing, which includes screening for infectious and genetic diseases. After processing it is placed in (frozen) storage in a blood bank, where it will stay until its possible future use as a source of stem cells for transplants or other therapies (current evidence suggests that freezing does not damage UCB).[2] The whole process is safe and painless, and takes just a couple of minutes.

Collection can only take place at the time of the delivery, so you need to decide beforehand if you want it done and let your doctor or midwife know.

UCB treatments

When the stored UCB is needed, it is thawed and delivered to the patient for treatment. When the stem cells are collected from a donor other than the patient, it is called an allogeneic treatment. When the cells are collected from the same patient for whom they will be used, it is called an autologous treatment. At the moment, UCB is being investigated for transplantation, gene therapy and stem-cell therapy. It is possible that more uses for UCB will be found in the future.

UCB transplants

There are several benefits in using UCB rather than the usual bone marrow for transplants. The cells proliferate more rapidly than bone marrow cells. UCB cells are immunologically immature compared to cells from adult bone marrow or peripheral blood stem cells, so they can tolerate an element of mismatch. As a result, there is less graft-versus-host disease (GVHD) following allogeneic transplantation. For patients with uncommon tissue types, UCB may be an option if an adult donor

---

2. A El Beshlawy, HG Metwally, K Abd El Khalek, RA Zayed, RF Hammoud and SM Mousa, 'The effect of freezing on the recovery and expansion of umbilical cord blood hematopoietic stem cells', *Experimental and Clinical Transplantation*, vol. 7, no. 1, March 2009, pp. 50-5.

cannot be found. It is already in storage, so there is no delay in collecting it from a donor. It can usually be ready to give within two weeks, whereas finding a bone marrow donor can take much longer. Disadvantages in using UCB include the fact that there is a small risk (1:10,000) that a genetic disease may be transmitted to the patient.

UCB has been used successfully in transplants for people related to the donor for both malignant and non-malignant diseases.[3]

UCB stem-cell therapy

UCB is also being investigated for use in stem-cell therapy. HSCs are being trialled to modify the body's immune system in diseases such as diabetes and arthritis. Researchers are currently using HSCs in gene therapy, as a way to deliver new genes to repair damaged cells. The benefits of using HSCs include the ease with which they are collected compared to all other stem cells. They are also believed to be more flexible, or *plastic* (able to turn into a larger number of different tissue types), than adult bone marrow stem cells.[4]

HSCs are being investigated for use in a wide variety of diseases, including heart, liver, eye, bone, nerve and hormonal diseases.[5]

UCB banks

UCB is stored by both public and private cord blood banks. Public cord blood banks store UCB for the benefit of the wider population. They are strongly supported by the medical community. Computerized registries allow the matching of patients needing a transplant to UCB supplies. Private cord blood banks are commercial organizations that store UCB for the exclusive use of the donor or the donor's relatives. Fathers and siblings have a 25% chance of matching their child's UCB stem cells. Of course, the match is perfect for the baby from whom the blood was collected. There is usually a collection fee, and then an ongoing storage fee. Private UCB banking is illegal in some parts of Europe.

There are arguments for both public and private banking. It should be

---

3. KK Ballen, 'New trends in umbilical cord blood transplantation', *Blood*, vol. 105, no. 10, 15 May 2005, pp. 3786-92.
4. S Ruhil, V Kumar and P Rathee, 'Umbilical cord stem cell: An overview', *Current Pharmaceutical Biotechnology*, vol. 10, no. 3, April 2009, pp. 327-34.
5. DT Harris and I Rogers, 'Umbilical cord blood: A unique source of pluripotent stem cells for regenerative medicine', *Current Stem Cell Research and Therapy*, vol. 2, no. 4, December 2007, pp. 301-9.

remembered that if the blood is stored in the public domain, the individual is still eligible to access it (before it is used by someone else). The probability of actually utilizing one's own UCB is very small. Estimates are difficult, but some put it as low as 0.0005% (1:200,000) within the first 20 years of life. This is partly because it is sometimes better to use stem cells from another donor. Your own UCB may contain the very same defect that means you need treatment. This is an argument for storing UCB in a public facility where more people will benefit from your donation.

However, private banking (where you are basically collecting and storing UCB for a family member) is recommended when there is a sibling with a disease that may be treated successfully with an allogeneic transplant.[6] In the end there is no absolutely wrong choice in ethical terms. You should discuss your own situation with your doctor. Several authorities warn parents to beware of misleading marketing by some private UCB banks.[7]

Ethics

It is ethical for Christians to use medical therapies to bring the body back to normal health so long as no other biblical principles are violated.[8] With UCB therapies in particular, as mentioned above, there are no ethical problems with the stem-cell treatments due to the ethical source of the stem cells. Regenerative therapy is a field of great promise to which no sensible person objects.

What about the ethics of *collecting* UCB? There are concerns that the rise of private UCB banks undermines the traditional idea that the donation of blood is a 'gift' to unknown others. Will private UCB banking allow those with sufficient money to keep blood for themselves, even though the chances of using your own blood may be very small? Some have also questioned whether it is right to take UCB without informed consent—since parents are often inadequately educated, and the child has no autonomy in giving permission for UCB to be taken.[9]

---

6.   KK Ballen, JN Barker, SK Stewart, MF Greene and TA Lane, 'Collection and preservation of cord blood for personal use', *Biology of Blood and Marrow Transplantation*, vol. 14, no. 3, March 2008, pp. 356-63.

7.   Royal College of Obstetricians and Gynaecologists (RCOG), *Umbilical Cord Blood Banking*, 2nd edn, Scientific Advisory Committee Opinion Paper 2, RCOG, London, 2006.

8.   See chapter 16.

9.   C Petrini, 'Umbilical cord blood collection, storage and use: ethical issues', *Blood Transfusion*, vol. 8, no. 3, 2010, pp. 139-48.

It is true that a market system discourages a sense of social solidarity, and undermines the altruism that is required for a society to exist successfully.[10] (This is why there have always been concerns about such practices as the selling of human organs for transplant.) Where private blood banking has been allowed, it has often led to unevenness in the quality of the product. This has prompted some to argue for a public system where all deliveries have cord blood collected, and where the government then regulates standards of quality.[11]

These discussions should not deter those who do have a high chance of using the UCB from taking advantage of the private system while it continues to exist, especially since there is a limit to how many cords public banks can store, and some are getting close to the limit.[12]

What of the infant autonomy argument? This seems disingenuous to me, given how quickly we have abandoned any autonomy for the fetus up to the moment of its birth. Besides, we allow parents to consent to treatment for minors, including the donation of renewable tissue (tissue that can replace itself). There is further ethical justification in collecting UCB in that it is beneficent (it does good) by making potential medical cures available for more people.

The issue, then, is making sure that parents are fully informed of what is involved. To achieve informed consent, we need agreement from mentally competent people who have not been pressured in any way, and who are aware of all the benefits, risks and burdens of the procedure. I would suggest this could be achieved by following these guidelines:

1. Doctors should be honest about their financial or other interests in private banks, and not accept rewards for providing private banks with UCB samples.

2. Collectors should be aware that both parents have the right to participate in the decision, and therefore both need to be informed. To avoid pressure to make a decision quickly, this should happen well before the birth, with written as well as verbal explanations in language the parents can understand.

3. Any explanation should cover both public and private banking and the benefits and burdens of each, in particular making sure private

---

10. RM Titmuss, *The Gift Relationship*, Allen and Unwin, London, 1970.

11. Petrini, loc. cit.

12. DE Roberts, 'Umbilical cord blood banking: public good or private benefit?', *Medical Journal of Australia*, vol. 189, no. 10, 17 November 2008, pp. 599.

banks don't offer more than they can deliver. There are detailed documents available which outline the information that should be covered.[13]

Theologian Andrew Cameron notes that this subject may bring an ancient biblical theme to mind: that the life of the creature is in the blood (Lev 17:11; cf. Gen 9:4; Lev 17:10-14; Deut 12:23). It is well known that some religions still regard this teaching as prohibiting treatment with blood products. But evangelical Christians will resist this interpretation, since we know that the laws of ancient Israel have been fulfilled in Jesus Christ. They are no longing binding on us (Gal 5:18).[14]

13.   Institute of Medicine (U.S.) Committee on Establishing a National Cord Blood Stem Cell Bank Program, *Cord Blood*, ed. EA Meyer, K Hanna and K Gebbie, National Academies Press, Washington DC, 2005, pp. 106-19; Council of Europe Committee of Ministers, *Recommendation Rec(2004)8 of the Committee of Ministers to Member States on Autologous Cord Blood Banks*, adopted by the Committee of Ministers at the 884th Meeting of the Ministers' Deputies, 19 May 2004.

14.   CFC Jordens, MAC O'Connor, IH Kerridge, C Stewart, A Cameron, D Keown, J Lawrence, A McGarrity, A Sachedina and B Tobin, 'Religious perspectives on umbilical cord blood banking', *Journal of Law and Medicine*, vol. 19, no. 3, March 2012, pp. 497-511.

Appendix V

Recommended resources

SOMETIMES IT IS EASIER to understand the issues when we think about them in the context of a personal story. Below are some recommended books and movies that explore in a helpful and/or interesting way the topics covered in this book. It is not an exhaustive list—just some good examples I have come across during my research.

Books

- Josh McDowell and Ed Stewart, *My Friend is Struggling with Unplanned Pregnancy*, Christian Focus Publications, 2009: a part of the Project 17:17 collection of stories, this book is an easy-to-follow 'crisis resource' for young Christians.
- Bernadette Black, *Brave Little Bear*, Inspire Publishing, 2006: a real-life story of an Australian teenage mother.
- Heather Gemmen, *Startling Beauty*, Life Journey, 2004: the author tells her story of the healing and forgiveness that is possible after rape. She decided to keep her 'rape' baby, and describes the joy a child can bring out of a place of darkness.
- Melinda Tankard Reist, *Giving Sorrow Words*, Duffy and Snellgrove, 2000: the author tells the stories of women grieving after abortion, and examines their experiences.
- Abby Johnson with Cindy Lambert, *Unplanned*, Tyndale, 2010: the personal story of a Planned Parenthood clinic director's change of heart in the abortion debate.
- Sarah Williams, *The Shaming of the Strong*, Kingsway, 2005: the personal story of a mother and her family learning to love and care for her disabled child, who was expected to die at birth.

- Madeleine Witham, *Ella*, Ark House, 2009: a mother's honest account of life with her daughter, who suffers from Cornelia de Lange Syndrome (CDLS).
- Kate Hurley, *Take Heart*, Blue Bottle, 2008: combines stories from families of children with disability with an honest look at the theological questions they raise.
- Melinda Tankard Reist, *Defiant Birth*, Spinifex Press, 2006: tells the stories of women who were told to abort because of disability, but decided to continue their pregnancies despite opposition.
- Kazuo Ishiguro, *Never Let Me Go*, Faber and Faber, 2005: a novel that tells the story of three friends growing up inside an English school that has been established for the raising of cloned children destined to become vital organ donors. Also a movie (2010).

Movies

Movies can be an easy way to start a group discussion about bioethics. Please check film ratings before viewing.

- *Juno*, 2007: a teenager becomes pregnant and has to decide what to do.
- *Vera Drake*, 2004: a working-class family woman in 1950s England secretly helps woman end their unwanted pregnancies.
- *The Elephant Man*, 1980: the story of John Merrick, the hideously deformed 19th-century Londoner known as 'The Elephant Man', who was treated as a sideshow freak.
- *Anonymous Father's Day*, 2011: a documentary exploring anonymous sperm donation from the perspective of the now adult offspring.
- *Eggsploitation*, 2010: a documentary exploring the human egg donation business in the USA.
- *My Sister's Keeper*, 2009: a family struggles as a saviour sibling seeks to stop donating tissue.
- *Lines that Divide*, 2009: a documentary that tells the story of stem-cell research.
- *The Island*, 2005: set in a future where cloning humans is an industry that provides tissue-matched transplant organs.
- *Gattaca*, 1997: set in a future where one's life is determined by genetic engineering.
- *Moon*, 2010: set in a future where cloning humans provides a reliable source of labour.

General index

Page numbers followed by *n* indicate footnotes.

Scripture index